HAFEZ, E. S. E., ed. Comparative reproduction of non-human primates. C. C. Thomas, 1971. 557p il tab 74-161162. 29.50

The experimental use of nonhuman primates has increased in recent years, yet detailed study of their reproductive biology has been largely neglected. This book provides a much-needed source of updated information on this aspect of their physiology and behavior. It consists of papers from 21 contributors that are divided into five sections: Classification and endocrinology, Male biology, Female and infant biology, Infertility, and Techniques. All of the papers are written clearly and concisely, and each includes an adequate bibliography with some citations as recent as 1971. The coverage of nonhuman primate reproduction is comprehensive, yet key comparisons are made to humans in several of the papers. The sections on infertility and techniques are especially useful to those who maintain breeding colonies and employ surgical techniques in their experimental procedures. The appendix provides a mixture of interesting and useful information, including classification, naming, handling, and growth. The format is pleasant and the quality of the photographs and illustrations is good. A very impressive book that should be well received by anyone interested in primate biology.

Comparative Reproduction of Nonhuman Primates

Comparative Reproduction of Nonhuman Primates

Edited by

E. S. E. HAFEZ
Departments of Gynecology-Obstetrics and Physiology
Wayne State University School of Medicine
Detroit, Michigan

CHARLES C THOMAS · PUBLISHER
Springfield · Illinois · U.S.A.

Published and Distributed Throughout the World by
CHARLES C THOMAS · PUBLISHER
BANNERSTONE HOUSE
301-327 East Lawrence Avenue, Springfield, Illinois, U.S.A.
NATCHEZ PLANTATION HOUSE
735 North Atlantic Boulevard, Fort Lauderdale, Florida, U.S.A.

Library of Congress Catalog Card Number 74-161162

With THOMAS BOOKS *careful attention is given to all details of manufacturing and design. It is the Publisher's desire to present books that are satisfactory as to their physical qualities and artistic possibilities and appropriate for their particular use.* THOMAS BOOKS *will be true to those laws of quality that assure a good name and good will.*

Printed in the United States of America

B-7

CONTRIBUTORS

W. J. Bo

Department of Anatomy
The Bowman Gray School of Medicine
Wake Forest University
Winston-Salem, North Carolina

J. Buettner-Janusch

Departments of Anatomy, Sociology, Anthropology and Zoology
Duke University Medical Center
Durham, North Carolina

D. H. Buss

Southwest Foundation for Research and Education
San Antonio, Texas

H. Butler

Department of Anatomy
University of Saskatchewan
Saskatoon, Canada

W. R. Dukelow

Center for Laboratory Animal Resources
Michigan State University
East Lansing, Michigan

A. A. Gerall

Department of Psychology
Tulane University
New Orleans, Louisiana

V. Giles Nelson

National Center for Primate Biology
University of California
Davis, California

E. S. E. Hafez

Department of Gynecology-Obstetrics
and Department of Physiology
Wayne State University School of Medicine
Detroit, Michigan

A. G. Hendrickx

National Center for Primate Biology
University of California
Davis, California

M. L. Houston

The University of Texas Dental School
San Antonio, Texas

J. M. Ioannou

Department of Anatomy
School of Medicine
The University of Leeds
Leeds, England

W. G. Kinzey

Department of Anthropology
The City College
City University of New York
New York, New York

D. C. Kraemer

Department of Reproductive Physiology
Southwest Foundation for Research and Education
San Antonio, Texas

C. Max Lang

Department of Comparative Medicine
The Milton S. Hershey Medical Center
Pennsylvania State University
Hershey, Pennsylvania

R. K. Meyer

Department of Zoology
The University of Wisconsin
Madison, Wisconsin

R. P. Michael

Primate Behavior Research Laboratories
Institute of Psychiatry
Bethlehem Royal Hospital
Beckenham, Kent, England

G. Mitchell

Department of Psychology
University of California
Davis, California

G. T. Moore

Department of Animal Resources
Southwest Foundation for Research and Education
San Antonio, Texas

N. C. Vera Cruz

Department of Reproductive Physiology
Southwest Foundation for Research and Education
San Antonio, Texas

R. C. Wolf

Department of Physiology
Service Memorial Institute
University of Wisconsin
Madison, Wisconsin

D. Zumpe

Primate Behavior Research Laboratories
Institute of Psychiatry
Bethlehem Royal Hospital
Beckenham, Kent, England

PREFACE

NONHUMAN primates are being used effectively for basic research in endocrinology, immunology, microbiology, toxicology, dermatology, ophthalmology, oncology, developmental biology, aging, drug metabolism, and other areas of biomedical research. In order to establish nonhuman primate species for use as laboratory animals, basic characteristics of their reproductive biology must be ascertained. Breeding colonies should be established to permit maximal utilization of species in those research areas requiring subjects of known age, condition, and experience.

Species differences occur in the gross anatomy, microanatomy, physiology, and biochemistry of the reproductive organs, germ cells, and placenta. The length of the breeding season, patterns of reproductive and parental behavior, estrous cycles, menstruation, gestation, fetal nutrition, litter size, lactation periods, susceptibility to reproductive disease and life span also differ from species to species. Reproductive biology has been studied systematically in only five nonhuman primate species.

The knowledge of nonhuman primate reproductive biology and its subsequent application to infertility and contraceptive problems is increasing very rapidly. Accordingly, the traditional textbook no longer provides specific aspects of current research in endocrinology, reproductive biology, and related experimental surgery of nonhuman primates required by medical research scientists, primatologists, veterinarians, and zoologists.

Available literature in these areas has been presented in a systematic, concise, and, where possible, tabular form. An attempt was made to avoid the mere propagation of unsifted and undigested fact by critically selecting material and by excluding data based on anecdotal or very limited observations. It is hoped that unavoidable errors were kept to a minimum and that avoidable errors, which are entirely the result of the editor's ignorance, are not too obtrusive. In the preparation of this book we have been made acutely aware of the gaps in our knowledge.

The reproductive biology of several families of nonhuman primates having a wide variety of reproductive patterns is described in this book which consists of five parts. Part I elucidates phylogenetics, genetic biology, and reproductive endocrinology of nonhuman primates. Part II covers the anatomy, physiology, and biochemistry of male reproduction, spermatogenesis, and artificial insemination. Part III deals with the anatomical, physiological, and developmental aspects of reproductive cycles, oogenesis, gestation, parturition, and parental and infant behavior. Part IV summarizes reproductive failure and infectious diseases affecting primate reproduction. Part V surveys techniques used in breeding, rearing of young, and the application of experimental surgery to studies in female and male reproduction.

E. S. E. HAFEZ

ACKNOWLEDGMENTS

WE are exceedingly grateful to a large number of friends and colleagues who have provided us with help. Without their generosity we could not have written this book.

Acknowledgments (Chap. 4) are due to Dr. W. R. Dukelow for helpful suggestions on "spermatogenesis," Mr. Leonid Pulchritudoff for technical assistance, University of Washington Primate Information Center for bibliographic assistance, and the Department of Mammalogy, American Museum of Natural History for use of facilities. Unpublished research described in Chapter 5 was supported by USPHS grant No. 5-P06-FR00366 to the Center for Laboratory Animal Resources, Michigan State University, NIH Contract 70-2061 for the Center for Population Research, and NIH Career Development Award 1-K04-HD35306-01; approved as Journal Article No. 5145 of the Michigan Agricultural Experiment Station. The manuscript of Chapter 7 was critically reviewed by Drs. H. Butler, F. Du Mond, C. E. Graham, J. K. Hampton, Jr., J. M. Ioannou, A. Joly, C. Max Lang, M. H. MacRoberts, R. M. Martin, T. Rowell, and R. M. Sadleir. Unpublished data in Chapter 7 are derived from an investigation supported in part by USPHS research grant (HD 00585) from the National Institute of Child Health and Human Development, by the Lillian Banta Research Fund and Ford Foundation Grant.

Drs. A. Gautier-Hion, Bob Martin, Alison Jolly and Gilbert Manley read parts of the manuscript of Chapter 8. The original work described in that chapter was supported by grants from the Medical Research Council, the National Institute of Mental Health (MH-10002), the Population Council and the Foundations' Fund for Research in Psychiatry, which are gratefully acknowledged. Unpublished data in Chapter 9 are part of investigations supported by grant No. MA-1833 of the Medical Research Council of Canada. The histological and ultrastructural specimens were prepared by Mrs. R. Acompanado and Dr. M. B. Juma; photography by Mr. F. Lawrence. The manuscript of Chapter 9 was critically reviewed by Dr. J. M. Newstead.

Unpublished data in Chapter 12 are part of an investigation supported by USPHS research grant (RR 00451) from the Division of Research Resources. The manuscript was critically reviewed by Drs. R. W. Cooper, D. C. Kraemer, W. C. Osman Hill, and N. C. Vera Cruz. The mammary gland sections in Figure 12-2 were kindly provided by Drs. J. E. Hamner, D. C. Kraemer, and A. S. Watnick. Unpublished data in Chapter 14 are supported in part by USPHS research grants FR-0169, HD04335-01, and MH17425-01 through the National Center for Primate Biology, the Department of Behavioral Biology and the Department of Psychology respectively, all of which are located at the University of California, Davis. The manuscript of Chapter 16 was critically reviewed by Drs. S. S. Kalter, R. W. Goy, and C. Max Lang, and Chapter 18 by Drs. R. H. Hamner and R. E. Vice. Chapters 16 and 18 were illustrated by Mr. G. T. Rote, Jr. Unpublished work in Chapters 16 and 18 was supported by U. S. Public Health Service grants RR00278 and RR00451 from the Division of Research Facilities and Resources. Dr. C. Max Lang acknowledges valuable assistance given by the Primate Information Center, University of Washington Regional Primate Research Center in the collection of references, and by Miss Patricia Burns and Miss Susan LaVia in the preparation of this manuscript.

Thanks are also due to the Zoological Society of San Diego, Zoological Gardens of San Diego, San Diego, California, and to several Regional Primate Centers for the photographs in the frontispiece. Our gratitude is also due to Miss Mary Brindley for indexing, and Mr. Payne Thomas and the staff of Charles C Thomas, Publisher, for their cooperation during the production of this book.

E. S. E. H.

CONTENTS

Comparative Reproduction
of
Nonhuman Primates

1. *Saimiri* (squirrel monkey)
2. *Nycticebus* (slow loris)
3. *Aotus* (night monkey)
4, 5. *Ateles* (spider monkey)
6. *Saguinus (Oedipomidas)* (pinché)
7. *Lemur variegatus* (ruffed lemur)
8. *Lemur macaco* (black lemur)
9. *Alouatta* (howler monkey)

10. *Pan* (chimpanzee)
11. *Macaca sylvanus* (Barbary ape)
12. *Presbytis* (langur)
13. *Macaca mulatta* (rhesus monkey)
14. *Nasalis* (proboscis monkey)
15. *Macaca silenus* (lion-tailed macaque)
16. *Cercocebus* (mangabey)
17. *G. g. gorilla* (gorilla)
18. *Pongo* (orangutan)
19. *Cynopithecus niger* (Celebes crested ape)
20. *Mandrillus leucophaeus* (drill)
21. *Hylobaes* (gibbon)
22. *Cercopithecus* (talapoin)

I. CLASSIFICATION AND ENDOCRINOLOGY

Chapter 1

PHYLOGENY AND EVOLUTIONARY BIOLOGY OF PRIMATES

J. BUETTNER-JANUSCH

I. EVOLUTION AND SYSTEMATICS

THE order Primates includes populations found on all continents except Australia. They most often live in arboreal or semiarboreal habitats. The remains, now fossilized, of a large number of different kinds of primates are found in deposits in North America and Europe as well as on the continents where the living primates are found. Australia, New Zealand, New Guinea, and the islands of Oceania did not have a native primate fauna on their shores before the advent of man. Today most primates are found in tropical and subtropical regions. The genus *Homo* is an exception to this, as are some Asiatic monkeys such as the macaques of Japan and those langurs and macaques found in the northern part of India and the southern part of China.

There are a number of characteristics unique to the Primates. Among the most significant, from an adaptive and evolutionary point of view, are the opposable thumb; the grasping, manipulative extremities; and the evolutionary potentials that this manipulative ability activated. Manipulative skills and excellent eye-hand coordination may not have been the basis for the adaptive, evolutionary radiation that produced the Primates. Nonetheless, manipulative skills and eye-hand coordination are fundamental aspects of the adaptive complex of living primates, and there is evidence in the fossil record that the anatomical characters upon which these are based appeared early in primate evolution. At one time it was desirable to include the tree shrews among the Primates, and simple characteristics such as the opposable thumb and the grasping extremities did not apply so well. Today we are less likely to include the Tupaiiformes among the Primates.

Studies of primate hands clearly demonstrate that the grasping hand is a most complex trait (Napier, 1960, 1961; Bishop, 1964). It is a basic adaptation that distinguishes the primate lineage from all others. The grasping hand and eye-hand coordination with consequent manipulative skills are not the result of changes in a single morphological system. The evolution of the brain must have been associated if not highly correlated with progressive changes in muscles, bones, and joints.

A. Evolutionary Trends

If we consider the basis for the evolutionary radiation that we call the order Primates, we do not necessarily look to the unique features of contemporary primates. The morphological basis for the divergence of the primate lineage from primitive mammals may, probably must, be sought in other features. All primates share certain general characteristics. There are certain trends evident in the record of their evolution that are believed to be unique to the order Primates and give us the basis for distinguishing them from other mammals. The development of the ability to adapt to a variety of environments and ecological opportunities is a major characteristic of the order *as a whole.* This ability to adapt has become increasingly evident throughout the fossil record, and it appears to be something rather different from the progressive or increasingly detailed adaptation to specific environments or ecological zones that is characteristic of many other mammalian groups. For this reason, the Primates are often considered more generalized and more primitive than other animals.

The principal evolutionary trends that make the Primates distinct include the following rather broadly conceived characteristics:

1. There is an increasing refinement of the hands and feet for grasping objects. Functionally, this is the development of a high degree of manual dexterity. Morphological features associated with this are flat nails on the digits of the hands and feet in place of the sharp claws of the primitive earlier mammals; the develop-

ment of sensitive tactile pads on the fingers and toes; retention of the earlier primitive mammalian pentadactylism; the increasing mobility of the digits, particularly the mobility and increasing opposability of the thumb and big toe. The so-called generalized limb pattern of the later mammals is also retained.

2. The special senses appear to have been reorganized. Certain skeletal structures associated with these special senses show modifications through time that suggest such reorganization was continuous. The olfactory center of the brain—the rhinencephalon—appears to have decreased in size proportionally to the rest of the brain. The length of the snout and the degree of protrusion of the face have gradually been reduced. The olfactory sense apparently has been reduced in importance functionally. The visual sense and the anatomical apparatus for vision appear to have been emphasized throughout primate evolution, leading to the very efficient binocular, stereoscopic, color vision of man. One should note that all members of the order Primates have binocular vision. It is also very likely that color vision has developed to some degree in all diurnal primates, although the evidence is not yet clear.

3. There has been a continuous development of the brain with special elaboration and differentiation of the cerebral cortex (Figure 1-1). A large brain-to-body ratio is characteristic of all members of the order. The reduction in the snout and the increased size of the cranium are related to this part of primate neurological evolution. The increasing degree of manual dexterity and eye-hand coordination, so prominent a feature of primate evolution and of modern living primates, required an enlargement of the coordinating centers in the cerebral cortex. These developments in the brain have, naturally, profound consequences on the morphology of the skull.

4. There appears to have been an increase and elaboration of the uterine and placental membranes and of the development of the gestational processes. The period of gestation has lengthened, quite likely as a direct consequence of this elaboration. Among the more primitive primates the period of gestation is as short as 50 to 60 days in, for example, *Microcebus,* although most of the Prosimii have a gestation of about four months. This period increases in length to about nine months among *Homo sapiens.*

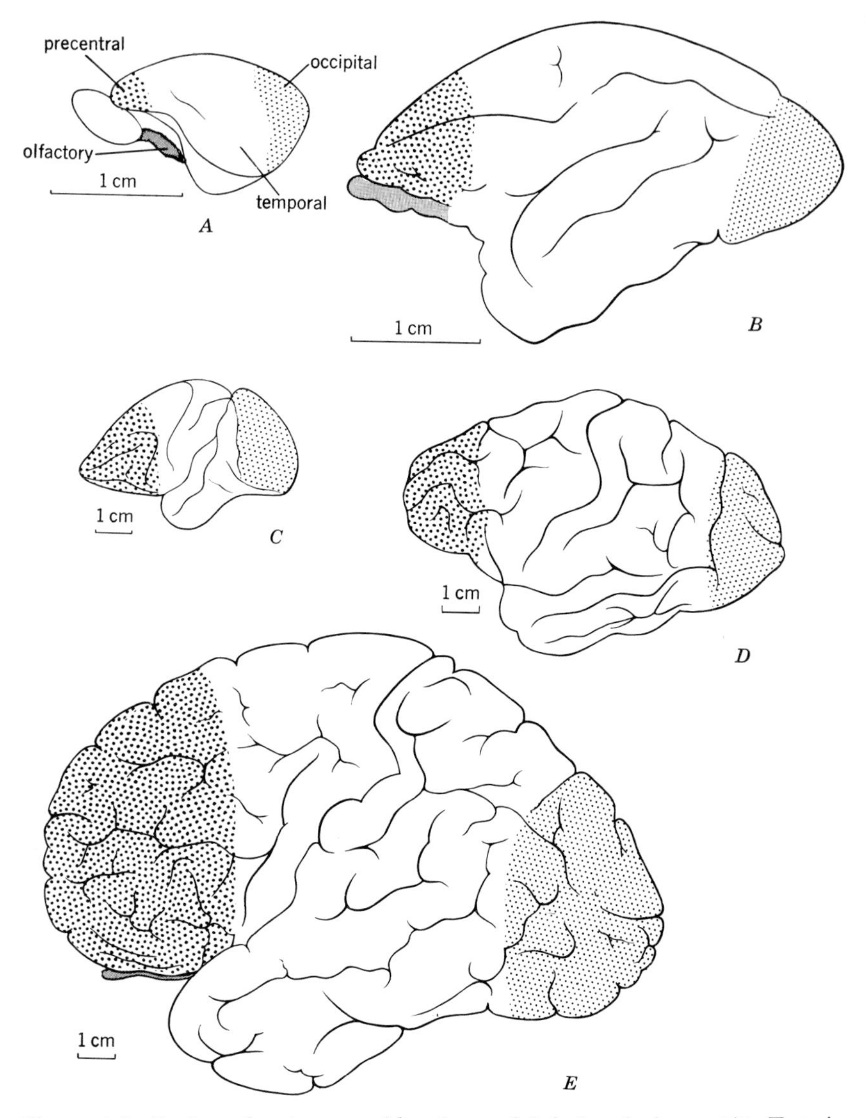

Figure 1-1. Brains of primates, side views of left hemisphere: (A) *Tupaia,* (B) *Lemur,* (C) *Cercopithecus,* (D) *Pan,* (E) *Homo.* [From Buettner-Janusch (1966a)]

5. The time during which infant primates are dependent upon their mothers or upon other adults is much longer than among most other mammals. This is related to the preceding trend; perhaps it is a consequence of it. This is not, of course, recognizable in the fossil record. But the fact that the length of the period of infant dependency increases from lower to higher living primates suggests that it is indeed a real evolutionary trend. The length of the period of postnatal growth and development to sexual maturity also markedly increases from lower to higher primates. This period ranges from less than one year among the nocturnal prosimian primates to almost twenty-one years in man.

6. There is a marked increase in longevity for all members of the order. Tiny mouse lemurs, *Microcebus murinus,* have lived for at least eight years in a laboratory colony. These are animals whose average weight is about 80 gm. Longevity is quite likely related to the relatively few offspring normally produced by the primates. Although often reported and very newsworthy, multiple births are rare in the majority of primate species. Many species normally have less than a single birth per female per year. The female sexual cycle varies from a single ovulation per year in some prosimians to as many as thirteen per year in higher primates. Trends four, five, and six could be categorized as part of a very complex adaptation that insures the survival of sufficient offspring to maintain the species. The primate approach to evolutionary survival may be characterized as conservative and with quality control. A small number of offspring are produced and mechanisms have developed to insure a high rate of survival. Other animals use the shotgun method, they produce a large number of offspring with the probability that only a few will survive.

7. There appears to have been a trend for the development of more and more complex social behavior. This trend is not interpretable from the fossil record, and one must base it upon study of living primates. Primate displays, vocalizations, and social behavior, such as grooming, infant care, and vigilance, are extremely varied and complex. Primates are the most social of mammals, and the higher primates are more social than the lower.

8. A simple cusp pattern on the molar teeth has been retained.

Certain elements of the primitive mammalian dentition have been lost, but the simple cusp pattern remains.

B. Eight Monophyletic Taxa

The eight principal groups, the major taxa, of the living primates (Table 1-I) are now believed to be monophyletic in origin. They occupy different levels in the taxonomic hierarchy. The members of any one taxon are more closely related to one another than they are to members of other taxa (Simpson, 1962).

Over a hundred years ago Huxley recognized a feature of the living primates that makes them so important in evolutionary studies. They appear to make up a series of successively advanced forms (Figure 1-2). Living representatives of many of the major adaptive advances that occurred in the long history of the order exist today. But we must use considerable caution if we make deductions from living forms about the past history of the order. Fortunately, there is an extensive fossil record that can be related to many of the living groups. It is not at all clear, nonetheless, whether any living primate populations can be taken to represent

TABLE 1-I

EIGHT MONOPHYLETIC TAXA OF LIVING PRIMATES

Taxon	*Common Names*	*Geographical Distribution*	*Habits*
Tupaiiformes	Tree shrews	Southeast Asia	Terrestrial and arboreal, nocturnal and diurnal
Lemuriformes	Lemurs	Madagascar, Comoro Islands	Arboreal, diurnal and nocturnal
Lorisiformes	Lorises, bush babies, pottos	Subsaharan Africa, Zanzibar, India, Ceylon, southeast Asia	Arboreal, nocturnal
Tarsiiformes	Tarsiers	Islands of southeast Asia	Arboreal, nocturnal
Ceboidea	New World monkeys	Central America, South America	Arboreal, diurnal, one genus nocturnal
Cercopithecoidea	Old World monkeys	Subsaharan Africa, Asia, adjacent islands	Arboreal and terrestrial, diurnal
Pongidae	Apes	Subsaharan Africa, southeast Asia, Borneo, Sumatra	Arboreal and terrestrial, diurnal
Hominidae	Men	Worldwide	Terrestrial, diurnal

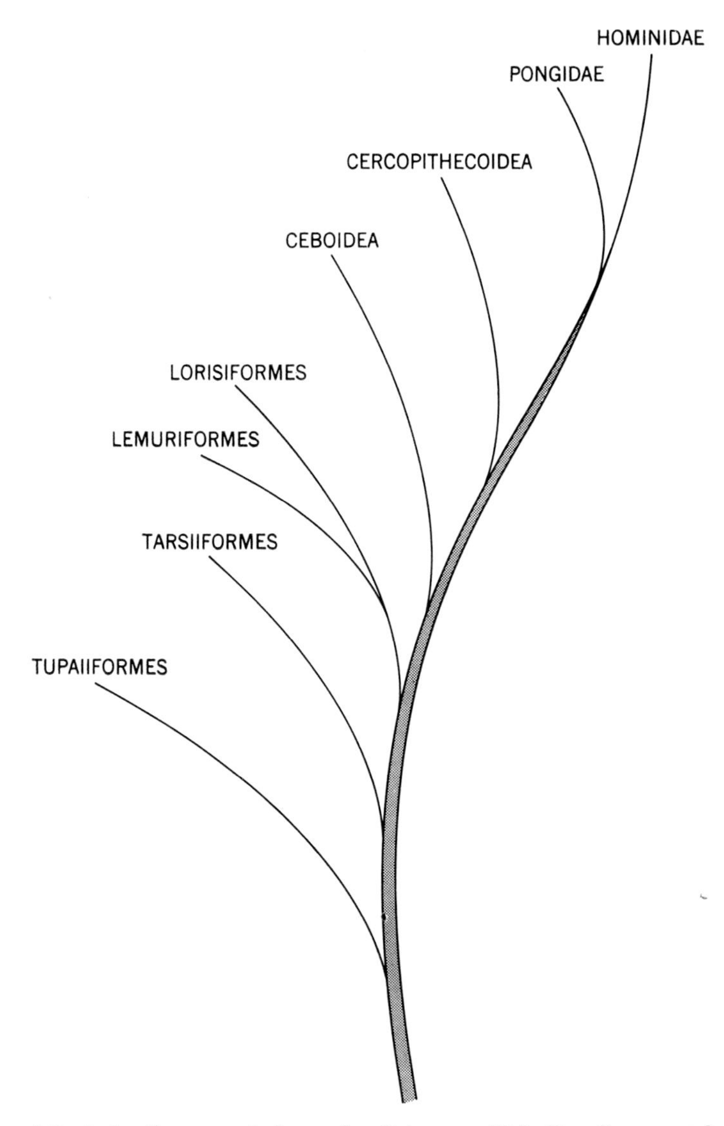

Figure 1-2. A family tree of the order Primates. This "tree" cannot be considered an authoritative presentation of primate phylogeny. It is simply a convenient device used to approximate graphically the sequence in which the eight major monophyletic taxa diverged. [From Buettner-Janusch (1966a)]

genuine transitional forms or new forms that led to the next most advanced adaptive radiation.

A number of populations of living primates are often considered to be very closely related to those groups out of which the more advanced forms developed. An example of the difficulties this assumption presents is the question of which living primates are most like the populations from which the hominids arose. This is the problem of finding man's closest relative or, in its crassest form, an inquiry to show from which apes man descended. Statements of this sort are not meaningful in modern evolutionary theory.

Every living primate species, genus, family, superfamily, infraorder, etc. has behind it a long evolutionary development. The more advanced are presumably those for whom phyletic splitting from the ancestral line occurred late. Some are considered less advanced, the lemurs for example, yet lemurs have a longer history of development along one particular line than do the more advanced forms. *Lemur* may be considered an Eocene primate, yet *Lemur* has had a long span of time during which it has diverged markedly from its Eocene progenitor. It is a metaphor to talk about lemurs or tarsiers or galagos as living fossils, a useful metaphor but only a metaphor.

Word-concepts such as primitive, advanced, lower, higher, when applied to the living primates, have very restricted meanings. Many writers, if one examines their words carefully, use primitive or lower to refer to the primates on the botton of the page on which a primate family tree is drawn. The assumption behind the use of these word-concepts is that a primitive primate is one who can reasonably be considered a lineal descendant of a primate group which is distinct early in the fossil record. Thus lemurs and galagos are considered primitive for they are reasonable lineal descendants of primates whose fossilized remains are found in geological deposits of the Eocene epoch. Gorillas, chimpanzees, and man are higher or advanced primates because they are descended from a lineage that is distinct later in the fossil record.

C. Concept of Relationship

The inquiry into which of the populations of living primates is most closely related to those groups out of which the more advanced forms have developed is difficult. Which of the living primates are most like the population out of which the hominids arose? Which primates are most closely related to man? We should consider at the outset what the phrase "most closely related to . . ." means. When an adaptive change occurs in one segment of a lineage of animals and this segment then diverges from the rest of the lineage, two kinds of things must be considered. First, there is the fact of phylectic divergence. Second, there is the time of divergence. We must deal with both the fact of phyletic divergence *and* the time at which phyletic divergence occurred. Relationship can be defined either with respect to time or with respect to the multitude of mutational, adaptive, selective events that occurred since phyletic splitting. But we must be quite clear what it is we are saying when relationship comes into the discussion.

It is debatable whether members of the genus *Pan,* chimpanzees and gorillas, are very closely related to man, for chimpanzees and gorillas are not at all like man. These primates occupy a totally different kind of ecological zone; the adaptive relationship these species have with their environment is unlike that of man. A large number of evolutionary events have occurred in the pongid lineage since phyletic divergence. Similarly, an enormous number of evolutionary events have occurred in the hominid lineage since it became distinct. The relationship of any two living primates may be seen in a large number of different ways depending upon the problem one investigates. It is not based upon any absolute scale.

Chimpanzees and gorillas are an extremely peculiar, specialized, and clearly maladapted group of higher primates. They are almost extinct, their relationship to the environment in which they live is very special, and they are unable, unlike the hominid lineage, to manipulate the environment sufficiently to insure their long-term evolutionary survival. It is just as and indeed perhaps more reasonable to examine prosimian primates, baboons, or arboreal monkeys than the great apes when we wish to examine living primates in an evolutionary and adaptive perspective. Because of an unmistakable anthropocentric projection onto the great apes by many members of the species *Homo sapiens,* it is taken as a given, an obvious fact, that pongids are our closest relatives. Modern evolutionary theory has suffered from the bias that chimpanzees and gorillas are the obvious models.

Today the discussion about the progenitor of the hominids centers on two or three kinds of animals. One popular view is that an arboreal brachiator, from which it is believed the pongids also developed, was a transitional stage between prehominids and hominids. Another view is that a social, terrestrial primate, something that resembles a baboon or a macaque, represents the population from which the Hominidae developed. Another view is that a semiterrestrial semibrachiator (whatever that is) is the morphological and behavioral type we should use as the model for the stage from which the Hominidae came. How to decide between alternative views of this sort? Some believe that the muscle-bone arrangements in the shoulder of *Homo* imply recent derivation from an animal that brachiated. There is equally good evidence that the hand of man resembles that of terrestrial primates, although there are some startling resemblances to the hand of gibbons (Figure 1-3).

Before one makes a serious study of such questions as, was an arboreal brachiator the progenitor of man, one might ask what is a brachiator? Is a brachiator an animal that swings by its arms, that hangs by its arms, that has a particular kind of morphological arrangement of muscles and bones in the shoulder joint, that has a particular shape to the head of the femur and the head of the hu-

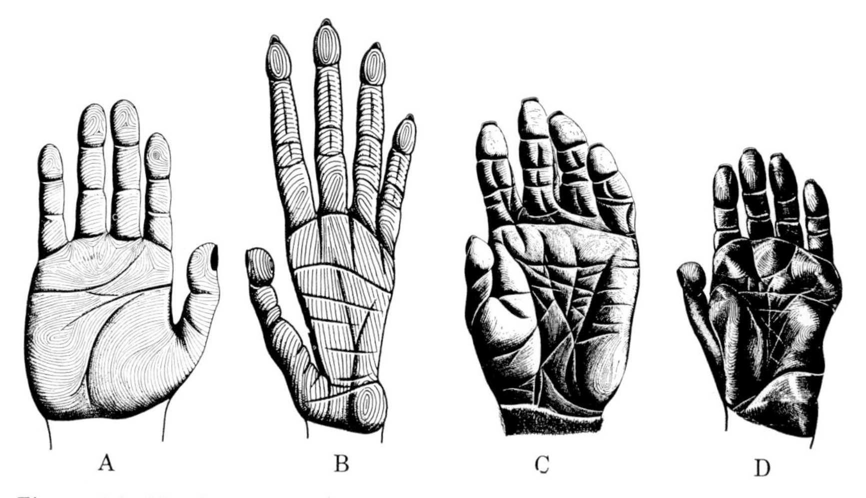

Figure 1-3. Hands of primates: (A) *Homo,* (B) *Hylobates,* (C) *Pan gorilla,* (D) *Papio.* [Drawings courtesy of Professor J. Biegert]

merus? All we know today about brachiation is that the most austere among us insist that the gibbon is the only primate that brachiates, that is, truly brachiates. But how do we go from fragmentary fossil postcranial bones to the behavior, the elaborate, elegant, acrobatic behavior, which the gibbon exhibits? The answer is, of course, we cannot. A number of inferences or speculations are possible, but it is essential that we recognize that these are speculations, inferences, that more than one set of inferences must be considered by students and investigators I shall not pursue the question further here. I have, I trust, shown how many other problems must be examined if we are to write sensibly about the question of which primates are most closely related to man and to each other.

D. Questions of Systematics

The classification of the Primates gives us a set of names for communicating with other scholars. The present taxonomic hierarchy of species, genus, family, and other categories has been built upon the work of many students and many years of experience with the Primates. It attempts to be and probably is phylogenetic in character, despite obvious inadequacies. It is a system with which to express one's ideas about primate evolution. The form is brief and organized and therefore useful. A classification based upon the Linnaean hierarchy cannot really be phylogenetic, since Linnaeus had no phylogenetic notions whatsoever, and his system is static. Nonetheless, discussion and argument about the adequacy of lumping or splitting certain taxa, putting a group of species into one genus, making one genus out of what is now placed in two genera, putting a number of genera into a single family or into two illuminate the development of general theories about the phylogeny and the evolution of the order Primates.

Systematic investigations of the primates have taken over a variety of techniques and characteristics not used in the past. Biochemical traits, particularly immunochemical reactions and the primary structures of molecules, have become fashionable in recent years. The data produced by these studies new to systematics are interpreted by some as undermining many divisions in the present classification of the Primates. Some authors consider that major revisions in our notions of the time and the nature of the phylogenetic divergences between major lineages of the Primates are in order. It is evident that some of these authors believe that there is a real, absolute, permanent classification or taxonomy that we will eventually discover, perhaps in the same way that Columbus discovered America or William Herschel discovered the planet Uranus. This view is naive, old-fashioned, and expresses an opinion that no longer counts in science. The real, the true, the genuine—the *real* system of classification is a mythological beast. The taxonomic hierarchy does not exist out there in the universe to be discovered by a particularly clever explorer.

The taxonomic system is constructed by man. It is constructed to enable him to handle biological data, systematic information, in a concise and convenient fashion. The taxonomic system of categories arranged in a hierarchy will change from time to time as our views of the nature of biological events change. The definitions of the categories, the hierarchy of categories, even the nature of the entire system will change. Taxonomic decisions, decisions on how to define taxa, are arbitrary. The fact the categories are arbitrary does not mean they should be formed capriciously or foolishly. Today most of us wish a set of categories that at the very least is not inconsistent with evolutionary and phylogenetic theory.

I have often been plagued by the following kinds of questions—do the categories in the classifications correspond to or reflect some supraindividual, real biological level of integration, or are the taxa at various levels arbitrary analytical devices invented by scientists? These sorts of questions rephrase in a biological context the old philosophical controversy between nominalism and realism. Briefly, the doctrine of nominalism states that abstract concepts or universals are merely names and the doctrine of realism states that universals or abstract concepts have objective existence. The objective existence of the species as a natural phenomenon is one thing, the construction of the analytical system, zoological classification, is another. It is probable that biological species and genera and families are real natural phenomena. It is quite certain that the taxa called species, genus, and family are not.

E. Biochemistry and Primate Systematics

A particuarly intriguing example of the use of immunochemical data to revise our notions of the relationships between the pongid and hominid lineages was presented in the work of Sarich and Wilson (1967b). They assert that their immunochemical analysis of albumin demonstrates that the pongid and hominid lineages diverged approximately five million years ago. There is no concordance at all between the interpretation of the immunochemical analyses of Sarich and Wilson (1966, 1967a, 1967b) and the interpretation of the data collected by paleontologists. The problem can briefly be summarized (Simpson, 1964). The immunochemists take paleontological data to verify a point in their time scale, then, having validated the time scale, they take their immunochemical data and attempt to reorganize and reorder the paleontological time scale. There are in this, as Simpson notes, the elements of a circular argument.

The problem raised by the interpretation of these data by Sarich and Wilson is most succinctly put by Read and Lestrel (1970). They point out that, with the meager data that immunochemists have at their command, several alternative explanatory models are equally reasonable. The model Sarich and Wilson chose is not the only one. Since each of the models, given the data available, is as good as the other, none can be chosen. For this reason, the particular dates picked by the immunochemists for evolutionary divergence must, for the time being, be rejected as an example of a muddle in the model, to paraphrase an anthropological colleague.

Another application of the immunological approach to systematics and phylogeny is illustrated in a recent paper by Goodman and his colleagues (1970). They investigated a variety of proteins, not only albumin, from many primates. They used many antisera produced by chickens, rabbits, cebid, and cercopithecid monkeys. They used a sophisticated mathematical and computer program to analyze their results. They avoided reliance on a single protein and a very small number of antisera. Yet their results do not substantially alter our understanding of primate systematics. They are faced with the same difficulty that confronts most who try to make an absolute time scale based upon data derived only from living, contemporary species. They cannot reconcile their time scale with the time scale provided by geologists and paleontologists (Pilbeam, 1969; Simons, 1967, 1968, 1969). Until the contradictions in the deductions about phylogeny and evolutionary rates made by immunologists are resolved, it is unlikely that much significant progress will be made in investigating other applications and aspects of the splendid corpus of information they have collected for us. I am convinced that immunological studies have greater value for other kinds of problems that we face in the study of primates and other mammals than the construction of phylogenies.

Excessive use of biochemical traits to revise primate taxonomy will unquestionably lead to further disputes and difficulties. It has never been clearly demonstrated that molecules or antibody-antigen reactions are more fundamental for the purposes of systematic biology, taxonomy, and classification than are the comparative morphology of bones and joints and the study of fossils. Since there are no fossil antibody-antigen reactions, or fossil molecules of hemoglobin or cytochrome c, I believe one must approach the use of molecules in systematic discussions with extreme caution.

Some molecular systematists argue that the Pongidae be divided into two groups, one including *Pongo* and *Hylobates,* that is, orangutans, gibbons, and siamangs, the other including the members of the genus *Pan,* that is, chimpanzees and gorillas. There are many reasons why this may be reasonable and useful. Most of the reasons have been known for at least two generations. During the past ten years several studies have demonstrated some differences between genetically controlled blood proteins of the apes of southeast Asia and those of Africa (Hill *et al.,* 1963; Buettner-Janusch and Hill, 1965; Goodman, 1963; Zuckerkandl *et al.,* 1960; Zuckerkandl, 1963). The suggestion was at once made that the Asian apes and the African apes be placed in separate families. It was even suggested by some that the African apes be put in the family Hominidae. Yet there was no discussion of what weight molecular characters should be given.

Analysis of the hemoglobins of chimpanzees and gorillas, that is, *Pan gorilla* and *Pan troglodytes,* shows that they differ rather little from human hemoglobin, while some organgutan hemoglobin appears to vary rather more. At first glance this might be taken to imply that African apes and man are genetically more closely linked with each other than they are with the Asiatic apes. Yet further work reveals that the hemoglobin of gibbons seems quite as similar to that of man as that of gorilla. Also, the differences found among the hemoglobins of orangutans are not any greater than the differences found within the group of abnormal or variant human hemoglobins. One orangutan hemoglobin even appears quite similar to one human variant hemoglobin.

A theoretical point of importance must be made at this juncture. We must take considerable care to analyze the generalizations and the assumptions we make about molecular data (Simpson, 1964; Buettner-Janusch, 1966a). The assumptions we make when we compare homologous molecules, for example hemoglobin, from two species are many and most of them are not particularly good (Simpson, 1964; Buettner-Janusch, 1966a). First, we assume that natural selection operated uniformly in both ancestral lineages, although natural selection is most unlikely to operate in this way. Second, because of the nature of the comparisons, we assume, implicitly or not, that all mutations occurred in one lineage, not in both. This is, of course, not reasonable. Third, it is not possible for us to distinguish back mutations. Fourth, it is impossible to be certain that if two amino acids at a particular position are identical in each homologous chain of the hemoglobin molecule of two species, they are identical because selection has put them there, or they are there because of different numbers of mutational steps from the ancestral hemoglobin. And these shaky assumptions involve only what we know today of the primary structure of proteins. These points should illustrate the enormous problems we must face when we try to turn differences in primary structures of proteins into evolutionary rates or taxonomy.

This discussion now returns us to the systematic or taxonomic point at issue. The two most extreme views are that the study of variations in and evolution of genetically controlled proteins supersedes the study of data used hitherto, usually gross morphological data, and that the inconsistencies between conclusions drawn from biochemical studies and those from paleontology demonstrate the lack of value of the former in taxonomy. Both of these positions are examples of extraordinary parochialism in scientific thinking. It is far more instructive to consider implications of supplementing classical taxonomic or systematic discussions with data from investigations of biological systems previously not considered. It is not clear at all whether the differences in the immunochemistry of albumin of African and Asiatic apes are symptomatic of a highly labile protein, in the evolutionary sense, or whether they reflect fundamental evolutionary differences between the two groups of primates. What about other more conservative proteins? How shall we weigh those that show few or no immunochemical differences in primate genera? What are we to make of the rather large genetic variation found among the transferrins of primates, man not excluded? Despite the immunochemical similarities of chimpanzee and human transferrin, other analyses of this protein imply rather large differences between the Pongidae and *Homo*. The fact that a protein shows an enormous genetic variation among members of the same taxonomic family may have no more fundamental phylogenetic significance than the variation that similar proteins show within a species.

There is a technical point with respect to the immunochemical approach to evolution of proteins that must be raised, although the complications of albumin chemistry are not wholly germane to this introductory chapter. It has not yet been demonstrated that the antibodies with which immunochemists work are some kind of absolute measure of the nature of the proteins. How do we know that making the antibody to human albumin in a horse, a guinea pig, or a turkey would not produce an antibody to human albumin that would recognize different receptor sites on the albumin of other primates? It is important to raise the question, because so many biologists dazzled by the complicated techniques and the eloquent assertions of molecular taxonomists have a habit of accepting the results without thinking.

The best classification—the best systematics, the best taxonomy—is basically phylogenetic and should express genetic similarities and differences among the animals classified. When genetic and anatomical data apparently imply different classificatory conclusions, we should recognize that a problem of fundamental interest in evolutionary biology exists.

Modification of the classification in use becomes necessary when we find gross inconsistencies between two lines of evidence. An example is provided by data on the chromosomes of *Lemur fulvus* and *L. macaco*. Several populations of lemurs usually considered to be subspecies or races of the species *Lemur fulvus* have different diploid chromosome numbers, with other morphological differences in karyotype as well. Variation in the pelage color of animals that seem basically similar led a number of workers to propose a variety of subspecies. An ecological dimension was added to such a division when it appeared that each color variety of the *L. fulvus* group inhabited separate forest areas. Since the forests of Madagascar have been reduced to noncontiguous remnants, and populations of *L. fulvus* became isolated, many of the *L. fulvus* populations may indeed be separable and given specific status. Petter (1962), commenting on the taxonomy of Madagascan lemurs, produced a system of classifying the lemurs, particularly *L. fulvus* subspp., which lumps most of them into a single species. Petter, using a suggestion Schwarz published in 1936, finds a continuum of traits among all *L. fulvus* groups and *L. macaco* and lumps all as subspecies of *L. macaco*. But if we take the available data on the diploid chromosome numbers (Table I-II) and karyotype morphology (Bender and Chu, 1963; Chu and Bender, 1962; Rumpler and Albignac, 1969a, 1969b, 1970; Buettner-Janusch and Bergeron, unpublished observations), the whole problem must be reconsidered. How shall the data presented in Table I-II be integrated with conventional interpretations? How could so much chromosome variation develop within what, on other grounds, is

TABLE 1-II

CHROMOSOME NUMBERS OF *LEMUR*[a]

Species	*2N*
L. catta	56
L. fulvus group	
L. f. albifrons	60
L. f. collaris (red collared)	48
L. f. collaris (red collared)	52
L. f. collaris (white collared)	52
L. f. fulvus	60
L. f. rufus	60
L. f. sanfordi	60
L. macaco	44
L. mongoz	60
L. variegatus	46

[a] Data from summaries reported by Bender and Chu (1963) and Rumpler and Albignac (1970).

TABLE 1-III

CHROMOSOME NUMBERS OF *LEMUR* HYBRIDS[a]

Hybrid			Male Parent		Female Parent	
No.	*Sex*	*2N*	*Species*	*2N*	*Species*	*2N*
1	Female	52	*L. macaco*	44	*L. fulvus rufus*	60
2	Male	52	*L. fulvus albifrons*	60	*L. macaco*	44
3	Female	46	*L. macaco*	44	*L. fulvus collaris*	48
4	Male	60	*L. fulvus fulvus*	60	*L. fulvus albifrons*	60
5	Female	60	*L. fulvus fulvus*	60	*L. fulvus rufus*	60
6	Female	60	Hybrid 4	60	Hybrid 5	60
7	Male	54	*L. fulvus collaris*	48	*L. fulvus rufus*	60
8	Female	60	*L. fulvus rufus*	60	*L. fulvus fulvus*	60
9	Female	60	*L. fulvus rufus*	60	*L. fulvus fulvus*	60
10	Female	60	*L. fulvus rufus*	60	*L. fulvus fulvus*	60
11	Female	60	*L. fulvus rufus*	60	*L. fulvus fulvus*	60
12	Female	60	*L. fulvus fulvus*	60	Hybrid 10	60
13	Male	60	*L. fulvus fulvus*	60	*L. fulvus rufus*	60
14	Male[b]	60	*L. fulvus fulvus*	60	*L. fulvus rufus*	60
15	Female[b]	60				
16	Female	52	*L. macaco*	44	Hybrid 12	60
17	Male	60	*L. fulvus fulvus*	60	Hybrid 8	60
18	Female	60	*L. fulvus fulvus*	60	Hybrid 8	60
19	Female	60	Hybrid 17	60	*L. fulvus rufus*	60

[a] Hybrids 1–6 from Rumpler and Albignac (1970); hybrids 7–19 from Buettner-Janusch and Bergeron (unpublished observations).

[b] Twins.

considered one population of animals? If they are one species with racial variation expressed by traits such as pelage color, then barriers to breeding cannot, by definition, exist. Variation in the chromosome complement may be interpreted as the first stage in the genetic differentiation which eventually produces the reproductive barriers that define species. Hybrids between lemurs of different chromosome numbers and karyotypes have been studied. The diploid numbers of the offspring appear to be the combination of a haploid set of the maternal with a haploid set of the paternal line (Table I-III). The fact that such hybrids occur does not, however, immediately suggest that the two parental lineages belong to the same species. Although some prefer to use these hybrids as evidence that these samples represent a single species, my own view is that the karyotypes and diploid numbers are good supporting evidence that several species should be defined. However, the original classification of the genus *Lemur* may have been made on the basis of incomplete observations of the distribution and relationships of the various populations and subpopulations of the animals. The implications we read from the karyotypes warrant reexamination of the older work.

The particular problem just noted is of more significance than sorting out the nomenclature and taxonomy of lemurs. Working on this problem contributes to our understanding of the reproductive biology, the evolutionary biology, and the phylogeny of all the Primates.

II. PROSIMII

Both fossil and living prosimians have features that make it impossible to produce an unequivocal distinction between Prosimii and Insectivora. The evolutionary development and differentiation of primates from insectivores was gradual. There is a continuous range or spectrum in various characters. There is no threshold in the fossil record over which insectivore lineages stepped to become primate lineages. A logical way to define the Primates would be to include only the Anthropoidea. The Prosimii are clearly distinct from the Anthropoidea, but they are not quite as distinct from the early Insectivora—which is the crux of the problem of defining the Primates. The Prosimii are a genetic and adaptive group of animals noticeably different but not completely distinct from shrews, moles, and hedgehogs. They are definitely related to the Anthropoidea. The best answer to the problem is that it is not reasonable to expect a clear distinction between the taxa Insectivora and Primates when no sharp distinction between them has ever existed in nature.

A. Tupaiiformes

Until recently there was general agreement that the tree shrews, Tupaiiformes, are to be classified with the Primates (Clark, 1962; Simpson, 1962; Straus, 1956). Grassé (1955) reaffirms the opinion that they belong to the order Insectivora, and Hill (1953) in his encyclopedic summary of Prosimii did not include them in the Primates. Other investigators have questioned inclusion of tree shrews in the Primates on such various grounds as reproductive behavior (Martin, 1968), reexamination of Paleocene and Eocene fossils (Szalay, 1968), and analytical attacks upon LeGros Clark's original premises. The Tupaiiformes, at the very least, represent an important link, the insectivore group presumably most closely related in a phylogenetic sense to the Primates. Much can be learned by studying a group of animals that may be said to have a foot in more than one order, although whether this situation is due to their truly transitional form or to our ignorance is yet to be determined. Much could undoubtedly be learned by study of *Galeopithecus,* the so-called flying lemur of Borneo. This strange animal has many superficial similarities to prosimian primates. However the taxonomic decision is finally made, students of the Primates are increasing the amount of attention that they pay to the Tupaiiformes. The list of names is a long one, and it is likely that many contemporary scholars would reduce the number of separate groups by a factor of two. Others might wish to increase the number. Many of the Tupaiiformes are island dwellers and such isolation will have emphasized tendencies toward divergence.

B. Lemuriformes

The lemurs of Madagascar are often considered important only because they are a survival from the Eocene. Had the lemurs not survived on Madagascar, it would be difficult to argue that any of the prosimian populations, deduced from Eocene fossils, included diurnal animals. But it is a metaphor to call lemurs a survival. The Madagascan lemurs have been isolated, presumably from the time of the divergence of the Lemuriformes, from the ancestral prosimians. What evidence exists seems to support the interpretation that the ancestral lineage of modern lemurs radiated completely on the island of Madagascar. Apparently, these interesting prosimians have not been subjected to the competitive pressure of presumably more intelligent, more cleverly manipulative monkeys (Andrew, 1962, 1963). The fossil evidence (Simons, 1963) implies a prosimian line leading directly to monkeys and another to modern prosimians.

Madagascar has been separate from the continent of Africa throughout the entire period of primate evolution, indeed probably during all of mammalian evolution. The lemurs as such are not represented in the Eocene fossil fauna. But it is reasonable to argue that lemurs are lineal descendants of certain Eocene populations now represented only in the fossil record of North America and Europe. The question of how the ancestors of lemurs got to the island of Madagascar is best answered by calling upon the Monte Carlo or the rafting hypothesis. Large rafts of floating vegetation, probably carried by rivers resembling the modern Zambezi, drifted across the Gulf of Mozambique, and eventually reached the island of Madagascar. The other mammals on Madagascar, rodents, insectivores, and, in particular, the curious fossa (*Cryptoprocta ferox;* family Viverridae), are consistent with this view.

Lemurs are various, divergent, and specialized. The specialization, diversity, and divergence support the belief of many that lemurs are a separate group of prosimians, to be ranked as an infraorder. This variation has also been the basis for a number of different, often conflicting, classifications of lemurs. Washburn (1950) argued that there seems to be little essential difference between lemurs, lorises, and tarsiers. There are a number of lemurs, all rather different from the nocturnal prosimians of the continents (Elliot, 1913; Hill, 1953; Jouffroy and Lessertisseur, 1959; Milne-Edwards and Grandidier, 1875, 1890-1896). There may be similarities, but the differences are sufficient to retain the infraorder Lemuriformes.

C. *Lorisiformes*

Lorisiformes are conveniently divided into two locomotor groups, the slow climbers and creepers and the fast hoppers. The slow climbers and creepers are usually placed in the subfamily Lorisinae, and the fast hoppers in the subfamily Galaginae. The principal differences between the two groups are structural modifications of the limbs that are consequences of rather advanced specializations for arboreal life.

The nocturnal, arboreal lorises probably are the remnants of what was once a widespread and variable prosimian population. The survival of some species of Lorisiformes is probably due to their occupation of a nocturnal, arboreal ecozone that does not bring them into competition with forms such as the monkeys.

The Lorisiformes present a number of problems in classification. It is not clear why *Arctocebus* and *Perodicticus* should be separated at the generic rather than the specific level. Both are relatively slow moving, arboreal, nocturnal forms. They are found in populations isolated by geographical barriers, and this fact may have given impetus to extreme splitting tendencies by naturalists and others who reported finding these animals. Separation of the various galagos into three genera, *Galagoides, Galago,* and *Euoticus,* always seemed extreme. Today one species, *Galago crassicaudatus crassicaudatus,* has been divided into a number of subspecies, some of which show pelage, skeletal, and size differences from *G. crassicaudatus crassicaudatus* that are at least as extreme as the differences between *Galago senegalensis* and *Galagoides demidovii. G. crassicaudatus crassicaudatus* and *G. c. argentatus* are still listed as variants in one species. The *G. c. argentatus* variety is not only radically different in pelage from the *G. c. crassicaudatus* group, but also is very much larger, with larger ears and bigger and broader skulls with rather large nasal bones. If these two are to be considered members of the same species, and they have not been separated yet, then the generic separation of some of the other African lorises is certainly unreasonable.

The classification of the Asiatic lorises is less complicated, there has been no excessive splitting of taxa. Only *Loris* and *Nycticebus* are recognized as generically different, and within each of the two genera, only a single species with racial variants is recognized. Many of these variants have been given the status of subspecies, but the variation has never been given any greater weight than that. And this relatively high degree of lumping includes island forms of *Loris* from Ceylon in the same species with mainland forms.

D. *Tarsiiformes*

The living Tarsiiformes comprise a single genus, *Tarsius.* Little research has been done on *Tarsius* in recent years. Data are not available on hematology, behavior, vocalizations, or biochemistry tnat are of comparable quality with the material assembled from studies on other primates. Yet *Tarsius* poses important problems to students of primate evolution. Its evolutionary position is hard to assess. There are many fossils assignable to a tarsioid group, but it is not clear, even today, what the essential differences, if any, between tarsioid and lemuroid fossil assemblages are (Simpson, 1940; Simons, 1963).

Tarsius has many features which argue for calling it the most primitive of the Primates. Despite the development of a number of specializations, *Tarsius* retains many traits that seem to be derived from the tupaiids (Hill, 1955). As many as thirty-two fossil genera have been allied to *Tarsius* (Hill, 1955). But this was before serious attention was directed to the difficulty of detecting the differences between lemuroid and tarsioid fossil assemblages.

The distinction between a fossil tarsioid and a fossil lemuroid is difficult to make. *Necrolemur* is the best example of a fossil tarsioid, and it is probable that the lineage from the ancestor common to *Necrolemur* and *Tarsius* is more or less unbroken (Simons and Russell, 1960; Simons, 1961).

Tarsius has had a vogue as representing an ancestor of man. Jones (1929) believed the Anthropoidea passed through a tarsioid stage. The difficulties in this view are many and not worth discussing in detail. Suffice to say here that it would be of great interest to examine biochemical, cytological, and physiological characteristics of *Tarsius*.

III. ANTHROPOIDEA

The Anthropoidea are distinctly different from the Prosimii. There are no forms that definitely bridge the morphological gap between prosimians and higher primates (Simpson, 1945). At one time this suborder was called Simia to make it nomenclaturally symmetrical with Prosimii. Unfortunately for symmetry, the name Simia is an illegal term in taxonomy. The International Commission ruled so because of an unreasonable ambiguity in the use of Simia.

A. Ceboidea

South American primates are said to be of the monkey grade of organization, and are called monkeys. This has stressed a probably spuriously close relationship between Old and New World forms.

Many consider it probable (Simpson, 1962; Simons, 1963) that at least two separate groups of prosimians gave rise to the two groups of monkeys that exist today, the ceboids of the NewWorld and the cercopithecoids of the Old World. Similarities between the two groups are startling, but the similarities are such that one is best advised to consider them the result of separate developments from different members of a common but remote prosimian ancestral group. The similarities probably are convergences due to continuing exploitation of similar econiches by evolving groups of primates. The similarities between the two groups are, as Simons (1963) points out, more apparent than real. It is for this reason that Ceboidea are potentially such an important group for students of primate evolution. The independent development, in a second primate stock, of structures and functional adaptations that appear exactly to parallel functional adaptations of the Old World monkeys is a datum about primate evolution that has not received proper consideration.

There are certain characteristics, aside from the obvious complete geographical separation, by which the New World monkeys are distinguished from those of the Old. The principal criterion used in the past for the distinction was the shape of the nose, which is presumably flat, hence, platyrrhine, flat-nosed, as opposed to catarrhine, sharp-nosed, monkeys and apes of the Old World. The expressions platyrrhine and catarrhine are reasonable enough when used colloquially but should not be used as taxonomic terms. We can add little to the mass of material about the Ceboidea collected by Hill (1957, 1960, 1962). There is little fossil material available to help us assess the relationship of the Prosimii to the South American Ceboidea. It is true that the oral tradition within paleontology suggests there are some important transitional but unpublished fossils. We are helpless until they become part of the scientific literature.

The cytogenetics of this group has been studied by Bender and Mettler (1958) and by Bender and Chu (1963). Hershkovitz (1963, 1966a, 1966b) has made notable contributions to clearing up the nomenclature of the Ceboidea and has made some intriguing observations on pelage color of several genera (Hershkovitz, 1968). However, the paucity of ecological and behavioral studies on this important group of primates, with the exception of the work of Carpenter and his students on the howler monkeys of Panama, makes it difficult to comment on the adequacy of the distinctions made in the past among the various species and genera. It is also very difficult to consider the history of any contemporary cebid group, for the fossil record is so poor. Indeed, it is almost nonexistent.

Two families have been defined in the Ceboidea, the Cebidae and the Callithricidae. In the past, the genus *Callimico*, Goeldi's monkey, has been placed among the Cebidae, in the subfamily Callimiconinae, or among the Callithricidae. Its affinities with cebids are no more obvious than its affinities with callithricids. It probably represents a lineage diverging from the line leading directly to the modern Callithricidae. Eventually a reassessment of its position must be made; for the present I have left it as a genus within the Callithricidae.

The systematics of New World monkeys is more confused than that of most primates. Much has already been done by a number of scholars to clean up this mess, and I hope that by the end of the century a better understanding of these primates from a systematic point of view will be generally available. The list I present is a compromise between those I know to be too long and somewhat confused (Hill, 1957, 1960, 1962; Napier and Napier, 1967) and the valiant attempts by Hershkovitz to rectify the situation.

B. Cercopithecoidea

The Old World monkeys, the Cercopithecoidea, are probably the most numerous and variable group in the order. They are found in Asia and in Africa and on nearby islands. There is a close relationship between Asiatic macaques and African baboons. The similarities are detailed, and Gray (1954) reports reliable accounts of hybrids between these two genera. It is best to consider them a single major group that has a continuous distribution from southern Africa to northeastern Asia, and they should be in a single genus (Buettner-Janusch, 1966b). Fossil baboons have been found in India (Simpson, 1945), and there were living populations in the Arabian peninsula recently. Baboons may have been superseded by macaques in Asia. *Macaca sylvana*, the Barbary ape, is found in North Africa. Since fossil macaques occur in European

Pleistocene deposits, it may be that *Macaca sylvana* is the survivor of a population with a continuous distribution around the Mediterranean and into Asia (Tappen, 1960).

The baboons of Africa have been classified in a large variety of ways (Hill, 1970). A simplified classification was proposed and rationalized (Buettner-Janusch, 1966b).

Among the other groups of monkeys only the leaf-eating monkeys, the Colobinae, are common to both continents. The colobines appear to require a relatively special diet of leaves and consequently a fairly specific and restricted ecozone in which they can survive. The occurrence of members in both continents may be taken to imply a continuous forest corridor which connected the two continents at one time.

The variability of species in the genus *Cercopithecus* has led to the definition of a larger number of species, subspecies, races, and local varieties than is useful even for the most extreme of splitters. An extreme is reached, perhaps, by attempts to define species and subspecies of the *C. aethiops* group on the basis of variations in the shades of blue and blue-green of the male testicles. Booth (1962) suggests that the color variation in male genitalia is conditioned by age and may be part of the apparent differences in mature and immature animals that are part of the repertory of social signals facilitating troop life and troop cohesion. Differences among the various species so far defined are undoubtedly real, but their meaning for understanding the history of this genus has not yet been explored.

The list of species and subspecies is vast and only a very small part of the systematics has been based upon ecological and field studies. Until recently almost no genetic investigations of cercopithecoids were undertaken. Both of these are essential in assessing the many debatable divisions made among these monkeys. Tappen (1960) summarized many of the problems that face anyone attempting to generalize about African monkeys. Most of his strictures apply equally well to study of the Asiatic monkeys.

Two problems in classifying various cercopithecid monkeys were cleared up by Verheyen (1962). The genera *"Allenopithecus"* and *"Erythrocebus"* have been eliminated. His excellent study of the craniology of the genus *Cercopithecus* shows that these two monkeys are to be included in that genus.

The *Cercopithecus* group is extremely widespread in Africa. Although considered arboreal animals, they can and do exploit the floor of the forest and such environments as sisal plantations and the heavy scrub land that lies between open bush-savanna country and the taller forests along the banks of rivers. As Tappen (1960) notes, the same species of *Cercopithecus* occur again and again throughout Africa.

There is no evidence that cercopithecine monkeys existed in Asia. This may imply that the cercopithecine group is more recent as an evolutionary development than the colobines. The known distribution of the African colobus monkeys may indicate they were once widespread and are now the remnant of an older population which has retreated to its special forest environments as the vegetation of Africa changed, the forests giving way to deserts, savannas, and scrub. The newer genus *Cercopithecus,* more versatile in exploiting the changing environment, grew in numbers and differentiated as extensively as it has because of the isolating effects of changes in the forest environment. This process was most certainly accelerated with the rise and expansion in size of agricultural populations that have destroyed many sections of forest land in Africa.

Tappen (1960) has argued that the cercopithecines are the more ancient inhabitants of Africa. The great number of types and the wide distribution are taken as evidence that they represent an older stratum in Africa. The colobines are viewed as a later incursion. If the colobus monkeys are a later invading group, I believe we must postulate that an extensive forest corridor existed between Asia and Africa in relatively recent times. Upon the disappearance of the forest, the leaf-eating monkeys of Africa were isolated from their Asian relatives. It is unfortunate that there is no geographical, geological, or botanical evidence which can be used to settle this question.

C. Pongidae

There are three distinct groups of pongids that have differentiated sufficiently from each other to be given generic status. "*Sym-*

phalangus" is clearly very closely related to *Hylobates,* but recent cytogenetic information tends to confirm the view that the former is distinct from the latter. This distinction is unlikely of generic significance and I no longer accept this genus. The large number of species and subspecies that have been named in the genus *Hylobates* is rather excessive. I cannot find any profound morphological differences in the pelage or skeletons. Pelage color differences, once thought important in defining species of gibbons, now appear to be another example of species polymorphism. Almost all the work done to support the excessive splitting that older name lists demonstrate is open to question.

The differences between the two island forms of *Pongo* might be expected to be great enough to warrant division into species, if the example of gibbon classification were followed. However, these populations are not distinct, and apparently subspecific status is accorded them only because of their island habitats. There are some minor genetic differences between the two strains, but they are clearly instances of polymorphism.

The African apes have been divided into a number of subspecies. The evidence for the usefulness of these subdivisions is not particularly convincing. The amazing florescence of specific and subspecific categories throughout the primate order is unquestionably the result of the fascination our closest mammalian relatives hold for hordes of variously trained explorers, naturalists, casual travelers, and overly enthusiastic zoologists. Many of the differences suggested by the long lists of subspecific names are of no greater and generally of lesser magnitude than the traits which are used to make racial divisions in the species *Homo sapiens.* The African apes exist as small populations comprising two or three species of a single genus (Simpson, 1963) and they are approaching extinction. The geographical separateness of these populations and the probable development of traits that are not common to all the separate groups has been taken by many naturalists as indicating greater genetic separation than is the case. At present I reluctantly list the so-called pygmy chimpanzee, *Pan paniscus,* as a separate species, but I do so because of tradition. I am not convinced of the usefulness or the validity of the taxon.

It is beyond the scope of this volume to do more than mention the most advanced of the Primates, the Hominidae. There has always been but a single species of the genus *Homo,* according to most informed contemporary paleontological and anthropological opinion. In recent years there has been a trend to increase the number of species represented by the fossils in the earlier segment of hominid evolution. But that is the subject of another essay.

IV. A CLASSIFICATION OF LIVING PRIMATES

The classification of the primates presented in Appendix I is based upon a variety of sources, many of which have been referred to in the preceding sections. This classification is not a revision of the Primates. An attempt is made to provide a list that has the smallest number of legitimate names and taxa.

There are several groups of primates that are still in a very unsystematic state. The most confused are those of South America. The Asiatic colobines, particularly the genus *Presbytis,* are anything but well-organized. There should be a thorough reexamination of the validity of the genera *Nasalis, Presbytis, Pygathrix, Rhinopithecus,* and *Simias.* The mangabeys (*Cercocebus*) have not been subjected to a modern reassessment. It is not unlikely that considerable changes in status of several taxa of mangabeys will occur. The macaques (*Macaca*) and baboons (*Papio*), closely related to mangabeys, are still not properly organized. These animals are often used in medical and behavioral research, and the benefits of a thorough reassessment of their phylogenetic positions as well as systematic relationships will be generally beneficial. The arboreal guenons (*Cercopithecus*) are another group that are almost hopelessly confused. I have resolved some contradictions in previously published lists. There are so many uncertainties to be resolved that another republication of the synonymies and curious reasoning found in the literature seems unnecessary at this time.

REFERENCES

Andrew, R. J. (1962): Evolution of intelligence and vocal mimicking. *Science, 137,* 585-589.

Andrew, R. J. (1963): The origin and evolution of the calls and facial expressions of the Primates. *Behaviour, 20,* 1-109.

Bender, M. A., and Chu, E. H. Y. (1963): The chromosomes of primates. In Buettner-Janusch, J. (Ed.): *Evolutionary and Genetic Biology of Primates.* New York, Academic Press, vol. I, pp. 261-310.

Bender, M. A., and Mettler, L. E. (1958): Chromosome studies of primates. *Science, 128,* 186-190.

Bishop, A. (1964): Use of the hand in lower primates. In Buettner-Janusch, J. (Ed.): *Evolutionary and Genetic Biology of Primates.* New York, Academic Press, vol. II, pp. 133-225.

Booth, C. (1962): Some observations on behavior of cercopithecus monkeys. *Ann NY Acad Sci, 102,* 477-487.

Buettner-Janusch, J. (1966a): *Origins of Man.* New York, Wiley, 674 pp.

Buettner-Janusch, J. (1966b): A problem in evolutionary systematics: Nomenclature and classification of baboons, genus *Papio. Folia Primat, 4,* 288-308.

Buettner-Janusch, J., and Hill, R. L. (1965): Molecules and monkeys. *Science, 147,* 836-842.

Chu, E. H. Y., and Bender, M. A. (1962): Cytogenetics and evolution of primates. *Ann NY Acad Sci, 102,* 253-266.

Clark, W. E. LeGros (1962). *The Antecedents of Man.* Edinburgh, Edin burgh University Press, 388 pp.

Elliot, D. G. (1913): *A Review of the Primates.* New York, American Museum of Natural History, vol. I, 317 pp.

Goodman, M. (1963): Man's place in the phylogeny of the Primates as reflected in serum proteins. In Washburn, S. L. (Ed.): *Classification and Human Evolution.* Chicago, Aldine, pp. 204-234.

Goodman, M.; Moore, G. W.; Farris, W., & Poulik, E. (1970): The evidence from genetically informative macromolecules on the phylogenetic relationships of the chimpanzees. In Bourne, G. H. (Ed): *The Chimpanzee.* Baltimore, University Park Press, vol. 2, pp. 318-360.

Grassé, P.-P. (1955): *Traité de Zoologie.* Paris, Masson, vol. 17, part II, pp. 1173-2300.

Gray, A. P. (1954): Mammalian hybrids. Tech. Commun. No. 10, Commonwealth Agricultural Bureau, Farnham Royal, England.

Hershkovitz, P. (1963): A systematic and zoogeographic account of the monkeys of the genus *Callicebus* (Cebidae) of the Amazonas and Orinoco river basins. *Mammalia, 27,* 1-79.

Hershkovitz, P. (1966a): Taxonomic notes on tamarins, genus *Saguinus* (Callithricidae, Primates), with descriptions of four new forms. *Folia Primat, 4,* 381-395.

Hershkovitz, P. (1966b): On the identification of some marmosets, family Callithricidae (Primates). *Mammalia, 30,* 327-332.

Hershkovitz, P. (1968): Metachromism or the principle of evolutionary changes in mammalian tegumentary colors. *Evolution, 22,* 556-575.

Hill, R. L.; Buettner-Janusch, J., and Buettner-Janusch, V. (1963): Evolution of hemoglobin in primates. *Proc Natl Acad Sci USA, 50,* 885-893.

Hill, W. C. O. (1953, 1955, 1957, 1960, 1962, 1966, 1970:) *Primates.* New York, Wiley-Interscience, vol. I-VI, VIII.

Jones, F. W. (1929): Some landmarks in the phylogeny of primates. *Hum Biol, 1,* 219-228.

Jouffroy, F. K., and Lessertisseur, J. (1959): La main des lémuriens malgaches comparée à celle des autres primates. *Mém Inst Sci Madagascar, A13,* 195-219.

Martin, R. D. (1968): Towards a new definition of primates. *Man, 3,* 377-401.

Milne-Edwards, A., and Grandidier, A. (1875, 1890-96): *Histoire Naturelle des Mammifères.* Paris, vol. 6, 9, 10.

Napier, J. R. (1960): Studies of the hands of living primates. *Proc Zool Soc London, 134,* 647-657.

Napier, J. R. (1961): Prehensility and opposability in the hands of primates. *Sympos Zool Soc London, 5,* 115-132.

Napier, J. R., and Napier, P. H. (1967): *A Handbook of Living Primates.* New York, Academic Press, 456 pp.

Petter, J.-J. (1962): Recherches sur l'écologie et l'éthologie des lémuriens malgaches. *Mém Mus Nat Hist nat,* Sér. A, *27,* 1-146.

Pilbeam, D. R. (1969): Tertiary Pongidae of East Africa: Evolutionary relationships and taxonomy. *Peabody Mus Nat Hist Yale Univ Bull, 31,* 1-185.

Read, D. W., and Lestrel, P. E. (1970): Hominid phylogeny and immunology: A critical appraisal. *Science, 168,* 578-580.

Rumpler, Y., and Albignac, R. (1969a): Etude cytogénétique de deux lémuriens, *Lemur macaco macaco,* Linné 1766, et *Lemur fulvus rufus* (Audebert 1800), et d'un hybride *macaco macaco/fulvus rufus. C R Soc Biol, 163,* 1247-1250.

Rumpler, Y., and Albignac, R. (1969b): Existence d'une variabilité chromosomique intraspecifique chez certains lémuriens. *C R Soc Biol, 163,* 1989-1992.

Rumpler, Y., and Albignac, R. (1970): Evolution chromosomique des lémuriens malgaches. *Ann Univ Madagascar, 12-13,* 123-131.

Sarich, V. M., and Wilson, A. C. (1966): Quantitative immunochemistry and the evolution of primate albumins: Micro-complement fixation. *Science, 154,* 1563-1566.

Sarich, V. M., and Wilson, A. C. (1967a): Rates of albumin evolution in primates. *Proc Nat Acad Sci, USA, 58,* 142-148.

Sarich, V. M., and Wilson, A. C. (1967b): Immunological time scale for hominid evolution. *Science, 158,* 1200-1203.

Schwarz, E. (1936): A propos du *"Lemur macaco"* Linnaeus. *Mammalia, 1,* 24-25.

Simons, E. L. (1961): Notes on Eocene tarsioids and a revision of some Necrolemurinae. *Bull Brit Mus Nat Hist Geol, 5,* 45-69.

Simons. E. L. (1963): A critical reappraisal of Tertiary primates. In Buettner-Janusch, J. (Ed.): *Evolutionary and Genetic Biology of Primates.* New York, Academic Press, vol. I, pp. 65-129.

Simons, E. L. (1967): The significance of primate paleontology for anthropological studies. *Amer J Phys Anthrop, 27,* 307-332.

Simons, E. L. (1968): A source for dental comparison of *Ramapithecus* with *Australopithecus* and *Homo. S Afr J Sci, 64,* 92-112.

Simons, E. L. (1969): The origin and radiation of the Primates. *Ann NY Acad Sci, 167,* 319-331.

Simons, E. L., and Russell, D. E. (1960): Notes on the cranial anatomy of *Necrolemur. Breviora, 127,* 1-14.

Simpson, G. G. (1940): Studies on the earliest primates. *Bull Amer Mus Nat Hist, 77,* 185-212.

Simpson, G. G. (1945): The principles of classification and a classification of mammals. *Bull Amer Mus Nat Hist, 85,* 1-350.

Simpson, G. G. (1962): Primate taxonomy and recent studies of nonhuman primates. *Ann NY Acad Sci, 102,* 497-514.

Simpson, G. G. (1963): The meaning of taxonomic statements. In Washburn, S. L. (Ed.): *Classification and Human Evolution.* Chicago, Aldine, pp. 1-31.

Simpson, G. G. (1964): Organisms and molecules in evolution. *Science, 146,* 1535-1538.

Straus, W. L., Jr. (1956): Review of *Primates I* and *II* by W. C. O. Hill. *Amer J Phys Anthrop, 14,* 668-673.

Szalay, F. S. (1968): The beginnings of primates. *Evolution, 22,* 19-36.

Tappen, N. C. (1960): Problems of distribution and adaptation of the African monkeys. *Curr Anthrop, 1,* 91-120.

Verheyen, W. N. (1962): Contribution à la craniologie comparée des Primates. *Ann Mus Roy Afr Cent-Tervuren, Belg, Sci Zool, 105,* 1-255.

Washburn, S. L. (1950): The analysis of primate evolution with particular reference to the origin of man. *Cold Spring Harbor Symp Quant Biol, 15,* 67-78.

Zuckerkandl, E. (1963): Perspectives in molecular anthropology. In Washburn, S. L. (Ed.): *Classification and Human Evolution.* Chicago, Aldine, pp. 243-272.

Zuckerkandl, E.; Jones, R. T., and Pauling, L. (1960): A comparison of animal hemoglobins by tryptic peptide analysis. *Proc Nat Acad Sci USA, 46,* 1349-1360.

Chapter 2

GONADOTROPINS AND GONADAL HORMONES

R. C. WOLF AND R. K. MEYER

THE role of the adenohypophysial and gonadal hormones on reproductive processes has been described for a variety of mammalian species. The kind and quantity of these hormones in tissues, blood and urine of nonhuman primates, however, has not been elucidated. In the present chapter the relationship of gonadotropins and gonadal hormones to selected phases of reproduction is described. It is outside the scope of this chapter to provide a detailed description of steroid biosynthetic and metabolic pathways. For information on these parameters standard biochemistry texts should be consulted.

I. PUBERTY

Puberty, the onset of those processes leading to sexual maturity, is accompanied by a number of anatomic and physiologic changes. These changes include the onset of spermatogenesis in males and cyclic follicular maturation and menarche in females. Growth and development of accessory reproductive organs and secondary sex characters such as the sexual skin, when present, also occur. A description of these and other changes in both primate and nonprimate species is described in a recent monograph (Donovan and van der Werff ten Bosch, 1965).

The precise factors responsible for the initiation of puberty in any species have not been clearly defined. It does appear, however, that maturation of the central nervous system is of fundamental importance, since an increase in gonadotropic hormones and, consequently, gonadal hormones occurs. That maturational alterations in the central nervous system are essential to initiation of puberty is well documented in rodents and is suggested by the observation that lesions in the neocortex or temporal lobe of the rhesus monkey (*Macaca mulatta*) bring about precocious puberty (Segal, 1964).

Testosterone is first detected in the peripheral plasma of rhesus monkeys at approximately three years of age (Resko, 1967). At this age granular cells appear in the testis (van Wagenen and Simpson, 1965). The possibility that lower, yet undetectable, amounts may be present in the circulation of younger animals arises from the observation that testicular homogenates contain this androgen. Resko (1967) also observed that androstenedione is present in the plasma of monkeys ranging in age from five days to over five years. In immature animals the ratio of testosterone to androstenedione is less than one, while in adult male monkeys the ratio is three or more. Since androstenedione levels in plasma do not vary with age, or following castration, the source of this steroid is probably the adrenal cortex. Dehydroepiandrosterone (DHEA) concentrations in the plasma of mature and immature male rhesus monkeys are identical and approximately four times higher than that of man (Snipes *et al.*, 1969).

Testosterone, epitestosterone, androsterone, etiocholanolone, and dehydroepiandrosterone are present in the urine of normal adult rhesus monkeys, but in amounts lower than those of man (Mougey *et al.*, 1969; Tolson *et al.*, 1966).

Androgen concentrations have also been determined by Snipes *et al.* (1969) in spider monkeys (*Ateles geoffroyi*), squirrel monkeys (*Saimiri sciureus*), capuchin monkeys (*Cebus apella*), cynomologus monkeys (*Macaca irus*), and baboons (*Papio cynocephalus*) (Table 2-I). In the nonmacaques, which were estimated as being adults, plasma testosterone concentrations tended to be higher than both rhesus and man. Testosterone is also present in the testicular lymph of baboons, but in concentrations approximately 0.1 to 0.7 of that in spermatic vein plasma (Daniel *et al.*, 1963).

The *in vitro* biosynthesis of testosterone from a variety of precursors by homogenates of rhesus (Hoschoian and Brownie, 1967), capuchin (Dorfman *et al.*, 1967) and baboon (Axelrod, 1967) testes has been described. In rhesus monkey testes homogenates an

TABLE 2-I

PLASMA ANDROGEN CONCENTRATIONS (mμg/100 ml) IN SEVERAL NONHUMAN PRIMATES*

Species	*Testosterone*	*Androstenedione*	*Dehydroepi-androsterone*
M. mulatta			
Mature	891 ± 204	141 ± 50	2121 ± 256
Immature	52 ± 27	199 ± 57	2120 ± 655
M. irus	68, 160, 564	64, 219, 155	250, 146
A. geoffroyi	444, 3890	140, 463, 303	52, 174, 138
C. apella	262, 5079, 1206	849, 538, 373	100, 112, 427
S. sciureus	3927, 1140, 1950	902	1138, 625, 674
P. cynocephalus	1152, 1792, 173	772, 364, 1130	711, 1288, 1190

* From Snipes *et al.*, 1970.

important pathway for testoterone synthesis involves pregnenolone and 17α hydroxypregnenolone, with Δ^5-androstenediol as a possible intermediate. This pathway is independent of androstenedione. Baboon testes homogenates also convert both pregnenolone and 17α hydroxypregnenolone to testosterone. The percent transformation of these precursors to testosterone is approximately the same as that observed in human testes.

Homogenates of capuchin monkey testes can synthesize testosterone, from progesterone, 17α hydroxyprogesterone, DHEA and androstenedione. In this species, the pathway, progesterone → 17α hydroxyprogesterone → testosterone, which is established in man and other species also operates.

The concentrations of gonadotropins in both immature and adult male and gonadal hormones in female prepuberal nonhuman primates are essentially unknown. This lack of information is due in large part to assay methods which until recently lacked sufficient specificity and sensitivity. Previous attempts to measure these hormones clearly indicated that the levels present in biological fluids were below the extinction points of the assays used.

The ovaries of immature monkeys can, however, respond to exogenous gonadotropins. In a series of twelve immature monkeys treated with varying doses of pregnant mare's serum gonadotropin (PMSG) seven animals demonstrated ovarian enlargement, sex skin development and withdrawal bleeding; ovulation, however, did not occur (Arslan *et al.,* 1968). The development of sex skin and induction of withdrawal bleeding may be regarded as positive, but indirect, evidence of estrogen secretion. Based upon uterine morphology, the ovaries of prepuberal langurs (*Presbytis entellus*) also secrete estrogen, but not progesterone following treatment with PMSG and human chorionic gonadotropin (HCG) (Kar and Chandra, 1965). The PMSG treated monkeys reached menarche one year earlier than both untreated control monkeys and the five monkeys which did not initially respond to the gonadotropin (Arslan *et al.,* 1968). Steroids other than estrogen also affect the time of puberty since sexual precocity occurs following testosterone administration to immature female monkeys (van Wagenen, 1949).

The testes of immature rhesus monkeys respond to both FSH and L.H. Testis weight, the diameter of the seminiferous tubules, and the number of spermatogonia increase following injection of FSH alone or in combination with LH. Stimulation of Leydig cells is induced by LH as is indicated by an increase in weight of the seminal vesicle and prostate gland. In addition, the concentration of prostatic acid phosphatase is elevated (Kar *et al.,* 1966).

II. MENSTRUAL CYCLES

Menstrual cycles are a characteristic feature of catarrhine monkeys and the anthropoid apes. Cyclic desquamation of the uterine endometrium accompanied by bleeding occurs in some, but not all, of the platyrrhine monkeys and is generally considered to be absent in the lorisiform primates.

The menstrual cycle of the rhesus monkey (*M. mulatta*) has a modal length of twenty-eight days. A typical cycle is generally considered to consist of four phases: (a) the follicular or proliferative phase; (b) ovulation; (c) the luteal or secretory phase; and (d) menstruation. Each of these terms is descriptive of events occurring in either the ovaries or uterus.

During the follicular phase of the cycle growth of the ovarian follicle occurs under the stimulus of FSH. Biological assays of anterior pituitary glands obtained from normal cycling rhesus monkeys indicate that the pituitary content of FSH is highest on day nine of the cycle (Simpson *et al.,* 1956). Although the amount of hormone present in the gland does not provide information on the circulating hormonal levels, this elevated gonadotropin level is consistent with the preovulatory growth spurt observed in the follicle at this time. In the adult female chimpanzee (*Pan troglodytes*) the urinary excretion of FSH is also maximal at this time (McArthur and Perley, 1969).

Pituitary gland content of LH is also high during the late follicular phase, although its concentration is low in plasma (Kirton *et al.*, 1970) and urine (Claybaugh, 1970). Using a sensitive double antibody radioimmunoassay for rhesus monkey LH, Monroe *et al.* (1970) detected approximately 4.5 μg LH/ml plasma in this stage of the cycle.

At the middle of the cycle, pituitary gland FSH is somewhat lower than that observed on day nine, while LH content is elevated. The increased ratio of LH to FSH at this time is compatible with the role of these gonadotropins in final follicular growth, and with the importance of LH to ovulation and corpus luteum formation. Plasma and urine concentrations of LH are also increased markedly at midcycle. Concentrations of 50 μg LH/ml of plasma have been measured (Monroe *et al.*, 1970). A surge in urinary LH is also observed at this time in the chimpanzee; FSH, however, is not detectable (McArthur and Perley, 1969).

Two days prior to ovulation a peak in excretion of estrone, the major urinary estrogen in the rhesus monkey, to approximately 8 μg/24 hours, occurs. Estradiol 17β and estriol are either not detectable or are excreted in amounts of 1.0 μg or 0.2 μg/24 hours respectively. Indeed, neither of these steroids is excreted in a predictable pattern or in amounts greater than these throughout the entire cycle (Hopper and Tullner, 1969). It is of interest that following administration of estradiol 17β-4-^{14}C to rhesus monkeys in the follicular stage of the menstrual cycle the majority of the injected steroid was excreted unmetabolized or as estrone. Small amounts of radioactivity, however, were associated with estriol and 16 epi-estriol (Flickinger and Wu, 1967).

Plasma progesterone concentrations also rise shortly before ovulation to levels of 3 to 4 mμg/ml. Prior to this time the concentration of this steroid is less than 0.5 mμg/ml of plasma (Neill *et al.*, 1967). The increased concentrations of both estrone and progesterone have been suggested as being useful indicators of impend-

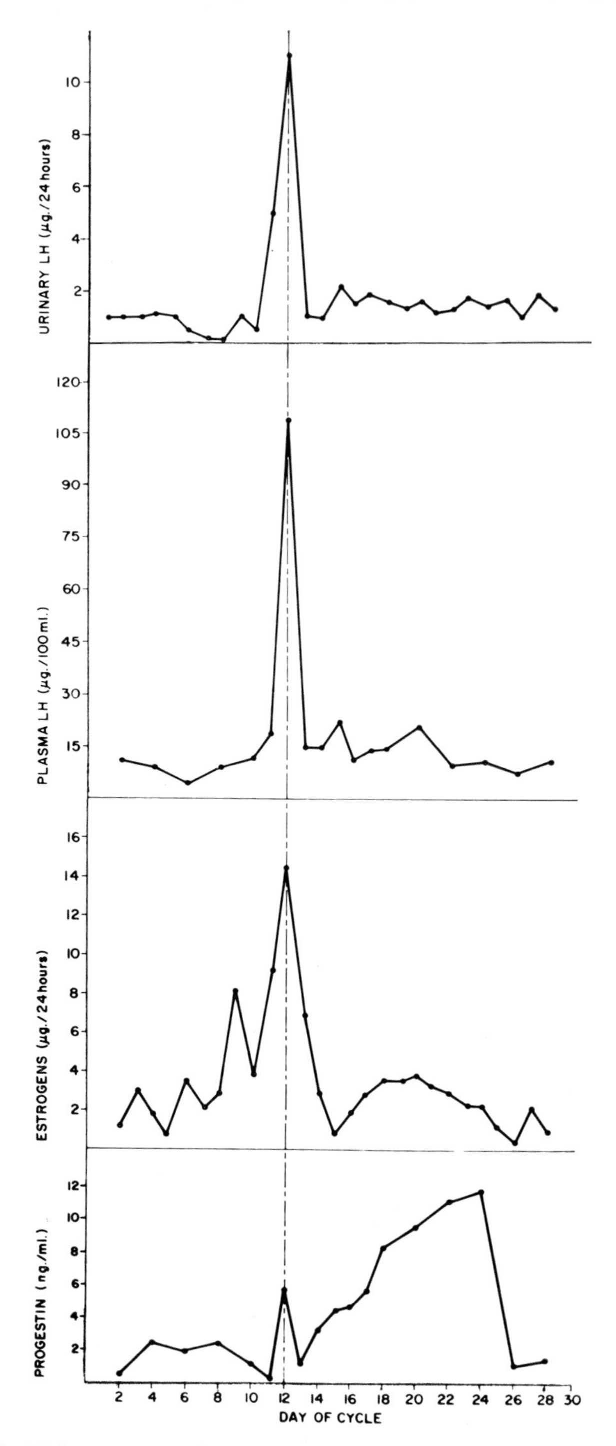

Figure 2-1. Urinary LH, plasma LH, urinary estrogens and plasma "progestins" during a baboon menstrual cycle.

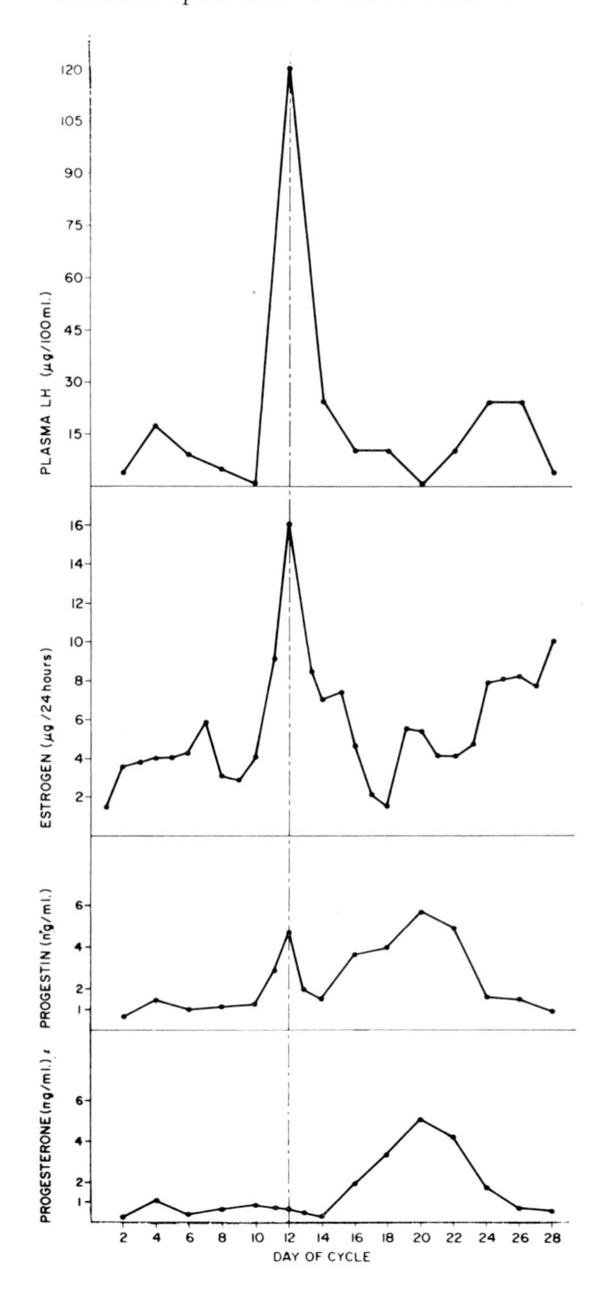

Figure 2-2. Plasma LH, urinary estrogens, plasma "progestins" and plasma progesterone during a baboon menstrual cycle.

ing ovulation (Hopper and Tullner, 1969; Johansson *et al.*, 1968).

At, or shortly after, ovulation the excretion of estrone decreases significantly. Plasma progesterone concentrations, however, remain elevated throughout most of the luteal phase. Approximately three days prior to the onset of menstruation the plasma concentration of this steroid is decreased to the level observed during the early part of the follicular phase. Urinary androsterone, a principal progesterone metabolite in the monkey, is also increased (Claybaugh, 1970). In baboons (*Papio ursinus*) pregnanediol, the principal urine metabolite of progesterone in this species, is greatly elevated (DuToit, 1956). These elevations in steroid concentration occur even though plasma LH levels are decreased to levels essentially identical to those measured during the follicular phase. In the chimpanzee, FSH was not detectable at midcycle, but is again present in measurable amounts in urine during the luteal phase (McArthur and Perley, 1969).

Ovarian venous plasma obtained from monkeys following treatment with ovulating doses of gonadotropins contains progesterone, 17α-hydroxy-progesterone and 20α hydroxy-4-en-3-one (Hayward *et al.*, 1963). Comparable studies have not been conducted at selected times in untreated cycling animals, although Riesen *et al.* (1970) reported a mean concentration of 400 mμg progesterone/ml of ovarian vein plasma obtained approximately one week following ovulation.

Concurrent measures of plasma and/or urine LH, estrogens and progestogens in the baboon (*Papio anubis*) have been measured (Stevens *et al.*, 1970) (Fig. 2-1, 2-2). The pattern of LH secretion throughout the cycle is fundamentally the same as that of the rhesus monkey in that a midcycle peak of LH is observed in both plasma and urine. Plasma progestins also peak at midcycle coincident with LH and remain elevated throughout the luteal phase of the cycle. Progesterone levels are also elevated during this stage of the cycle but no peak at midcycle is detected. These data suggest that most of the luteal progestin is progesterone, but that, as in man, the progestin peak is primarily the result of a sudden increase in 17-hydroxyprogesterone. Urinary estrogens increased during the follicular phase of the cycle with a sudden elevation taking place at midcycle. In contrast with most human data, however, the urinary LH and estrogen peaks occurred on the same day of the cycle.

The onset of menstruation is characterized by low concentrations of pregnanediol in the urine of the baboon, and low plasma progesterone and urinary estrone in the monkey. These depressed steroid levels are consistent with the finding that a decrease in either estrogen or progesterone will induce uterine bleeding in both intact and ovariectomized animals. The possibility that other hormonal factors are necessary, however, for the initiation of menstruation cannot be ignored. In hypophysectomized monkeys estrogen withdrawal bleeding occurred only if pituitary extracts were administered (Hartman *et al.*, 1930). In the hypophysectomized baboon, estrogen induced uterine bleeding will only ensue if thyroxin and ACTH are administered prior to estrogen treatment (Gilbert and Gillman, 1956).

III. PREGNANCY

The information available concerning endocrine changes which occur during pregnancy in primates indicates that certain similarities exist between nonhuman primates and human females. Most information on nonhuman primates has been derived from studies on monkeys, principally the rhesus monkey (*M. mulatta*). In this species, like the human female, ovariectomy or hypophysectomy after the placenta is well established does not terminate pregnancy. Evidence from the human female, and in more limited amounts from nonhuman primates, indicates that the conceptus (fetal compartment) is the source of both gonadotropins and steroids which supplement the pituitary gland and ovaries during the establishment of the embryo in the uterus, and is the primary source of hormones required for the maintenance of pregnancy.

A. Gonadotropins

Much remains to be learned about the regulation of pituitary and ovarian function, especially the corpus luteum, in primates during the transition from the fertile postovulatory menstrual phase to the establishment of the embryo in the uterus. During the postovulatory phase of the nonfertile and fertile menstrual cycle in *M. mulatta* LH and FSH are low. Available evidence from serum and urinary data indicates that the gonadotropic stimulus for ovarian function during the early phases of pregnancy is provided by the chorionic gonadotropin (MCG) at the time of implantation (Neill and Knobil, 1969). The level of MCG reaches a maximum between three to five weeks after mating depending upon whether measurements are made on serum or urine; measurable amounts are rarely found seven weeks after mating (Tullner and Hertz, 1966a; Kinzey, 1965; Arslan *et al.*, 1967). Unlike *M. mulatta* in which MCG excretion appears to be restricted to the early stages of pregnancy, chorionic gonadotropin is excreted during the most of pregnancy in man, gorilla (*Gorilla gorilla*) (Tullner and Gray, 1968), chimpanzee (Elder and Bruhn, 1939), baboon (Hobson, 1970), squirrel monkey (*S. sciureus*) (Nathan *et al.*, 1966), and marmoset (*Callithrix jacchus*) (Hampton, *et al.*, 1969). Ovariectomy during early post-implantation stages in *M. mulatta* does not alter the normal patterns of MCG excretion nor interfere with pregnancy or the delivery of normal young (Tullner and Hertz, 1966b). Hypophysectomy or sham hypophysectomy in *M. mulatta* seventeen to twenty days after conception, however, causes a sudden marked decrease in the excretion of MCG and termination of pregnancy. However, progesterone administered just prior to hypophysectomy does not prevent the decrease in MCG and abortion (Arslan *et al.*, 1969). Sham hypophysectomy performed at known times after ovulation in a nonfertile cycle in the rhesus monkey causes a rapid and marked decrease in blood progesterone (Knobil *et al.*, 1968).

Immunological cross reactivity, as demonstrated by radioimmunoassay systems, exists between MCG and HCG and supports the biological similarity of these two placental gonadotropins (Bagshawe *et al.*, 1968; Tullner *et al.*, 1969).

B. Gonadal Steroids

There are both similarities and differences in the kind and production patterns of steroid hormones during pregnancy between human and nonhuman females. Data from the baboon (*P. cynocephalus*) (Merkatz and Beling, 1969) and rhesus monkey (Hopper and Tullner, 1967; Liskowski *et al.*, 1970) show that urinary excretion of *estrogenic activity* increases during pregnancy as in women. However, the total estrogenic activity is lower in both the baboon and monkey, and although estradiol-17β, estriol and estrone are excreted, estrone is the principal estrogen in the monkey (Liskowski *et al.*, 1966). The peak in estrogenic activity in the rhesus monkey, which is largely due to estrone, is attained approximately one week prior to parturition and decreases to very low levels on the day of delivery. The marked rise in estriol observed typically during pregnancy in the human female does not occur in either the baboon or monkey. In the lowland gorilla (*G. gorilla*), however, estriol exhibits a marked rise similar to that seen in pregnant women (Hopper *et al.*, 1968). Indicative data, although limited, suggest that this is true also for the pregnant chimpanzee (*P. satyrus*) (Jirku and Layne, 1965). The likeness of the estriol excretory patterns in these two higher primates and pregnant women suggests that the fetal compartment is contributing more to the estriol component than it is in baboons and rhesus monkeys.

Although much is known about the metabolism of progesterone and the excretion of its principal metabolite, pregnanediol, during pregnancy in women and some nonhuman primates, information concerning blood levels of progesterone has been very limited. Recently the development of the competitive protein binding methods for measuring circulating steroids has been applied to the measurement of progesterone in the rhesus monkey during both fertile and nonfertile cycles and pregnancy (Neill *et al.*, 1969). Progesterone begins to decrease at approximately the twenty-second day of the nonfertile cycle when the corpus luteum is presumably involuting. At about this time in the fertile cycle there is a sharp but temporary elevation in plasma progesterone which coincides with days nine to eleven of pregnancy. It is at this time that the embryo is implanting and the syncytiotrophoblast is developing and beginning to secrete chorionic gonadotropin. Presumably the surge in progesterone is initiated by a luteotropic stimulus (Neill and Knobil, 1969). The short-lived increase is followed by a decline to concentrations observed at the eighteenth to twentieth days of the nonfertile cycle. The depression in plasma progesterone occurs at the same time that chorionic gonadotropin is increasing rapidly and reaching peak levels. These events are correlated with the appearance of the placental sign. A second longer-lived and more prolonged peak exists between twenty-three to forty days, which is the time during which the ovary or hypophysis can be removed without causing abortion. It is reasonable to assume that the placenta is capable of producing sufficient progesterone to maintain pregnancy during and after this time. Shortly after the fortieth day the concentration decreases to levels observed just prior to ovulation which persist until parturition. This decline is associated with a decrease of chorionic gonadotropin to unmeasurable quantities.

Figure 2-3 represents in schematic form the correlation of the requirement of the ovary and pituitary gland for the initiation and maintenance of pregnancy in *M. mulatta* with the levels of progesterone and chorionic gonadotropin, the secretory phases of the corpus luteum and the differentiation of the placenta.

The plasma concentrations of progesterone during gestation in the rhesus monkey are very low compared to those observed in women in the last third of pregnancy (Wiest, 1967). Short and Eckstein (1961) showed that both plasma and placental progesterone in the monkey are much lower than those in the pregnant woman.

Limited data are available concerning the biosynthesis and metabolism of estrogens and progestins in nonhuman primates. It is clear, however, from these data that marked differences in gonadal steroid metabolism exist among the primates.

The primary urinary metabolite of progesterone in the rhesus monkey (Liskowski *et al.,* 1970) and pig-tail monkey (*Macaca nemestrina*) (Jeffery, 1966) is androsterone (3 α-hydroxy-5α-androstan-17-one). This and other information indicate that the major conversion of progesterone to androgen in these species is in contrast to women in which pregnanediol is the primary metabolite.

On the basis of data obtained from *in vitro* studies with placental tissue, Ainsworth *et al.* (1969) demonstrated that placental tissue of the baboon (*P. cynocephalus*) and rhesus (*M. mulatta*), squirrel (*S. sciureus*) and *M. cynomologus* monkeys metabolize pregnenolone and progesterone. They isolated 6β hydroxyprogesterone as well as compounds having a 5α configuration from the incubation media.

These data suggest that the metabolism of progesterone by these species may be more closely related to that of domestic animals than to the human female. In women, pregnenolone is converted

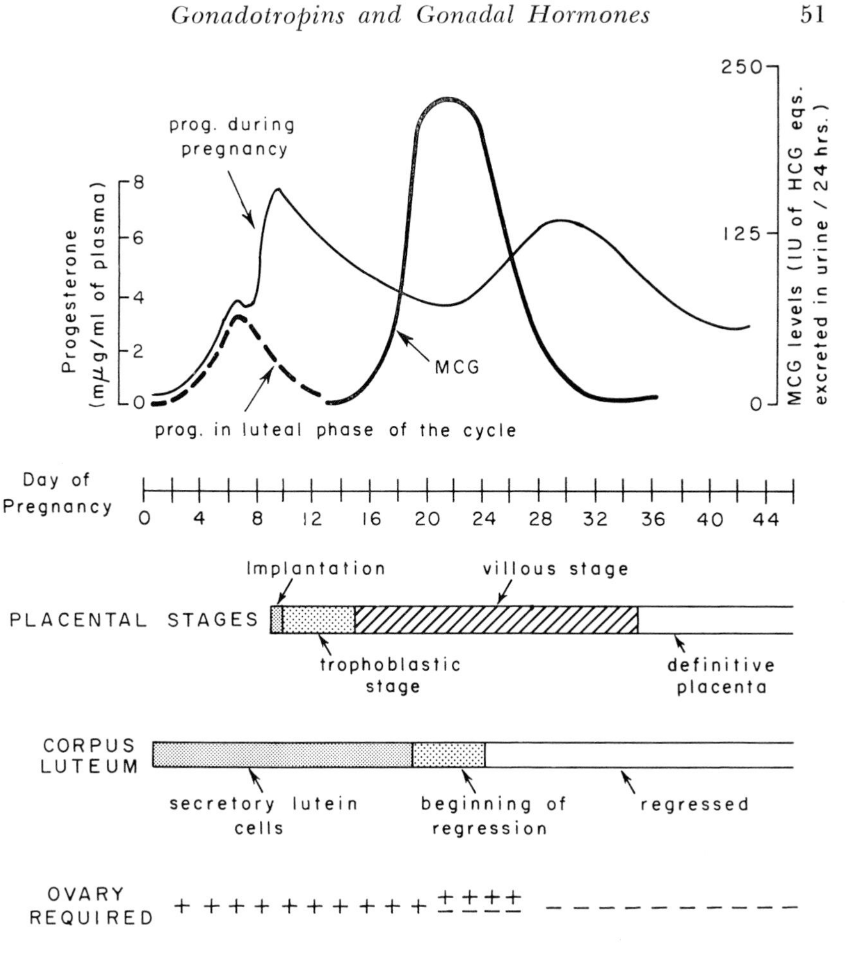

Figure 2-3. Ovarian, pituitary and placental relations during pregnancy in *M. mulatta*. [From (Arslan, M. 1969): *Hormonal Requirements During Early Pregnancy and Effects of Gonadotrophins in the Rhesus Monkey (Macaca Mulatta)*. Ph.D. thesis, University of Wisconsin.]

to progesterone, but progesterone is not extensively metabolized (Solomon, 1966). In contrast, orangutan placental tissue metabolism resembles that of human placenta with the single exception that in the orangutan a Δ^4-5α reductase system is present which has not been identified in human placentae. Ainsworth and Ryan (1969) have reported the conversion of Δ^4-androstenedione to estrone and estradiol 17β in the same species. The formation of estrone from the same substrate also occurs in the marmoset *(Leontocebus rosalia)* (Ryan *et al.*, 1961).

As indicated earlier, estrogen excretion in the pregnant chimpanzee (*P. satyrus*) is like that of women. In addition, the pregnant chimpanzee converts injected estrone to estradiol 17β, estriol and 2-methoxyestrone. The latter steroid has not been reported to be present in any other mammalian species except man (Jirku and Layne, 1965).

IV. LACTATION

The factors involved in the growth, development and function of the female mammary gland can be conveniently described in relation to those changes which occur in the gland from birth to puberty, during the menstrual cycle, pregnancy and lactation. Rapid advances concerning hormonal involvement in these changes occurred in the period between 1935 and 1945. Since that time this facet of endocrinology in nonhuman primates has not been extensively studied.

In the rhesus monkey the duct system of the mammary gland undergoes extension in the period between birth and puberty. Although the duct system is extended and shows some arborization, no alveolar tissue is present (Folley *et al.*, 1939; Allen *et al.*, 1935). With the initiation of cyclic ovarian function an increase in the mammary gland and the development of lobule-alveolar tissue ensues. Of particular interest is the observation that immediately following menarche, when menstrual cycles are generally anovulatory, alveolar tissue is not present. However, when ovulation occurs alveoli are present in the gland.

Cyclic changes in the mammary gland of the rhesus monkey which depend upon ovulation have been established (Speert, 1941). Approximately one week prior to menstruation in ovulatory cycles lobular enlargement, an increased vascularity of the lobule and acinar dilatation occur. These changes reach their apogee at the time of menstruation and then regress during the postmenstrual period. In anovulatory cycles, these changes are not observed.

In the single detailed description of the glandular changes during pregnancy (Speert, 1948), little change in ducts or lobules occurred during the first two months of gestation. During the third month lobule hypertrophy and alveolar growth was observed. Shortly before parturition the lobules were enlarged further and the alveoli distended. Lactation occurred two days after delivery at which time the lumina of the alveoli were distended with milk.

Experimental evidence indicates that, in contrast to women, estrogen alone causes both duct and lobule-alveolar development in the rhesus monkey. The complete mammary development following estrogen stimulation is not only observed in intact females (Gardner, 1941), but also in ovariectomized immature animals (Gardner and van Wagenen, 1938). Although other steroids are not required for normal gland development, a mammary growth promoting action has been reported for progesterone (Hartman and Speert, 1941), testosterone and desoxycorticosterone (Speert, 1948).

Direct evidence concerning the well-documented role of other hormones, particularly prolactin and oxytocin, on initiation and maintenance of lactation in other species is not available for the nonhuman primate. That these or other hormones may be involved in these processes can be inferred, however, from studies of hypophysectomized pregnant rhesus monkeys (Agate, 1952). In nineteen monkeys hypophysectomized at stages ranging from early to late pregnancy, no significant difference in either the size or development of mammary glands was observed between intact and operated animals. At term secretory activity was noted in the glands of hypophysectomized monkeys during each of the first three days following delivery and milk could be expressed from the nipples. These data indicate clearly that milk secretion and lactation can be initiated in the absence of the pituitary gland. Continued milk production and lactation did not appear to be comparable to that of intact monkeys since nursing infants lost weight (Smith, 1954).

REFERENCES

Agate, F. J., Jr. (1952): The growth and secretory activity of the mammary glands of the pregnant rhesus monkey *(Macaca mulatta)* following hypophysectomy. *Amer J Anat, 90,* 257-283.

Ainsworth, L.; Daenen, M., and Ryan, K. J. (1969): Steroid hormone transformations by endocrine organs from pregnant mammals. IV. Biosynthesis and metabolism of estrogens and progesterone by primate placental preparations *in vitro. Endocrinology, 84,* 1421-1429.

Ainsworth, L., and Ryan, K. J. (1969): Steroid hormone transformations by endocrine organs from pregnant mammals. V. The biosynthesis and metabolism of progesterone and estrogens by orangutan placental tissue *in vitro. Steroids, 14,* 301-314.

Allen, E.; Gardner, W. U., and Diddle, A. W. (1935): Experiments with theelin and galactin on growth and function of the mammary glands of the monkey. *Endocrinology, 19,* 305-313.

Arslan, M.; Meyer, R. K., and Wolf, R. C. (1967): Chorionic gonadotropin in the blood and urine of pregnant rhesus monkeys *(Macaca mulatta). Proc Soc Exp Biol Med, 125,* 349-352.

Arslan, M.; Wolf, R. C., and Meyer, R. K. (1969): Effects of hypophysectomy on early-phase of gestation and levels of chorionic gonadotrophin in the rhesus monkey *(Macaca mulatta). Soc Stud Reprod, 2,* 3.

Arslan, M.; Wolf, R. C; Meyer, R. K., and Prasad, M. R. N. (1968): Evidence of precocious puberty in the immature female rhesus monkey *(Macaca mulatta)* treated with pregnant mare's serum gonadotrophin. *J Reprod Fertil, 17,* 119-123.

Axelrod, L. R. (1967): The synthesis of testosterone from precursors by the baboon testes. In Vagtborg, H. (Ed.): *The Baboon in Medical Research.* Austin, University of Texas Press, vol. 2, pp. 633-636.

Bagshawe, K. D.; Orr, A. H., and Godden, J. (1968): Cross-reaction in radioimmunoassay between human chorionic gonadotrophin and plasma from various species. *J Endocr, 42,* 513-518.

Claybaugh, J. (1970): *The Secretion of Pituitary Gonadotrophins in the Female Rhesus Monkey (Macaca Mulatta).* Ph.D. Thesis, University of Wisconsin.

Daniel, P. M.; Gale, M. M., and Pratt, O. E. (1963): Hormones and related substances in the lymph leaving four endocrine glands—the testis, ovary, adrenal, and thyroid. *Lancet, 1,* 1232-1234.

Donovan, B. T., and van der Werff ten Bosch, J. J. (1965): *Physiology of Puberty.* Baltimore, Williams & Wilkins.

Dorfman, R. I.; Menon, K. M. J.; Sharma, D. C.; Joshi, S., and Forchielli, E. (1967): Steroid hormone biosynthesis in rat, rabbit, and capuchine testis. *Ciba Fdn Colloq Endocr, 16,* 91-104.

DuToit, D. S. (1956): Preliminary report on the excretion of pregnanediol during the menstrual cycle of the baboon *(Papio ursinus). S Afr J Med Sci, 21,* 47-48.

Elder, J. H., and Bruhn, J. M. (1939): Use of the Friedman test for pregnancy with chimpanzees. *Yale J Biol Med, 12,* 155-160.

Flickinger, G. L., and Wu, C. (1967): Metabolism of estradiol-17β-4^{14}C in a non-pregnant rhesus monkey. *Proc Soc Exp Biol Med, 124,* 1310-1313.

Folley, S. J.; Guthkelch, A. N., and Zuckerman, S. (1939): The mammary gland of the rhesus monkey under normal and experimental conditions.

Proc Roy Soc, London, B126, 469-491.

Gardner, W. U. (1941): Inhibition of mammary growth by large amounts of estrogen. *Endocrinology, 28,* 53-61.

Gardner, W. U., and van Wagenen, G. (1938): Experimental development of the mammary gland of the monkey. *Endocrinology, 22,* 164-172.

Gilbert, C., and Gillman, J. (1956): The role of the adrenal and thyroid in promoting bleeding in hypophysectomized baboons *(Papio ursinus). Endocrinology, 58,* 753-766.

Hampton, J. K., Jr.; Levy, B. M., and Sweet, P. M. (1969): Chorionic gonadotropin excretion during pregnancy in the marmoset *(Callithrix jacchus). Endocrinology, 85,* 171-174.

Hartman, C. G.; Firor, W. M., and Geiling, E. M. K. (1930): The anterior lobe and menstruation. *Am J Physiol, 95,* 662-669.

Hartman, C. G., and Speert, H. (1941): Action of progesterone on the genital organs of the unprimed rhesus monkey. *Endocrinology, 29,* 639-648.

Hayward, J. N.; Hilliard, J., and Sawyer, C. H. (1963): Preovulatory and postovulatory progestins in monkey ovary and ovarian vein blood. *Proc Soc Exp Biol Med, 113,* 256-259.

Hobson, B. M. (1970): Excretion of gonadotrophin by the pregnant baboon *(Papio cynocephalus). Folia Primat, 12,* 111-115.

Hopper, B. R., and Tullner, W. W. (1967): Urinary estrogen excretion patterns in pregnant rhesus monkeys. *Steroids, 9,* 517-527.

Hopper, B. R., and Tullner, W. W. (1969): Relationship of urinary estrogen level to ovulation in the rhesus monkey. *Fed Proc Abst,* no. 2866.

Hopper, B. R.; Tullner, W. W., and Gray, C. W. (1968): Urinary estrogen excretion during pregnancy in a gorilla *(Gorilla gorilla). Proc Soc Exp Biol Med, 129,* 213-214.

Hoschoian, J. C., and Brownie, A. C. (1967): Pathways for androgen biosynthesis in monkey testis. *Steroids, 10,* 49-69.

Jeffery, J. D'A. (1966): Metabolism of progesterone in the pig-tail monkey *(Macaca nemestrina). J Endocr, 34,* 387-392.

Jirku, H., and Layne, D. S. (1965): The metabolism of estrone-^{14}C in a pregnant chimpanzee. *Steroids,* 5, 37-44.

Johansson, E. D. B.; Neill, J. D., and Knobil, E. (1968): Periovulatory progesterone concentration in the peripheral plasma of the rhesus monkey with a methodologic note on the detection of ovulation. *Endocrinology, 82,* 143-148.

Kar, A. B., and Chandra, H. (1965): Response of the ovary of prepuberal langoors *(Presbytis entellus)* to heterologous mammalian gonadotrophins. *Acta Anat, 60,* 608-615.

Kar, A. B.; Chandra, H., and Kamboj, V. P. (1966): Effect of non-primate gonadotrophins on the testis of prepuberal rhesus monkeys. *Acta Biol Med German, 16,* 450-455.

Kinzey, W. G. (1965): Concentration of gonadotropin in the urine of the pregnant monkey, *M. mulatta. Anat Rec, 151,* 372-373.

Kirton, K. T.; Niswender, G. G.; Midgley, A. R.; Jaffe, R. B., and Forbes, A. D. (1970): Serum luteinizing hormone and progesterone concentration during the menstrual cycle of the rhesus monkey. *J Clin Endocr, 30,* 105-110.

Knobil, E.; Neill, J. D., and Johansson, E. D. B. (1968): Influence of hypophysectomy, sham hypophysectomy and other surgical procedures on luteal function in the rhesus monkey. *Endocrinology, 82,* 410-415.

Liskowski, L.; Wolf, R. C.; Chandler, S., and Meyer, R. K. (1970): Urinary estrogen excretion in pregnant rhesus monkeys. *Biol Reprod, 3,* 55-60.

Liskowski, L.; Wolf, R. C., and Meyer, R. K. (1966): Urinary excretion of estrogens and metabolites of progesterone during pregnancy in rhesus monkeys. *Proc III Internat Pharmacol Cong,* Abst. no. 357.

McArthur, J. W., and Perley, R. (1969): Urinary gonadotropin excretion by infrahuman primates. *Endocrinology, 84,* 508-513.

Merkatz, I. R., and Beling, C. G. (1969): Urinary excretion of oestrogens and pregnanediol in the pregnant baboon. *J Reprod Fertil (Suppl), 6,* 129-135.

Monroe, S. E.; Peckham, W. D.; Neill, J. D., and Knobil, E. (1970): A radioimmunoassay for rhesus monkey luteinizing hormone (RhLH). *Endocrinology, 86,* 1012-1018.

Mougey, E. H.; Collins, D. R.; Rose, R. M., and Mason, J. W. (1969): Measurement of testosterone and epitestosterone in human and monkey urine by gas-liquid chromatography. *Anal Biochem, 27,* 343-358.

Nathan, T. S., Rosenblum, L. A.; Limson, G., and Nelson, J. H., Jr. (1966): Diagnosis of pregnancy in the squirrel monkey. *Anat Rec, 155,* 531-536.

Neill, J. D.; Johansson, E. D. B., and Knobil, E. (1967): Levels of progesterone in peripheral plasma during the menstrual cycle of the rhesus monkey. *Endocrinology, 81,* 1161-1164.

Neill, J. D.; Johansson, E. D. B., and Knobil, E. (1969): Patterns of circulating progesterone concentrations during the fertile menstrual cycle and the remainder of gestation in the rhesus monkey. *Endocrinology, 84,* 45-48.

Neill, J. D., and Knobil, E. (1969): On the nature of the initial luteotropic stimulus of pregnancy in the rhesus monkey. *Fed Proc Abst,* no. 2871.

Resko, J. A. (1967): Plasma androgen levels of the rhesus monkey: Effects of age and season. *Endocrinology, 81,* 1203-1212.

Riesen, J. W.; Koering, M. J.; Meyer, R. K., and Wolf, R. C. (1970): Origin of ovarian venous progesterone in the rhesus monkey. *Endocrinology, 86,* 1212-1214.

Ryan, K. J.; Benirschke, K., and Smith, O. W. (1961): Conversion of androstenedione-4-C^{14} to estrone by the marmoset placenta. *Endrocrinology, 69,* 613-618.

Segal, S. J. (1964): The testis: Development and maturation. In Lloyd, C. W. (Ed.): *Human Reproduction and Sexual Behavior.* Philadelphia, Lea & Febiger, pp. 50-64.

Short, R. V., and Eckstein, P. (1961): Oestrogen and progesterone levels in pregnant rhesus monkeys. *J Endocr, 22,* 15-22.

Simpson, M. E.; van Wagenen, G., and Carter, F. (1956): Hormone content of anterior pituitary of monkey *(Macaca mulatta)* with special reference to gonadotrophins. *Proc Soc Exp Biol Med, 91,* 6-11.

Smith, P. E. (1954): Continuation of pregnancy in rhesus monkeys *(Macaca mulatta)* following hypophysectomy. *Endocrinology, 55,* 655-664.

Snipes, C. A.; Forest, M. G., and Migeon, C. J. (1969): Plasma androgen concentrations in several species of old and new world monkeys. *Endocrinology, 85,* 941-945.

Solomon, S. (1966): Formation and metabolism of neutral steroids in the human placenta and fetus. *J Clin Endocr, 26,* 762-772.

Speert, H. (1941): Cyclic changes in the mammary gland of the rhesus monkey. *Surg Gynec Obstet, 73,* 388-390.

Speert, H. (1948): The normal and experimental development of the mammary gland in the rhesus monkey, with some pathological correlations. *Contr Embr Carn Wash, 32,* 9-65.

Stevens, V. C.; Sparks, S. J., and Powell, J. E. (1970): Levels of estrogens, progestogens and luteinizing hormone during the menstrual cycle of the baboon. *Endocrinology, 87,* 658-666.

Tolson, W. W.; Johnson, T. R., and Mason, J. W. (1966): The determination of urinary androsterone, etiocholanolone, and dehydroepiandrosterone in the normal male rhesus monkey. *J Lab Clin Med, 68,* 981-990.

Tullner, W. W., and Gray, C. W. (1968): Chorionic gonadotropin excretion during pregnancy in a gorilla. *Proc Soc Exp Biol Med, 128,* 954-956.

Tullner, W. W., and Hertz, R. (1966a): Chorionic gonadotropin levels in the rhesus monkey during early pregnancy. *Endocrinology, 78,* 204-207.

Tullner, W. W., and Hertz, R. (1966b): Normal gestation and chorionic gonadotropin levels in the monkey after ovariectomy in early pregnancy. *Endocrinology, 78,* 1076-1078.

Tullner, W. W.; Rayford, P. L., and Ross, G. T. (1969): Evidence for similar antigenic determinants in gonadotropins from urine of man and monkey *(Macaca mulatta). Endocrinology, 84,* 908-911.

van Wagenen, G. (1949): Accelerated growth with sexual precocity in female monkeys receiving testosterone propionate. *Endocrinology, 45,* 544-546.

van Wagenen, G., and Simpson, M. E. (1965): *Embryology of the Ovary and Testis Homo sapiens and Macaca mulatta.* New Haven, Yale University Press.

Wiest, W. G. (1967): Estimation of progesterone in biological tissues and fluids from pregnant women by double isotope derivative assay. *Steroids, 10,* 279-290.

Chapter 3

ROLE OF THE NERVOUS SYSTEM IN REPRODUCTIVE BEHAVIOR

A. A. GERALL

THE most significant neural modifications occurring in primate evolution have been in those structures which can be correlated with transition toward upright posture, increased manual dexterity, shift in dependence from olfactory to auditory and visual stimuli, and enhanced learning and memory facilities. In general, these functional changes permit sensitive and varied responses to stimuli, thereby enabling the animal to be more independent of immediate environmental events. Corresponding to the attainment of these attributes and skills is an increase in the relative size and complexity of the neocortex, the lemniscal systems, and their intervening subcortical synaptic relay stations. Most comparative analyses of the primate brain have focused upon these parts of the evolving nervous system, since their progressive structural changes are profound and their phylogenetic implications meaningful (Clark, 1960; Noback and Muskowitz, 1963; Kappers *et al.*, 1960). In contrast, the phylogenetically older limbic system, which mediates vegetative and emotive processes in general and reproductive activities in particular, has elaborated only slightly during primate evolution. Morphological and functional analyses support the contention made by Broca (1878) and contemporary scientists (MacLean, 1966; Russell, 1961) that the limbic system is the common denominator of the mammalian brain. The characteristic patterns of behavioral and physiological processes integrated by this system are essentially similar in most species. What is different is the environmental setting in which these responses are expressed and their dependence on and relation to internal events. Ovulation and uterine endometrial proliferation occur at highly regular intervals and at specific times in the diurnal cycle in spontaneously ovulating mammals. Also, in these species, mating is restricted to intact females and to a limited period near the ovulatory event. Higher primates, in contrast, have variable menstrual periods and engage in copulation when fertilization is not possible. In observations of approximately one thousand menstrual periods in rhesus monkeys, while the modal interval was twenty-seven to twenty-eight days, the distribution extended from fourteen to fifty-four days (Corner, 1923; Hartman, 1932). Of 421 copulations, only 12.5 percent were fertile. Baboons, chimpanzees, squirrel and rhesus females permit intromissions during nonestrous periods and the rhesus is receptive to males after ovariectomy (Phoenix *et al.*, 1968). To the extent that comparative information is available, the greater variance in primate reproductive function is associated with development of telencephalic structures. Neural endocrine relationships involving the diencephalon, hypophysis, and gonads appear to involve similar substances and principles of interactions in most mammals studied in the laboratory.

I. HORMONAL-NEURAL INTERACTIONS

A. Hormones and the Menstrual Cycle

The focal target organ controlled by the central nervous system is the gonad, which not only generates and releases mature germ cells, but estrogenic, progestational, and androgenic hormones, which serve as the direct conditioners of sexual organs and neural processes. These gonadal activities are governed by the anterior pituitary gonadotrophic hormones, follicle stimulating hormone (FSH), luteinizing hormone (LH), and possibly, luteotrophic hormone (LTH). The trophic nature of these hormones is easily demonstrated in the rhesus, which exhibits gonadal atrophy within two weeks after pituitary stalk sectioning. Folliculogenesis and the key event of ovulation are dependent upon appropriate ratios of FSH and LH. In the rhesus, plasma FSH and LH remain at relatively low levels until approximately five days before ovulation. Thereafter, while FSH increases slightly, LH has been recorded to increase ten-fold at midcycle (Kirton *et al.*, 1970). Ovulation occurs within thirty hours after the LH surge. Estrogen reaches its highest blood concentration four days before ovulation, whereas progesterone increases markedly after ovulation, corresponding to the development of corpora lutea. Menstruation, although a highly variable event, usually starts four to five days after progesterone level has reached its plateau (Neill *et al.*, 1967). General behavioral activity tends to increase during the follicular phase and attains highest amplitude a day or two after ovulation. While copulation can take place throughout the twenty-eight-day period, it is more likely to be permitted or solicited within approximately seven days around the time of the LH surge. Control of these events resides in the interrelation between these hormones, the organs which produce them, and the brain. The major regulatory organ, however, is the pituitary gland.

B. Anterior Pituitary

An outline of the pituitary gland of the rhesus monkey is provided in Fig. 3-1. Considerable differences exist among primates in the relative topology and size of the various parts of this gland. For example, in lower primates, such as the slender loris, the pars tuberalis is either nonexistent or greatly reduced. In higher primates, such as apes and man, the pars intermedia is regressed in comparison to other forms. The pars distalis, which is most crucial for reproductive function, has essentially common cytological and functional characteristics among mammals. Located in it are basophilic cells, the source of gonadotrophic hormones. The pars distalis, pars intermedia, and pars tuberalis originate from oral epithelium and have characteristics of glandular tissue. The median eminence, pars nervosa, and infundibular process differentiate from central nervous system tissue. The median eminence forms part of the ventral surface of the hypothalamus and adjoins the infundibular stem.

Functional connection between the median eminence and pars distalis is by a complex vascular portal system. A capillary plexus located in the median eminence anastomoses into portal vessels which descend into the pars distalis, at which point they disperse into sinusoids interlacing with secretory cells. Blood leaving these sinusoids flows through venous sinuses and then enters the systemic circulation. It is now well established that the output of go-

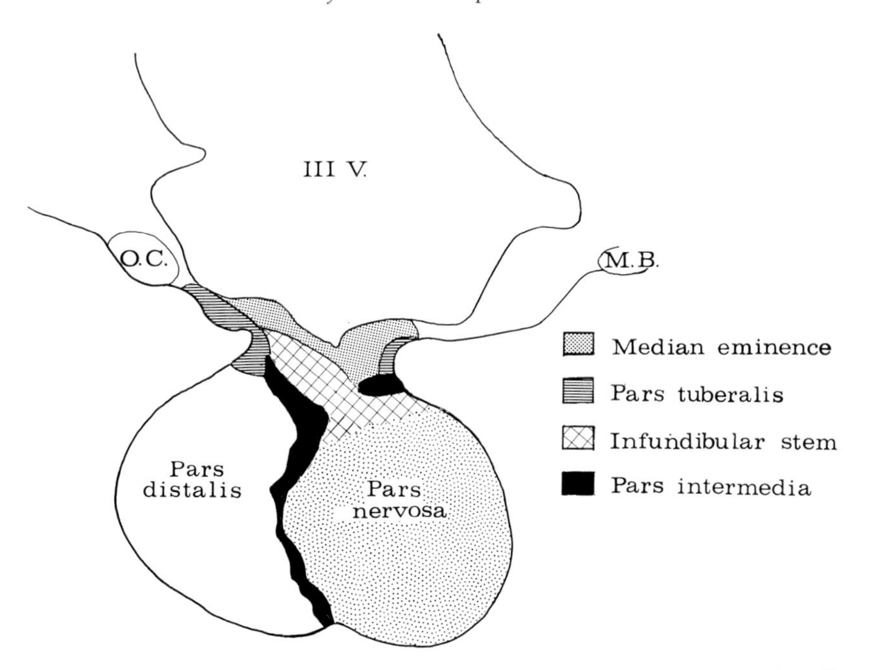

Figure 3-1. Approximate appearance of hypophysis of the rhesus monkey. In this primate the infundibular stem is solid and contiguous with the median eminence and pars nervosa. Its relatively small pars tuberalis adjoins the pars intermedia and pars distalis.

nadotrophic hormones is governed by chemical substances called "releasing factors," which are transported from the median eminence through the portal system to the pars distalis. The two active principles, follicle stimulating hormone-releasing factor (FRF) and luteinizing hormone-releasing factor (LRF) are elaborated by secretory neurons located in the median eminence and probably other diencephalic regions. Storage and discharge to the pars distalis of releasing factors occur only in the median eminence. Thus, the median eminence represents a critical final pathway for instigating hypophyseal activity.

C. Anterior Pituitary Feedback Systems

An outline of the basic reciprocal relationship between the gonads, the hypophysis, and the central nervous system is provided in Figure 3-2. Both negative and positive feedback relationships are present in this system. The classical negative feedback or inhibi-

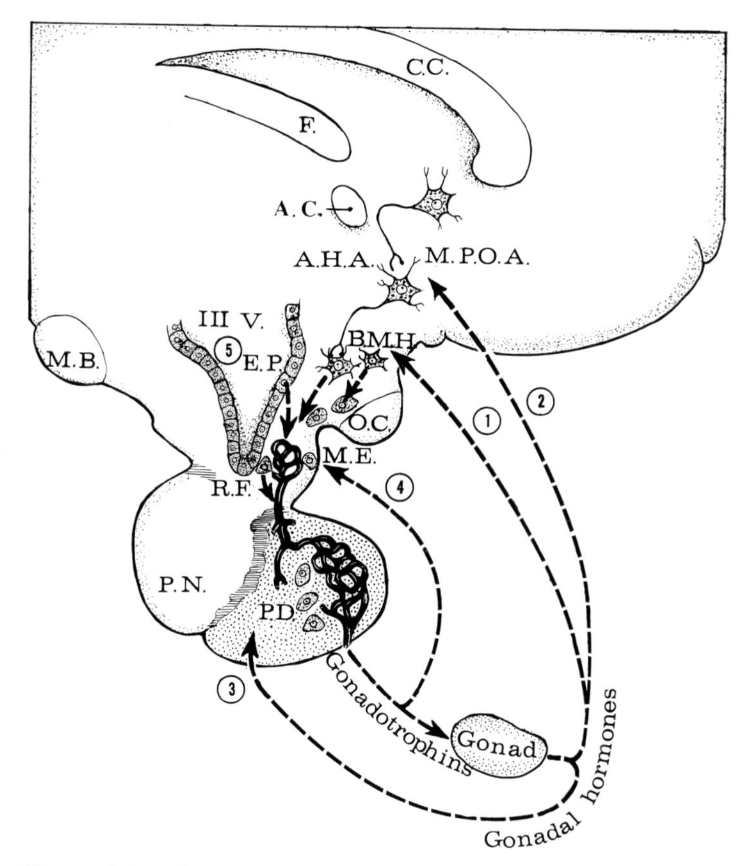

Figure 3-2. Schematic description of feedback relationships between hypophyseal and gonadal secretions. The best established feedback interactions are numbered 1 and 2 and are indirect in the sense that gonadal hormones act on or are sensed by neural tissue in the B.M.H., basomedial area of the hypothalamus or in the A.H.A., anterior hypothalamus and M.P.O.A., medial preoptic area. The consequent neural activity, then, in some unknown way, regulates the flow of the R.F., releasing factors, through the portal system to the basophilic cells of the P.D., pars distalis. The route labelled 3 is more direct in that gonadal hormones affect the release of hormones from the P.D. by acting upon structures in the P.D. The last two routes, numbered 4 and 5, are in the early stages of investigation and include the action of gonadotrophins on the release of R.F. substances in the M.E., median eminence. Route 5 is between agents conveyed in the III V., third ventricle, acting on ependymal cells which extend from the ventricle to the portal vessels in the M.E. Other abbreviations include A.C., anterior commissure; C.C., corpus callosum; F., fornix; M.B., mammillary bodies; O.C., optic chiasma; P.N., pars nervosa.

tory relationship is between FSH and estrogen secretion. FSH increases gonadal estrogen output, which in turn decreases the amount of FSH released from the pars distalis. Estrogen and progesterone possess both negative and positive feedback capabilities with regard to LH. Which of the two effects will occur depends upon many factors, including the relative amounts of these hormones, the phase of the estral cycle, etc. Progesterone appears to have a positive feedback relationship to LTH.

For a hormone to effect change in the tissue generating or releasing another substance, there must be a sensor or receptor site which can respond to it. A multiple of experimental procedures have located estrogen responsive sites in the basomedial and anterior regions of the hypothalamus and the anterior pituitary. The basomedial hypothalamic region includes the median eminence, arcuate and ventromedial nuclei. Uniformly, it has been shown that this region is responsive to changes in estrogen and androgen blood levels. Although limited, research with the rhesus tends to confirm the importance of the basomedial region of the hypothalamus for the integrity of estral cycles. Relatively small lesions placed in the ventromedial region permanently disrupt menstrual cycles (Chatterjee and Anand, 1967); stimulation leads to ovulation or menstruation depending upon the day in the cycle on which it is delivered (Anand *et al.*, 1957). When the basomedial region is neurally isolated from the remainder of the brain by surgical procedures (Halász and Pupp, 1965) without interrupting its vascular connection with the systemic and portal circulatory systems, sufficient gonadotrophins are released to maintain gonadal tissue, folliculogenesis, and spermatogenesis. Ovulation, however, does not take place, indicating the absence of the phasic surge of LH.

These data are congruent with the hypothesis that the basomedial hypothalamic region is largely responsible for tonic release of FSH and LH in both sexes (Gorski, 1968). Ovulation is present when this basomedial region is permitted neural continuity with anterior hypothalamic and medial preoptic areas. Thus, it has been concluded that exteroceptively and endogenously induced rhythmicities modulate gonadotrophic output via anteriorly located diencephalic nuclei. Support for this view comes from studies in which electrical stimulation of the anterior hypothalamus of the rhesus alters the temporal pattern of estrogen flow and menstruation. After cessation of the stimulation period, the ovarian cyclicity returns to normal (Chatterjee and Anand, 1967).

Feedback paths not involving the intervention of the hypothalamus include a direct loop between the gonads and the pars distalis, and a short loop between the pars distalis and the median eminence. In the former case, steroid hormones directly alter the release of gonadotrophins, and in the latter, gonadotrophins regulate the output of releasing factors. The importance of the latter two feedback relationships for gonadotrophin release is in the early stages of determination. It is likely that they complement the action of the gonad-hypothalamic-hypophyseal network.

A fourth and novel feedback loop has been outlined by Knowles and Anand Kumar (1970). Specific ependymal cells, labelled Type B tanycytes, lining the third ventricle in the region of the tuber cinerium in the rhesus have been found to retain selectively tritium-labelled estrogen. They also possess globular electron dense masses when estrogen is present and have bulbous projections that vary systematically in size with the stage of the menstrual cycle (Anand Kumar and Knowles, 1967; Anand Kumar, 1968). The feedback relationship is physically possible because the ependymal tanycyte cells have large processes reaching blood vessels in the median eminence. It is possible that they secrete active substances into the portal system. Exactly what is being sensed in the cerebral spinal fluid which might influence release of pituitary hormones remains undetermined.

D. Hormonal Neural Difference Between the Sexes

The same gonadotrophic releasing factors and hormones are synthesized by both sexes, but their cyclic release is a characteristic of only the female. The basomedial region of the male is responsive to increases in androgen and estrogen, indicating a negative feedback or inhibitory capability. However, neither estrogen nor androgen acting on anterior hypothalamic and medial preoptic regions alters consistently the flow of gonadotrophic hormones in the male. Thus, a sexual dimorphism exists in this part of the hypothalamus. Sex differences have also been found in the effects of releasing factors produced by gonadal hormones. Gonadectomy enhances FRH hypothalamic concentrations in both sexes. Estrogen and progesterone, but not testosterone replacement, reduces these levels in spayed females. On the other hand, testosterone, but not progesterone, is effective in decreasing FRH levels in the castrated male (Mittler and Meites, 1966; Dávid *et al.*, 1965). Another interesting sex difference in structures possibly involved in feedback is in the ependymal lining in the rhesus. Ependymal cells are arranged in a double layer separated by a space only in the male. Injections of estrogen do not alter the space in the castrated male nor do they produce bulbous projections in the B tanycyte cells (Knowles and Anand Kumar, 1970).

E. Posterior Pituitary Hormones

The pars nervosa is a storage area for oxytocin and the antidiuretic hormone (ADH). These substances originate in the supraoptic and paraventricular nuclei of the hypothalamus and travel along nerve fibers to the pars nervosa. Oxytocin acts directly on the uterine myometrium and therefore is critical in the process of parturition. It also stimulates mammary myoepithelium, thereby mediating milk let-down. Whether oxytocin has other functions relevant to reproduction is a matter of conjecture. It is released by stimulation of the uterus, cervix, and vagina. It has been suggested that the uterine contractions induced during copulation aid in the transport of sperm to the oviducts. Midspinal section or hypophysectomy abolishes uterine contractions evoked by vaginal stimulation. Oxytocin has also been implicated in facilitating seminal emission by constricting smooth muscles in male secondary sexual organs. However, it has not been shown to be necessary for successful fertilization.

II. NEURAL BEHAVIORAL RELATIONSHIPS

A. Neocortex and Limbic Lobe

A listing of much of the research on the relationship between neural function and reproductive processes is provided in Table 3-I. Inspection of this table immediately reveals the paucity of information relevant to neural-behavioral mechanisms and especially for species other than the rhesus and squirrel monkey. Al-

TABLE 3-I

RELATIONSHIP BETWEEN LIMBIC SYSTEM AND REPRODUCTIVE BEHAVIOR IN MALE AND FEMALE MACACA MULATTA* AND SAIMIRI SCIUREUS†

Structure	*Treatment*	*Male*	*Female*
Putamen*	S	Erection and complete copulatory sequence in social situation	
Putamen*	R		No specific unit response to vaginal stimulation
Caudate nucleus†	S	No consistent effect on erection	
Cingular gyrus*	L	No permanent effect on sexual behavior	No effect on receptivity
Posterior cingular gyrus*	S	No effect on penile erection	
Anterior cingular gyrus*	S	Penile erection	
Cingular gyrus†	S	Low-rated erection	
Hippocampus*	R	No specific effect on EEG of genital manipulation in immature *S*s before or after androgen injection	
Hippocampus*	S	No effect on penile erection	
Temporal lobe resection: (large lesions)*	L	Hypersexuality: increased frequency of copulatory activity, indiscriminate choice of objects in lab situation, increased orality, hypermetamorphosis, lessened fear, psychic blindness, alteration of social behavior (Kluver-Bucy phenomenon) hypersexuality eliminated by castration	Increased tameness; effects on sexual behavior either lacking or temporary; pregnancy and parturition normal; offspring neglected or abused
Medial temporal lobe, anterior half of right and ventral half of left amygdala, rostral hippocampus*	L	Normal heterosexual activity	
Bilateral 2/3 of amygdaloid complex*	L	Apathetic, but frequent normal heterosexual contact	
Medial surface temporal lobe, left side rostral and middle third amygdaloid complex*	L	Temporary tameness; normal heterosexual behavior	
Right uncus and amygdala, left temporal cortex, basal portion of amygdala*	L	Apathetic; normal sexual behavior	
Basal lateral medial cortical nuclei*	L	Temporary tameness; hypersexuality in approximately two months	
Amygdala and uncus*	L	Juveniles; pre-testosterone injections: greater frequency of mounting; exhibit erection when mounted; post-testosterone injections: increased mounting and grooming	
Amygdala*	L	Neonates; no hypersexuality at 1–2 years of age	
Amygdala*	R		Excitation of unit activity and both excitation and inhibition in animals with estrogen in response to vaginal stimulation
Amygdala and temporal lobe*	R	No specific effect on EEG of genital manipulation in immature *S*s before or after androgen injection	

TABLE 3-I—*Continued*

Structure	*Treat-ment*	*Male*	*Female*
Amygdala corticomedial nucleus*	S	Penile erection	
Stria terminalis and its bed nucleus*	S	Penile erection	
Stria terminalis†	S	Negative effect on erection	
Basal septal region*	L	No effect on copulatory behavior	No effect on copulatory behavior; interference with maternal behavior
Septum, not including area of bed nucleus of stria terminalis*	S	No effect on erection	
Septum*	R		Unit response to vaginal stimulation; same as amygdala
Medial septopreoptic region†	S	Nodal point for erection	
Midline nuclei, thalamus*	S	Penile erection	
Anterior and midline thalamic nuclei†	S	Penile erection	Clitoral enlargement
Mediodorsal nucleus†	S	Penile erection	Clitoral enlargement
Centralis lateralis nucleus†	S	Seminal discharge independent of scratching	
Preoptic*	S	Erection, pelvic thrusting, and ejaculation exhibited when restrained; erection in free social situation and suppression of sexual mounting and intromission	
Preoptic*	R		Spindle EEG's evoked in immature *S*s by genital stimulation after estrogen priming
Preoptic and suprachiasmatic*	R		Inhibition of single units in estrogen-primed immature and adult animals in response to vaginal stimulation
Anterior hypothalamus and ventromedial nucleus*	L	No effect	No effect
Rostral supraoptic region*	R	High amplitude slow waves in immature androgenized males in response to genital stimulation	
Anterior hypothalamic area*	R		Frequent inhibition of single unit activity in estrogenized females in response to vaginal stimulation
Ventromedial region*	L, S		Disrupted menstrual cycles
Ventromedial region*	R		Inhibition of single unit activity in estrogen-primed animals
Ventromedial region*	S	No penile erection	
Medial hypothalamus*	S	Penile erection	
Dorsomedial region*	L		Temporary and minimal effects on menstrual cycle
Dorsomedial region*	S		Disrupted menstrual cycles
Anterior tuberal region*	S		No effect on menstrual cycles
Anteromedial region of median eminence*	S		Accelerated onset of either vaginal cornification or flow depending on time of cycle
Ependymal cells in tuber cinereum*	M		Selective cytological reaction to estrogen
Medial hypothalamus, dorsal to VMN, lateral hypothalamus*	S	Penile erection	
Posterior hypothalamus*	L		Temporary disruption of menstrual cycles
Posterior hypothalamus*	S		Prolonged cycles for duration of stimulation
Posterior hypothalamus*	S	Penile erection	

TABLE 3-I—*Continued*

Structure	*Treat-ment*	*Male*	*Female*
Posterolateral hypothalamus*	R		Increased tendency toward unit activity following vaginal stimulation regardless of hormone condition
Mammillary bodies*	S	No effect on penile erection	
Mammillary bodies*	R	High amplitude slow waves following genital stimulation in immature males injected with estrogen for at least 5 days	No distinctive pattern of unit response evoked by genital stimulation
Medial forebrain bundle*	S	Nodal tract for erection	
Mammillothalamic tract*	S	No effect on penile erection	
Medial preoptic, anteromedial nucleus, and supraoptic†	S	Penile erection; no emission	Clitoral enlargement
Ventromedial area†	S	Aversive effects	
Lateral hypothalamus†	S	Positive loci for erection	
Mammillary bodies†	S	Penile erection	
Mammillothalamic tract†	S	Nodal tract for erection	Clitoral enlargement
Medial forebrain bundle†	S	Nodal tract for erection	Clitoral enlargement
Nucleus tegmenti ventralis, nucleus opticus tegmenti, medial segment of substantia nigra†	S	Penile erection	
Regions near spinothalamic tract†	S	Genital scratching and manipulation often accompanied by emission	

S—Electrical stimulation R—Recording *—Macaca mulatta
L—Lesion M—Microscopic analysis †—Saimiri sciureus

though most studies of the primate neocortex have been concerned with sensory, motor, and learning processes, investigators often include observations of social and sexual behavior. No neocortical region in the primate has been reported to be directly involved in either sexual arousal or expression. Even when partial paralysis or hyperactivity ensue from cortical extirpation, copulatory attempts are made by both sexes, and females become pregnant and successfully give birth. However, the sparse evidence of direct relationship between neocortical structures and reproductive physiology and behavior precludes drawing firm conclusions of the role the phylogenetically newest portion of the brain plays in procreation.

The total number of neural regions and structures included in the limbic system tends to increase as new investigations reveal additional neural or response interrelationships. While many limbic system structures are often listed as part of the rhinencephalon, the use of the latter functional classification is finding less acceptance since the size and function of many of these areas are not correlated with those of the olfactory bulb. Usually subsumed in the limbic system are the limbic lobe, basal ganglia, septal area, amygdala, anterior thalamus, and hypothalamus. As shown in Figure 3-3, the limbic lobe, which forms a collar beneath the neocortical mantle and encircles the inner core of basal ganglia, diencephalon, and corpus callosum, consists of the cingular gyrus, presubiculum, hippocampal formation, and parts of the uncus. The cingular gyrus dominates the mesial surface of the brain and possesses morphological characteristics phylogenetically intermediate between neocortical and paleocortical types of cortices.

In the cebus, rhesus, and squirrel monkey, as shown in Table 3-I, lesions placed primarily in the anterior agranular region of the cingular gyrus, but in the posterior aspect as well, have not interfered with male copulation or female receptivity, pregnancy, or parturition (Glees *et al.*, 1950; Poirier, 1962; Smith, 1944; Walker *et al.*, 1953). Ablation of much of the cingular gyrus, including some neocortical areas, resulted in extensive motor impairment (Nicholson and Turner, 1963). One paraplegic male rhesus continued to exhibit erection, and another, with partial right-side paralysis, attempted to copulate. The most frequently reported alterations accompanying ablation of parts of the cingular gyrus are increased tameness, diminution in fear arousal, increased vocalization, and greater autonomic reactivity. Gradual return to former behavioral states usually occurs. Electrical stimulation of a restricted section of the anterior cingular gyrus has been reported to produce erection in the rhesus (Robinson and Mishkin, 1968) and in the squirrel monkey (MacLean and Ploog, 1962). Stimulation often leads to sound patterns and autonomic reactions similar to those present during sexual interactions.

As in the case of the cingular gyrus, the hippocampal formation, though extensive in size and complexity, has not been found necessary for reproductive function in primates. Because of its enclosed position, ablation is difficult without damaging other areas. However, absence of considerable portions of the hippocampus has not led to either hyper- or hyposexual behavior in primates. In the rhesus, stimulation of the hippocampal formation has not produced changes in the genital organs (Robinson and Mishkin, 1968), nor are specific evoked potentials present in it when the genital organs are manipulated (Chhina and Anand, 1969). However, penile erection in squirrel monkeys has been reported (MacLean

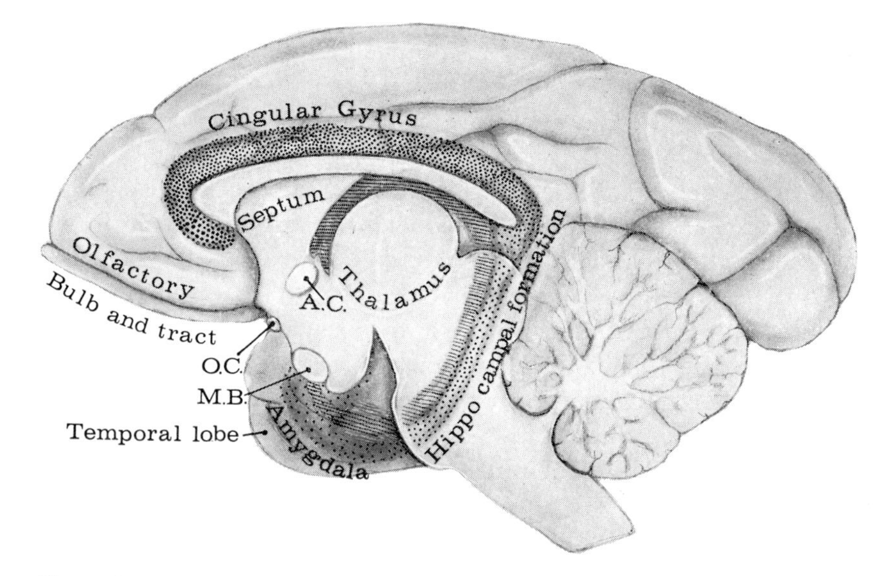

Figure 3-3. Diagrammatic presentation of the primate's limbic lobe and some areas of its limbic system shown in a midsagittal plane of the squirrel monkey's brain. The cingular gyrus occupies the midline area above the corpus callosum. The hippocampal formation, as it descends from its dorsal location, proceeds laterally and reaches into the temporal lobe. Fibers coursing through the fornix arise largely in the hippocampus and terminate in the mammillary bodies. Abbreviations include A.C., anterior commissure; O.C., optic chiasma; M.B., mammillary bodies.

and Ploog, 1962) following stimulation of the posterior ventral hippocampus. Results of hippocampal stimulation are difficult to interpret because of the presence of seizure activity and rebound phenomena. Also, hippocampal after-discharge frequently occurs concurrently with penile erection when other limbic structures are stimulated (MacLean *et al.,* 1963). Penile erection resulting from hippocampal stimulation itself might be due to secondary reactions rather than to a specific structure-behavior relationship. Many researchers suggest that the hippocampus primarily inhibits activity present in or mediated by other neural regions. Evocation of sexual-type responses during the rebound phase may indicate a release from inhibition exerted by other areas. In summary, the limbic cortex, i.e. cingular gyrus and hippocampal formation, is functionally related to multiple states of arousal, attention, and integrative activity rather than to evocation of specific actions. Its relevance to sexual behavior is probably that of supporting background states of arousal, somatic, and autonomic activities. If these are its functions, simple topographical specificity for reproductive responses might not exist in these structures.

B. Temporal Lobe

Limbic structures encased in the temporal lobe drew considerable research attention after Kluver and Bucy's (1937) finding that in the rhesus monkey excision leads to dramatic behavioral changes. Bilateral temporal lobectomy resulting in removal of the pyriform cortex, most of the amygdaloid complex, dorsal hippocampus, entorhinal gyrus, and many temporal lobe pathways to the other locations in the brain produced subjects exhibiting hypersexuality, increased orality, and tameness. Attempts to discern which one of the diverse structures ablated is relevant to a specific behavioral phenomenon have not been too successful because of difficulty in resecting specifically and in identifying the critical behavioral alteration from the complex syndrome of interdependent psychological modifications. Two areas most often related to the appearance of the hypersexual phenomenon in primates are the basolateral nucleus of the amygdala and pyriform cortex. However, removal of other temporal lobe structures in conjunction with these areas could either facilitate or inhibit the hypersexuality for which these critical areas might be responsible. Stimulation of the basolateral nucleus in the rhesus leads to erection. The juxtaposition of both inhibitory and excitatory possibilities in the amygdala is indicated by the finding that genital stimulation (Chhina and Anand, 1969) leads to both a decreased and an increased rate of discharge of single units located in it. Genital stimulation decreases frequency of single unit discharge in females only when estrogen is circulating in an amount at least equivalent to that present in adult animals.

Temporal lobe hypersexuality is limited to the male and is androgen-dependent in that it is absent in amygdalectomized animals during the neonatal period, one or two years of age, but present at juvenile and postpuberal ages. It disappears after castration and is restored by androgen replacement (Kling, 1968; Kling and Green,

1967; Schreiner and Kling, 1956). The hypersexuality takes the form of increased auto-, homo-, and heterosexual behavior and includes copulatory attempts with animals of other species and with objects. The increased frequency of copulation with members of its own species is in relation to the laboratory setting; this rate, however, may not be beyond that actually engaged in by the rhesus in its wild habitat (Beach, 1967). The hypersexuality may be, at least in part, due to modification of perception of territoriality, dangers associated with captivity, or foreign objects. Congruent with this interpretation is the observation (Walker *et al.*, 1953) that the amygdalectomized rhesus mother does not manifest normal maternal attention. She often ignores or inadvertently harms her offspring. The maternal inattention, hypersexuality, orality, and tameness all can be related to an alteration of the perceptual relationship of the self to other animals and objects.

C. Septal Area

More lateral regions of the limbic system often act upon more medially or caudally placed limbic components such as the septum and hypothalamus. An illustration of this relationship is the suppression of hypothalamically induced aggressive responses by simultaneous stimulation of the amygdala (Egger and Flynn, 1962). Of the two major pathways between the amygdala and other limbic areas, the stria terminalis is the more compact and defined. It is a two-way bundle of fibers with the efferent portion arising in the basal nucleus and terminating in the septopreoptic area and paraventricular nuclei. The phylogenetically more recent basolateral nuclei have no direct olfactory afferents. The second fiber system, more diffuse and ventrally placed than the stria, originates mainly in the lateral and basal amygdaloid nuclei and connects with the olfactory tubercle, lateral preoptic, hypothalamic areas, and temporal cortex. Stimulation of the stria terminalis evokes erection in the rhesus (Robinson and Mishkin, 1968) and squirrel monkey (MacLean and Ploog, 1962), although requiring different parameters in the two. The bed nucleus of the stria terminalis is located adjacent to the lateral ventricle between the caudate nucleus and septum. Stimulation of the septal area does not elicit erection in the rhesus but it does so in the squirrel monkey. Numerous fibers conveyed through the well-defined fornix extend to the septal area from the mammillary bodies. As might be expected, stimulation of the mammillary bodies leads to erection in the squirrel but not in the rhesus monkey (MacLean *et al.*, 1963; Robinson and Mishkin, 1968). The disparity in septal function between the two species might reflect a general difference in the significance of genital erection. Whereas in the rhesus erection is primarily related to sexual situations, in the squirrel monkey it is a pervasive display pattern appearing soon after birth in both males and females (Maurus *et al.*, 1965). According to many observers, penile erection is used frequently in initiating threat reactions or defining social position (Ploog and MacLean, 1963; Wickler, 1966). This difference between the rhesus and squirrel monkeys fosters a conservative interpretation that the septal area in primates plays a greater role in mediating agonistic and other social behaviors than in consummatory sexual activities.

D. Diencephalon

Mapping of diencephalic and functionally interrelated limbic system sites involved in penile or clitoral erection and implicated in mediating genital sensations represents the most systematic research on the neural basis of primate reproduction. Using permanently implanted depth-adjustable electrodes in awake but restrained subjects, MacLean *et al.* (1962, 1963, 1963) stimulated several thousand loci and observed the effect on penile erection and emission, clitoral enlargement, and genital scratching in the squirrel monkey. Positive loci for erection aggregate along three major subdivisions of the limbic system: (a) the hippocampal connections with the septum, including anterior midline thalamus and parts of the hypothalamus; (b) components included in the Papez circuit, particularly the mammillary bodies, mammillothalamic tract, regions of the anterior thalamic nucleus and cingular gyrus; (c) connections involving medial orbital gyrus and medial part of the medial dorsal nucleus. Nodal points for clitoral enlargement coincide with those for penile erection. Efferent pathways for erection arising from the thalamus and septum pass through the hypothalamus either via the periventricular or medial forebrain bundle tracts. The latter is the most important tract for erection and contributes to a pathway coursing through the ventral tegmentum, dorsolaterally through the substantia nigra, and thence ventrolaterally through the pons, eventually extending medially to a location near the exit of the VIth nerve.

In the squirrel monkey, stimulation of the areas associated with the three systems, although leading to erection of various degrees, does not concomitantly cause emission. Stimulation of sites coinciding with the spinothalamic tract up to the level of the midbrain and caudal intralaminar region of the thalamus frequently leads to emission which either is not accompanied by or precedes erection (MacLean *et al.,* 1963; MacLean, 1966). Genital scratching elicited during stimulation of these sites is not merely a motor reflex but an integrated response to sensation (MacLean, 1966). Efferent and afferent pathways and central integrative nuclei involved in erection and emission have been defined for the squirrel monkey. The implication of this research for reproduction is complicated by the fact that evocation of erection and emission at a given site is dependent upon specific stimulus parameters. Changes in frequency, amplitude, or duration of the stimulus can alter a positive site into one which leads to general aversive reactions or genital shrinkage. That none of the activated hypothalamic sites produces a throbbing type of erection and emission implies that many of them in the squirrel monkey may be associated with the nonsexual aspect of penile usage.

Research using the rhesus has contributed to the interpretation and meaningfulness of the inferences drawn from the squirrel monkey. Robinson and Mishkin (1966, 1968) stimulated 5,880 sites and found that 126 of them led to penile erection in the rhesus. There is considerable correspondence among positive loci in anterior hypothalamic and midline thalamic areas in the two species. Sixty-five positive points clustered in the preoptic area, lateral, and dorsal hypothalamus. Other positive loci were in the medial hypothalamus, midline thalamus, corticomedial amygdala, and the bed nucleus of the stria terminalis. The medial preoptic was the only area in which stimulation evoked both erection and projectile ejaculation in the restrained subjects. Stimulation by a telemetering device of the medial preoptic area in unrestrained rhesus monkeys leads to large erections, but interferes with or arrests copulatory attempts with estrous females. The only area in the unrestrained rhesus from which the complete mating sequence, including intromission and ejaculation, has been elicited by stimulation is not in the diencephalon but in the putamen (Perachio *et al.,* 1969).

E. Spinal Cord and Peripheral Nerves

Although the forebrain may be necessary for coordinating the mating sequences of two interacting animals, most of the component acts or reflexes are independently organized at a spinal level. Evidence concerning spinal location of various reflexive mechanisms involved in copulatory behavior is not available in primates. However, there are ample data from human subjects, and since the anatomy and physiology of the spinal cord are essentially similar in all primates, extrapolation would probably yield few errors. Male patients with cord transections uniformly demonstrate that erection, emission, and ejaculation occur without suprasegmental influences. Somatic efferents in the internal pudendal nerves innervate the bulbocavernosus and ischiocavernosus muscles which support erection and the constrictor urethrae muscles which participate in erection and ejaculation. Autonomic innervation is involved in the vascular dilation. Autonomic innervation is involved in the vascular dilatation required for tumescence and activation of a variety of smooth muscles in secondary organs that eject semen and sperm. Evaluation of paraplegic patients reveals that erection can survive any injury above the sacral level (Munro *et al.,* 1948). Ejaculation, which involves primarily sympathetic but also parasympathetic action, is lost after extensive damage located between the third and sixth lumbar segments. No single center exists for this response, since it can be evoked if lesions are located at only one thoracic or lumbar level. Spastic contractions of the musculature in the pelvic region and legs can be evoked in paraplegic men by genital stimulation (Zeitlin *et al.,* 1957).

Distribution of autonomic nerves to the gonads and secondary organs is similar in males and females. Most organs are innervated by both parasympathetic and sympathetic efferents and visceral afferents. Sympathetic neurons originate primarily in the intermediolateral column in the thoracic and upper two or three lumbar segments of the spinal cord. Their axons emerge in the splanchnics as preganglionic fibers and establish synapses in prevertebral ganglia located either on the descending aorta or in close proximity to a specific organ. Relatively short postganglionic fibers terminate either in smooth muscles in blood vessels or specific reproductive organs, or occasionally in nonmuscular areas. Parasympathetic preganglionic fibers emanating from the sacral plexus are conveyed in the nervi erigentes and synapse in ganglia near the organs to be innervated. Afferents course through sympathetic plexuses to lower lumbar and upper thoracic nerves and through parasympathetic plexuses in the pelvic nerve trunk.

Nerve fibers in the ovary are nonmyelinated. They enter primarily via the ovarian plexus and the majority of them terminate near or in the blood vessels. In the squirrel monkey (Jacobowitz and Wallach, 1967) and in the baboon (LePere *et al.*, 1966), some fibers terminate in the stroma. There is no demonstration that neural fibers innervate follicles or corpora lutea. While some cholinergic fibers can be found in the ovaries, no function has been attributed to them. The evidence consistently supports the view that ovarian cyclicity can occur in the absence of neural contribution. As early as 1900, Sherrington reported no lasting interference in the rhesus monkey's menstrual cycle resulting from transection at the twelfth thoracic level. Similarly, uterine cyclicity is present in rhesus monkeys after spinal sections between T6-T12 (Markee *et al.*, 1936). Women with spinal cord injuries between T1-12 can have normal menstrual periods and, when pregnant, do not necessarily abort (Comarr, 1966). Bilateral removal of the abdominal sympathetic chain and coeliac ganglia does not affect ovulation or catamenia in the rhesus (Brooks and Bard, 1942). Ovarian cyclicity is not impaired by bilateral vagotomy, superior cervical ganglionectomy, or hysterectomy in the rhesus, nor does careful transection or stripping nerve fibers entering the ovary disrupt reproductive capacity of the baboon. Complete sympathectomy does not alter ovarian function in other mammals studied (Bard, 1935; Bacq, 1932). The function of autonomic nerves in the gonads is unknown.

III. CONCLUDING REMARKS

Many reflexes, visceral reactions, and action patterns typically occurring during courtship and copulation are exhibited not only before puberty, but in social and emotional situations not having coitus as an objective. On the other hand, many oral and aggressive responses involved in feeding can be seen in sexual situations. Meaningful definitions depend upon the type of relationships being investigated as well as the current state of the knowledge. In this review, a common sense approach was taken, in which physiological processes and behavior were labelled reproductive or sexual if they involved generation and transport of germ cells or coitus. Although a multitude of physiological and behavioral processes occur in a regular sequence in each species, many of the components possess a degree of independence from each other. One task of investigators has been to identify these components, describe their stimulus-response (input-output) parameters, and establish their influence on each other and the total system.

Underlying reproductive behavior are hormonal and neural systems having a common core in the hypothalamus but becoming functionally more independent from each other as their distance from this region increases. At the peripheral level, the gonads do not require innervation from the central nervous system for production and release of germ cells and hormones. These functions are regulated by short and long feedback loops involving chemicals transported through vascular channels to local tissue, the pituitary, and hypothalamus. Secretions are formed in secondary sexual organs without neural influences, but their expulsion is, at least partially, under neural control. Emission and erection have a degree of independence from each other and are mediated by separate autonomic reflexes. Their reflexive integrity to local stimuli survives all spinal cord transections except those at lower lumbar segments. Some skeletal muscle patterns, such as those involved in pelvic thrusting and lordosis, can be elicited in spinal animals. It is not known if or how circulating gonadal hormones alter the excitability of the interneurons involved in these reflexes. They are, however, subjected to suprasegmental influences in a manner similar to other reflexes.

Stimuli from receptors in the genitalia and pudendal area are part of the suprasegmental reflex system and initiate sensations attending coitus. These afferent impulses are conducted to the nucleus centralis lateralis and neighboring nuclei in the thalamus via the spinothalamic tract to the level of the pons and from there by fibers mingled with the medial lemniscus (MacLean *et al.,* 1963). Changes in neural potential are also recorded in the anterior hypothalamus, septum, and amygdala following vaginal stimulation of intact females. Efferent impulses from the hypothalamus to lower centers affecting genital tumescence and ejaculation are propagated primarily through the medial forebrain bundle and, to a lesser extent, the periventricular fiber system (MacLean *et al.,* 1963). The medial forebrain bundle is a massive, longitudinally oriented, bidirectional tract containing short and long fibers interconnecting many nuclear groupings throughout the entire extent of the hypothalamus. Thus, at least one ascending and descending pathway for influencing spinal mechanisms involved in sex has been outlined. Correspondingly, an afferent-efferent loop for control of gonadotrophic hormone can be identified in the hypothalamus. Neurons sensitive to level of circulating gonadal hormone and influencing the output of releasing factors from the median eminence have been located in the basomedial and the anterior hypothalamic areas. The basomedial region controls tonic release of gonadotrophic hormones. Its integrity is not directly necessary for behavior. Animals with large basomedial lesions perform adequately when provided with gonadal hormone replacement therapy. The anterior hypothalamic and medial preoptic areas are more complex in function in that they probably control phasic release of hormone in the female and influence behavior in both sexes.

The region qualifying as the most likely candidate for integrating impulses from forebrain structures for the neural system and translating them for action on the hormonal system is the medial preoptic area. Although only two primate species have been investigated, the evidence from them and other mammals is that it receives input from many sensory sources and utilizes them to determine general sexual arousal, evocation of erection, and ejaculation. Many limbic structures which are nodal points for erection have neural pathways to the medial preoptic area. Spontaneous firing of neurons in it is dramatically altered by genital manipulation in the female, and locally implanted steroid hormones alter the excitability of its neurons. Therefore, it represents the forebrain area which is a focal point for averaging neuronal and hormonal inputs influencing both hormonal and behavioral processes.

Limbic structures, like the diencephalon, have retained their basic organization and characteristics throughout primate phylogeny. In spite of the extensive literature on the limbic system, particularly the limbic lobe, little is known about how it influences reproductive activities. It is often suggested that the limbic rim influences behavior by inhibiting diencephalic centers. While a useful working hypothesis, this is an oversimplification. In many instances, actions called inhibitory and excitatory are characteristic of the same nucleus. Also, ablations of limbic lobe structures in primates do not typically lead to behaviors which reflect release from inhibition or disruption of sequential sexual responses. The hypersexuality associated with amygdalectomy may be due to perceptual deficits rather than release of inhibition of sexual responses. The influence of most limbic structures, therefore, remains to be discovered. Research involving limbic lesions and observations of the presence or absence of copulation in a cage is not likely to clarify their normal behavioral influences. Using telemetering devices in freely moving animals should be a useful approach. Thus far, it has revealed that stimulation of the putamen is followed by execution of the complete copulatory sequence in males (Perachio *et al.*, 1969). Perhaps because this experiment used unrestricted animals, it is the first one to clearly implicate the extrapyramidal system as an initiating and integrating area for the complex array of autonomic and somatic reactions present during mating.

REFERENCES

Anand, B. K.; Malkani, P. K., and Dua, S. (1957): Effect of electrical stimulation on the hypothalamus on menstrual cycle in the monkey. *Indian J Med Res, 45,* 499-502.

Anand Kumar, T. C. (1968): Modified ependymal cells in the ventral hypothalamus of the rhesus monkey and their possible role in the hypothalamic regulation of anterior pituitary function. *J Endocr, 41,* 17-18.

Anand Kumar, T. C., and Knowles, F. (1967): Structure of the pituitary gland and cytophysiology of the adenohypophysis in the slender loris, Loris tardigradua, *Nature (London), 215,* 54-55.

Bard, P. (1935): The effects of denervation of the genitalia on the oestral behavior of cats. *Amer J Physiol, 113,* 5.

Bacq, Z. M. (1932): Effect of sympathectomy on the sexual function, lactation, and maternal behavior in the albino rat with a description of the technic of sympathectomy in the rat. *Amer J Physiol, 99,* 444-453.

Beach, F. A. (1967): Cerebral and hormonal control of reflexive mechanisms involved in copulatory behavior. *Physiol Rev, 47,* 289-316.

Broca, P. (1878): Anatomie comparée des circonvolutions cérébrales. Legrand lobe limbique et la scissure limbique dans le série des mammifères. *Rev Anthrop,* Ser. 2, *1,* 385-498.

Brooks, C., and Bard, P. (1942): Effect of hypothalamic lesions and of subtotal sympathectomies on menstrual and ovulatory cycles of the monkey. *Endocrinology, 30,* S1026-1027.

Chatterjee, S., and Anand, B. K. (1967): Effect of hypothalamic lesions and stimulation on urinary oestrogen excretion in female monkeys. *Indian J Med Res, 55,* 981-990.

Chhina, G. S., and Anand, B. K. (1969): Responses of neurones in the hypothalamus and limbic system to genital stimulation in adult and immature monkeys. *Brain Res, 13,* 511-521.

Chhina, G. S.; Chakrabarty, A. S.; Kaur, K., and Anand, B. K. (1968): Electroencephalographic responses produced by genital stimulation and hormone administration in sexually immature rhesus monkeys. *Physiol Behav, 3,* 579-584.

Clark, W. E. LeGros (1960): *The Antecedents of Man.* Chicago, Quadrangle Books.

Comarr, A. E. (1966): Interesting observations on females with spinal injury. *Med Serv J Canada, 22,* 651-661.

Corner, G. W. (1923): Observation in Macaca rhesus. *Contrib Embryol, 75,* 75-101.

Dávid, M. A.; Fraschini, F., and Martini, L. (1965): Parallelisme entre le contenu hypophysaire en FSH et le contenu hypothalamique en FSH-RF (FSH-Releasing Factor). *C R Acad Sci (Paris), 261,* 2249.

Glees, P.; Cole, C. W.; Whitty, M., and Cairns, H. (1950): The effects of lesions in the cingular gyrus and adjacent areas in monkeys. *J Neurol Neurosurg Psychiat, 13,* 178-190.

Gorski, R. A. (1968): Neural control of ovulation. In Assali, N. S. (Ed.): *Biology of Gestation.* New York, Academic Press, vol. 1, pp. 1-66.

Halász, B., and Pupp, L. (1965): Hormone secretion of the anterior pituitary gland after physical interruption of all nervous pathways to the hypophysiotrophic area. *Endocrinology, 77,* 553-562.

Hartman, C. G. (1932): Studies in the reproduction of the monkey Macacus (Pitheus) rhesus with special reference to menstruation and pregnancy. *Contrib Embryol, 23,* 1-159.

Jacobowitz, D., and Wallach, E. E. (1967): Histochemical and chemical studies of the autonomic innervation of the ovary. *Endocrinology, 81,* 1132-1139.

Kappers, A. C. U.; Huber, G. C., and Crosby, E. C. (1960): *The Comparative Anatomy of the Nervous System of Vertebrates, Including Man.* New York, Hafner.

Kirton, K. T.; Niswender, G. G.; Midgley, A. R.; Jaffe, R. B., and Forbes, A. D. (1970): Serum luteinizing hormone and progesterone concentration during the menstrual cycle of the rhesus monkey. *J Clin Endocr, 30,* 105-110.

Kling, A. (1968): Effects of amygdalectomy and testosterone on sexual behavior of male senile macaques. *J Comp Physiol Psychol, 65,* 466-471.

Kling, A. and Green, P. C. (1967): Effects of amygdalectomy in the maternally reared and maternally deprived neonatal and juvenile Macaque. *Nature (London), 213,* 742.

Kluver, H., and Bucy, P. C. (1939): Preliminary analysis of functions of the temporal lobes in monkeys. *AMA Arch Neurol Psychiat, 42,* 979.

Kluver, H., and Bucy, P. C. (1937): "Psychic blindness" and other symptoms following bilateral temporal lobectomy in rhesus monkeys. *Amer J Physiol, 119,* 352-353.

Knowles, F., and Anand Kumar, T. C. (1970): Structural changes, related to reproduction, in the hypothalamus and in the pars tuberalis of the rhesus monkey. In *Philosophical Transactions of the Royal Society of London,* Series B, vol. 256, pp. 1-66, Cambridge.

LePere, R. H.; Benoit, P. E.; Hardy, R. C., and Goldzieber, J. W. (1966): The origin and function of the ovarian nerve supply in the baboon. *Fertil Steril, 17,* 68-75.

MacLean, P. D. (1966): Studies on the cerebral representation of certain basic sexual functions. In Gorski, R. A., and Whalen, R. E. (Eds.): *Brain and Behavior: the Brain and Gonadal Functions.* Berkeley, University of California Press, vol. 3, pp. 35-80.

MacLean, P. D.; Denniston, R. H., and Dua, S. (1963): Further studies on cerebral representation of penile erection: Caudal thalamus, midbrain and pons (Squirrel monkey). *J Neurophysiol, 26,* 273-293.

MacLean, P. D.; Dua, S., and Denniston, R. H. (1963): Cerebral localization for scratching and seminal discharge. *Arch Neurol, 9,* 485-497.

MacLean, P. D., and Ploog, D. W. (1962): Cerebral representation of penile erection. *J Neurophysiol, 25,* 29-55.

Markee, J. E.; Davis, J. H., and Hinsey, J. C. (1936): Uterine bleeding in spinal monkeys. *Anat Rec, 64,* 231-245.

Maurus, M.; Mitra, J., and Ploog, D. (1965): Cerebral representation of the clitoris in ovariectomized squirrel monkeys. *Exp Neurol, 13,* 283-288.

Mittler, J. C., and Meites, J. (1966): Effects of hypothalamic extract and androgen on pituitary FSH release *in vitro. Endocrinology, 78,* 500-504.

Munro, D.; Horne, H. W., and Paull, D. P. (1948): The effect of injury to the spinal cord and cauda equina on the sexual potency of men. *New Eng J Med, 239,* 903-911.

Neill, J. D.; Johansson, E. D. B., and Knobil, E. (1967): Levels of progesterone in peripheral plasma during menstrual cycle of the rhesus monkey. *Endocrinology, 81,* 1161-1164.

Nicholson, A. N., and Turner, E. A. (1963): Mesial surface of the brain and genital function (rhesus monkeys). *Nature (London), 200,* 788.

Noback, C. R., and Moskowitz, N. (1963): The primate nervous system: Functional and structural aspects in phylogeny. In Buettner-Janusch, J. (Ed.): *Evolutionary and Genetic Biology of Primates.* New York, Academic Press, chap. 3, pp. 131-177.

Perachio, A. A.; Alexander, M., and Robinson, B. W. (1969): Sexual behavior evoked by telestimulation. *Proc 2nd Int Congr Primat.* Basel/New York, Karger, vol. 3, pp. 68-74.

Phoenix, C. H.; Goy, R. W.; Resko, J. A., and Koering, M. (1968): Probability of mating during various stages of the ovarian cycle in Macaca mulatta. *Anat Rec, 160,* 490.

Ploog, D. W.; and MacLean, P. D. (1963): Display of penile erection in squirrel monkey (Saimiri sciureus). *Anim Behav, 11,* 32-39.

Poirier, L. J. (1962): Anatomical and experimental studies on the temporal lobe of the macaque. *J Comp Neurol 96,* 209-248.

Robinson, B. W., and Mishkin, M. (1968): Penile erection evoked from forebrain structures in Macaca mulatta. *Arch Neurol 19,* 184-198.

Robinson, B. W., and Mishkin, M. (1966): Ejaculation evoked by stimulation of the preoptic area in monkeys. *Physiol Behav, 1,* 269-272.

Russell, G. V. (1961): Interrelationships within the limbic and centrencephalic systems. In Sheer, D. E. (Ed.): *Electrical Stimulation of the Brain.* Austin, University of Texas Press, Chap. 15, pp. 167-181.

Schreiner, L, and Kling, A. (1956): Rhinencephalon and behavior. *Amer J Physiol, 184,* 486-490.

Sherrington, C. S. (1900): In Schafer, E. A. (Ed.): *The Spinal Cord. A Textbook of Physiology.* Edinburgh, Pentland, vol. 2.

Smith, W. K. (1944): The results of ablation in the cingular region of the cerebral cortex. *Fed Proc, 3,* 42.

Walker, A. E.; Thomson, A. F., and McQueen, J. D. (1953): Behavior and the temporal rhinencephalon in the monkey. *Bull Hopkins Hosp, 93,* 65-93.

Ward, A. A. (1948): The cingular gyrus: Area 24. *J Neurophysiol 11,* 13-23.

Wickler, W. (1966): Origin and biological significance of genital presentation of male primates. *Z Tierpsychol, 23,* 422-427.

Zeitlin, A. B.; Cottrell, T. L., and Lloyd, F. A. (1957): Sexology of the paraplegic male. *Fertil Steril, 8,* 337-344.

II. MALE BIOLOGY

Chapter 4

MALE REPRODUCTIVE SYSTEM AND SPERMATOGENESIS

W. G. KINZEY

THE male reproductive organs comprise the male gonads, or testes, together with their coverings, and the accessory organs which include a series of ducts (ductus epididymidis, ductus deferens, ejaculatory duct, and urethra), glands (seminal vesicles, prostate, and bulbourethral glands), and the external genital organs (penis and scrotum).

I. TESTIS

A. Descent of Testis

In the great majority of adult primates the testes are permanently scrotal. Only among a few of the prosimians with (apparently) restricted breeding seasons do the testes descend seasonally.

The testes develop in the connective tissue of the dorsal wall of the peritoneal cavity and, until at least the latter part of intrauterine life, remain in the abdominal cavity. Later, they "migrate" through the future inguinal canal to the scrotum, each carrying with it an outpocketing of the peritoneum, the tunica vaginalis, which forms a serous cavity, the processus vaginalis, around each testis. The inguinal canal, from the deep to the superficial inguinal ring, marks the pathway of descent through the anterior abdominal wall. The general pattern of the canal is the same for all primates regardless of posture, except that in man the canal is very short and is supported by an inguinal ligament which is absent from all other primates (Miller, 1947).

Within the Tupaiidae, although the testes in the adult do not retain their embryonic position near the kidneys as in the closely related macroscelid insectivores, *Elephantulus* and *Macroscelides,* the testes are abdominal in the Indian treeshrew, *Anathana,* having migrated to lie at the deep inguinal ring with only the large highly coiled tail of the epididymis extending through the inguinal canal (Verma, 1965). In the pen-tailed treeshrew, *Ptilocercus,* the testes descend seasonally from the abdominal cavity to the scrotum (Clark, 1926), while in *Tupaia* the testes are permanently descended (Eckstein, 1958) arriving in the scrotum at about the time of puberty. The inguinal canal in *Tupaia* remains sufficiently large to allow the testis to pass back into the abdomen in the adult, but contraction of the muscular wall of the superficial inguinal ring prevents reascent into the canal.

In the Lemurinae and in *Galago* descent of the testes is permanent; whereas in the Cheirogaleinae the testes regress between sexual seasons to the inguinal canal, but never completely to the abdominal cavity (Petter-Rousseaux, 1962). In the adult slender loris, *Loris tardigradus,* even when sexually active, the testes are inguinal and do not usually descend, except temporarily, into the scrotum (Ramakrishna and Prasad, 1962).

In the remainder of adult primates the testes, once descended, do not return to the abdominal cavity.

In the Platyrrhini the testes are undescended until puberty in *Saguinus geoffroyi, Aotus, Saimiri, Cebus capucinus,* and *Alouatta villosa,* but are already permanently descended at birth in *Ateles geoffroyi* (Wislocki, 1936).

In most of the Catarrhini studied, permanent descent of the testes does not occur until near or at the time of puberty. But, in the macaque, *M. mulatta, M. sinica* (Wislocki, 1933), they descend to the scrotum during the latter half of intrauterine life and are found in the scrotum at birth; they then reascend to the inguinal canal shortly after birth and do not regain the scrotum finally until puberty. Development of the testes has been described in detail for *M. mulatta* (Van Wagenen and Simpson, 1954). Whether or not the testes are descended at birth in other Cercopithecoidea, and then reascend as in the macaque, is a matter for further research.

In the chimpanzee, *Pan troglodytes, P. paniscus* (Wislocki, 1933 , as in man, the testes descend to the scrotum before birth and remain there. In the gorilla, *G. g. beringei* (Wislocki, 1942), and the Bornean orang, *Pongo p. pygmaeus* (Wislocki, 1936), data are incomplete, but descent of the testes has taken place by the time of infancy.

The processus vaginalis becomes completely obliterated in man, the chimpanzee, the gorilla, and the capuchin, *Cebus capucinus,* and the spider monkey, *Ateles,* but in all other primates free communication between abdominal cavity and scrotum persists into adult life.

B. Gross Structure and Coverings

The surface of the testis is completely covered in most primates by the visceral layer of the tunica vaginalis except where it is attached to the epididymis. In *Tupaia* (Jones, 1917) and in the macaque (Wislocki, 1933) only the upper pole of the testis is covered, an important consideration in orchidectomy. Underlying the tunica vaginalis is a thick fibrous capsule, the tunica albuginea. On the dorsal aspect of the organ, a thickening of the capsule projects into the gland as the mediastinum. Thin fibrous septa extend from the inner surface of the tunica albuginea, converging toward the mediastinum and divide the testis into pyramidal compartments, the lobuli. Septa are lacking and the mediastinum is rudimentary in the gibbon, *H. agilis* (Matthews, 1946). Each lobule contains one or more highly convoluted seminiferous tubules, which constitute the testis' exocrine portion whose secretory product is whole cells, the spermatozoa. The tubules are highly convoluted loops, but they may branch or end blindly. At the apex of each lobule its tubules pass into the tubuli recti which comprise the first segment of the system of excretory ducts. They in turn are confluent with the rete, a labyrinth of spaces in the connective tissue of the mediastinum. From the rete several ducts, the ductuli efferentes, pass directly into the epididymis to communicate with a single common duct, the ductus epididymidis.

On the inner aspect of the tunica albuginea, dense connective tissue gives way to a looser layer provided with numerous blood vessels and lymphatics which enter and leave the testis through the mediastinum. This loose connective tissue extends in to fill all of the interstices among the seminiferous tubules, and it contains, *inter alia,* the interstitial cells, the endocrine tissue of the testis.

The size of the testis, both absolutely and relatively, has been

TABLE 4-I

SIZE AND WEIGHT OF TESTES IN VARIOUS PRIMATES*

	Size (cm)	*Weight (gm)*	*% of Body Weight*
Galago demidovii	1.1×0.7		
Galago elegantulus	1.5×0.5		
Perodicticus potto	2.0×1.7		
Loris tardigradus		1.7	.65 (138)
Avahi laniger	1.5×1.1		
Lemur macaco fulvus	3.0×1.5		
Microcebus murinis (active)	1.5×1.2		
Microcebus murinis (inactive	0.75×0.6		
Callithrix geoffroyi		1.8	.32
Aotus trivirgatus		1.2	.12
Alouatta villosa palliata		25.0 (8)	.34 (8)
Lagothrix lagothricha		11.2	.22
Ateles geoffroyi		13.4	.17
Macaca fascicularis		30.8 (12)	.67
Macaca radiata		57.6	.69
Macaca nemestrina		66.7	.67
Macaca mulatta		76.0 (2)	.73 (2)
Papio sphinx		88.9	.28
Papio anubis		114.5 (4)	.42 (4)
Papio hamadryas		30.1 (6)	.14 (6)
Theropithecus gelada		21.5	.10
Cercopithecus aethiops		18.5 (6)	.36 (6)
Colobus polykomos		13.7 (3)	.14 (3)
Presbytis cristatus		5.5 (14)	.09 (14)
Presbytis rubicundus		3.6 (12)	.06 (12)
Nasalis larvatus		11.9 (8)	.06 (8)
Hylobates moloch		4.6 (7)	.08 (7)
Hylobates agilis	2.8×1.4		
Pongo pygmaeus	3.9×3.0	35.3 (2)	.05 (2)
Pan troglodytes		118.8 (3)	.27 (3)
Pan paniscus		250.0	.55
Gorilla g. berengei	5.5×3.5	36.0	.017
Homo sapiens	5.0×3.0	50.2 (3)	.08 (3)

* The number in parentheses indicates the number of animals, if more than one. (Adapted from Hall-Craggs, 1962; Hill, 1939; Jones, 1969; Kinsky, 1960; Matthews, 1946; Petter-Rousseaux, 1963; Ramakrishna and Prasad, 1967; Schultz, 1938; Wislocki, 1942).

considered in detail by Schultz (1938). There is enormous variation among species and genera, and testis size is independent of body weight (Table 4-I). The testes are proportionately most heavy in the genus *Macaca* and smallest in the Hominoidea. Compared to man, the testes are relatively smaller in the gorilla and orang. The weight and/or the size of the testis has proved very useful as a measure of functional activity of the seminiferous tubules in prosimians (Ramakrishna and Prasad, 1967) as well as in macaques (Sade, 1964).

C. Seminiferous Epithelium

In the adult primate the seminiferous tubules are lined with stratified epithelium composed of two types of cells, sustentacular cells and spermatogenic cells.

Each sustentacular cell (supporting cell, nursing cell, or Sertoli cell), the only nongerminal cell in the tubule, is located next to the basement membrane of the seminiferous epithelium and is most easily identified by the characteristically oval shape of its nucleus, folded nuclear membrane, and large nucleolus. The cytoplasm of the sustentacular cell is elaborate in shape, conforming to the surface of adjacent spermatogenic cells, and cell boundaries are not easily delimited in histological sections. The nucleus may even appear to be separated from the basement membrane by a continuous layer of spermatogonia. The sustentacular cells provide mechanical support and protection for developing spermatogenic cells, probably play a role in their nutrition, and may phagocytize degenerating spermatogonia (Gondos and Zemjanis, 1970).

The spermatogenic cells include several morphologically distinct stages of development: spermatogonia (the mitotic stage), primary and secondary spermatocytes (the meiotic stages), spermatids (the postmeiotic stage), and spermatozoa (the male germ cells after they are released from the wall of the tubule).

Spermatogenesis. Spermatogenesis is the process by which the primordial germ cells (spermatogonia) develop into mature spermatozoa. The youngest cells are located at the basement membrane of the epithelium and progressively more advanced stages of the spermatogenic process occur towards the lumen of the seminiferous tubule. The process is described in a sequence of three phases: spermatocytogenesis, meiosis, and spermiogenesis. Spermatogenesis has been reviewed in several mammalian species (Roosen-Runge, 1962; Leblond *et al.*, 1963). In nonhuman primates thus far studied in detail (*Macaca mulatta* and *Cercopithecus aethiops*) spermatogenesis appears to follow a pattern similar to that

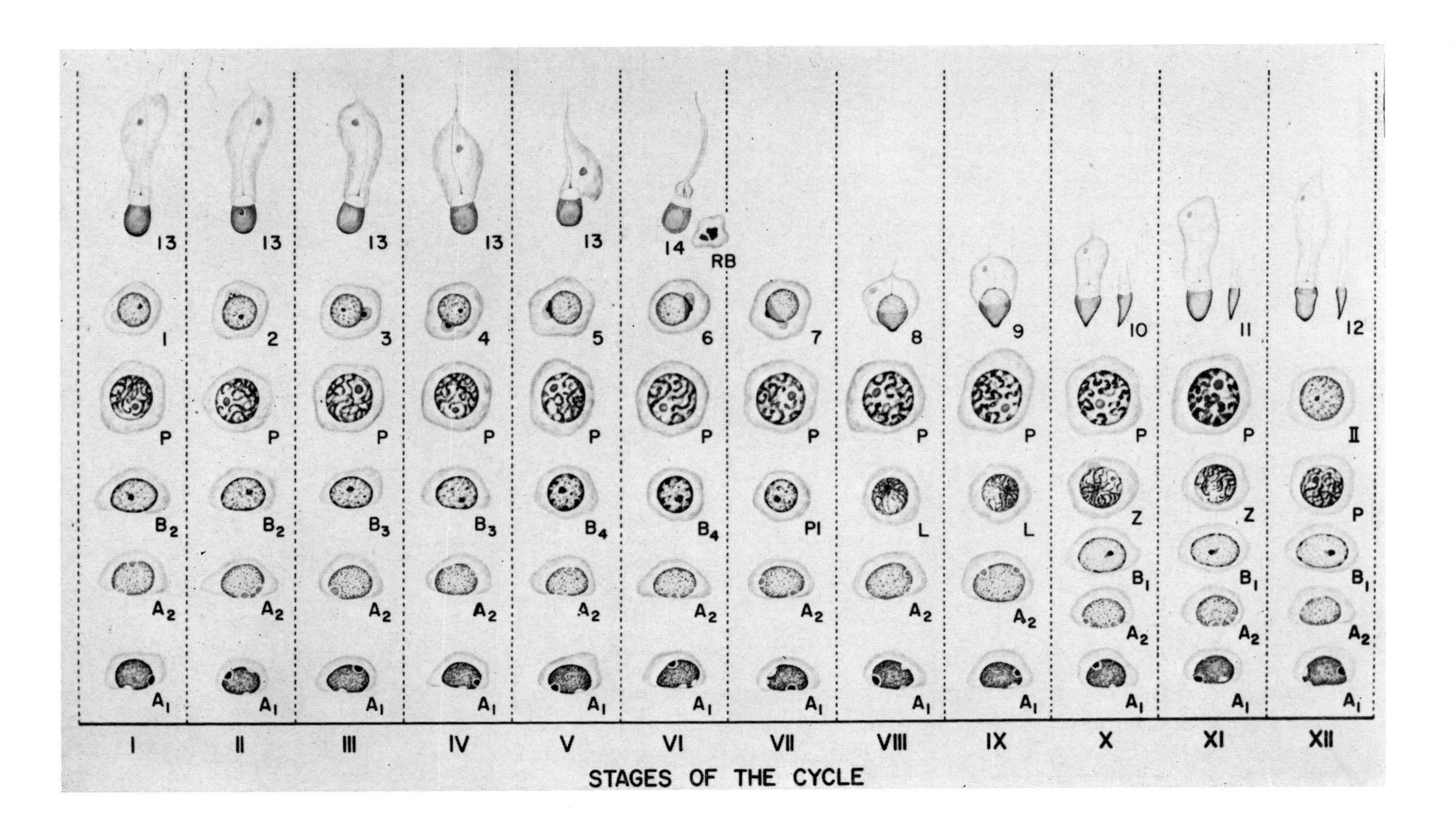
13
13
13
13
13
14
RB
1
2
3
4
5
6
7
8
9
10
11
12
P
P
P
P
P
P
P
P
P
P
P
II
B_2
B_2
B_3
B_3
B_4
B_4
Pl
L
L
Z
Z
P
B_1
B_1
B_1
A_2
A_2
A_2
A_2
A_2
A_2
A_2
A_2
A_2
A_2
A_2
A_2
A_1
A_1
A_1
A_1
A_1
A_1
A_1
A_1
A_1
A_1
A_1
A_1
I
II
III
IV
V
VI
VII
VIII
IX
X
XI
XII
STAGES OF THE CYCLE

found in laboratory rodents. The gonadotropic hormones of the anterior pituitary gland exert a stimulatory effect on spermatogenesis beginning shortly before puberty. The exact mechanism of this action is not clearly defined, especially since some primates undergo a seasonal arrest of spermatogenesis (Petter-Rousseaux, 1962; Conaway and Sade, 1965; DuMond and Hutchinson, 1967).

The mitotic proliferation of spermatogonia and their development into spermatocytes is termed spermatocytogenesis. Individual spermatogonia may be distinguished in the fetal monkey, *M. mulatta,* as early as fifty four days after conception (Van Wagenen and Simpson, 1965). Spermatogonial stem cells are of two types—those which serve as an emergency source of new stem cells ("reserve" stem cells; A_1 in Fig. 4-1), and those which may begin the process of differentiation into spermatozoa ("renewing" stem cells; A_2 in Fig. 4-1). "Reserve" stem cells remain quiescent unless the supply of "renewing" stem cells divide to form either new A_2 spermatogonia or B_1 spermatogonia. The latter differentiate by a series of stages B_{1-4} into primary spermatocytes, and thus type B cells are referred to as "differentiated" spermatogonia (Clermont, 1969; Clermont and Leblond, 1959).

In the second phase of spermatogenesis, meiosis, each primary spermatocyte undergoes two maturation divisions which reduce the number of chromosomes from the diploid to the haploid num-

---

Figure 4-1. Cellular composition of the 12 stages of the cycle of the seminiferous epithelium in the monkey, *M. mulatta and C. aethiops.* Each column numbered with a roman numeral shows the cell types present in one of the cellular associations found in cross-sections of seminiferous tubules. The cellular associations or stages of the cycle succeed one another in time in any given area of seminiferous tubule according to the sequence indicated from left to the right in the figure. Following cellular association XII, cellular association I reappears, so that the sequence starts over again. A_1, A_2, represent type A_1 and A_2 spermatogonia; B_{1-4}, generations of type B spermatogonia; Pl, preleptotene primary spermatocyte; L, leptotene spermatocyte; Z, zygotene spermatocyte; P, pachytene spermatocyte; II, secondary spermatocyte; numbers 1-14, the steps in spermiogenesis. Associated with step 14, the residual body (Rb) is illustrated. (From Clermont, 1969)

ber and produce a cluster of four spermatids. Primary spermatocytes at first resemble the B_4 spermatogonia from which they differentiate (P1 in Fig. 4-1), but as they move away from the basement membrane they become larger (stages L, Z, and P) until in the first maturation division each primary spermatocyte divides to form two secondary spermatocytes (II in column XII of Fig. 4-1). The latter remain in interphase only briefly, then quickly undergo the second maturation division to become spermatids (1 in column I of Fig. 4-1).

The third phase of spermatogenesis, spermiogenesis, is the differentiation of spermatids into spermatozoa which are released into the lumen of the seminiferous tubule. During spermiogenesis cytoplasm containing Golgi membranes, vesicles, mitochondrial remnants, lipid, and most of the RNA is lost from the cell. The cytoplasm so removed (residual bodies) moves gradually down the tail of the spermatid and persists during much of the spermatozoon's passage through the epididymis. A high percentage of spermatozoa in the ejaculated semen of the squirrel monkey, *Saimiri sciureus*, contains these "cytoplasmic droplets." In all mammals an acrosomic system (acrosome, head cap, and their precursors) develops in the spermatid from the Golgi apparatus (Clermont and Leblond, 1955). Four phases (Golgi, cap, acrosome, and maturation) are recognized in the development of this system in the monkey, as well as in most other mammals. In primates, in contrast to other mammals, the acrosome is not present in the spermatozoon. Man differs from nonhuman primates in lacking a clear-cut separation between the acrosome and maturation phases. A large acrosomal head cap has been described in the marmoset, *Saguinus oedipus* (Rattner and Brinkley, 1970).

After release into the lumen of the seminiferous tubule, spermatozoa begin their passage through the system of excretory ducts, and are stored in the tail of the epididymis prior to ejaculation. While in the epididymis they develop motility, the ability to survive *in vitro,* and the ability to fertilize ova when placed in the female reproductive tract. Also during this time the sperm become coated with decapacitation factor (DF), a substance which must be removed from the sperm within the female reproductive tract as part of the capacitation process (Dukelow and Chernoff, 1969).

During ejaculation spermatozoa travel through the remainder of the system of excretory ducts and are mixed with secretions of the various accessory glands to form semen. Immobilization of the pig-tail macaque, *M. nemestrina,* for more than fourteen days arrests spermatogenesis (Cockett *et al.,* 1970). Other environmental factors which affect development of spermatozoa are discussed by Leblond *et al.,* 1963).

Cycle of the Seminiferous Epithelium. In any histological section of a seminiferous tubule several stages of development are seen at different levels in the epithelium, with the more primitive cells near the basement membrane and the more differentiated cells closer to the lumen of the tubule. The cells of different stages are not randomly distributed, however, but occur in a series of well-defined combinations. In the monkey, *M. mulatta* and *C. aethiops,* twelve such combinations are recognized (Clermont and Leblond, 1959; Clermont, 1969) corresponding to the twelve vertical columns in Figure 4-1. In man only six such combinations or stages occur (Clermont, 1963). This sequence of stages which takes place in any given area of the seminiferous epithelium is called the "cycle of the seminiferous epithelium." The presence of intercellular bridges between spermatogonia is probably a factor in synchronization of the cycle (Gondos and Zemjanis, 1970). A model of the twelve combinations in the monkey is presented (Fig. 4-2) to show the mode of development of spermatocytes from a single stem cell and the peaks of mitotic activity which occur in stages II, IV, VI, IX-X, and XII of the cycle. The duration of a single cycle of spermatogonial renewal has not been determined for any nonhuman primate, but the length of the cycle in man is sixteen days (Leblond *et al.,* 1967), and thus the length of time for a single human spermatogonium to become a spermatozoon (four consecutive cycles) is sixty-four days.

II. ACCESSORY ORGANS

A. Epididymis

The epididymis, together with the lowest portion of the spermatic cord, is attached to the posterior margin of the testis. In many primates (*Cebus, Lagothrix,* Cercopithecoidea) the epididymis is suspended from the parietal layer of the tunica vaginalis

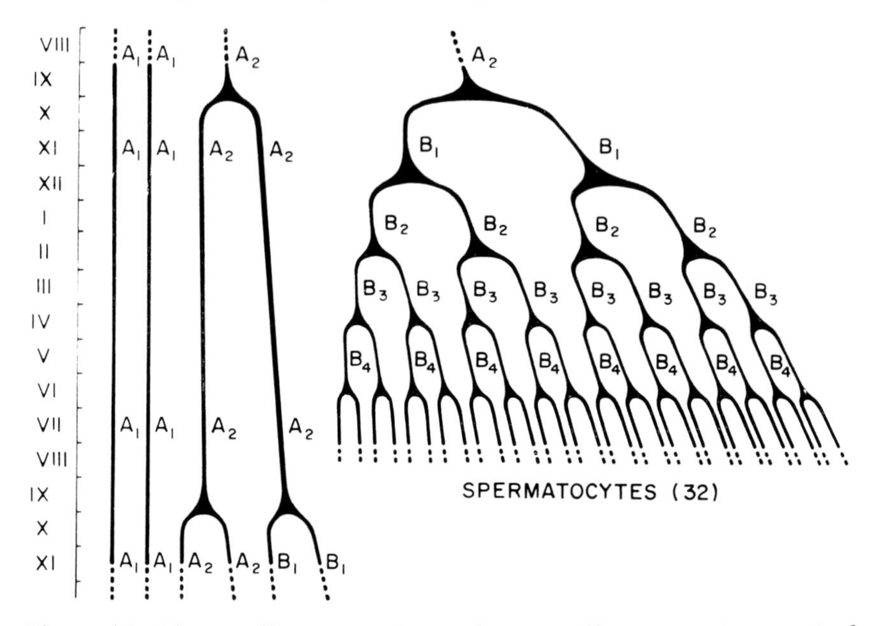

Figure 4-2. Diagram illustrating the mode of proliferation and renewal of spermatogonia in the monkey, *M. mulatta and C. aethiops*. The stages of the cycle are indicated on the left of the diagram by Roman numerals. Lettering of cell as in Figure 4-1. On the left of the diagram, a pair of type A_1 spermatogonia is represented as two parallel unbranched lines to indicate that these cells do not proliferate to any significant extent during the cycle of the seminiferous epithelium of normal adult animals. A pair of type A_2 spermatogonia is shown to divide at stages IX-X of the cycle, one of them would yield a new pair of type A_2 spermatogonia that would remain dormant until stages IX-X of the next cycle. The other (right of diagram) would yield a pair of type B_1 spermatogonia which in stage XII would produce type B_2 cells. Type B_2 spermatogonia would give rise, during stage II, to type B_3 spermatogonia which in stage IV would produce type B_4 cells which finally divide in stage VI to yield spermatocytes. (From Clermont, 1969)

by a meso-epididymis. The organ has a body (corpus), a head (caput) which lies against the superior pole of the testis, and a tail (cauda), attached to the inferior extremity. The relative size of the head and tail varies in different primates; the tail is particularly large and lobulated in Tupaiidae and *Tarsius,* and the head is particularly large in the Platyrrhini. Between the epididymis and the testis is an invaginated reflection of the tunica vaginalis called the sinus of the epididymis. This cleft is absent from the

Cercopithecinae, but present in the langur (Ayer, 1948); shallow in Lorisiformes, but deep and clearly separating the epididymis from the testis in Lemuriformes, especially in Hapalemur (Hill and Davies, 1954).

The main mass of the epididymis is comprised of an irregularly convoluted duct, the ductus epididymidis which is connected to the rete testis by numerous (e.g. 15-20 in man) efferent ductules which pierce the tunica albuginea of the testis and enter the head of the epididymis. The duct of the epididymis is much longer than the epididymis itself (over six meters long in man), and terminates by becoming the ductus deferens.

Appendices testis and/or epididymidis (hydatids of Morgani) have been described in all male primates whose reproductive organs are known, except the Lorisdae (Eckstein, 1958).

B. Ductus Deferens and Ejaculatory Duct

The ductus deferens is the direct continuation of the ductus epididymidis. Beginning at the lower pole of the epididymis it ascends to the superficial inguinal ring (provided the testis is descended), passes through the inguinal canal and, upon entering the abdomen, bends medially and posteriorly to end behind the neck of the urinary vesicle (bladder) in either the prostatic portion of the urethra, or to join the duct of the seminal vesicle to become the ejaculatory duct. The ejaculatory duct is absent from the Lorisidae (Butler, 1964) and from the Indriidae (Hill, 1953) (Fig. 4-3). In *Ptilocercus* the duct of only one lobe of the seminal vesicle (the upper) joins the ductus deferens, the other emptying directly into the urethra near the entrance of the prostatic utricle. In the *Lemur* the two ejaculatory ducts join to form a common (ejaculatory) duct, although in *Hapalemur* the ducts merely share a common urethral opening. In man, *Presbytis entellus,* and *Hylobates* the ductus deferens, immediately before it ends, expands into an ampulla in which the epithelial lining is thrown into numerous irregular folds. The ampulla is absent from other primates.

C. Seminal Vesicle

The paired seminal vesicles are present in all known primates except *Daubentonia, Callicebus,* and *Pithecia pithecia* (Hill,

1953, 1960). They are generally large organs, except in gorilla. They are particularly large in the tarsier in which they are roughly pear-shaped, and extend beyond the cranial surface of the bladder. In Lorisiformes and Lemuriformes they are very elongated (Fig. 4-3) and in the Indriidae and Lemuridae, unlike other primates, they are bent at their upper poles. In *Ptilocercus* each gland is divided into two lobes, the cranial joining the ductus deferens by a simple straight tube to form an ejaculatory duct, the more complex caudal lobe emptying directly into the urethra (Clark, 1926). In other primates they are simple coiled tubes; in the gibbon, *H. agilis,* each seminal vesicle is 2 cm long and 4.3 cm long when uncoiled (Matthews, 1946). Compare Figure 4-4 in which one tube is shown uncoiled in the orang. In most primates except the apes the seminal vesicles are relatively larger than those of man (Fig. 4-4 to 4-6).

D. Prostate

The prostate of most nonhuman primates comprises at least two distinct parts known as the cranial and caudal lobes (Figs. 4-5, 4-6). As a rule each lobe is confined to the dorsal aspect of the urethra. In man, *Daubentonia, Cheirogaleus,* the Indriidae, and *Ptilocercus,* however, the prostate completely surrounds the urethra. In all primates the ejaculatory ducts (or in their absence, the ductus deferens) together with the ducts of the prostate drain into the posterior wall of the urethra on or near the colliculus seminalis. The caudal lobe is traversed by the ejaculatory ducts (Fig. 4-7).

The size and shape of the prostate vary markedly even within families of primates. Among Tupaiidae, the prostate is quite small in *Tupaia* and relatively large in *Ptilocercus.* The prostate is unilobular in the Tupaiidae, in marmosets, in the orang (Fig. 4-4), and in *Loris* (Fig. 4-3) and *Galago* (Butler, 1964).

The cranial lobe has a different histological structure from the caudal lobe (Schoones *et al.,* 1968), and is functionally comparable to the "coagulating gland" of rodents (van Wagenen, 1936). Its secretion coagulates seminal plasma, and this is responsible for the formation of the vaginal plug during copulation.

The prostatic utricle is described in section IV A.

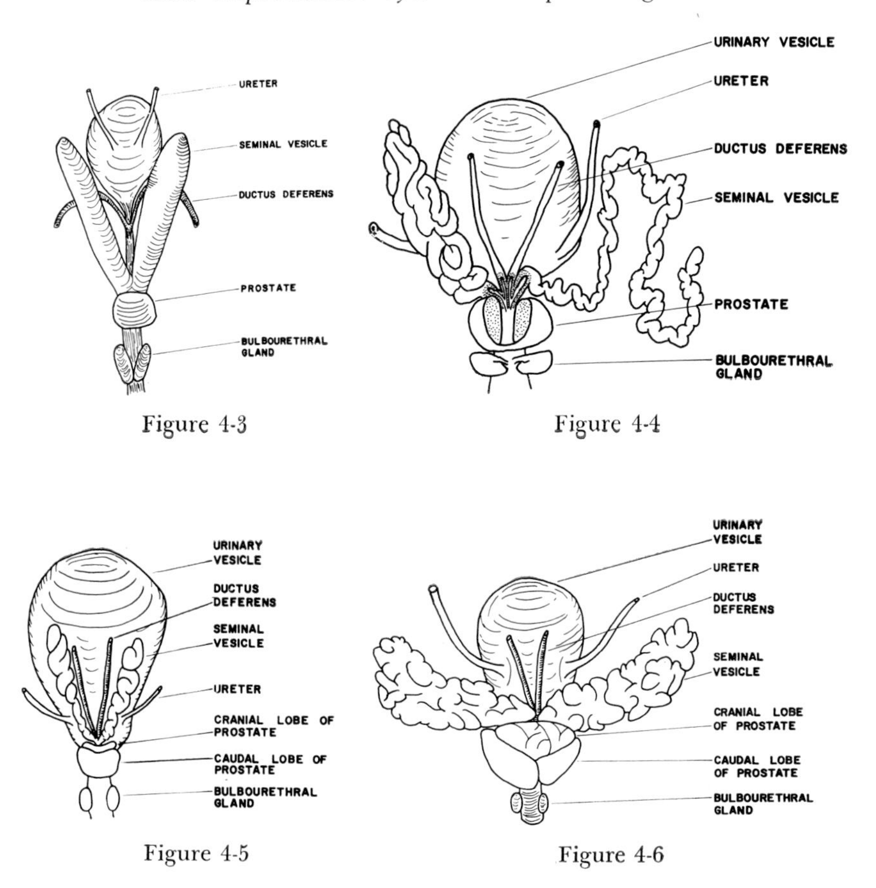

Figure 4-3

Figure 4-4

Figure 4-5

Figure 4-6

Figure 4-3. The internal male reproductive organs of the slender loris, *Loris tardigradus,* dorsal view. Note (1) lack of an ejaculatory duct as the ductus deferens terminates separately in the urethra from the duct of the seminal vesicle; and, (2) presence of only one lobe in the prostate. (After Klaar and Krasa, 1921)

Figure 4-4. The internal male reproductive organs of the orang, *Pongo pygmaeus,* dorsal view. The right seminal vesicle has been uncoiled to show its extent, and the prostate and prostatic urethra have been cut to show the union of the ductus deferens with the duct of the seminal vesicle to form a short ejaculatory duct. (Adapted from Pousargues, 1895)

Figure 4-5. The internal male reproductive organs of the spider monkey, *Ateles paniscus,* dorsal view. (After Klaar and Krasa, 1921)

Figure 4-6. The internal male reproductive organs of the rhesus monkey, *M. mulatta,* dorsal view. (After Klaar and Krasa, 1921)

E. Bulbourethral Gland

The paired bulbourethral (Cowper's) glands which are present in all primates, except the gorilla, are branched tubulo-alveolar glands, lined with simple low cuboidal to columnar epithelium. They are located on either side of the membranous portion of the

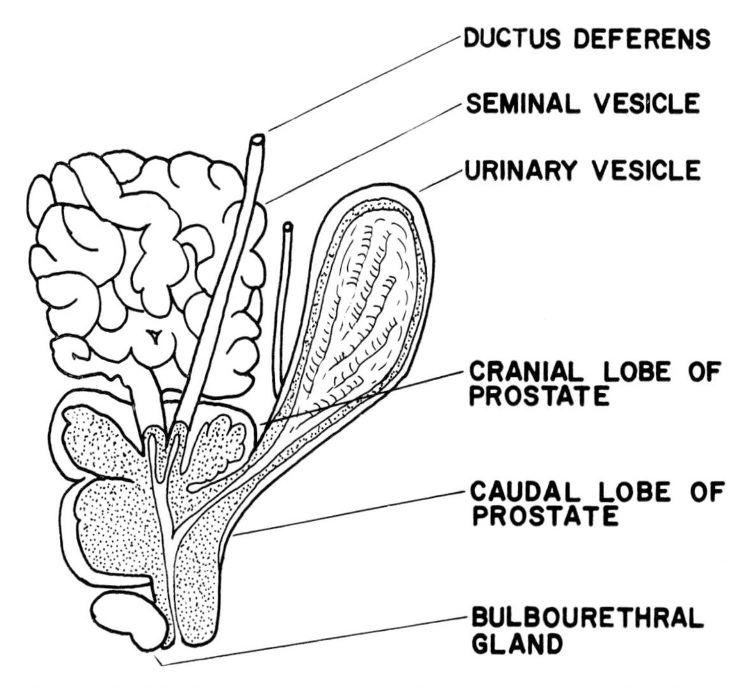

Figure 4-7 Median sagittal section through the internal male reproductive organs of the rhesus monkey, *M. mulatta.* (After van Wagenen, 1936)

urethra (Figs. 4-3 to 4-7), and each empties its secretion by a single duct into the first part of the cavernous urethra. The glands are usually well-developed, oval structures. They measure 3.5 mm in greatest diameter in *Ptilocercus* (Clark, 1926), 3.5 mm in *Galago* (Butler, 1964), 5 mm in *Presbytis entellus,* 3 mm in the gibbon, *H. agilis,* and "about the size of a pea" in man.

The physiology of the male accessory organs has been reviewed by Risley (1963).

III. EXTERNAL GENITAL ORGANS

A. Penis

The penis is composed chiefly of cavernous (erectile) tissue, and is traversed by the urethra. The skin of the penis is thin and freely movable, and, except near the pubis, is free from hairs. On the urethral aspect the skin is usually marked by a median raphe, continuous with the raphe of the scrotum, although the raphe is absent from *Callicebus* and *Aotus* (Hill, 1960). Towards the base of the glans, the skin forms a free fold, the prepuce, or foreskin (Fig. 4-8), which overlaps the glans to a variable extent. Man is exceptional in attachment of the prepuce very close to the glans. From the deep surface of the prepuce the skin is reflected on to the neck of the glans, and is continued over the entire glans to the external urethral orifice.

The penis is invariably pendulous to some degree, although least so in the Tupaiidae. In this the primates differ from most other mammals, except bats and bears. The penis is particularly long in macaques and baboons, in correlation with the sexual swelling of the perineum in the female.

The glans, together with other parts of the organ clothed by the prepuce, is covered by an epithelium intermediate between ordinary epidermis and mucous membrane. The final transition to mucous membrane occurs a short distance within the external urinary orifice. A specialization of the epithelium of the glans is the tendency for local keratinization giving rise to horny papillae (e.g. in langurs), spicules (e.g. in the chimpanzee), or even quite large recurved hooks (e.g. in Galagidae and Indriidae, (Fig. 4-8). Details of these specializations are described by Hill (1958).

Structurally, the penis consists of three rods of erectile tissue which over most of their extent are bound together by their fibrous outer sheaths (tunica albuginea) to form a firm cylinder. Two (corpora cavernosa) form the dorsum of the organ while the other (corpus spongiosum) is ventral. Proximally the three elements diverge, the two corpora cavernosa becoming attached to the margins of the subpubic arch (where they form the crura penis), the median corpus spongiosum to the urogenital fascia, where it enlarges to form the bulb of the penis and is enclosed by

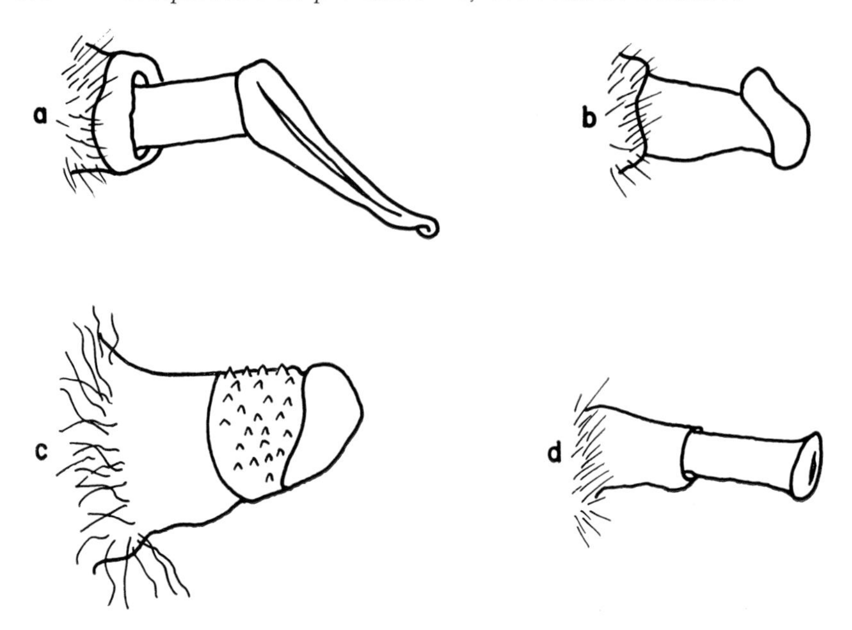

Figure 4-8. Various forms of the penis in anthropoid primates: (a) stumptail macaque, *M. arctoides,* with highly specialized glans; (b) *M. sinica,* with typically catarrhine acorn-shaped glans; (c) gibbon, *H. agilis,* with spicules; (d) *Cebus,* with mushroom shaped glans. The prepuce has been retracted in each case. (After Pocock, 1920, 1921, 1925)

the bulbocavernosus muscle. The urethra enters the cranial surface of the bulb and courses through the corpus spongiosum to its distal end, where it terminates in the external urinary orifice. The tip of the penis is formed by the corpus spongiosum (Fig. 4-9), which typically expands over the distal end of the fused corpora cavernosa as a cap (the glans penis), except in the howler monkey, *Alouatta,* and the chimpanzee. The glans is more or less acorn-shaped in all the catarrhine primates, except the specialized stumptail macaque, *M. arctoides,* the chimpanzee (which lacks a differentiated glan), gibbon and orang. The glans penis of the gorilla is most like that of man (Hill and Matthews, 1949). The shape of the glans in macaques has been correlated with the shape of the female genital canal (Fooden, 1967). The shape of the glans is highly variable in prosimians and New World monkeys (Fig. 4-8).

TABLE 4-II

LENGTH OF BACULUM (IN MM) IN PRIMATES*

Species	Length	Species	Length
Galago crassicaudatus	21, 24	*Papio leucophaeus*	21, 25
Nycticebus coucang	17	*Papio hamadryas*	21, 21.6, 22
Lemur variegatus	11, 15	*Theropithecus gelada*	19.05; 26
Lemur macaco fulvus	15, 9	*Cercopithecus mona*	14, 23.7
Hapalemur griseus	11	*Cercopithecus mitis*	11.5
Microcebus murinus	11, 12.5	*Cercopithecus neglectus*	17.7
Cheirogaleus medius	14	*Cercopithecus aethiops*	12, 13.2, 17.9, 21.5
Propithecus diadema	9, 10	*Cercopithecus albogularis*	17
Daubentonia madagascarensis	28	*Presbytis senex*	12.5
Saimiri sciureus	10	*Colobus verus*	7.5
Cebus apella	14	*Colobus badius*	20
Cebus capucinus	17	*Hylobates lar*	8.5
Pithecia pithecia	2.0	*Hylobates moloch*	2.75
Macaca sinica	20, 20	*Hylobates concolor*	2.7
Macaca fascicularis	10, 12	*Pongo pygmaeus*	11, 11.4, 12.8, 13.7, 14.7, .15
Macaca fuscata	10	*Gorilla g. gorilla*	5.0, 7.9
Macaca niger	25	*Gorilla g. berengei*	11.7, 12.7
Cercocebus troquatus	13, 15, 17.9, 19	*Pan troglodytes*	6.0, 8.4, 8.5, 11
Papio sphinx	21, 23, 25		
Papio anubis	23.7, 30		
Papio papio	22		

* Adapted form Chaine, 1926; Fiedler, 1959; Hill, 1958, 1960, 1966, 1970; Hill and Matthews, 1949; Pohl, 1910.

Baculum. The penis in primates typically contains a bone (os penis, os priapi, or baculum), as it does in several other orders of mammals (Saban, 1967). The bone is completely absent, however, from Tupaiidae, *Tarsius,* Atelinae, *Cebuella, Callimico,* and *Homo* (Eckstein, 1958; Hill, 1957, 1959). In *Aotus* it is cartilagenous (Hill, 1960). The baculum varies in length among adult primates from less than 3 mm in some gibbons, to 55 mm in *Macaca arctoides* (Table 4-II). For taxonomic purposes the length of the baculum must be used with caution, since the bone continues to grow during (early) adulthood and there is considerable intraspecies variation in shape and size (Fig. 4-10 and Table 4-III). Structurally the baculum varies from a single osteon when small to a typical long bone with compacta and spongiosa when large (Ruth, 1934). The baculum is usually bifid distally in Lemuroidea, with the urethra passing between the distal rami to the external urethral meatus. In all other primates the baculum, when present, is a

TABLE 4-III
THE LENGTH OF BACULA IN ADULT MACAQUES

	No. of Cases	*Measurements in mm*	
		Average	*Range*
Macaca mulatta	7	15.1	12.4–17.2
Macaca nemestrina	6	18.8	16.5–20.8
Macaca arctoides	5	49.3	46.9–55.0

straight or slightly curved rod of bone, frequently with an enlargement at the proximal end (Fig. 4-11). The baculum parallels the long axis of the penis, extending dorsal to the urethra, within the substance of the glans, its proximal extremity attached by collagenous fibers to the distal end of the septum joining the two corpora cavernosa (Fig. 4-9).

Muscles of the penis include the bulbospongiosus, ischiocavernosus and levator. Bulbospongiosus is a thick layer covering the bulb of the corpus spongiosum. It arises from a median raphe on the surface of the bulb and from the central tendon of the perineum. Its fibers diverge from the median raphe in V-fashion, with the apex of the V directed towards the anus. Fibers encircle the corpus spongiosum and end mainly in fascia.

The ischiocavernosus muscle originates from the caudal end of the ischium and inserts on the corpus cavernosum after coursing over the corresponding crus.

The levator penis muscle arises from the ischium medial to the

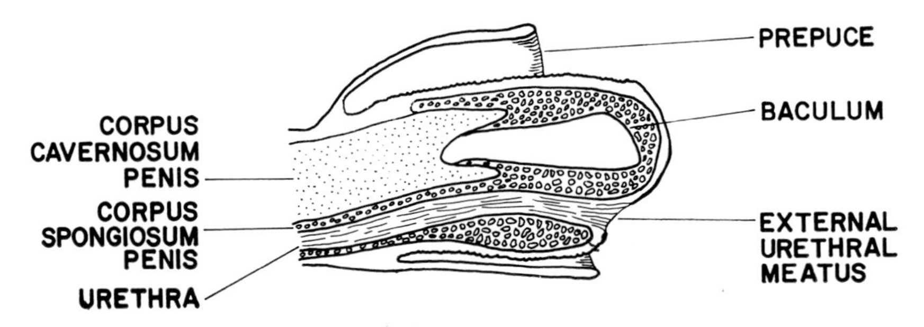

Figure 4-9. Median sagittal section through the terminal end of the penis in the orang, *Pongo pygmaeus*. The relationship of the baculum to the corpus cavernosum and the corpus spongiosum is shown. (After Pousargues, 1895)

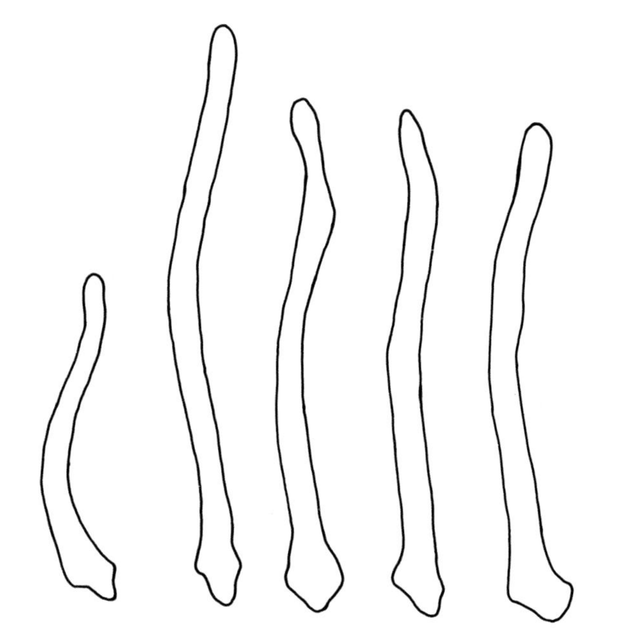

Figure 4-10. Bacula of the stumptail macaque, *M. arctoides,* showing range in size and shape of five individual adult penis bones. All to same scale. The actual length of the longest bone is 55 mm. The proximal end of each bone is at the bottom of the figure.

ischiocavernosus, near the midline. Its fibers converge with those of the opposite side and run a variable distance along the dorsum of the penis, ending in a tendinous expansion. The muscle is absent from man and is replaced by the suspensory ligament.

B. Scrotum

Like the penis this sac is more or less pendulous. In gibbon, orang, and gorilla, however, it is sessile and inconspicuous; in the macaque and chimpanzee it is semipendulous, and exceedingly pendulous in some animals such as *Alouatta.* The scrotum is located entirely posterior to the penis in most primates (postpenile), although it is parapenile in marmosets and some prosimians, and either prepenile or parapenile in the Tupaiidae and the Hylobatidae.

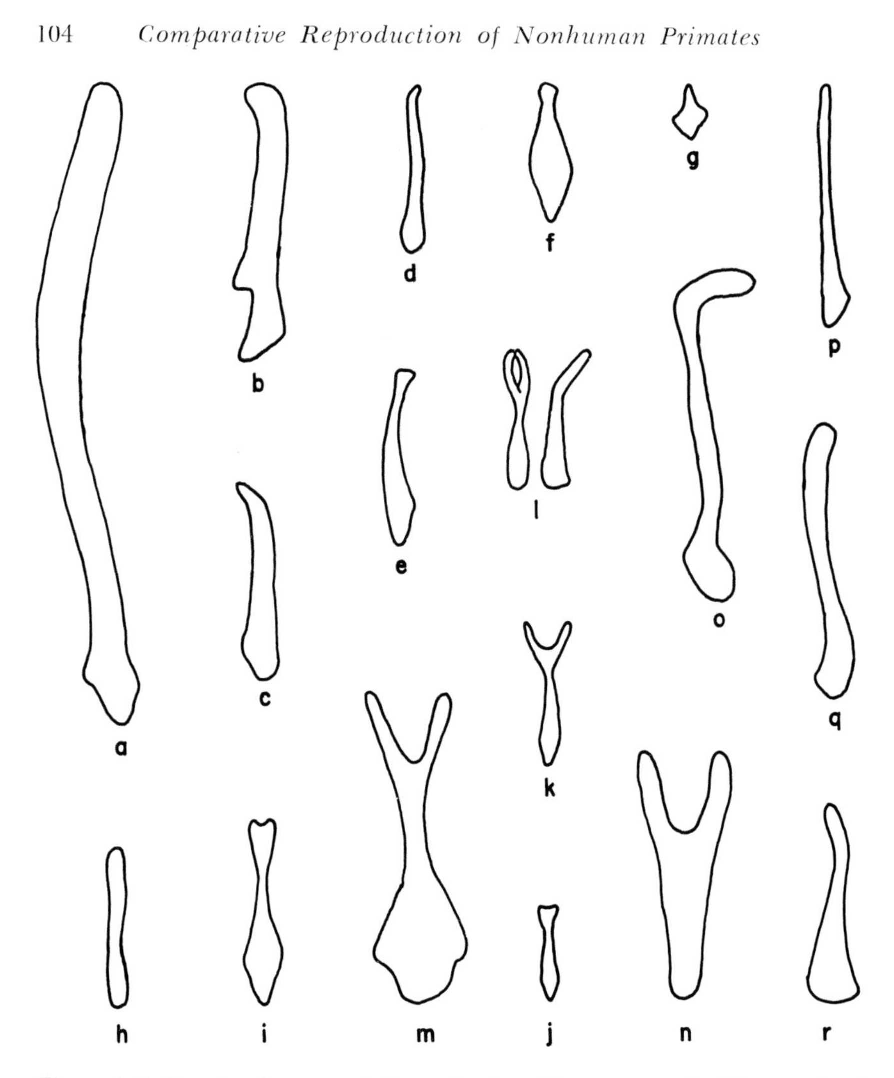

Figure 4-11. Bacula of representative primates. All to same scale. The proximal end of each bone is at the bottom of the figure: (a) stumptail macaque, *M. arctoides;* (b) Celebes macque, *M. niger;* (c) pigtail macaque, *M. nemestrina;* (d) siamang, *Symphalangus syndactylus;* (e) orang, *P. pygmaeus;* (f) mountain gorilla, *G. g. beringei;* (g) lowland gorilla, *G. g. gorilla;* (h) capuchin, *Cebus apella;* (i) *Lemur variegatus;* (j) *L. macaco;* (k) *Lepilemur mustelinus;* (l) mouse lemur, *Microcebus murinus,* dorsal and lateral views; (m) *Avahi laniger;* (n) *Indri indri;* (o) aye-aye, *Daubentonia madagascariensis;* (p, q) thick-tailed galago, *Galago crassicaudatus;* (r) slow loris, *Nycticebus coucang.* (After Chaine, 1926; Davis, 1951; Fooden, 1969; Gerhardt, 1909; Kaudern, 1911; Pocock, 1921; Pohn, 1910; and Pousargues, 1895)

The scrotum is a cutaneous bag composed of skin, variously modified and histologically different from normal skin, lined by a layer of muscular fibers (dartos muscle), but lacking subcutaneous adipose tissue except in *Lagothrix*. The dartos is lacking in prosimians and marmosets (Hill, 1953, 1955, 1957). The scrotum is frequently brightly colored, especially in *Cercopithecus* in which it is various shades of blue and green, depending upon the species. It frequently is of a contrasting color from the neighboring skin, as in *Cebus, Alouatta,* some macaques, and Colobinae. It is almost always more sparsely haired than surrounding skin and may be completely hairless as in *Lemur catta* and *Cacajao*. Occasionally, as in the gibbons, it is heavily covered with hair. Usually there is a well marked median raphe, although this is lacking in *Callicebus* and *Aotus*. The scrotum is so small as not to be visible in *Ateles paniscus, Erythrocebus patas pyrronotus, Procolobus, Piliocolobus,* and some species of *Hylobates*. The structure of the scrotum in various species has been described in detail by Hill (1958). Comparative anatomy of the skin of the scrotum of primates has been described in detail by Machida and Giacometti (1967).

IV. MALE URETHRA

The male urethra is a channel which leads from the urinary vesicle (bladder) to the external urethral orifice at the end of the glans penis. Although it is generally considered together with the urinary portion of the urogenital system, it is considered here since the canal not only serves for the passage of urine, but also serves for the passage of seminal fluid.

As it passes from the internal urethral orifice to its external opening the urethra describes an s-shaped course, and it is customary to divide it into three sections for descriptive purposes. The first part, the prostatic part, is within the pelvis, and traverses or passes ventral to the prostate. Turning ventrally, the urethra passes posterior to the pubic symphysis, pierces the urogenital diaphragm, and enters the bulb of the penis. Throughout the rest of its course it lies in the erectile tissue of the corpus spongiosum and the glans. That part of the urethra between the prostatic part and the bulb of the penis is the membranous part, so named because in man it follows a very short course through the urogenital diaphragm. The part surrounded by the corpus spongiosum is the spongy part.

A. Prostatic Part

The male urethra passes ventral to all of the prostate in most nonhuman primates. In *Ptilocercus, Daubentonia, Cheirogaleus,* the Indriidae and man the prostate surrounds the urethra, although the major portion of the gland lies dorsal to it. The posterior wall of the prostatic urethra presents a distinct median ridge called the urethral crest which projects into the urethra to such an extent that the canal in transverse section presents a crescentic outline. The groove on each side of the crest is known as the prostatic sinus and into it the ducts of the prostate open by minute apertures. At its highest point the urethral crest forms an eminence, the colliculus seminalis (verumontanum); on the apex of this there is variably present a small opening, the orifice of the prostatic utricle. On each side of the colliculus seminalis is the opening, when present, of the ejaculatory duct.

The Prostatic Utricle. The size and structure of the utricle vary greatly among different species of primates, and major differences are found even within a single genus. It is completely absent from Lemuridae, Lorisidae, and Galagidae (*L. catta, L. fulvus, Nycticebus coucang, Perodicticus potto, Galago senegalensis*) (Zuckerman and Parkes, 1935; Hill, 1953; Butler, 1964), and from some treeshrews (*Dendrogale frenata,* Davis, 1938; *Anathana wroughtoni,* Verma, 1965), although it is present in at least one lemuriform, the aye-aye, *Daubentonia* (Hill, 1953).

The utricle is present in most primates as a blind pouch extending cranially for a variable distance into the substance of the prostate or dorsal to the prostatic urethra and urinary vesicle. The utricle consists either of an evagination of the prostatic urethra (vagina masculina; an outgrowth of the embryonic urogenital sinus), or a uterus masculinus (a remnant of the fused paramesonephric—Mullerian—ducts), or both. In several species of tree shrew, *Tarsius, M. mulatta,* and *P. papio,* it is represented by a small, simple, nonglandular diverticulum, lined with stratified cuboidal (transitional) epithelium and surrounded by layers of fibromuscular tissue. In closely related species the utricle consists of pseudostratified columnar epithelium (e.g. in *Papio hamadryas, Cercopithecus mona, Pan troglodytes*), while a truly "uterine" microscopic structure, with many branched tubular glands and a simple glandular epithelium, is present in *Cercopithecus aethiops* and *Presbytis entellus* (Zuckerman and Parkes, 1935). Anatomical variations have been reported in the utricle in *M. mulatta;* thus, the utricle may open into one ejaculatory duct, or both ejaculatory ducts may join the utricle before they open by a common orifice on the colliculus seminalis (Zuckerman, 1938).

The term "prostatic utricle" has been used here because of the uncertainty of its embryonic origin in all primates; however, the results of estrogenic stimulation are informative. The utricle of Platyrrhini does not respond to exogenous estrogen; that of nearly all Catarrhini responds with hyperplasia and squamous keratinization; while that of *P. entellus* and *Tupaia minor* responds with glandular proliferation (Zuckerman and Parkes, 1936; Alcala and Conaway, 1968). Obviously the "prostatic utricle" in primates subsumes two (or more) nonhomologous structures.

B. Membranous Part

This, the shortest part of the male urethra, is surrounded by the muscles of the urogenital diaphragm. On either side are the bulbourethral glands. No peculiarities of this part of the urethra have been reported in respect to the reproductive system.

C. Spongy Part

This part begins where the urethra passes into the corpus spongiosum penis traversing it for its entire extent from the bulb to the glans. Thus, unlike the female urethra except in Lorisiformes, it is entirely surrounded by erectile tissue in the whole of its length. When the penis is erect, the direction of the terminal half of the canal is changed, and at the same time the whole spongy urethra becomes more uniformly curved.

In those Lemuroidea in which the baculum is bifid (Fig. 4-11, i through n), the urethra, after passing ventral to the main shaft of the bone, passes through its bifurcation to open dorsal to the cornified pad overlying the end of the bone (Hill, 1953).

The spongy part of the urethra does not present a uniform calibre throughout; it is wider in the bulb and glans than in the corpus spongiosum. In the glans the urethra expands to form a terminal dilated part (the fossa navicularis) and it opens on the surface of the glans by a vertical slit (horizontal in some marmosets), the external urethral meatus which is frequently the narrowest and least dilatable part of the entire urethra.

The ducts of the bulbourethral glands, when present, open by very minute apertures in the inferior wall of the proximal part of the spongy urethra. Before opening into the canal they lie for some distance immediately outside its mucous membrane.

V. EVOLUTIONARY ASPECTS

A. Parallel Evolution

According to G. G. Simpson, "The development of the same sort of evolutionary opportunity by different groups of organisms produces the evolutionary phenomenon known as parallelism [in which] groups already adaptively and structurally similar independently undergo changes in the same direction." (Simpson, 1949, p. 181). Within the Order Primates many examples of parallelism exist. The prostate has undergone enlargement to encircle completely the urethra in at least two evolutionary lines including man and the most specialized prosimians, the Indriidae. The development of a frenulum on the ventral surface of the glans penis has taken place independently in the tarsier, in some marmosets, in some catarrhine monkeys, and in man. The tendency for the penis, and particularly the glans penis, to keratinize has resulted in the development of specializations such as spicules, horny papillae, and recurved hooks in different genera. The spider monkey, *Ateles,* one of the most specialized platyrrhine monkeys, and man have developed several similarities in detail. These include absence of a baculum, complete obliteration of the processus vaginalis, permanent descent of the testes by the time of birth, and small testes in relation to body weight. All the above cases are examples of parallel evolution since the features apparently were not present in a common ancestor. The more distantly related two species are, the easier it is to determine whether their similarities are due to parallelism; the more closely related, the more difficult. Thus, similarities between ape and man, presented below, may be due to parallelism, rather than to close genetic relationship, as is usually assumed.

B. Evolutionary Changes in the Male Reproductive System

Anticipating the morphology of the male reproductive tract to demonstrate close correspondence between the African apes and man (as has so well been demonstrated by immunologic, biochemical, karytological, parasitological, paleontological, behavioral, and other anatomical evidence; Washburn, 1963; Sarich, 1968), one is disappointed. In many details of the male reproductive system the apes and man differ sharply; in certain characteristics, such as in the size of the inguinal canal, the difference is clearly due to man's assumption of upright posture; in others the reasons for the differences are less clear. In man the prostate surrounds the urethra, in the apes it does not; the seminal vesicles are much smaller in the apes than in man; man has bulbourethral glands, the gorilla does not; only in man is the prepuce of the penis attached very close to the glans; the scrotum is sessile or only semipendulous in apes, quite pendulous in man; the baculum is present in apes, absent from man; levator penis muscle is present in the apes, absent from man; the epidermis of the scrotum is heavily pigmented in the apes, hardly at all in man.

These differences are not completely without explanation. Although man lacks a baculum, he merely demonstrates the culmination of a trend of retarded ossification already present in the apes, and representative of the general hominoid trend of delayed bony ossification. In catarrhine monkeys the baculum is present at birth; in *Gorilla* it is only cartilaginous at birth and ossifies later in life; whereas, in man a cartilaginous anlage may occasionally develop, but it does not ossify.

The testicular artery is a highly convoluted vessel on the surface of the testis and spermatic cord in the catarrhine monkeys (Harrison, 1949). In the chimpanzee and man there is a tendency for the artery to be straight, thus reducing the arterial surface area for temperature exchange. This may be correlated with the slightly lower body temperature in the apes and man compared with the monkeys.

A seasonal cycle of spermatogenic activity is known in prosimians and in monkeys. In the mouse lemur, *Microcebus murinus,* spermatogenesis is limited to the period from July to a maximum activity in October at which time the female becomes sexually active (Petter-Rousseaux, 1963). Change in size of the testis and epididymis is also correlated with the spermatogenic cycle (Table 4-I). A shift of the cycle to begin in January when animals are moved to the northern hemisphere demonstrates that climatological factors are important in determining the cycle; a corresponding shift takes place in the female estrous cycle. (Spermatogenesis is active all year in the slender loris, however. Ramakrishna and Prasad, 1967). In the squirrel monkey, *Saimiri sciureus,* a seasonal cycle of spermatogenesis is correlated with a seasonal "fatted" appearance of the male (DuMond and Hutchinson, 1967). In the rhesus monkey, *M. mulatta,* a similar seasonal cycle of spermatogenesis has been described (Sade, 1964; Conaway and Sade, 1965). A cycle has not been demonstrated in the Hominoidea, and the lack of such a cycle in apes and man may be a significant factor in human evolution.

In delay of ossification, in loss of a seasonal cycle of spermatogenesis, in earlier descent of the testis, in closing of the processus vaginalis, and in the configuration of the testicular artery, differences between catarrhine monkey, ape, and man represent evolutionary trends culminating in the African apes and/or in man. In the Platyrrhini parallel development of some of these trends culminated in similar specializations in the spider monkey. These trends suggest that in the higher primates selection has favored increased independence from environmental factors in the neuroendocrine control of reproduction, a delay in certain phases of maturation, and a more constant sexual potency in the male.

REFERENCES

Alcala, J. R., and Conaway, C. H. (1968): The gross and microscopic anatomy of the uterus masculinus of tree shrews. *Folia Primat, 9,* 216-245.

Ayer, A. A. (1948): *The Anatomy of Semnopithecus Entellus.* Madras, Indian Publishing House.

Butler, H. (1964): The reproductive biology of a strepsirhine *(Galago senegalensis senegalensis). Int Rev Gen Exp Zool, 1,* 241-296.

Chaine, J. (1926): L'os pénien, étude descriptive et comparative. *Actes Soc Linné (Bordeaux), 78,* 5-195.

Clark, W. E. Le Gros (1926): On the anatomy of the pen-tailed tree-shrew (Ptilocercus lowii). *Proc. Zool Soc London, 1926,* 1179-1309.

Clermont, Y. (1963): The cycle of the seminiferous epithelium in man. *Amer J Anat, 112,* 35-51.

Clermont, Y. (1969): Two classes of spermatogonial stem cells in the monkey *(Cercopithecus aethiops). Amer J Anat, 126,* 57-71.

Clermont, Y., and Leblond, C. P. (1955): Spermiogenesis of man, monkey, ram and other mammals as shown by the "periodic acid-Schiff" technique. *Amer J Anat, 96,* 229-253.

Clermont, Y., and Leblond, C. P. (1959): Differentiation and renewal of spermatogonia in the monkey, *Macacus rhesus. Amer J Anat, 104,* 237-273.

Cockett, A. T. K.; Elbadawi, A.; Zemjanis, R., and Adey, W. R. (1970): The effects of immobilization on spermatogenesis in subhuman primates. *Fertil Steril, 21,* 610-614.

Conaway, C. H., and Sade, D. S. (1965): The seasonal spermatogenic cycle in free ranging rhesus monkeys. *Folia Primat, 3,* 1-12.

Davis, D. D. (1938): Notes on the anatomy of the tree shrew, *Dendrogale. Field Mus Publ Zool, 20,* 383-404.

Davis, D. D. (1951): The baculum of the gorilla. *Fieldiana Zool, 31,* 645-647.

Dukelow, W. R., and Chernoff, H. N. (1969): Primate sperm survival and capacitation in a foreign uterine environment. *Amer J Physiol, 216,* 682-686.

Dumond, F. V., and Hutchinson, T. C. (1967): Squirrel monkey reproduction: The "fatted" male phenomenon and seasonal spermatogenesis. *Science, 158,* 1467-1470.

Eckstein, P. (1958): Internal reproductive organs. In Hofer, H.; Shultz, A. H., and Starck, D. (Eds.): *Handbuch der Primatenkunde.* Basel, Karger, vol. 3, part 1.

Fielder, W. (1959): Über das Baculum der Cheirogaleinae (Primates). *Zool Anz, 163,* 57-63.

Fooden, J. (1967): Complementary specialization of male and female reproductive structures in the bear macaque, *Macaca arctoides. Nature, 214,* 939-941.

Fooden, J. (1969): Taxonomy and evolution of the monkeys of Celebes. *Bibl Primat, 10,* 1-148.

Gerhardt, U. (1909): Über das Vorkommen eines Penis- und Clitorisknochens bei Hylobatiden. *Anat Anz, 35,* 353-358.

Gondos, B., and Zemjanis, R. (1970): Fine structure of spermatogonia and intercellular bridges in *Macaca nemestrina. J Morph, 131,* 431-446.

Hall-Craggs, E. C. B. (1962): The testis of *Gorilla gorilla beringei. Proc Zool Soc London, 139,* 511-514.

Harrison, R. G. (1949): The comparative anatomy of the blood supply of the mammalian testis. *Proc Zool Soc London, 119,* 325-344.

Hill, W. C. O. (1939): Observations on a giant Sumatran Orang. *Amer J Phys Anthrop, 24,* 449-510.

Hill, W. C. O. (1953): *Primates—Comparative Anatomy and Taxonomy.* I. Strepsirhini. Edinburgh, University Press.

Hill, W. C. O. (1955): *Primates—Comparative Anatomy and Taxonomy.* II. Tarsioidea. Edinburgh, University Press.

Hill, W. C. O. (1957): *Primates—Comparative Anatomy and Taxonomy.* III. Pithecoidea. Platyrrhini-Hapalidae. Edinburgh, University Press.

Hill, W. C. O. (1958): External genitalia. In Hofer, H.; Schultz, A. H., and Starck, D. (Eds.): *Handbuch der Primatenkunde.* Basel, Karger, vol. 3, part 1.

Hill, W. C. O. (1959): The anatomy of *Callimico goeldii* (Thomas). *Trans Amer Phil Soc, 49* (5), 1-116.

Hill, W. C. O. (1960): *Primates—Comparative Anatomy and Taxonomy.* IV. Cebidae, Part A. Edinburgh, University Press.

Hill, W. C. O. (1966): *Primates—Comparative Anatomy and Taxonomy.* VI. Cercopithecinae. Edinburgh, University Press.

Hill, W. C. O. (1970): *Primates—Comparative Anatomy and Taxonomy.* VIII. Cynopithecinae. Edinburgh, University Press.

Hill, W. C. O., and Davies, D. V. (1954): The reproductive organs in *Hapalemur* and *Lepilemur. Proc Roy Soc (Edinburgh) (B), 65,* 251-270.

Hill, W. C. O., and Matthews, L. H. (1949): The male external genitalia of the gorilla, with remarks on the os penis of other Hominoidea. *Proc. Zool Soc London, 119,* 363-378.

Jones, C. (1969): Notes on ecological relationships of four species of lorisids in Rio Muni, West Africa. *Folia Primat, 11,* 255-267.

Jones, F. W. (1917): The genitalia of *Tupaia. J Anat, 51,* 118-126.

Kaudern, W. (1911): Studien über die männlichen Geschlechtsorgane von Insektivoren und Lemuriden. *Zool Jb Jena, 31,* 1-106.

Kinsky, M. (1960): Quantitative Untersuchungen an äthiopischen Säugetieren. II. Absolute und relative Gewichte der Hoden äthiopischer Affen. *Anat Anz, 108,* 65-82.

Klaar, J., and Krasa, F. C. (1921): Zur Anatomie der akzessorischen Geschlichtsdrüsen der Prosimier und Primaten. I. Vesicula seminalis und Prostata. *Zeit Anat Entwickl, 61,* 41-75.

Leblond, C. P.; Clermont, Y., and Nadler, N. J. (1967): The pattern of stem cell renewal in three epithelia. *Canad Cancer Conf, 7,* 3-30.

Leblond, C. P.; Steinberger, E., and Roosen-Runge, E. C. (1963): Spermatogenesis. In Hartman, C. G. (Ed.): *Mechanisms Concerned with Contraception.* New York, Macmillan.

Machida, H., and Giacometti, L. (1967): The anatomical and histochemical properties of the skin of the external genitalia of the primates. *Folia Primat, 6,* 48-69.

Matthews, L. H. (1946): Notes on the genital anatomy and physiology of the gibbon *(Hylobates). Proc Zool Soc London, 116,* 339-364.

Miller, R. A. (1947): The inguinal canal of primates. *Amer J Anat, 80,* 117-142.

Petter-Rousseaux, A. (1962): Recherches sur la biologie de la reproduction des inférieurs. *Mammalia, 26,* 1-88.

Petter-Rousseaux, A. (1963): Reproductive physiology and behavior of the Lemuroidea. In Buettner-Janusch (Ed.): *Evolutionary and Genetic Biology of Primates.* New York, Academic Press, vol. 2.

Pocock, R. I. (1920): On the external characters of the South American monkeys. *Proc Zool Soc London, 1920,* 91-113.

Pocock, R. I. (1921): The systematic value of the glans penis in macaque monkeys. *Ann Mag Nat Hist (9), 7,* 224-229.

Pocock, R. I. (1925): The external characters of the catarrhine monkeys and apes. *Proc Zool Soc London, 1925,* 1479-1579.

Pohl, L. (1910): Beiträge zur Kenntnis des Os penis der Prosimier. *Anat Anz, 37,* 225-231.

Pousargues, E. de (1895): Note sur l'appareil génital male des orang-outans. *Nouv Arch Mus d'Hist Nat (Paris) (3), 7,* 57-82.

Ramakrishna, P. A., and Prasad, M. R. N. (1962): Reproduction in the male slender loris, *Loris tardigradus lydekkerianus* (Cabrera). *Curr Sci 31,* 468-469.

Ramakrishna, P. A., and Prasad, M. R. N. (1967): Changes in the male reproductive organs of *Loris tardigradus lydekkerianus* (Cabrera). *Folia Primat, 5,* 176-189.

Rattner, J. B., and Brinkley, B. R. (1970): Ultrastructure of mammalian spermiogenesis. I. A tubular complex in developing sperm of cottontop marmoset *Saguinus oedipus. J Ultrastruct Res 32,* 316-322.

Risley, P. L. (1963): Physiology of the male accessory organs. In Hartman, C. G. (Ed.): *Mechanisms Concerned with Contraception.* New York, Macmillan, chap. 2.

Roosen-Runge, E. C. (1962): The process of spermatogenesis in mammals. *Biol Rev, 37,* 343-377.

Ruth, E. B. (1934): The os priapi: A study in bone development. *Anat Rec, 60,* 231-249.

Saban, R. (1967): Enderostes. In Grassé, P.-P. (Ed.): *Traité de Zoologie. Anatomie, Systématique, Biologie.* Paris, Masson, vol. 16, part 1, pp. 1079-1087, 1122-1123.

Sade, D. S. (1964): Seasonal cycle in size of testes of free-ranging *Macaca mulatta. Folia Primat, 2,* 171-180.

Sarich, V. M. (1968): The origin of the hominids: An immunological approach. In Washburn, S. L., and Jay, P. C. (Eds.): New York, Holt, Rinehart and Winston, chap. 6.

Schoonees, R., Klerk, J. N. de, and Murphy, G. P. (1968): Anatomy, radioisotopic blood flow and glandular secretory activity of the baboon prostate. *S Afr Med J, 42 (Suppl.),* 87-94.

Schultz, A. H. (1938): The relative weight of the testes in primates. *Anat. Rec, 72,* 387-394.

Simpson, G. G. (1949): *The Meaning of Evolution.* New Haven, Yale University Press.

Verma, K. (1965): Notes on the biology and anatomy of the Indian tree-shrew, *Anathana wroughtoni. Mammalia, 29,* 289-330.

Wagenen, G. van (1936): The coagulating function of the cranial lobe of the prostate gland in the monkey. *Anat Rec, 66,* 411-421.

Wagenen, G. van, and Simpson, M. E. (1954): Testicular development in the rhesus monkey. *Anat Rec, 118,* 231-251.

Wagenen, G. van, and Simpson, M. E. (1965): *Embryology of the Ovary and Testis, Homo Sapiens and Macaca mulatta.* New Haven, Yale University Press.

Washburn, S. L. (1963): *Classification and Human Evolution.* Chicago, Aldine.

Wislocki, G. B. (1933): Observations on the descent of the testes in the macaque and in the chimpanzee. *Anat Rec, 57,* 133-148.

Wislocki, G. B. (1933): The reproductive systems. In Hartman, C. G., and Straus, W. L., Jr. (Eds.): *The Anatomy of the Rhesus Monkey.* Baltimore, Williams and Wilkins.

Wislocki, G. B. (1936): The external genitalia of the simian primates. *Hum. Biol, 8,* 309-347.

Wislocki, G. B. (1942): Size, weight, and histology of the testes in the gorilla. *J. Mammal, 23,* 281-287.

Zuckerman, S. (1938): The effects of prolonged oestrogenic stimulation on the prostate of the rhesus monkey. *J Anat, 72,* 264-276.

Zuckerman, S., and Parkes, A. S. (1935): Observations on the structure of the uterus masculinus in various primates. *J Anat, 69,* 484-496.

Zuckerman, S., and Parkes, A. S. (1936): The effects of oestrone on the prostate and uterus masculinus of various species of primate. *J Anat, 70,* 323-330.

Chapter 5

SEMEN AND ARTIFICIAL INSEMINATION

W. R. DUKELOW

I. SEMEN PROPERTIES

SEMEN of nearly all monkeys, as with the rat and the guinea pig, is characterized by very rapid coagulation immediately after ejaculation. This is caused by a reaction between the secretions of the cranial prostate gland and the vesicular gland (van Wagenen, 1936). Coagulation appears to be similar to that found in the rat, and enzymes removed from the rat coagulating gland have the ability to coagulate monkey semen. The reverse situation is also true, i.e. the enzymes extracted from the cranial prostate of the rhesus monkey (*Macaca mulatta*) have the ability to coagulate rat seminal plasma. The formation of the coagulum begins within seconds of ejaculation and is normally complete within one minute. The autolysis of this coagulum does not take place to a significant degree *in vitro*. Normal ejaculates from rhesus monkeys weigh 4 to 5 gm and will autolize only 0.5 to 0.7 ml of sperm-rich fluid after thirty to forty minutes at 37°C. Variations in the dissolution of the coagulum either by natural or experimental means have led to wide variations in reported constituents of the semen and in the sperm concentration of various species. Table 5-I indicates the most recently reported values for sperm concentration and volume of ejaculate of several species of nonhuman primates.

The morphology of nonhuman primate sperm has not been extensively studied. Table 5-II indicates the dimensions of the head midpiece and tail of sperm from thirteen species. In a comparison of semen from *Galago senegalensis* and man the sperm of the former had a complex system of membranes which envelope the neck and the anterior midpiece (Bedford, 1967). The nonhu-

TABLE 5-I

SEMEN VOLUME, SPERM MOTILITY AND SPERM NUMBERS FROM TWELVE PRIMATE SPECIES*

Species	*Semen Volume (ml)*		*Sperm Motility (%)*		*Sperm Concentration per ml* ($\times 10^6$)	
	Mean	*Range*	*Mean*	*Range*	*Mean*	*Range*
Cebus apella	0.6	0.3–1.0	24	10–50	161.1	56.0– 740.2
Cercopithecus aethiops	0.9	0.3–2.0	39	15–70	439.6	165.8– 810.8
Cercocebus galeritus	1.3	1.1–1.5	60	55–65	575.5	541.8– 609.2
Erythrocebus-patas	0.6	0.4–1.0	45	10–70	1,153.4	250.6–3,600.0
Hylobates lar	1.3	0.5–4.0	9	0–20	152.4	51.0– 350.4
Macaca fasicularis	1.2	0.6–3.0	57	25–75	458.2	160.5– 830.1
Macaca mulatta	1.1	0.2–4.5	58	10–85	1,069.1	100.2–3,600.2
Macaca speciosa	1.6	0.4–4.0	49	10–80	468.2	214.1–1,268.1
Pan troglodytes	1.9	0.5–6.2	30	10–60	608.8	230.9–1,268.9
Saimiri sciureus	0.4	0.2–1.5	52	40–80	205.9	80.8– 310.9
Theropitheius gelada	1.0	0.5–2.0	21	5–30	502.9	350.8– 650.6
Tupaia	0.1	0.1–0.1	52	50–60	103.2	90.1– 116.8

* (Roussel and Austin, 1968).

TABLE 5-II

SUBHUMAN PRIMATE SPERMATOZOON DIMENSIONS*

Mean of Subhuman Primate Spermatozoon (μ)

Species	*Head*		*Midpiece*	*Flagellum*
	Length	*Width*	*Length*	*Length*
Cebus apella	8.35	5.38	11.95	75.75
Cercopithecus aethiops	7.48	4.94	14.13	87.08
Cercocebus galeritus	6.80	4.87	13.30	86.30
Erythrocebus-patas	7.60	5.65	12.57	81.86
Hylobates lar	6.85	5.60	7.85	56.65
Macaca fasicularis	7.74	5.39	14.71	87.47
Macaca mulatta	7.31	5.21	13.57	82.95
Macaca nemestrina	7.30	5.27	13.25	83.10
Macaca speciosa	7.82	5.64	14.79	93.38
Pan troglodytes	6.00	4.85	8.67	76.40
Saimiri sciureus	7.84	5.88	12.87	86.85
Theropitheius gelada	6.70	4.98	12.15	80.60
Tupaia	9.18	8.81	14.03	84.23

* Roussel, J. D., Personal Communication.

man primate sperm had a subacrosomal space or "perforatorium," a structure not found in human spermatozoa. Generally speaking, far fewer abnormalities of sperm morphology are found in the nonhuman primates than in man.

B. Biochemical Characteristics

The fructose content of liquified semen in *Macaca nemestrina* (Pigtailed macaque) ranges from 371 to 547 mg per 100 ml (Reznichek *et al.*, 1968.) Lactic acid content ranges from 40–109 mgs per 100 ml and citric acid 59–174 mg per 100 ml. When the coagulum is dissolved with tryspin for one hour there is a decrease in the fructose concentration and an increase in the lactic acid concentration. Rhesus monkey vesicular secretions contain several glycosidases, e.g. α-mannosidase, β-N-acetylglucostminidase and β-glucuronidase (Mann, 1964). There is no evidence for the presence of glucosidase or galactosidase. Inositol is present in high concentration in rhesus seminal plasma (145 mg/100 ml) a level second only to that found in boar seminal plasma. Monkey vesicular secretions contain phosphorylcholine, but no glyceryl phosphorycholine nor glyceryl phosphoryl ethanolamine. The enzyme phosphofructokinase has been isolated from rhesus sperm (Hoskins and Stephens, 1969) and has a regulatory role in sperm cell glycolysis.

Nonhuman primate sperm appears to follow metabolic pathways similar to those that have been reported in domestic mammals (Mann, 1964). A high but variable rate of aerobic fructolysis was seen in a complete study of rhesus sperm metabolism. (Hoskins and Patterson, 1968). They reported a rate of endogenous respiration comparable to sperm of other domestic animals and found a mechanism for the decarboxylation of pyruvate independent of respiration in the rhesus monkey. This pathway was termed pyruvate dismutation.

It is a well-established phenomenon in all mammals which have been studied that sperm undergo final maturation within the female reproductive tract. This maturation has been termed "capacitation" and generally requires a period of several hours. Capacitation has been demonstrated in several species of primates by various indirect techniques. Direct demonstration of capacitation, however, requires the recovery of a nonhuman primate egg and its fertilization either *in vivo* or *in vitro* with primate sperm. This had not been accomplished to this date. Once sperm are capacitated their metabolic rate is rapidly increased and this phenomenon has been demonstrated after the incubation of sperm in the monkey uterus (Dukelow and Chernoff, 1968, 1969).

II. SEMEN COLLECTION

Many techniques commonly used in domestic animals have been applied to the nonhuman primates as a means of semen collection. However, most of the commonly used techniques with primates involve electrical stimulation of either the penis or the accessory sexual glands. Certain criteria must be used in selecting the males which will be utilized for semen collection, and it is a well-recognized phenomenon that not all males are capable of artificial ejaculation. In the case of the rhesus monkey, the proper choice of males is of prime importance. They should be in a strong physical state and of proven fertility through use in natural mating schemes. Since larger animals can be quite dangerous, and because of the close working relationship of the male and the animal technician, the canine teeth should be removed from all experimental subjects before they are used. Young animals from 5 to 8 kg in weight are preferable since they can be more easily trained to the ejaculation procedure. For continuous collection of a large number of males the male is restrained every day for a period of ten minutes by means of a collar. This procedure continues for two weeks prior to the initial attempt at ejaculation. By this method, the animal learns to accept restraint as a routine part of his daily life.

It is desirable to have the same personnel involved in the ejaculation procedure each day. Artificial ejaculation should be done at intervals of two to three times per week, regardless of the need for semen. This results in semen of a continuous, predictable quality.

The penile electrode technique (Mastroianni and Manson, 1963) has been widely used. The animal is restrained with collar and chain and all four limbs are tied to an extended position within the cage by means of leather thongs. A strip of aluminum foil, 0.5 cm wide is then lubricated with a high electroyte cream and placed about the base of the penile shaft. There it is held in position with an alligator clip electrode. A second aluminum foil strip is placed immediately posterior to the glans and using a gloved hand the operator holds the penile shaft and the two electrodes. Intermittent charges of from 8 to 20 volts are then delivered at a frequency between ten to twenty impulses per second for a duration of 25 to 50 milliseconds using a monophasic alternating current. The semen is usually collected in 50 ml beakers and the coagulum is allowed to incubate in a 37° water bath for thirty minutes to yield liquified semen. In some species which lack a distinct glans, such as the chimpanzee, this technique is not possible because of the inability to keep the electrodes on the penile shaft. To prevent this, a plastic sheath can be used, which has brass ring electrodes inbedded in the inner surface (Fig. 5-1). Placing this over the penis eliminates the necessity for the foil strips and clip electrodes.

Another form of electroejaculation frequently used is that of the rectal probe. This was first described in monkeys in 1965 and was used for several species of primates. The construction of the rectal probes that are utilized has been described in several publications (Weisbroth and Young, 1965; Healey and Sadleir, 1966; Fussell, Roussel and Austin, 1967; Lang, 1967; Roussel and Austin, 1968; Balerio, Ellis, Clark and Thompson, 1969; and Gilman, 1969). The voltage requirement for rectal probe electroejaculation is less than that required by penile probe, ranging from 2 to 8 volts. The probe electrodes are placed within the rectum in the vicinity of the male accessory glands, and through their simulation elicit ejaculation. The rectal probe has been used in the squirrel monkey (Lang, 1967), (Bennett, 1967-a 1967b) and has also been utilized (Roussel and Austin, 1968) for collection of semen from the chimpanzee, the gibbon, the Gelada baboon, the Mangabey, the rhesus, the Stumptail macaque, the cynomologous, the African green, the Patas, the capuchin, and the tree shrew. While ejaculation by the penile probe technique is normally done with an unanesthesized animal, anesthesia is used with rectal ejaculation. Small-sized species can be suspended in a sling-like arrangement. Larger species are restrained on a movable table or rack. Electroejaculation of the adult male chimpanzee is illustrated in Figure 5-2. Care should

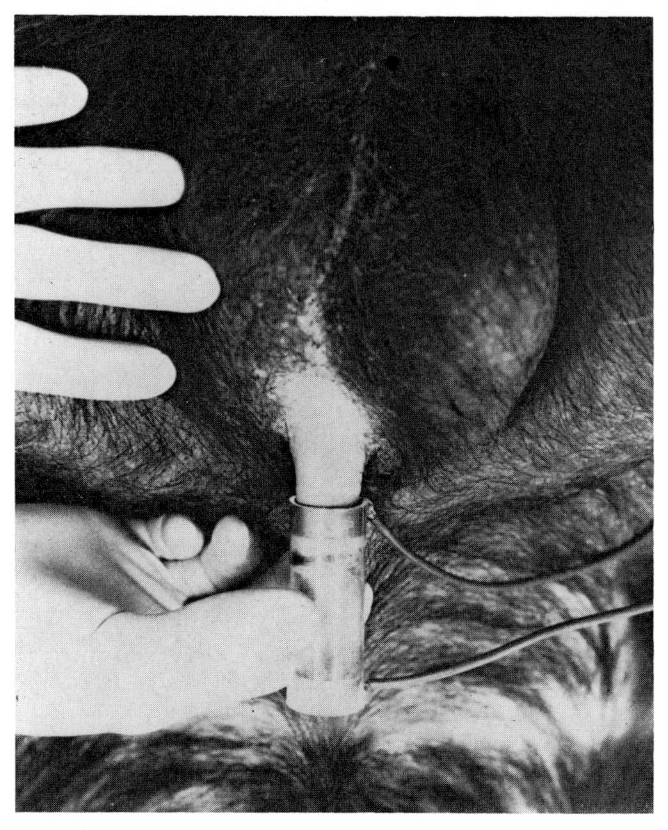

Figure 5-1. Tubular penile electrodes used with the chimpanzee. (Courtesy of Drs. N. B. Guilloud & M. Keeling)

always be used to protect handlers from accidental injury from these animals. Atropine should be avoided when electroejaculating these animals. This compound is often given to primates to reduce salivation, but its administration before electroejaculation will prevent the successful collection of the ejaculate.

The artificial vagina, used extensively in domestic species, has been tried with several species of nonhuman primates, but generally without success. Experiences with condoms in rhesus and cynomologus monkeys have been similarily unsuccessful. The condoms were placed on the animals and mating allowed, but in no case was an ejaculate obtained. Since the coagulation of monkey semen is

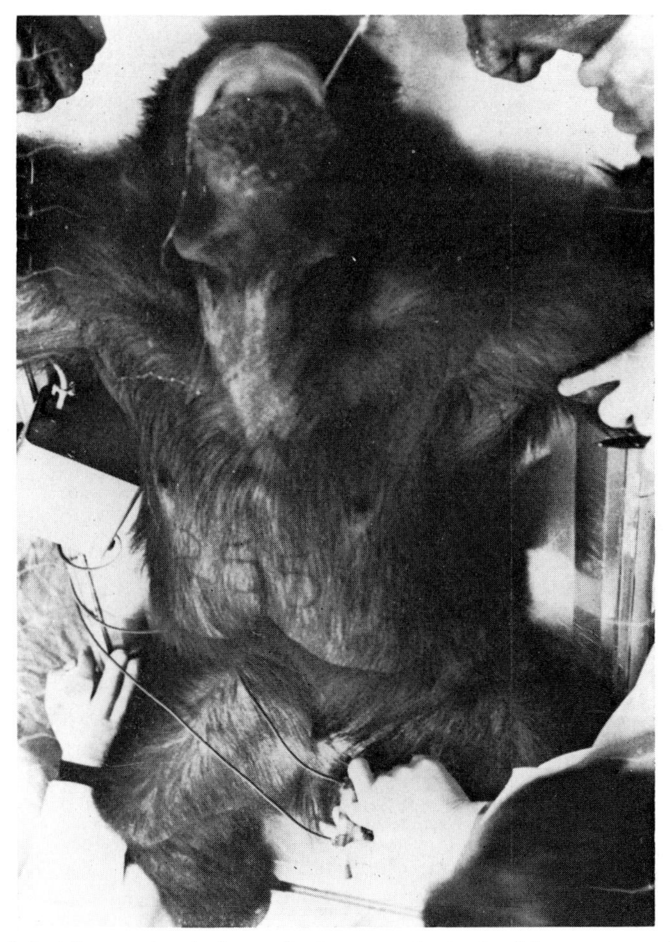

Figure 5-2. Electroejaculation of the anesthetized chimpanzee using the tubular penile electrode technique. (Courtesy of Drs. N. B. Guilloud & M. Keeling)

caused by secretions of cranial prostate (Greer *et al.*, 1968) an attempt to prevent coagulation by removal of this gland and subsequent ejaculation by the rectal probe technique has been used. This procedure resulted in a liquified ejaculate whose volume was not significantly different from ejaculates obtained prior to the operation, nor was there an effect on sperm motility. This technique may have application in future studies. However, the operative procedure is technically difficult and a great deal of dissection is necessary to obtain even small exposure of the surgical field. A massage vibrator, used with humans unable to obtain an erection (Sobrero *et al.*, 1965) has been used in several laboratories on rhesus monkeys. Generally, the technique consists of placing the vibrator over the glans penis and subjecting it to several minutes of vibration. This technique results in a few ejaculates, but it had a very high failure rate and the technique is not recommended for routine semen collection.

III. ARTIFICIAL INSEMINATION

A. Liquification of the Coagulum

As previously mentioned, primate semen coagula will liquify to a small degree by incubation at 37°C. The coagula is not affected by compounds capable of dissolving fibrin coagula such as Evans Blue, cysteinamine, N-acetyl cysteine and bromsulphalein.

Many enzyme preparations have been used in attempts to liquify the coagulum. Varizyme (streptokinase-human plasminogen-streptodoronase) was used without success (Weisbroth and Young, 1965).

Collagenase, α-amylase and β-amylase are ineffective. The best results have been obtained with 1 percent solutions of Pronase, α-chymotrypsin and trypsin (bovine pancrease, type I) (Roussel and Austin, 1967a). Lipase also has a dissolving effect on the coagula (Roussel and Austin, 1968) at a concentration of 1 percent in a 3 percent sodium glutamate solution. A 2 percent lipase solution dissolves the squirrel monkey coagulum, but the time requirement for this incubation precludes the recovery of motile sperm.

One interesting approach to the prevention of the formation of the coagulum is the collection of semen directly into a 2 percent chymotrypsin solution (Hoskins and Patterson, 1967). By this procedure complete dissolution was obtained within five minutes.

B. Semen Preservation

As with other species, the motility of the sperm decreases with prolonged storage at 4°C. The death rate of sperm over twenty hours ranges from 40 to 80 percent. A sperm death rate of 30 percent occurs in humans, which would indicate that nonhuman primate sperm are more susceptible to cold-induced death.

Several workers have successfully frozen and thawed nonhuman primate semen, but no fertilization has occurred using semen which has been frozen. The semen of rhesus, stumptail, patas, African green monkey, and the chimpanzee have been frozen and thawed with recoveries of motile sperm ranging from 50 to 54 percent (Roussel and Austin, 1967b). The semen was frozen in an extender consisting of 20 percent egg yolk, 64 percent of a 3.0 percent w/v sodium glutamate solution and 14 percent glycerol. Semen was added to the extender in ratio of 1 : 10 and equilibrated for thirty minutes at room temperature. The semen was ampuled (0.5 ml in 1.2 ml glass ampules) and lowered for three minutes into the neck of a liquid nitrogen refrigerator, then lowered into the nitrogen refrigerator for deep-freezing.

The best semen extenders reported for freezing chimpanzee semen, (Sadleir, 1966) were (a) egg yolk—2.9 percent sodium citrate with 10 percent glycerol; (b) milk-egg yolk with 10 percent glycerol; and (c) glucose-egg yolk 7 percent glycerol.

Baboon semen has been frozen by the nitrogen vapor techniques

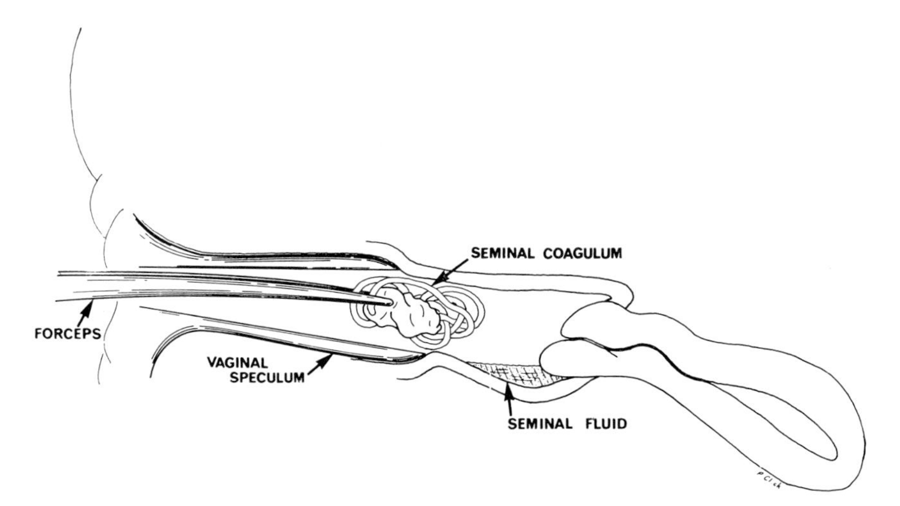

Figure 5-3. Semen deposition technique in the rhesus. The vagina is opened with a vaginal speculum, the liquid portion of the semen is placed in the anterior vagina and then the seminal coagulum is added with forceps. (Hendrick & Kraemer (1970), Hafez, E. S. E. (Ed): *Reproduction and Breeding Techniques in Laboratory Animals.* Philadelphia, Lea & Febiger.)

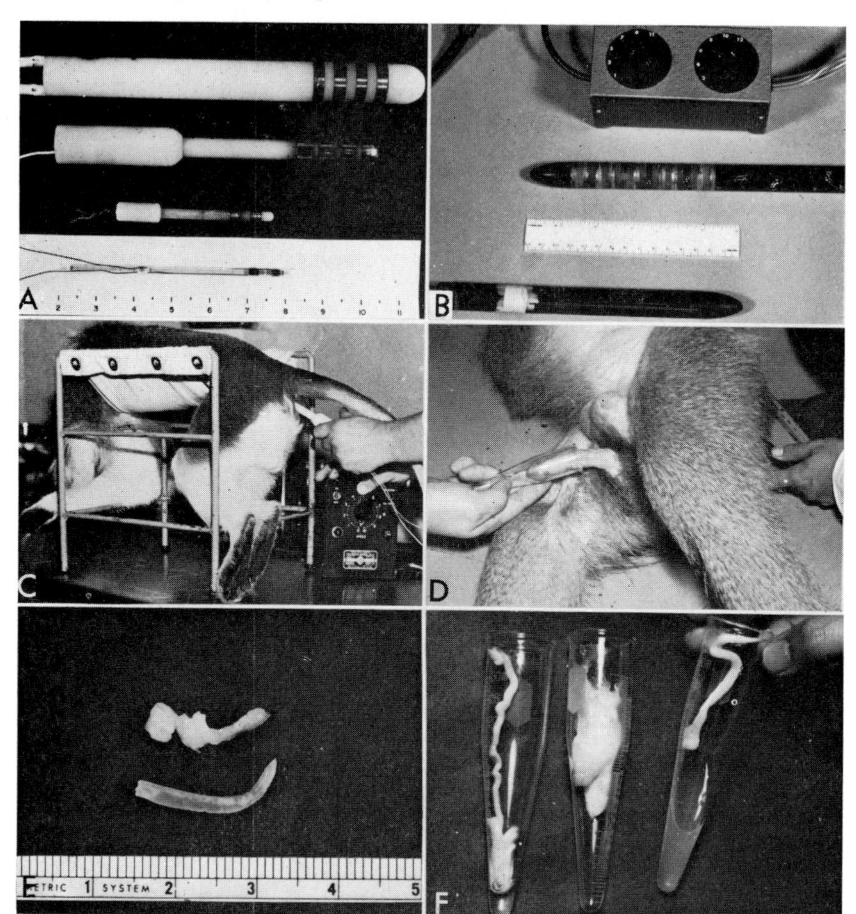

Figure 5-4. A. Rectal probes used for electroejaculation of various species of primates. B. Rectal probes used for electroejaculation of baboons showing horizontal ring electrodes, which can be selected in any combination of 2 using the switch box shown in the top of the picture, and longitudinal electrodes. C. Electroejaculation of a patas monkey using a sling to support the animal in a convenient position. D. Electroejaculation of a baboon lying on its side in an extended position. E. Seminal coagulum from a rhesus monkey showing an amorphous mass characteristic of coagulation after ejaculation and a mass conforming to the urethra that is formed during ejaculation. F. Semen collected from baboons showing a liquid fraction and 2 types of coagulum. The amorphous mass coagulated after ejaculation and the strings of coagulum formed during ejaculation. (Fig. A from Fussell *et al.,* 1967; C and E from Roussel and Austin, 1968)

just described, with the semen extended in the sodium glutamate-egg yolk solution of Roussel and Austin (1967b) containing 500 i.u. penicillin and 500 μg streptomycin per ml (Kraemer and Vera Cruz, 1969).

C. Artificial Insemination

Attempts at artificial insemination in nonhuman primates have involved placement of the coagulum into the vagina without dilution of the semen. This is normally done with (unanesthetized) females held in an inverted position, and the liquified semen is sprayed onto the cervix with a syringe. The coagulum is then inserted into the vagina and the female is held in the inverted position for fifteen to twenty minutes (Figs. 5-3 and 5-4). In the squirrel monkey (Bennett, 1967b) three females were inseminated and seventy-two hours later ova were recovered up to the four cell stage.

Nearly all work has involved artificially induced ovulation either with superovulation (Bennett 1967b) or single (Dukelow, 1970) ovulations. There was no difference in the fertility of either spontaneous or induced ovulation in rhesus with natural mating or artificial insemination (Dede and Plentl, 1966), however, the overall conception rate (12.8 percent) was low. There is some indication that superovulation treatments increase ovum transport through the oviduct (Bennett, 1967b) and this would lower the fertilization rate.

It is possible to inseminate rhesus monkeys intraperitoneally (Van Pelt, 1970). In eight animals so treated, three became pregnant on the first cycle. Two of these pregnancies were terminated by Cesarean section in the eighth week, one pregnancy went full term. The semen was collected by the penile electrode technique, diluted and washed, and injected intraperitoneally in volumes varying from 22 to 183 ml.

REFERENCES

Bedford, J. M. (1967): Observations on the fine structure of spermatozoa of the bushbaby *(Galago senegalensis)*, the African green monkey *(Cercopithecus aethiops)* and man. *Amer J Anat, 121,* 443-460.

Bennett, J. P. (1967a): Semen collection in the squirrel monkey. *J Reprod Fertil, 13,* 353-355.

Bennett, J. P. (1967b): Artificial insemination of the squirrel monkey. *J Endocr, 37,* 473-474.

Dede, J. A., and Plentl, A. A. (1966): Induced ovulation in a rhesus colony. *Fertil Steril, 17,* 757-764.

Dukelow, W. R. (1970): Induction and timing of single and multiple ovulations in the squirrel monkey *(Saimiri sciureus.) J Reprod Fertil, 22,* 303-309.

Dukelow, W. R., and Chernoff, H. N. (1968): Capacitation of primate spermatozoa. *VI Int Cong Anim Reprod Artif Insem (Paris), 1,* 51-53.

Dukelow, W. R., and Chernoff, H. N. (1969): Primate sperm survival and capacitation in a foreign uterine environment. *Amer J Physiol, 216,* 682-686.

Fussell, E. N.; Roussel, J. D., and Austin, C. R. (1967): Use of the rectal probe method for electrical ejaculation of apes, monkeys and a prosimian. *Lab Anim Care, 17,* 528-530.

Gilman, S. C. (1969): Relationship between internal resistance, stimulation voltage, and electroejaculation in the pigtail monkey *(Macaca nemestrina):* A preliminary report, *Lab Anim Care, 19,* 800-803.

Greer, W. E.; Roussel, J. D., and Austin, C. R. (1968): Prevention of coagulation in monkey semen by surgery. *J Reprod Fertil, 15,* 153-155.

Healey, P., and Sadleir, R. M. F. S. (1966): The construction of rectal electrodes for electroejaculation. *J Reprod Fertil, 11,* 299-301.

Hoskins, D. D., and Patterson, D. L. (1967): Prevention of coagulum formation with recovery of motile spermatozoa from rhesus monkey semen. *J Reprod Fertil, 13,* 337-440.

Hoskins, D. D., and Patterson, D. L. (1968): Metabolism of rhesus monkey spermatozoa. *J Reprod Fertil, 16,* 183-195.

Hoskins, D. D., and Stephens, D. T. (1969): Regulatory properties of primate sperm phosphofructokinase. *Biochim Biophys Acta, 191,* 292-302.

Kraemer, D. C., and Vera Cruz, N. C. (1969): Collection, gross characteristics and freezing of baboon semen. *J Reprod Fertil, 20,* 345-348.

Lang, C. M. (1967): A technique for the collection of semen from squirrel monkeys *(Saimiri sciureus)* by electroejaculation. *Lab Anim Care, 17,* 218-221.

Mann, T. (1964): Biochemistry of Semen and of the Male Reproductive Tract. New York, John Wiley & Sons.

Mastroianni, L., and Manson, W. A. (1963): Collection of monkey semen by electroejaculation. *Proc Soc Expt Biol Med, 112,* 1025-1027.

Reznichek, R. C.; Roussel, J. D.; Mangelson, N. L.; Kado, R. T., and Cockett, A. T. K. (1968): Some morphologic and biochemical observations of semen in *Nemestrina* monkeys destined for space flight. *Fertil Steril, 19,* 376-381.

Roussel, J. D., and Austin, C. R. (1967a): Enzymatic liquefaction of primate semen. *Int J Fertil 12,* 288-290.

Roussel, J. D., and Austin, C. R. (1967b): Preservation of primate spermatozoa by freezing. *J Reprod Fertil, 13,* 333-335.

Roussel, J. D., and Austin, C. R. (1968): Improved electroejaculation of primates. *J Inst Anim Tech 19,* 22-32.

Sadleir, R. M. F. S. (1966): The preservation of mammalian spermatozoa by freezing. *Lab Pract, 15,* 413.

Sobrero, A. J.; Stearns, H. E., and Blair, J. H. (1965): Technic for the induction of ejaculation in humans. *Fertil Steril, 16,* 765-767.

Valerio, D. A.; Ellis, E. B.; Clark, M. L., and Thompson, G. E. (1969): Collection of semen from macaques by electroejaculation. *Lab Anim Care, 19,* 250-252.

van Pelt, L. F. (1970): Intraperitoneal insemination of *Macaca mulatta. Fertil Steril, 21,* 159-162.

van Wagenen, G. (1936): The coagulating function of the cranial lobe of the prostate gland in the monkey. *Anat Rec, 66,* 411-421.

Weisbroth, S., and Young, F. A. (1965): The collection of primate semen by electroejaculation. *Fertil Steril, 16,* 229-235.

III. FEMALE AND INFANT BIOLOGY

Chapter 6

FEMALE REPRODUCTIVE ORGANS

J. M. IOANNOU

A COMPARATIVE study of any organ or system must start from a generally accepted basic pattern. For this reason the descriptions which follow will refer for comparison to the condition found in the human female. A number of excellent texts are available on the development and morphology of the human reproductive tract (Davies, 1962; Hamilton *et al.*, 1962).

I. THE ORGANS IN THE HUMAN FEMALE

A. Development of the Reproductive Tract

Gonadal primordia appear in the embryo at about five weeks *post coitum* as paired genital ridges on the medial side of the mesonephros. Cords of cells proliferate from the thickened coelomic epithelium and extend into the underlying mesenchyme. Soon after, the primordial germ cells appear in the genital ridges and start multiplying (Chap. 9). This cell proliferation causes the developing gonad to project more and more from the dorsal abdominal wall so that it becomes distinct from the mesonephros, although still closely associated with the mesonephric duct.

In the fourth week of development both male and female embryos have two pairs of genital ducts: the mesonephric ducts, extending from the mesonephros to the cloaca, and the paramesonephric ducts, newly formed, lying parallel to the former and likewise entering the cloaca (Fig. 6-1). Each paramesonephric duct arises as a longitudinal invagination of the coelomic epithelium, and is normally in open communication with the coelomic cavity. From here the newly formed duct runs lateral to the mesonephric duct and then crosses it anteriorly, growing caudo-medial to fuse with the duct on the opposite side. In this way is formed the utero-vagi-

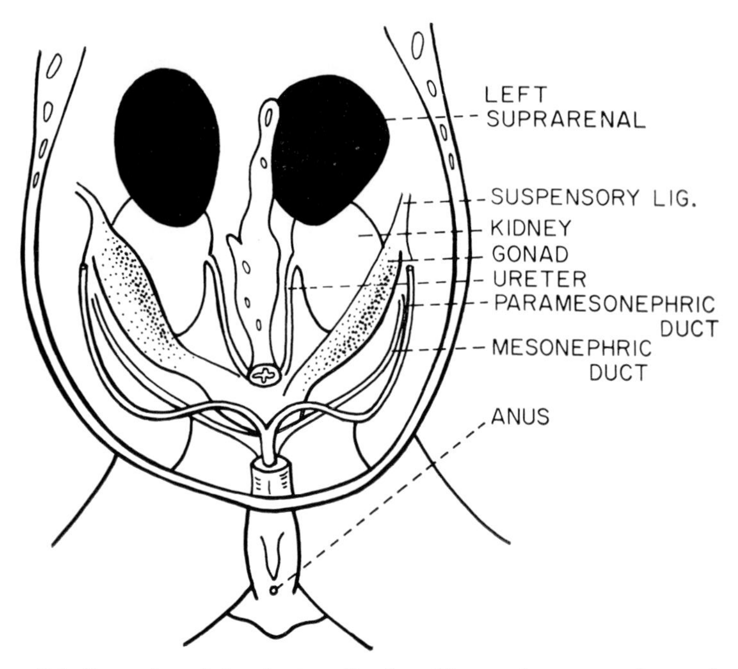

Figure 6-1. Posterior abdominal wall of a 26 mm human embryo, showing relationships of the urogenital apparatus and associated ducts. (Hamilton *et al.,* 1962)

nal canal. Depending on the sex of the embryo, either the mesonephric (male) or the paramesonephric (female) ducts complete their differentiation into the definitive system.

In the female, the paramesonephric duct may be considered in three parts: a cranial portion, a horizontal part, and a caudal part. The first two parts develop into the uterine tubes, the site where the two tubes meet marking the fundus of the uterus. From here to the entrance into the urogenital sinus the two ducts gradually fuse to become the utero-vaginal canal, initially a solid cord, but later canalized.

The musculature of the utero-vaginal canal is derived from the surrounding mesenchyme. Cranially the mesenchyme forms the myometrium of the corpus and cervix of the uterus. In the caudal portion, the future vagina, only a few muscle fibres are formed at this stage.

The lumen of the vagina remains separated from that of the urogenital sinus by a thin plate of tissue known as the hymen.

In the third week of development the cloacal membrane is gradually surrounded by mesenchyme, forming a pair of slightly elevated cloacal folds. These fuse directly in front of the cloacal membrane to form the cloacal eminence, which gradually lengthens as the genital tubercle and eventually becomes the clitoris. The anterior three-quarters of the cloacal folds become the genital folds and later the labia minora. On each side, lateral to the genital folds, a pair of genital swellings arise, and enlarge greatly to form the labia majora. The urogenital groove opens to the surface and forms the vestibule (Fig. 6-2).

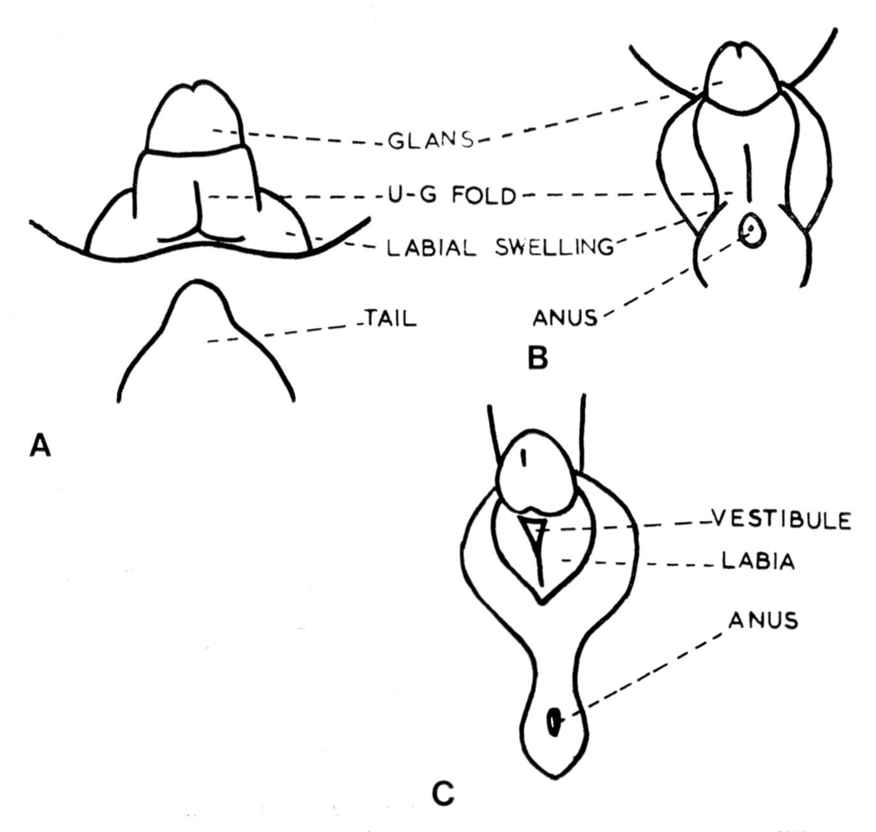

Figure 6-2. Differentiation of the human external genitalia: (A) the indifferent period, about 8 weeks; (B, C) the female, at 10 and 12 weeks. (Arey, 1961)

B. Adult Morphology

The reproductive organs in the nonpregnant female are situated in the pelvis (Fig. 6-3). The uterus is a pear-shaped muscular organ lined with a glandular endometrium, and lying between the urinary bladder in front and the rectum behind. It consists of a moveable part, or body, and a lower part—the cervix—anchored to the pelvic diaphragm. The lower part of the cervix projects into the vagina. Into either side of the body of the uterus opens a uterine tube, a convoluted structure about 10 cm long, which passes laterally to the side wall of the pelvis in a double layer of peritoneum known as the broad ligament. The lateral extremity of the uterine tube is open to the peritoneal cavity through an ostium surrounded by a fringe of irregular processes called the fimbriae. On either side of the uterus, close to the fimbriated end of each tube,

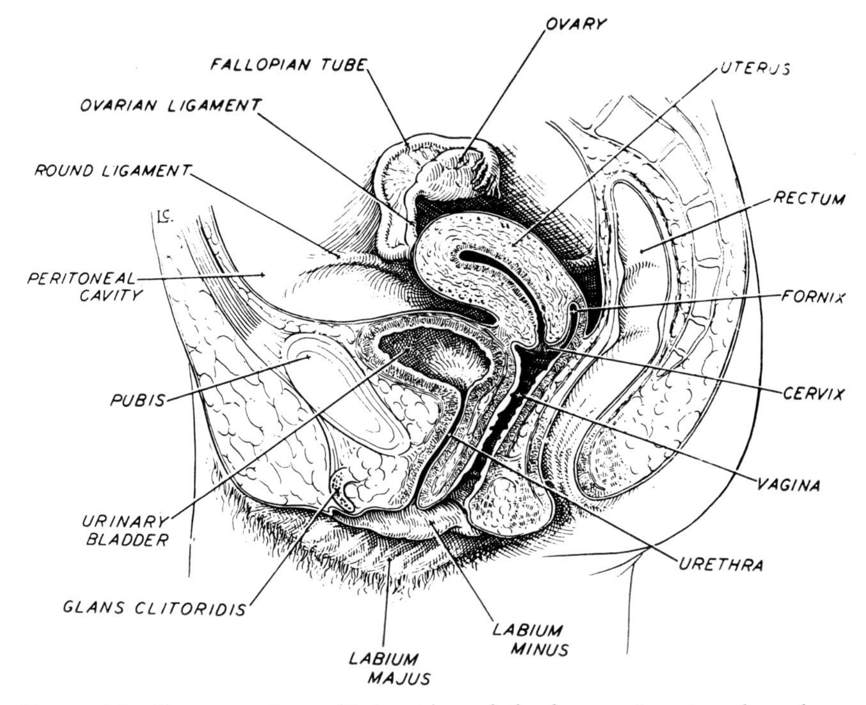

Figure 6-3. Diagrammatic sagittal section of the human female pelvis, showing the genital organs and their relations to the bladder and urethra. (Turner, 1966)

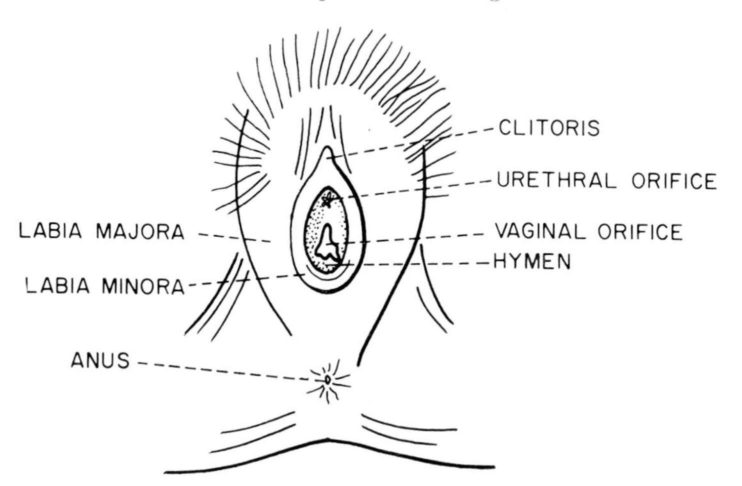

Figure 6-4. Surface view of the external genitalia in a virgin human female. (Davies, 1962)

is an ovary, from which the female germ cells are released. Its upper pole is connected to the side wall of the pelvis, and its lower pole to the uterus. The anterior border is attached by a fold of peritoneum—the mesovarium—to the back of the broad ligament of the uterus.

The uterine cavity opens into the vagina, which passes downwards and forwards, more or less at right-angles to the long axis of the uterus, to open into the vestibule.

The general term vulva is applied to the external genitalia of the female, which consist of the mons pubis, the labia majora et minora pudendi, the clitoris and the hymen (Fig. 6-4). The mons pubis, a rounded eminence in front of the pubic symphysis, is formed by a collection of fatty tissue beneath the skin. It becomes covered with hair at the time of puberty.

The labia majora are two prominent longitudinal cutaneous folds extending downwards and backwards from the mons pubis and forming the lateral boundaries of the pudendal cleft (into which the vagina and urethra open). Each labium has two surfaces, an outer, pigmented and covered with coarse hairs, and an inner, smooth, and covered with large sebaceous glands. The labia are thicker in front, where they form by their meeting the anterior commissure. Posteriorly they become lost in the neighbouring integument; together with the connecting skin between them this constitutes a posterior commissure.

The labia minora are two small cutaneous folds, situated between the labia majora. They extend from the clitoris obliquely downwards, laterally and backwards, on either side of the orifice of the vagina, between which and the labia majora they end. In the virgin the posterior ends of the labia minora are usually joined across the median plane by a fold of skin, the frenulum of the labia. Anteriorly, each labium minus divides into two portions: the upper division passing above the clitoris to meet its fellow of the opposite side, thus forming a fold overhanging the glans clitoridis —the praeputium clitoridis. The lower division passes below the clitoris and is united to its under surface forming, with its fellow of the opposite side, the frenulum clitoridis. Numerous sebaceous follicles are found on the apposed surfaces of the labia minora.

The clitoris is an erectile structure homologous with the penis. It is situated caudal to the anterior commissure, partially hidden between the anterior ends of the labia minora. The free extremity, or glans clitoridis, is a small rounded tubercle. The hymen vaginae is a thin fold of mucous membrane situated at the orifice of the vagina; the inner surfaces of the fold are normally in contact with each other, and the vaginal orifice appears as a cleft between them. The hymen varies much in shape and, indeed, may be competely absent.

II. COMPARATIVE MORPHOLOGY

A. Internal Genitalia

The reproductive tract in female primates shows great diversity of form. In prosimians, and *Tarsius,* for instance, the uterus is bicornuate in type, whereas it is unilocular in apes and man. Among apes the size and structure of the cervix uteri, as well as the shape of the fundus, vary greatly both between and within different groups.

The size of the ovaries is subject to great variation. In prosimians, catarrhine monkeys and three of the great apes they are relatively small. In platyrrhines and the gibbon, by contrast, they are disproportionately large—these animals are thus distinct from all other primates and women. This difference is mainly due to the large amounts of interstitial luteal tissue present in the ovary, and less so to the relatively larger size of the Graafian follicle.

The uterine tubes are usually coiled in lower primates, but in *Saimiri* and *Callithrix* (both platyrrhines) they are nearly straight. A superior mesosalpinx (a thin membraneous fold formed by the free border and adjacent parts of the broad ligament) is generally present, running along the upper border of the tube. It takes part in the formation of a bursa which wholly or partly surrounds the ovary. No such bursa is present in *Tarsius,* anthropoid apes or women. The ovarian end and ostium of the tube is usually surrounded by complex folds and fimbriae, except in *Tarsius* where the infundibulum is usually smooth.

The size and shape of the uterus is also variable. In man the fundus is usually flattened, but in catarrhines and *Gorilla* it is characteristically rounded.

The cervix is both absolutely and relatively more developed in lower monkeys than in anthropoids. In some catarrhines it is highly contorted (e.g. *M. mulatta*), and with a complex gladular epithelium (e.g. *M. radiata*). In others and in anthropoids the cervical canal is straight, and resembles the human.

The vagina is a thick walled muscular structure, with longitudinal and transverse folds. In *Ateles* the vaginal epithelium is covered with many squamous keratinized denticles. The lower end of the vagina widens into a funnel-shaped vestibule, and contains the external orifice of the urethra, usually on a raised papilla. This is true for most catarrhines and anthropoids, which thus differ from man.

1. Ovary. The histological structure of the ovary, and the development and atresia of follicles, have been the subject of numerous reviews (Harrison 1948; Brambell 1956 and Franchi *et al.,* 1962).

In *Tupaia* and *Ptilocercus* the ovary is partly surrounded by a bursa (Wood Jones 1917). The abdominal ostia of the uterine tubes open into the ovarian capsules. More or less complete bursae are found in other prosimians, except for *Tarsius,* where the ovary is naked, as in higher primates. In *Hapalemur* the ovarian bursa is formed from dorsal and ventral prolongations of the mesosalpinx, and a hoodlike fold which joins the two, thereby constricting the bursal opening. In *Tarsius* the ovaries may be markedly asymmetrical: during the luteal phase, and in early pregnancy, the ovary containing a corpus luteum grows to about twice the size of the contralateral ovary.

The ovaries of platyrrhine monkeys are usually thick and compact, and much larger than those of catarrhine species. This is mainly due to the large quantities of interstitial tissue found in the ovarian stroma (Wislocki, 1932; Dempsey, 1939, 1940). This feature is sufficiently striking to distinguish New World from Old World monkeys and apes. The interstitial cells arise by a process of luteal transformation of atretic follicles, and this occurs both during the normal cycle and during pregnancy. It has been reported

TABLE 6-I

SIZE OF THE OVARIES IN PRIMATES (MM)*

1. *Ateles* (mean of 2)	16×10×10
2. *Cebus* (mean of 2)	13× 9× 8
3. *Lagothrix*	13× 4× 2
4. *Callithrix*	6× 3
5. *Macaca*	10×81× 7
6. *Presbytis entellus*	20× 7× 4
7. *Colobus versus*	15×10× 6
8. *Papio*	15×10× 8
9. *Homo*	13×15×10
10. *Lepilemur*	4× 2× 1

* 1, 2, and 5. from Wislocki, 1932; 3. Hill, 1953c; 4. Eckstein, 1958; 6. Ayer, 1948; 7. Hill, 1952; 8. Zuckerman and Parkes, 1932; 9. Davies, 1962; 10. Hill and Davies, 1954.

for spider and howler monkeys (Dempsey, 1939) and marmosets (Wislocki, 1939). During pregnancy, all the interstitial elements undergo transformation so that the ovaries become a mass of solid luteal tissue. Thecal luteinization during pregnancy has also been recorded for *Papio* and *Gorilla.*

In *Ateles* and *Alouatta* the large size of the ovary is partly due to enormous Graafian follicles (up to 6 mm in diameter). *Lagothrix* is distinctive in having a fusiform ovary, like the fetal human organ (Table 6-I).

The ovary in the catarrhine monkeys is usually small, and lacks the extensive luteinization typically found in platyrrhines. A shallow capsule is sometimes present. In *Papio* the maximum size of the ovary (Table 6-I) is reached late in the luteal phase of the cycle. Unlike platyrrhines there is no increase in ovarian size during pregnancy.

Among the Hominoidea the ovaries are relatively larger and more elongate than in man. Except for *Gorilla* they are normally smaller in absolute size (Wislocki, 1932; Table 6-I).

2. *Uterine Tubes.* The uterine tubes are only slightly coiled in Tupaidae, in other prosimians they tend to be highly convoluted. The lorisiform and lemuriform species have coiled tubes with an expanded fimbriated end closely applied to the ovary. The coils of uterine tube are partly hidden by raised folds of peritoneum which are laterally continuous with the ovarian fimbriae. Each tube arises from the caudally bent extremity of a uterine horn, and runs parallel with, and dorsal to, the free border of the broad ligament, contrasting with the condition in man. The tube opens into the ovarian bursa near the upper pole of the ovary by a minute funnel-shaped abdominal ostium.

In *Tarsius* the tubes are short. The degree of coiling varies with the cycle, being most pronounced in the follicular phase (Hill, 1953a).

In *Callithrix, Saimiri* and *Lagothrix* the tubes are nearly straight; most other catarrhines have coiled tubes (Beattie, 1927; Hill, 1953b), opening into a bursa that practically encloses the ovary.

In *Papio* the fimbriated end of the tube is expanded and attached both to the ovary and to the broad ligament, surrounding and roofing over the ovary. The tube is highly vascular and active immediately after ovulation (Eckstein, 1958). In *Presbytis* the tube lies within peritoneal folds constituting the superior mesosalpinx.

A bursa is lacking in the hominoids, except for *Hylobates.* In general the uterine tubes are similar to those found in women, although differing in detail. In *Gorilla* the muscular layer is especially well developed.

3. *Uterus.* A bicornuate uterus is found throughout the prosimians. In *Tupaia* the horns are much longer than the body of the uterus, a primitive condition (Clark, 1934); the uterine cavity is marked off by a well-developed external os (Wood Jones, 1917).

The corpus uteri in lemurs and lorises is usually equal to, or greater than, the cornua in length, which is a less primitive condition than that of tree shrews (in *Perodicticus* and *Indri,* however, the cornua are long and conspicuous). The horns are usually tapered slightly (e.g. *Lemur, Lepilemur*), and diverge from the corpus in a Y shape; they are connected near their point of origin by a short intercornual ligament which may be greatly reduced in aged animals.

The topographical position of the uterus differs from that in women, in that the uterine axis is continuous with that of the vagina—the uterus is neither anteverted nor anteflexed.

Little is known about microscopical changes in the uterine endometrium of prosimians. Rao (1927, 1932) reported a slight sanguineous discharge in *Loris* twice a year, but the general opinion is that lemuroids do not experience menstruation.

A menstruation-like process has been reported for *Tarsius* (Catchpole and Fulton, 1943; Hill *et al.*, 1952), but appears to be inconstant and requires further study. The uterus in *Tarsius* foreshadows the unilocular uterus of monkeys and man in having a well developed corpus and short lateral horns. The cervix is well-marked and conical, projecting into the vaginal vault and with dorsal and ventral fornices.

The size of the platyrrhine uterus varies very greatly. *Ateles* has a bigger uterus than the anthropoids *Hylobates* or *Pongo,* for instance, but *Cebus,* and *Lagothrix* are much smaller. These size differences are partly due to differences in the cervical segment. In *Callithrix,* the fundus of the uterus is bulbous, as in *Gorilla;* in women it is dorso-ventrally flattened. The cranial aspect of the fundus in *Lagothrix* has a membraneous free border which may represent a rudimentary intercornual ligament (such as is commonly found in lemurs). On transverse section the fundus appears triangular in *Cebus* and *Ateles,* owing to the thickening of the dorsal wall. Lateral projections and a median groove suggest that *Callithrix* might have a bicornuate uterus, but this appearance is not borne out by sectioning.

Phases of slight uterine hemorrhage occur in *Cebus, Ateles* and *Alouatta.* This bleeding is qualitatively similar to, but less marked than, that found catarrhine monkeys and women.

The uterus of *Macaca* may be taken as an example of the catarrhine type. (Fig. 6-5). It is roughly divided into an upper segment

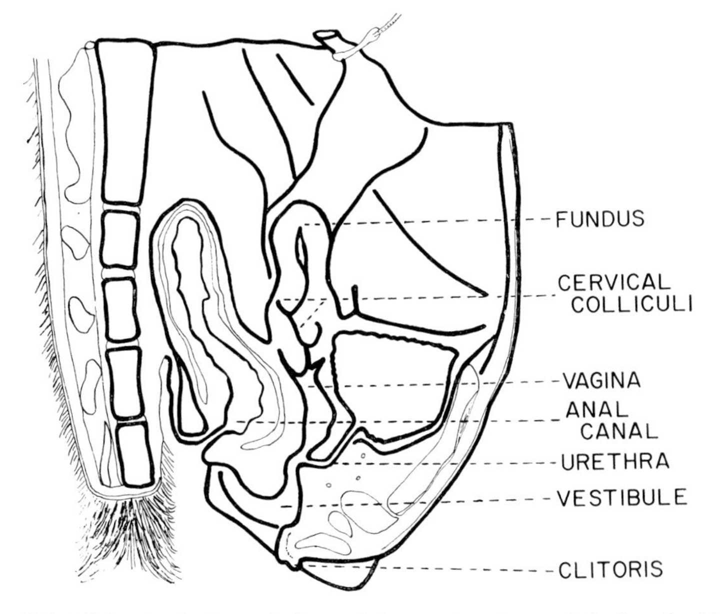

Figure 6-5. Midsagittal view of the pelvic organs of an adult female *Macaca mulatta*. Note the cervical colliculi. (Wislocki, 1933)

consisting of the body and the fundus, and a lower part formed by the thick-walled, complexly folded, cervix. A transverse section through the fundus shows a distinctly bicornuate cavity, but fusion is complete below that level. The size of the uterus varies with the stage of the menstrual cycle, but rarely exceeds 21 mm in length in the nonpregnant state. The microscopic structure of the endometrium and its cyclical changes have been reviewed by Eckstein and Zuckerman (1956b) and Everett (1961).

The size of the uterus in *Papio* varies depending on the species. The lumen is single, but may show a median constriction as in *Macaca*. In the upper part of the body the lumen is a transverse slit, but lower down it becomes circular. The uterus in *Gorilla* is much larger than in women, while that of *Pan* is much smaller. All the Hominoidea except *Gorilla* show a marked antero-posterior flattening of the fundus, but in *Gorilla* (as in catarrhine monkeys) it is globular. The uterus of the *Gorilla* is more or less in a straight line with the vagina, unlike the anteverted, anteflexed human condition (Fig. 6-6).

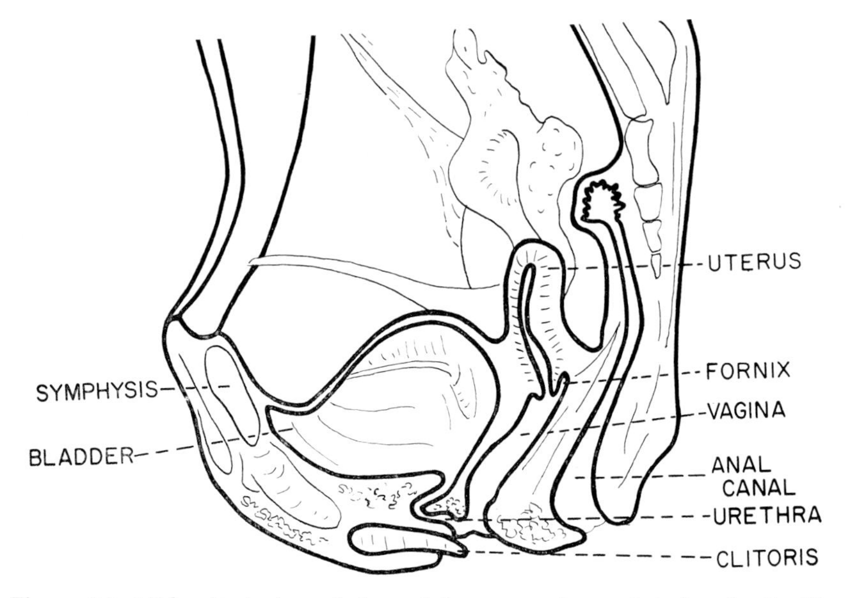

Figure 6-6. Midsagittal view of the pelvic organs of an adult female *Gorilla*. (Atkinson and Elftman, 1950)

4. Cervix. The corpus uteri ends distally in a cervical segment possessing both dorsal and ventral lips and surrounded by vaginal fornices. In *Loris* the cervical canal is ill-defined owing to indistinct internal and external oris uteri. By contrast, the external os is conspicuous in *Lemur* and *Hapalemur,* and surrounded by deep vaginal fornices.

The cervix is both relatively and absolutely more developed in lower monkeys than in anthropoids. For instance, in *Ateles* and *Callithrix* the "portio" extends far into the vagina. *Aotes,* by contrast (like *Hylobates*) has a minute cervix with no intravaginal segment. In *Lagothrix* the cervix does not protrude, but merges gradually into the vagina so that there is neither external os nor vaginal fornix, and only an abrupt change in calibre identifies the lower limit of the canal (Hill 1953b). The cervical canal in *Callithrix* is essentially straight, and this differs from that of the macaques, where it is of massive size and complexity (Fig. 6-5). In *Macaca,* unlike most other primates (including women) the cervix is not straight, but bent into two near right-angled turns. This unusual arrangement is due to the presence of two or three elevations or "colliculi" which project into the uterus and distort it. Thus the central cervical colliculus is a prominent median eminence protruding dorsally from the floor of the cervical canal midway between the external and internal uterine openings. Interdigitation of this colliculus with a pair of variably developed dorsal colliculi results in a marked dorso-ventral sinuosity of the cervical canal. Such colliculi have been described for *Macaca nemestrina, mulatta, radiata* and *sinica* (Wislocki, 1933; Clark and Corner, 1935; Hill, 1939). The latter two species have an even more complex cervix than *mulatta*. These cervical obstructions should not be confused with the vestibular colliculus found in *M. arctoides* (see below).

The portio vaginalis is variable in size and position. The external os is slit-like; because the os lies nearer the anterior aspect, its dorsal lip is thicker than the ventral, and the posterior fornix of the vagina is deeper than the anterior.

In *Papio,* the cervical canal is straight, and the external os a coronal slit between thick anterior and thinner posterior lips. The "portio" is surrounded by a well-marked ring of vaginal fornices. Neither *Presbytis* nor *Colobus* have a curved cervix as in macaques, though the cervical canal in *Colobus* is ridged longitudinally. The ventral fornix in *Colobus* is deeper than the dorsal, unlike women; in *Presbytis* (as in macaques) the posterior is the deeper.

Gorilla also has a highly muscular cervix whereas in the remaining anthropoids it is quite small, especially in *Hylobates.* The entire cervix in the latter species is barely 1 cm long, and hardly protrudes into the vagina.

5. *Vagina.* A distinct external os marks off the uterus from the vagina in Tupaiidae. The thin-walled vagina opens into a slightly longer smooth-walled urogenital sinus which itself opens by an elongated orifice to the outside.

The vagina in the lemurs is a flattened tube, running a straight course to the base of a conspicuous clitoris. The cyclical changes of the vaginal epithelium of *Galago* (Manley, 1965) and *Peredicticus* (Ioannou, 1966) are well-marked and comparable to those described for laboratory rodents. Marked keratinization of the vaginal mucosa of *Hapalemur* may be associated with the follicular part of the ovarian cycle (Hill and Davies, 1954).

A conical cervix is found in *Tarsius,* projecting into the vault of the vagina, which is almost twice as long as the uterus, and is continued into a longitudinally folded urogenital sinus. The lower part of the urethra is embedded in the ventral wall of the vagina and opens into the vestibule separately from the clitoris. Catchpole and Fulton (1943) describe cyclical changes in the vagina of *Tarsius.*

A distinctive feature of the vagina in platyrrhines is the presence of low, mucosal "bosses," either smooth or papillated (Wislocki, 1932). In *Ateles* the surface epithelium forms scales projecting into the vaginal epithelium, similar to structures found on the skin of the male's penis. Although some keratinization persists throughout the cycle, some of these denticles are sloughed off at midcycle (Dempsey, 1939). Cyclic changes in the vagina are inconspicuous in *Alouatta,* but well marked in *Cebus* (Hamlett, 1939).

The vagina in *Macaca* is thick walled and muscular, with an elaborately folded mucosa. The lower end widens into a deep, funnel-shaped vestibule. The urethral orifice is more concealed than in women and lies on a raised papilla at the junction of the vagina and vestibule. A vestibular colliculus has been described for *M. arctoides* (Fooden, 1967), and in this species the urethral orifice is nearer the clitoris and more exposed than in *M. mulatta* (Fig. 6-7). The colliculus is 2 cm long, a middorsal ellipsoid mass which protrudes ventrally from the roof of the vestibule.

In *Papio* the urethra opens about 3 cm from the vulva. A hymen-like annular fold is found in *Presbytis* at the junction of vagina and vestibule.

B. External Genitalia

1. Clitoris. The clitoris in primates shows a wide range in general form, size and structure. In certain species it is channelled throughout by the urethra; in other groups it is merely grooved on its under surface. In the latter cases the urethra may open into a vestibule or at the base of the clitoral sulcus. In some species a more or less rudimentary os clitoridis may be present.

In *Tupaia* a small ossicle is present at the tip of the clitoris

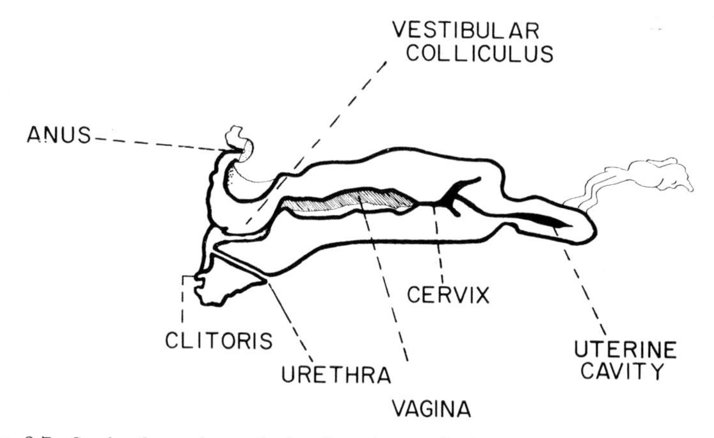

Figure 6-7. Sagittal section of the female genital canal of *Macaca arctoides*. Note the large vestibular colliculus. (Fooden, 1967)

(Wood Jones, 1917). In *Ptilocercus* the small clitoris may be hidden by the labia (Clark, 1934).

In *Loris* the clitoris is usually longer than the male penis, and pierced by the urethra, which opens between the lateral lips of the bifid glans. Each lobe of the glans has a glandular pocket at the apex, and a tuft of long hairs is usually present dorsal to the glandular pockets. A prepuce, attached by a frenulum, forms a distinct collar around the glans clitoridis.

Arctocebus also has a long, thin clitoris, which projects backwards over the vaginal opening. In this species a specialized area of naked skin is found anterior to the root of the clitoris and extending in the midline on to the belly. By contrast with *Loris* and *Arctocebus, Nycticebus* and *Perodicticus* both have a short and thick clitoris, although again the urethra opens at the apex. In *Nycticebus* the clitoris has an apical gland, while in *Perodicticus* the tip bears a tuft of long hairs.

Both *Galagoides* and *Hemigalago* typically have a small baculum at the tip of the clitoris. The clitoris in this family tends to be long (up to 15 mm), and thin (in *G. crassicaudatus* it is thicker), tufted at the apex (*Galagoides*), with a glandular pocket (*Hemigalago, Galagoides, Galago*) either encircling or adjacent to the urethral orifice. In *G. senegalensis* the urethra opens on the ventral surface distally, rather than at the apex.

The urethral opening in the Lemuroidea usually lies at the base of the long and often pendulous clitoris, contrasting with the apical position it occupies in the lorisoids. The clitoris has a tufted tip in *Microcebus* and *Hapalemur,* and a baculum is present in *Hapalemur, Cheirogaleus, Lemur mongoz* and *L. variegatus.* In *Cheirogaleus* the clitoris may be short and fleshy, as in *L. variegatus,* and grooved on the dorsal surface with the urethra opening into the dorsal part of the groove, so that urine is directed away from the body. In *Lepilemur* the urethra opens at the base of a broad, leaf-shaped clitoris, at the distal end of a wide and shallow urethral sulcus.

Among the Indriidae a glandular pit is found at the clitoral apex. In *L. variegatus* the clitoris arises from an area of naked skin and is itself naked. The median groove on its dorsal surface is flanked by raised fleshy lips. In *Daubentonia* the urethra fails to channel the clitoris, but opens into the vestibule directly. The clitoris and vaginal opening are hidden by a circular fold of skin homologous either with a hymen, or a prepuce. The clitoris is short, and has a bifid glans. The clitoris in *Tarsius* is small, and lies concealed by the prominent labia minora. The urethra opens on the anterior wall of the vagina, well away from the clitoris, and between a pair of longitudinal rugae which form a groove along which urine passes to the outside. This gutter is quite distinct from the groove on the dorsal surface of the clitoris. The bifid glans clitoridis is often plum coloured.

The Hapalidae have a small clitoris, hidden between the labial folds, and usually with a bifid glans. In *Tamarin* each part of the glans is anchored laterally to the inner surface of the base of the clitoris.

Tamarinus has a prepuce former from the anterior commissure of the labia; as in *Tamarin* a narrow frenulum is given off to the under surface of the glans from each side of the prepuce. Both the prepuce and the glans are darkly pigmented, although no pigment is found elsewhere on the genital region. In *Marikina, Oedipomidas, Leontocebus,* and *Cebuella* the clitoris is entirely hidden in the labial mass. The labia are prominent and swollen in *Hapale,* so that the clitoris is again entirely hidden (Beattie 1927; Clark, 1934). Dorsally the clitoris is cleft, the two halves of the glans being continuous with the thickened inner ventral divisions of the labia minora. *Lagothrix* (Hill, 1953c) has a small and thick clitoris, with a smooth glans not very distinct from the corpus. A shallow median groove on the perineal half of the glans, in both *Lagothrix* and *Cacajao,* is continued on to the perineal aspect of the corpus as a cleft between the frenula, and then runs into the rima. *Cacajao* has a short clitoris on a low conical eminence—the apex anteriorily is formed by the glans, separated by a distinct cleft from the prepuce anteriorly and laterally. The clitoral eminence is marked by a reticular formation of sulci, some of which delineate the labia. *Aotes* has a very short and narrow urogenital orifice, such that at first no clitoris is visible; when exposed the clitoris is small and broad with a bifid glans supported on a narrow neck and covered by a well-developed prepuce. In *Callicebus* the clitoris is again short and concealed, with a median groove continuous from the apex (resulting in a bifid glans), to the base and into the pudental cleft.

Chiropotes again shows a bifid glans, with the lobes widely splayed. The glans is pigmented a bluish color.

In *Brachyteles, Ateles, Alouatta, Cebus, Saimiri* and *pithecia* the clitoris is hypertophied, and may (as in *Ateles,* for instance) be even larger than the penis of the male. *Saimiri* has a horny, claw like apex to the clitoris, covered with a distinct prepuce. In *Brachyteles* the organ is covered with black hairs. *Ateles* has sparse hairs only (Wislocki, 1936) and the clitoris is unpigmented except in *A. marginalis.* The dorsal median groove is continued into the vestibule. The truncated glans is hidden in an ample prepuce, and baculum may be present. *Alouatta* has an elongated and flattened clitoris (Wislocki, 1936). In *Cebus* the long and pendulous clitoris may contain a small os clitoridis (e.g. *C. capucinus.* Clark, 1934; Wislocki, 1936). The groove is continued to the apex, and a prepuce is present. The dorsal part of the clitoris is hairy, while distally it is smooth and pigmented.

Among the Cercopithecidae a large clitoris is found in *Cercocebus, Macaca mulatta* and *Miopithecus.* Of the remaining species, *Semiopithecus, Colobus, Papio, Erythrocebus, Allenopithecus,* and *Theropithecus* all have an inconspicuous organ. In *Miopithecus* the glans is cleft, without a prepuce and about 4.6 mm across, 6 mm long and 5 mm dorsoventrally. The fetus has a more prominent glans, which is enclosed in a prepuce (Eckstein, 1958).

Cercocebus has a conspicuous prepuce. *Cercopithecus* has a small clitoris, acorn-like, with a median notch. It is pigmented bright pink to scarlet, and the corpus is enclosed in a pigmented sheath, ending in a crenulated frill around the glans. Scattered glandular papillae may be present on the prepuce (Eckstein, 1958).

In *Semnopithecus* the clitoris is indistinctly bilobed and small, while in *Papio* the clitoris, although small, is distinctly bilobed. *Erythrocebus,* like *Cercopithecus,* has a red and globular glans, although again it is small, and hardly raised above the labia. *Theropithecus* has a short clitoris, concealed within the labia and with a median groove at the apex.

Among the Anthropoidea, the clitoris is generally larger. Thus in both *Pan* and *Gorilla* it is large, and grooved below as far as the rima. In *Hylobates* the clitoris lies outside the vulva (Matthews, 1946), has a notched glans but is not grooved. No frenulum is present, and the prepuce is simply a low ridge of skin at the base. Finally, in man the clitoris is less well-developed than in the great apes, although during fetal life the similarities are greater.

2. *Labia.* In *Tupaia* the labia are enclosed within two folds (possibly homologues of the labia minora) which run back around the rima pudendis to form a dorsal commissure, from which a median raphe passes to the anus. *Ptilocercus* has prominent labia minora and less developed labia majora, fusing dorsally to form a median raphe. The clitoris lies hidden within the labia.

Loris has hairy skin right up to the vaginal orifice. Ashley Montagu (1937) describes labia minora in this species as two simple folds continuous posteriorly with the edges of the vulva, ending on the ventro-lateral aspect of the base of the clitoris. *Arctocebus* has no distinct labia, although there is an area of naked skin, anterior to the root of the clitoris, merging with it and extending on to the belly in the midline. *Perodicticus* has a spherical, scrotum-like swelling on which the clitoris is mounted (Fig. 6-8). This swelling is bifid posteriorly, and the vagina opens into the cleft. The entire surface is covered with a reticular pattern of sulci, and is thought to be glandular.

Labia are found in both *Galago* and *Galagoides.* A hymen is present in the virgin.

Labia minora are found in all the Lemuridae, although labia majora are much less well-defined. In *Microcebus,* the lips of the clitoral groove form a pair of naked-edged labia minora, longitudinally folded on their inner surface. In *Cheirogaleus* the labia minora are continuous with the large, hoodlike, clitoral prepuce. *Lemur* has thick labia minora, and a hymen covers the urethra and vagina in the virgin (Fig. 6-8). In *L. catta* the labia majora are glandular and pigmented. They diverge from around the vaginal orifice and fade out inferiorly in the area of naked skin from which the clitoris takes origin. In *L. fulvus* this area of naked skin is lilac or slate colored.

The labia minora in *Propithecus* continue dorsally to form the margins of a large prepuce. Labia majora are present as rounded pseudoscrotal prominences. The vulva in *Daubentonia* is raised on a transverse fold of skin and bounded ventrally by a thick, hoodlike, labial commissure, separated from the glans by a thick groove (Eckstein, 1958).

In *Tarsius* the prominent labia minora conceal the clitoris. Labia majora show a cyclic congestion and regression, the swelling coinciding with a proestrous vaginal smear (Fig. 6-8). When turgid, the labia are crenulated (see also under Sexual Skin).

The labia minora in *Tamarin* are thick, pigmented, and with small glandular papillae. Unpigmented fatty labia majora are present in some species, external to the minora. Ventrally the outer labia unite to form a thick commissure with a distinct shallow median sulcus. Dorsally the labia gradually lose height and disappear, so there is no dorsal commissura laborium. *T. midas* (like *Perodicticus*) has roughly hexagonal facets covering the "friction pads" of the labia majora. These are naked and smooth, and are kept moist by sebaceous secretions. In *T. tamarin* this glandular area extends on to the pubes as a thickened pad with large pores (Sanderson, 1949). *Tamarinus* has no labia majora; the labia minora are less well-developed than in *Tamarin,* and bear no obvious glandular pustules. The labia are prolonged posteriorly as paired lobes while anteriorly they form a darkly colored commissural prepuce. In *Marikina* the labia project up to 9 mm, and have a deep groove around the outside. A semilunar fourchette is revealed dor-

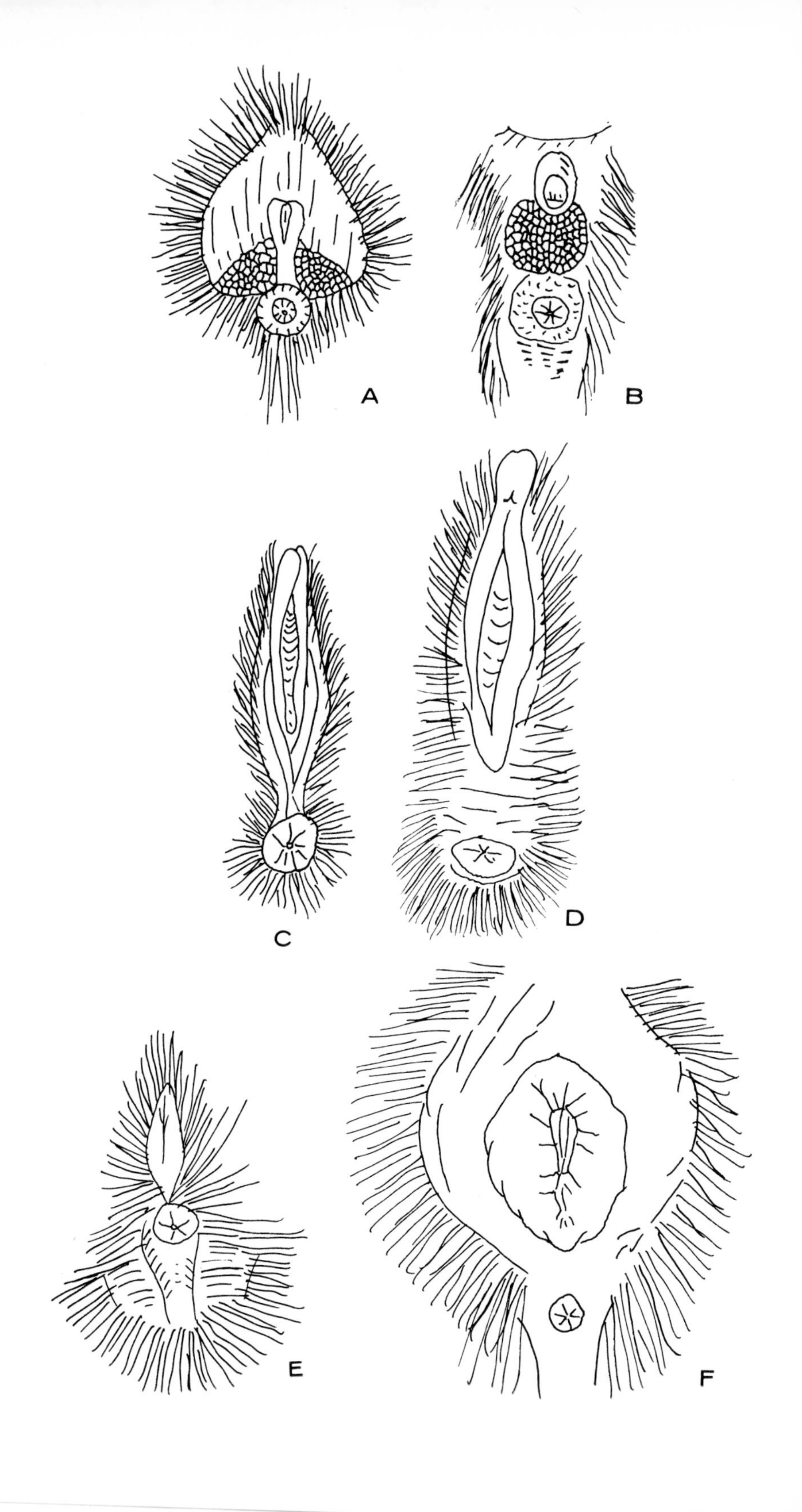
A
B
C
D
E
F

sally when the labia are separated. Deeply pigmented labia majora are present in *Oedipomidas,* making two conspicuous cushions over the pubes, and separated by a median furrow. Their surface is covered with minute whitish nodules, said by Wislocki (1936) to form a specialized scent gland. The labia minora are delicate and fusiform, prominent ventrally and vanishing dorsally. In *Leontocebus* the labia majora are not raised folds, but are studded with papillae marking the position of underlying scent glands. Labia minora about 4 mm high enclose the clitoris. *Callithrix* has glandular labia minora projecting into free lobes dorsally. *Hapale* has minute labia minora. White and swollen, pseudoscrotal labia are found in *Mico,* standing out from the narrow crimson zone around the vulva. The labia are highly glandular, and deeply cleft caudally.

Pseudoscrotal labia majora occur in *Saimiri* (Fig. 6-8) and *Cebus.* Labia minora are also well-defined, forming a white domelike structure just dorsal to the root of the clitoris, and extending as far as the anal hillock. During the follicular phase of the cycle the labial glands thicken to hard parallel ridges 4-6 mm high. A hymen is present in the virgin *C. capucinus.*

Both labia majora and minora are greatly developed in *Alousatta,* forming a labial pad similar in form, colour and location to the scrotum of the male. In *A. belzebuth* the labia majora and minora form a single sheet, no distinction being visible. *Ateles* has variable and inconspicuous labia majora (Eckstein and Zuckerman, 1956a), with labia minora lying within the vestibule. A projecting ventral commissura labiorum is found in *Brachyteles,* covered with a tuft of brown hair. In *Callicebus,* thickened labia contribute to a preputial hood over the clitoris. *Aotes* has well-devel-

---

←

Figure 6-8. External genitalia of adult female *Perodicticus* (Hill, 1953a). Note the pseudoscrotal labia majora; B. External genitalia of female *Saimiri* (Hill, 1960); C and D. External genitalia of female *Lemur,* in quiescent (C) and sexually active state (D) (Hill, 1953a); E and F. External genitalia of female *Tarsius,* in quiescent (E) and sexually active state (F). (Hill, 1955)

oped labia minora and majora, on which sparse yellow hairs may be present. Swollen labia majora and thin labia minora occur in *Lagothrix* (Hill, 1953c).

The clitoral eminence in *Cacajao* is marked by a reticular pattern of sulci, some of which delineate labia minora and majora. Ventrally the labia minora bifurcate to contribute to the frenulum and prepuce on each side. Dorsally the labia majora may form a broad commissure peripheral to the root of the prepuce.

Labia in the Cercopithecidae are very variable. *Theropithecus* and *Cercocebus* both have turgid and well-defined labia, flanking the vaginal orifice above and the clitoris below. In *Erythrocebus,* the rima pudendis is flanked by labia, which merge ventrally to form the clitoral sheath. *Semnopithecus* has distinct black labia majora, but labia minora are indistinct, as in *Cercopithecus.* Scattered glandular papillae are found on the labia and prepuce, and a slight puffiness occurs associated with menstruation. In *Macaca,* poorly developed labia minora unite to form a prepuce, although no distinct frenulum is present. Neither labia majora nor mons veneris are present, except possibly in *M. radiata* (Hartman, 1938). *Miopithecus,* similarly, has no mons or prepuce, although labia form the lateral lobes of the sex skin swelling found at the follicular phase of the cycle (see below).

The labia majora are well-developed in late fetal and early postnatal life in all the anthropoids (Hill, 1951). But in *Pan, Pongo* and *Gorilla,* they undergo marked reduction during growth to maturity, whereas in man they persist. By contrast, in *Hylobates* the labia majora are found throughout postnatal life, resembling man more closely than the other anthropoids. The labia minora (particularly the frenulum and prepuce) are well developed in the great apes except for *Hylobates.* A hymen-like thickening of the vaginal mucosa at the junction of vagina and vestibule is found in most anthropoids.

3. *Sexual Skin* (see also Chap. 7). The term "sexual skin" denotes that area of the integument which becomes flushed during the menstrual cycle or which responds to estrogenic stimulation by reddening or by swelling. The swelling of the sex skin is associated with an increase in body weight resulting from the development of edema of the genital region. The increase in body weight is due to

water retention, since deturgescence is associated with an enormous increase in daily urine output (Krohn and Zuckerman, 1937).

A true sexual skin is not found in lower primates, although some do show cyclic changes in the external genitalia. In *Loris,* proestrus is marked by a swelling of the pendulous clitoris and adjacent skin. Phases of cyclical congestion and regression of the labia minora of *Tarsius* (Fig. 6-8) sometimes involve the anal region, tail and buttocks. Most authorities agree that New World monkeys rarely exhibit external genital changes; Russell and Zuckerman (1935), however, observed swelling in *Hapale jacchus* extending from the pubic symphysis as far as the anus, the ventral two-thirds being cleft by the urogenital sinus. This turgid circumgenital swelling resembles true sexual skin, and appears to be the only recorded instance of such a swelling in a New World Monkey.

Sex skin swelling is most marked among the catarrhine monkeys. The mature rhesus monkey (*Macaca mulatta*) is characterized by a vivid red coloration of the hind quarters, from the iliac crest as far as the popliteal fossa, and sometimes up on to the back. Anteriorly, it forms a sharp triangle over the pubes; the face and nipples also go a bright red. The intensity of coloration reaches a sharp peak during the third postmenstrual week (i.e. at the time of ovulation) and fades before the next menstrual flow. Intense reddening occurs during pregnancy, and after estrogen stimulation. It may also continue through lactation (while the ovaries involute) and in aged specimens past the reproductive phase. Sex skin activity is slight in *M. sinica* and *M. rediata,* except during pregnancy, when a purple-red coloration is most obvious. *Cercocebus* shows a moderate degree of cyclical swelling, and in addition the sex skin is active for one to two weeks after parturition. The sex skin swelling in *Papio* is enormous (Fig. 6-9), beginning during or after menstruation, and reaching its peak in a week. The red and swollen mass overlaps the base of the tail, hiding the ischial callosities, and may reach a diameter of eighteen inches. The median area beneath the clitoris becomes a large and scrotum-like pendulous mass. The changes found in *Miopithecus* are particularly well-marked because the perinium is hairless (Fig. 6-10).

In *Procolobus* the swelling develops at puberty and remains as a solid structure, without regressing (Hill, 1952). *Theropithecus* shows an unusual specialization in having two distinct areas of pigmented sex skin (Matthews, 1956). A perineal area extends dorsally from the pubes to the base of the tail, and expands laterally to two patches alongside the ventral vulval commissure. In addition there is a pectoral area on the ventral aspect of the throat, and a second area on the front of the chest. Both areas of sex skin undergo cyclic swelling, intensification of red coloration, and development of conspicuous cutaneous vesicles. The colour fades with menstruation, when the skin becomes pallid and taut; after menstruation finishes the colour returns, together with flaccidity (thus contrasting with *Papio,* where the coloration is associated with turgescence).

Among the anthropoids, *Hylobates* shows no true sex skin swelling. *Pan* shows a marked cyclical swelling, which increases to about four times the size of a clenched fist. A preswelling phase lasts about seven days, followed by a swollen phase of eighteen

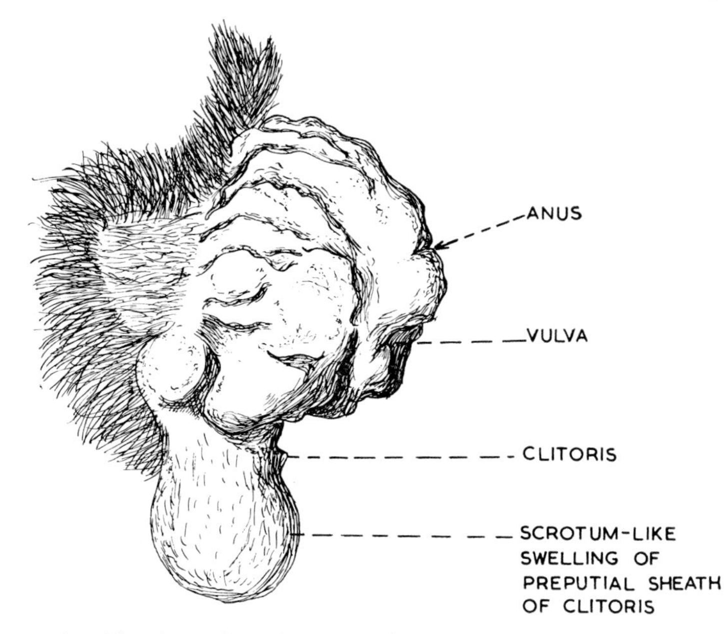

Figure 6-9. Side view of anal and genital area of adult female *Papio* with catamenial swelling at its height. (Pocock, 1925)

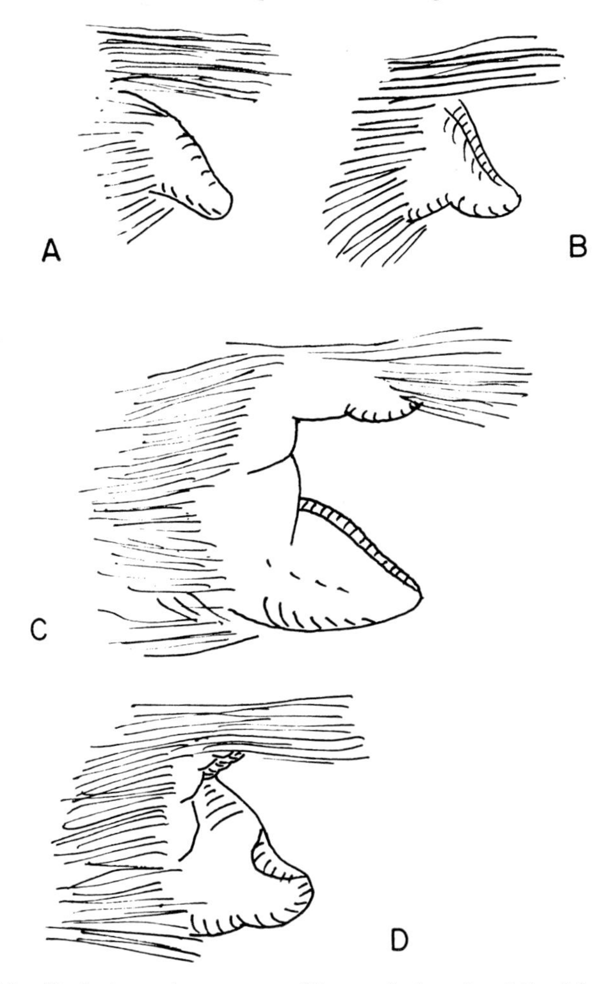

Figure 6-10. Variations in sex swelling of female *Miopithecus.* (Hill, 1966)

days, which coincides with the follicular phase of the ovarian cycle. A stage of detumescence last ten days, and coincides with the luteal phase; this leads to the menstrual period (Young and Yerkes, 1943).

No true sex skin swelling occurs in the nonpregnant *Pongo.* During pregnancy, however, a paravulval swelling appears and disappears again after parturition.

In *Macaca mulatta, Papio,* and *Mandrillus* the male of the species may also show a bright coloration and swelling of the anal and genital region (Zuckerman and Parkes, 1932). In male drills and mandrills the tail region may be raised in the form of either a hemispherical protuberance, or as two superimposed domes of swelling. These swellings are composed of a fatty fibrous tissue, while the swelling of the female is typically gelatinous and edematous.

4. Ischial Callosities. In all catarrhines the skin over the ischial tuberosities is greatly thickened to form horny sitting pads. Among higher primates only gibbons (*Hylobates*) have them regularly; sometimes *Pan* and *Gorilla,* and rarely *Pongo,* also show them. They have never been reported for man, and are quite absent in platyrrhines.

In the lower catarrhines, and in gibbons, the callosities constitute a hairless, well-defined area of thick skin, immovably attached to the tuberosity by dense fibrous tissue so that the hamstring muscles are limited to the edges of the tuberosity. In *Pan, Gorilla* and *Pongo,* the callosities are toughened cushions, movable over the tuberosities, and intervening between the skin and the origin of the hamstrings. They are formed of loose connective tissue and fat, and are thus little more than skin pads.

C. Mammary Gland (see also Chap. 12)

Mammary glands may occur as a single pair, or several pairs may be present, found anywhere along the "milk line," extending in embryos from the axilla obliquely down and across the body to the inguinal region. One pair is typical for most species, but two or three pairs have been reported for several species of prosimians, and others (Schultz, 1948).

Tarsius has two pairs of mammae, situated in the axilla and above the navel; all are functional. In *Galago alleni* two or three pairs of mammae are commonly found, one near the axillary fold, and another far back on the thorax. In addition, an abdominal pair is sometimes present. *Loris* has one pectoral and one abdominal pair, a single naked area enclosing all four nipples during lactation. *Arctocebus,* like *Galago,* has three pairs. *Nycticebus* may have three pairs, all enclosed (like Loris) within a single naked area. Among the lemurs, there may be one pair (as in *L. catta*), or two pairs (as in *L. variegatus*). *Hapalemur* has two pairs, axillary and abdominal.

Daubentonia is unique among the Lemuriforms in having a pair of glands in the inguinal region (Hill, 1953a). These have elongated cylindrical nipples, with numerous duct holes at the apex.

Pithecia, Ateles and Lagothrix all have one pair of axillary glands. In *Brachyteles,* the nipples, bluntly rounded, are a purplish colour around the base. The nipples in *Macaca* lie opposite the sixth sternocostal junction, about 3 cm apart. Their size depends on the endocrine state of the reproductive organs, on parity, and on the length of elapsed time since nursing; they may be up to 12 mm long. After lactation stops the nipples often involute to the virginal size.

In other Cercopithecidae, the mammary gland is poorly developed except in pregnancy, and is hardly palpable until late in gestation.

Of the anthropoids, only *Pongo* shows any peculiarity, in that the nipples grow long and pendulous late in pregnancy.

REFERENCES

Ashley Montagu, M. F. (1937): Note on the external genitalia in three female old world primates. *Anat Rec, 69,* 389-485.

Ayer, A. A. (1948): *The Anatomy of Semnopithecus entellus.* Madras, Indian Publ House Ltd.

Beattie, J. (1927): The anatomy of the common marmoset (*Hapale jacchus* Kuhl.). *Proc Zool Soc, London, 1927,* 593-718.

Brambell, F. W. R. (1956): Ovarian changes. In *Marshall's Physiology of Reproduction,* 3rd ed. London, Longmans, Green & Co., vol. 1, part I, chap. 5.

Catchpole, H. R., and Fulton, J. F. (1943): The oestrous cycle in *Tarsius:* Observations on a captive pair. *J Mammal, 24,* 90-93.

Clark, O. H., and Corner, G. W. (1935): The cervix uteri of the rhesus monkey. *Anat Rec, 63,* 247-252.

Clark, W. E. le G. (1934): *Early Forerunners of Man.* London, Bailliere, Tindall & Cox.

Davies, D. V. (Ed.) (1962): *Gray's Anatomy,* 34th ed. London, Longmans, Green.

Dempsey, E. W. (1939): The reproductive cycle of New World monkeys. *Amer J Anat, 64,* 381-405.

Dempsey, E. W. (1940): The structure of the reproductive tract in the female gibbon. *Amer J Anat, 67,* 229-253.

Eckstein, P. (1958): Internal reproductive organs. In Hofer, H.; Schultz, A. H., and Starck, D. (Eds.): *Primatologia.* Basel, S. Karger, vol. III, part 1.

Eckstein, P., and Zuckerman, S. (1956a): Morphology of the reproductive tract. *Marshall's Physiology of Reproduction,* 3rd ed. London, Longmans Green, vol. 1, chap. 2.

Eckstein, D., and Zuckerman, S. (1956b): Changes in the accessory reproductive organs of the nonpregnant female. In *Marshall's Physiology of Reproduction,* 3rd ed. London, Longmans, Green, vol. 1, part 1.

Everett, J. W. (1961): The mammalian female reproductive cycle and its controlling mechanism. In Young, W. C. (Ed.): *Sex and Internal Secretions.* London, Bailliere, Tindall & Cox, vol. 1.

Fooden, J. (1967): Complementary specialization of male and female reproductive structures in the bear macaque, *Macaca arctoides. Nature (London), 214,* 939-941.

Franchi, L. L.; Mandl, A. M., and Zuckerman, S. (1962): The development of the ovary and the process of oogenesis. In Zuckerman, S. (Ed.): *The Ovary.* London, Academic Press.

Hamilton, W. D.; Boyd, J. D., and Mossman, H. W. (1962): *Human Embryology,* 3rd ed. Cambridge, England, Heffer.

Hamlett, G. W. D. (1939): Reproduction in American monkeys. I. Estrous cycle, ovulation and menstruation in *Cebus. Anat Rec, 73,* 171-187.

Harrison, R. J. (1948): The development and fate of the corpus luteum in the vertebrate series. *Biol Rev, 23,* 296-324.

Hartman, C. G. (1938): Some observations on the bonnet macaque. *J. Mammal, 19,* 469-474.

Hill, W. C. O. (1939): Observations on a giant Sumatran orang. *Amer J Phys Anthrop, 24,* 449-505.

Hill, W. C. O. (1951): The internal genitalia of the female chimpanzee; with observations on the mammary apparatus. *Proc Zool Soc, London, 121,* 133-145.

Hill, W. C. O. (1952): The external and visceral anatomy of the olive colobus monkey *(Procolobus verus). Proc Zool Soc, London, 122,* 127-186.

Hill, W. C. O. (1953a): *Primates. Vol. 1, Strepsirhini.* Edinburgh, Edinburgh University Press.

Hill, W. C. O. (1953b): The female reproductive organs of *Tarsius,* with observations on the physiological changes therein. *Proc Zool Soc, London, 123,* 589-598.

Hill, W. C. O. (1953c): Observations on the genitalia of the woolly monkey *(Lagothrix). Proc Zool Soc, London, 122,* 973-984.

Hill, W. C. O., and Davies, D. V. (1954): The reproductive organs in *Hapalemur* and *Lepilemur. Proc Roy Soc, Edinburgh, B., 65,* 251-270.

Hill, W. C. O.; Porter A., and Southwick, M. D. (1952): The natural history, endoparasites and pseudoparasites of the *Tarsiers (Tarsius carbonarius)* recently living in the Society's gardens. *Proc. Zool Soc, London, 122,* 79-119.

Ioannou, J. M. (1966): The oestrous cycle of the potto. *J Reprod Fertil, 11,* 455-457.

Krohn, P. L., and Zuckerman, S. (1937): Water metabolism in relation to the mentrual cycle. *J Physiol, 88,* 369-387.

Manley, G. H. (1965): Reproduction in Lorisoid primates. *J Reprod Fertil, 9,* 390-391 (abstract).

Matthews, L. H. (1946): Notes on the genital anatomy and physiology of the gibbon *(Hylobates). Proc Zool Soc, London, 116,* 339-364.

Matthews, L. H. (1956): The sexual skin of the Gelada Baboon *(Theropithecus gelada). Trans Zool Soc, London, 28,* 543-545.

Rao, C. R. N. (1927): On the structure of the ovary and the ovarian ovum of *Loris lydekkerianus. Quart J Micr Sci, 71,* 57-74.

Rao, C. R. N. (1932): On the occurrence of glycogen and fat in the liquor folliculi and uterine secretion in *Loris lydekkerianus. J Mysore Univ, 6,* 140-170.

Russell, A. E. and Zuckerman, S. (1935): A "sexual skin" in a marmoset. *J Anat, 69,* 356-362.

Sanderson, I. T. (1949): A brief review of the mammals of Suriname (Dutch Guiana) based upon a collection made in 1938. *Proc. Zool Soc, London, 119,* 755-789.

Schultz, A. H. (1948): The number of young at birth and the number of nipples in primates. *Amer J Phys Anthrop* (New Series), *6,* 1-25

Wislocki, G. B. (1932): On the female reproductive tract of the gorilla with a comparison of that of other primates. *Contr Embryol Carneg Instn, Wash DC, 23,* 163-204.

Wislocki, G. B. (1933): The reproductive systems. In Hartman, C. G., and Strauss, W. L. (Eds.): *The Anatomy of the Rhesus Monkey.* London, Bailliere, Tindall & Cox.

Wislocki, G. B. (1936): The external genitalia of the simian primates. *Hum Biol, 8,* 309-347.

Wislocki, G. B. (1939): Observations on twinning in marmosets. *Amer J Anat, 64,* 445-483.

Wood Jones, F. (1917): The genitalia of *Tupaia. J Anat, London, 51,* 118-126.

Young, W. C., and Yerkes, R. M. (1943): Factors influencing the reproductive cycle in the chimpanzee; the period of adolescent sterility and related problems. *Endocrinology, 33,* 121-154.

Zuckerman, S. and Parkes, A. S. (1932): The menstrual cycle of the primates. Part V. The cycle of the baboon. *Proc Zool Soc, London, 1932,* 139-191.

Chapter 7

REPRODUCTIVE CYCLES

E. S. E. HAFEZ

I. PUBERTY

PUBERTY in female nonhuman primates occurs at one to eight years of age, depending on the species: 2 to 3.5 years in *Macaca mulatta* (rhesus monkey), 3 to 4 years in *Papio* (baboon), and 8 to 11 years in *Pan* (chimpanzee). It occurs before mature body weight is attained, but when growth rate is decreasing.

Sexual maturity is accompanied by physical changes such as the development of mammary glands, appearance of pubic sex skin and perineal swelling (*M. mulatta*), opening of vaginal orifice, full canalization of the vagina (*Cercopithecus aethiops,* green monkey), secretion of cervical mucus (*M. sinica,* toque monkey), or swelling of the vulva (*Erythrocebus,* patas). In *M. mulatta* and *Papio,* menarche may occur without previous swelling of the sexual skin. The major gonadotropins involved in the development of the gonads during puberty are FSH, LH, and LTH.

For several months after sexual maturity, females frequently have irregular and anovulatory cycles and abortions; thereafter, ovulation and regular cycles become established. "Adolescent sterility" may last one to two years in *Pan.* The sexual skin of *Papio* in captivity increases in size progressively with successive cycles for one to two years, until adult proportions are reached. The menstrual flow tends to be longer and more profuse in pubertal than in fully grown females. Menstruation and breeding may continue until age seventeen to twenty in *M. mulatta* and *Papio,* and even longer in *Pan.*

Active spermatogenesis begins at three years of age in *M. mulatta* and *Papio,* and at ten years in *Pan.* The male *M. mulatta* is sexually mature at 3 to 3.5 years and socially mature at 4.5 to 5 years. In *Presbytis entellus* (langur) the female shows the first signs of sexual receptivity at 3.5 years and the male attains complete adulthood at six to seven years (Jay, 1965).

II. BREEDING SEASON

A. Breeding Season of Females

Seasonal reproductive cycles are indicated by seasonal variations in (a) occurrence of births, (b) state of the female reproductive tract, or (c) behavior.

Free-ranging Conditions. Under free-ranging conditions many species have a restricted breeding season, but the degree of seasonality varies with the species and the physical environment Table 7-I). During certain months, several cycles occur in free-ranging *M. mulatta* in Puerto Rico (Vandenbergh and Vessey, 1968) and India (Southwick *et al.,* 1961) and native *M. fuscata* (Japanese macaque). In the introduced population of *M. mulatta* in Puerto Rico, copulation generally begins in late August or September, reaches a peak during November and December, and ceases in March or April. The sexual season is clearly indicated by the occurrence of distinct estrous periods during which the consort relation and copulation and its associated behavior occur. *Pan* copulate frequently during September and October but rarely in other months. Menstrual cycles are relatively rare in the life of the adult female *Papio:* noncycling periods of pregnancy (6 months) and lactation (5 months) are separated by one to three cycles.

Commercial dealers of *Saimiri* (squirrel monkey) in both major supply areas, Iquitos, Peru, and Leticia, Colombia, find pregnant females in the collecting compounds from October to January and newborn infants with their mothers from January to March. Such species undergo considerable enlargement of their external reproductive organs during a distinct season. The female *Langur* experiences menstrual cycles and sexual activity throughout the year, although in the wild there are concentrations of breeding behavior and birth. Assuming a pregnancy duration of six months, Sugiyama *et al.* (1965) estimated the most sexually active season to be June to October. The period of maximal sexual activity varies greatly annually and also among troops. This varia-

TABLE 7-I

AGE AT PUBERTY, SEXUAL SEASON, AND LENGTH OF SEXUAL CYCLE OF SOME PRIMATES[a]

Species	*Age at Puberty of Female*	*Sexual Season*	*Length of Sexual Cycle (Days)*
Allouatta palliata		all year	
Ateles geoffroyi		all year	24–27
Callicebus		all year	
Callithrix jacchus	14 mo	all year	
Cebus albifrons		all year	16–20
Cercocebus		Apr.–Nov. (for no. hemis.)	29–33 (irreg.)
Cercopithecus		May–Sept.	
C. aethiops			31
Erythrocebus	3–4 yr	all year	30
Galago senegalensis	20 mo	Apr.–Oct. or twice a year	32 (19–39)
Gorilla	5–8 yr		39
Hylobates hoolock	7 yr		28
Lagothrix lagothricha			23–26
Lemur catta		end Mar.–early July	
Loris		twice a year	42 (37–54)
L. tardigradus		June–July & Sep.–Nov.	
Macaca fascicularis	4 yr	all year	25–39
M. fuscata	3–4 yr	Oct.–Apr.	28
M. mulatta	3–4 yr	menstruate all year; estrus and birth rate fluctuate seasonally	(23–33)
M. nemestrina	4 yr	all year	32 (29–33)
M. radiata	3–4 yr	all year	31
M. sinica	3 yr		29.5
M. sylvanus			27–33
Pan	8–11 yr	all year	36 (33–38)
Papio sp.	3–4 yr	all year	32–36
Perodicticus		all year	38 (21–47)
Pongo pygmaeus			39–32
Presbytis entellus	3–5 yr		22
Saguinus	15 mo	Feb.	
Saimiri sciurea	3 yr	restricted season	12
Tarsius spectrum		all year	23–24
Theropithecus gelada	5 yr	all year	

[a] From the literature.

tion may be due to drastic social and behavioral changes resulting from displacement of a troop's leader male.

In certain species local conditions may induce either phases of anestrous or additional breeding periods. For example, in the Sudan two annual sexual seasons seem to occur among captive and wild *Galago senegalensis* (Butler, 1967 a, b), but south of the equator *Galago* breed only once a year. Variations in climate or geography thus seem to affect the breeding season. *M. fuscata* experience a restricted mating season from October to March (Sugiyama *et al.*, 1965). *Propithecus verreauxi* (sifaka), *Lemur catta* (ringtail lemur), and *Cheirogaleus major* (mouse lemur) have well-defined breeding seasons.

Captive conditions. Some species that breed seasonally in the wild [e.g. *M. mulatta, Papio, Pan* and *Callithrix* (marmoset)] breed all year around under laboratory conditions of consistent diet and management. Peaks of conception and birth do occur and vary with the locality (Fig. 7-1 and 7-2). Captive *M. mulatta* show fairly regular cycles from October to April, and less regular and frequent ones at other times; maximal conception rates are noted between January and March.

Loris tardigradus lydekkerianus show two sexual seasons, June

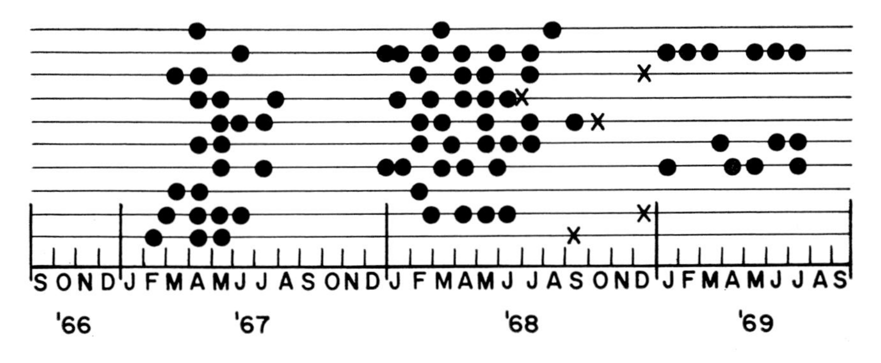

Figure 7-1. The breeding season of pubertal *Galago senegalensis senegalensis* kept in isolation in Saskatoon, Canada, over a period of 3 years. Estrus commenced between February and July during the 2nd year of life. In subsequent years the sexual season was prolonged. Note the distinct period of anestrus. (H. Butler, unpublished data)

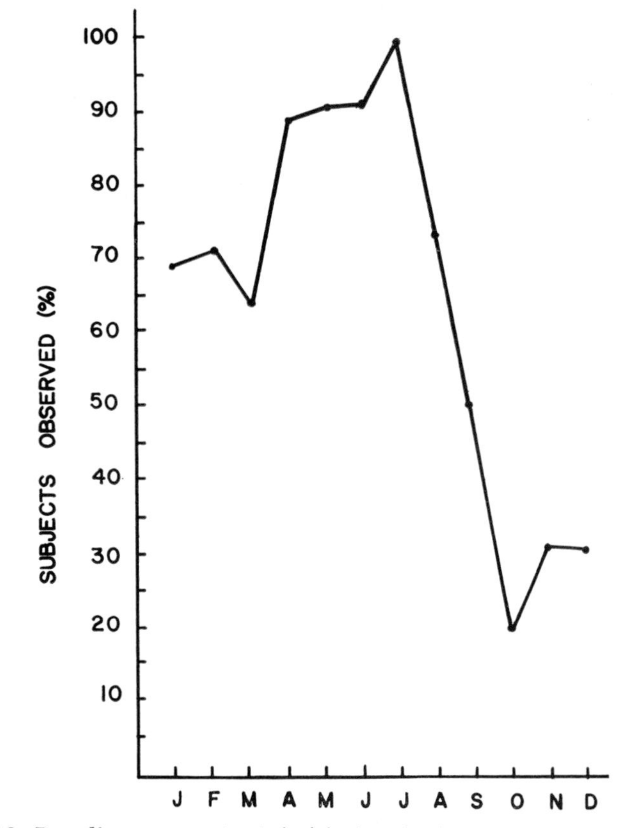

Figure 7-2. Breeding season in *Saimiri*. Graph shows percentage of subjects with estrus-criterion smears in each calendar month. (Rosenblum, 1969)

to July and September to October (Ramaswami and Anand Kumar, 1962, 1965), but pregnancy is possible during only one of them. Like other prosimians, *Loris* have estrous cycles but never any sanguineous discharge or even micromenstruation.

It is not known to what degree observed patterns of reproduction in the laboratory are attributable to the constancy of captive conditions. Several rodents often breed all year under laboratory conditions, but have a restricted sexual season in the wild.

Under laboratory conditions, true seasonality of breeding is found in *L. catta, Propithecus verreauxi* (Joly, 1966), *Cheirogaleus major* (Petter-Rousseaux, 1964), *Loris* (Manley, 1966), *Saimiri* and *M. fuscata*. In *Loris tardigradus,* for example, there are two estrous periods per year of which the first is shorter. If fertilization fails at the second estrus, there is a long anestrus until the next period of sexual receptivity. Each animal can breed only once a year (Ramaswami and Anand Kumar, 1962).

Environmental Factors and Breeding Season. Seasonality of reproduction is apparently an adaptation to rainfall and to quantity and quality of vegetation. The similarities in the reproductive cycles of *M. sylvanus* (Barbary ape) on Gibraltar and *M. fuscata* at Takasakiyama, Japan, are due to independent adaptations to local environments (MacRoberts and MacRoberts, 1966). In these two species, the onset of the sexual season seems to be coincident with the autumnal decrease in daylength, temperature, or both (Fig. 7-3).

There are numerous examples of environmental effects on the breeding season. The breeding season of *Lemurinae* is changed when the animals are transported from the southern to the northern hemisphere. Copulation in *Microcebus murinus* occurs between March and August in Paris, and between October and February in Madagascar (Petter-Rousseaux, 1964). Similarly, the breeding season of prosimians in the northern hemisphere is a reversal of their natural sexual season in the southern hemisphere. On the other hand, *Saimiri* and *M. fuscata* maintain their usual reproductive cycles in captivity, in spite of a uniform diet.

Controlling Mechanisms. The mechanism by which the photoperiod controls the breeding season in primates is not fully understood. It apparently involves photosensitive receptor cells acting in concert with the pituitary and the C.N.S. The commonly accepted locations of photoreceptor cells are the retina, pineal gland, and hypothalamus, although other locations have been suggested. Seasonal shifts in sun position and in the relative amounts of dust particle and water vapor in the air affect total intensity of illumination and cause differential filtering effects throughout the visual, infrared and ultraviolet spectra. The effects of changing or constant photoperiod on the menstrual pattern and seasonality of reproduction need further investigation.

In captivity *Galago senegalensis senegalensis* have a long period of anestrus between September and December, but this is much less apparent in *G. senegalensis braccatus* (Butler, unpublished

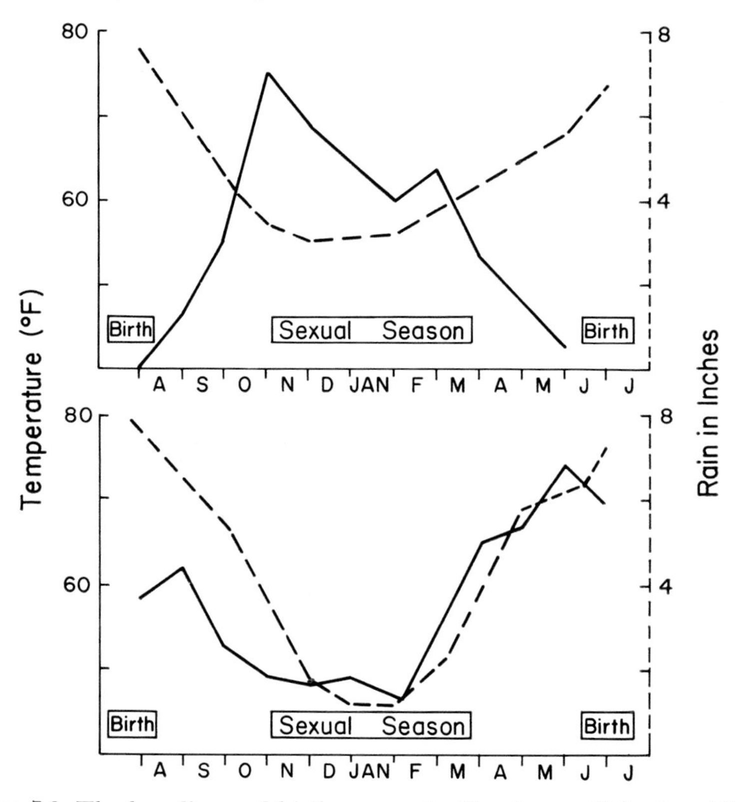

Figure 7-3. The breeding and birth seasons in *M. sylvanus* (Gibraltar, 36° N) and Takasakiyama *M. fuscata* (Japan, 35° N) in relation to mean monthly temperature (————) and rainfall (..............). Note the similarity in the annual reproductive cycles at both localities at similar latitudes. Copulation occurs in both localities in the fall, during decreasing daylength. Copulation begins with increased rainfall in Gibraltar and decreased rainfall in Japan (MacRoberts and MacRoberts, 1960)

data). In this species and with certain other species some internal factors may be responsible in stimulating the onset of the breeding season.

B. Breeding Season of Males

The nature and degree of seasonality in spermatogenic activity vary with species, locality, and constancy of laboratory conditions.

Spermatogenesis may continue throughout the year, but seasonal variations are observed in frequency and intensity of sexual behavior, testicular size (Fig. 7-4), semen characteristics, and the ease of semen collection by electroejaculation.

Slade (1964) observed that *M. mulatta* males in the free-ranging colony on Puerto Rico show an annual spermatogenic cycle; spermatogenesis is maximal during the fall breeding season. During the spring, there is extensive regression of the seminiferous tubules and spermatogenesis ceases; in midsummer prior to the breeding season the testis begins redevelopment. A similar cycle occurs in the epididymis. Male sex skin color is brightest during the breeding season when testes are large, and least intense during the nonbreeding season when testes are smaller.

Testicular size variation is most striking in *Microcebus murinus,* the smallest species of *Lemuroidea. Lemur* and *Saimiri* adult males show annual cycles of testicular size and body weight; in *Lemur* spermatogenesis ceases during the nonbreeding season. During the breeding season (December-March) the male *Saimiri* is heavy with subcutaneous fat at the upper torso, shoulders, and arms, which is gradually lost during April and is absent by May (Du Mond and Hutchinson, 1967). In the *Cheirogaleus* male subcutaneous fat increases during the nonbreeding season (Petter-Rousseaux, 1964).

Peak spermatogenesis in *Microcebus murinus* of southern Madagascar occurs during October-November at the height of the dry season; during the shorter rainy season, this species is spermatogenically inactive (Ramakrishna and Prasad, 1967). Conversely, the breeding season in Madagascar *Lepilemur mustelinus* and *Cheirogaleus* extends from the end of May to the beginning of August (Petter-Rousseaux, 1964).

Even when spermatogenic activity extends throughout the year, male breeding activity may be restricted to certain seasons to coincide with the secretory activity of the male accessory sex glands. For example, the male *Loris* is spermatogenically active all year but sexual activity is seasonal. The approach of breeding season is indicated by an increase in the weight of the vesicular glands, prostate and bulbourethral glands, as well as the testicles (Ramakrishna and Prasad, 1967).

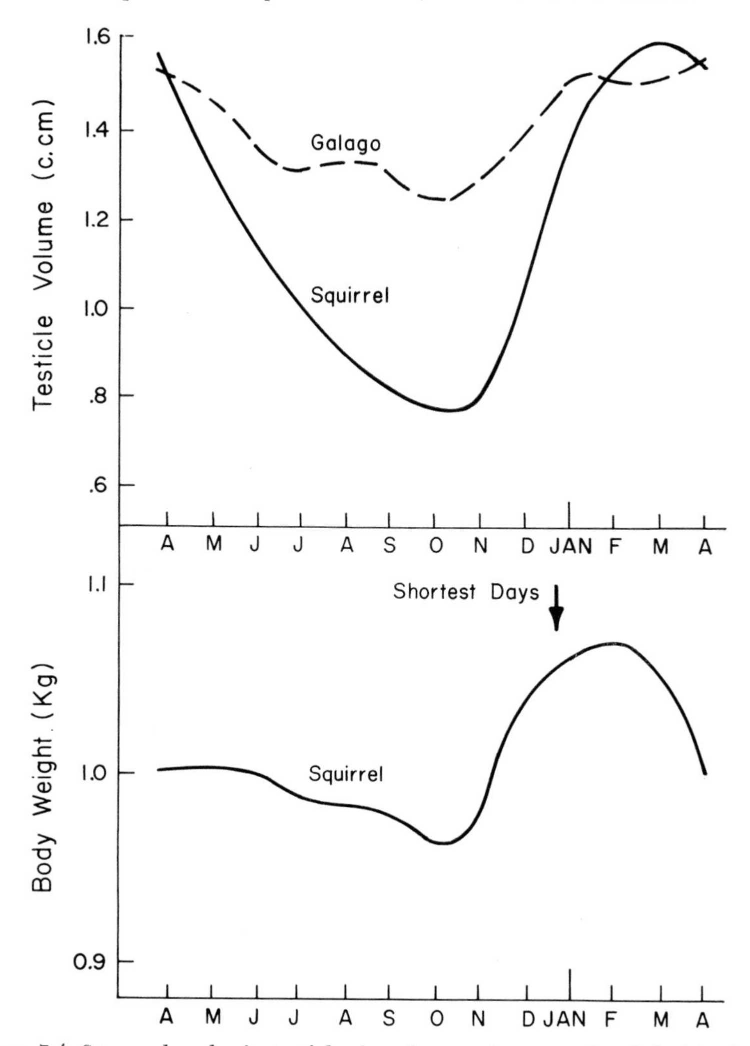

Figure 7-4. Seasonal cycles in testicle size of two colony species, *Saimiri sciureus* and *Galago crassicaudatus panganiensis,* imported from Leticia, Colombia, to San Diego, California. In the squirrel monkey there is marked seasonal increase in testicle size; the sexual season of the females extends only from February to May. In the galago, there is less seasonal fluctuation in testicle size and the female sexual season lasts all year except for a short period of anestrus during August to December. During the sexual season body weight increases in the male squirrel monkey but not in the female. (R. W. Cooper, unpublished data)

C. Season of Birth

In captivity, *Papio, Callithrix,* and twelve species of *Macaca* breed readily and may give birth during any month, but peaks of birth vary with the physical and social environment (Fig 7-5 and 7-6).

In northern India, free-ranging *M. mulatta* have two seasons of birth: most births occur during April, and a few during September (Southwick *et al.*, 1961). In captivity in the northern hemisphere,

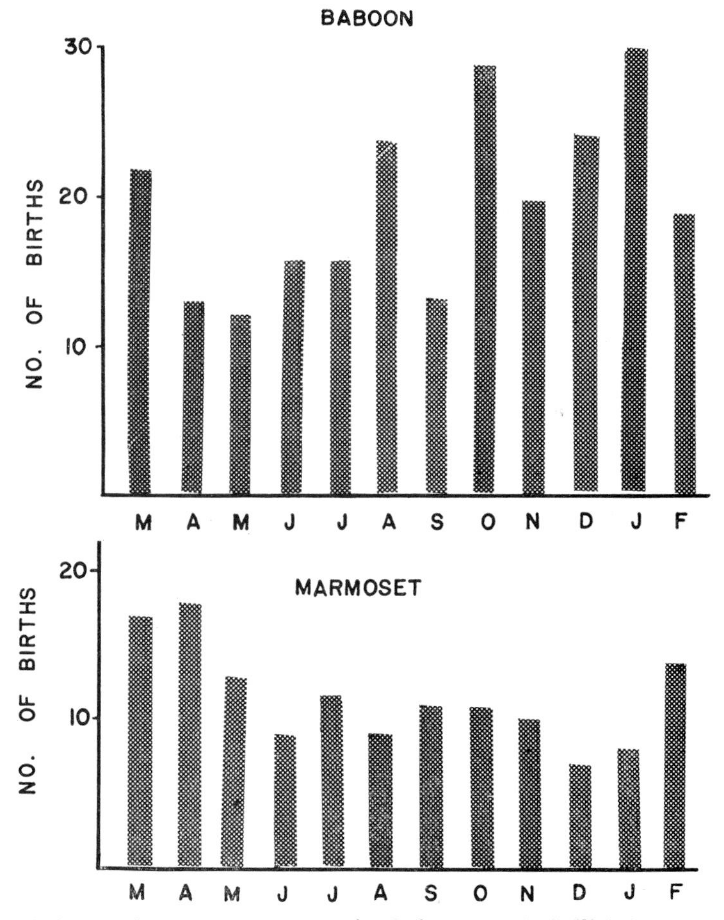

Figure 7-5. Breeding seasons in *Papio* (baboon) and *Callithrix* (marmoset). These two species breed all year but have peaks of birth at certain seasons. (Hampton and Hampton, 1965; Kriewaldt and Hendrickx, 1968)

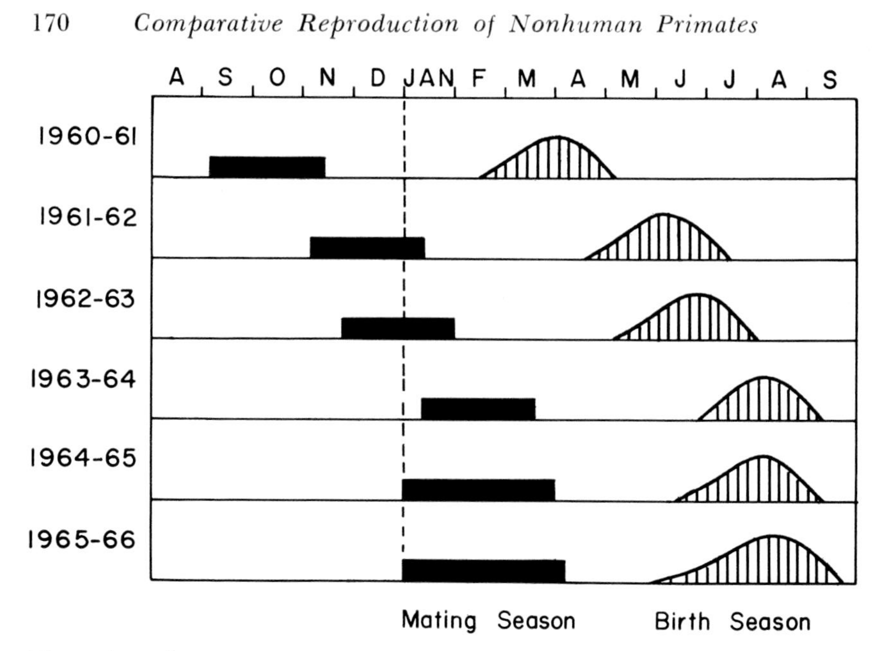

Figure 7-6. Six-year record of reproduction of 37 *Saimiri* (squirrel monkeys) imported from Iquitos, Peru, to the Monkey Jungle, Miami, Florida. The birth season is illustrated as a curve, the high portion of which indicates a peak of births. For 3 years, all births were confined to very discrete annual periods. The birth season shifted from winter (February-March) to summer (June- August) to coincide with the local ecological cycle.

most *M. mulatta* are born from March to May. Births in baboons are less seasonal but peaks occur from October to January. Different monkey groups in Japan (latitude 31° to 41° N) have different birth seasons. Variations seem to be regional (Kawai *et al.,* 1967). The seasonal and monthly birth distribution patterns are affected when the organization and integration of a group are disturbed. Two to three years may be required before a new system is stabilized.

Saimiri in their natural habitat usually give birth during February or March, whereas those bred in laboratories in the northern hemisphere usually give birth during August or September. When a colony of *Saimiri* was imported into the Monkey Jungle, Miami, Florida, from Iquitos, Peru, the season of birth shifted from the winter to the summer over a three-year period (Fig. 7-6).

Birth interval for *Presbytis* is probably twenty to twenty-four months (Jay, 1963a, b). The birth season, which extends from November to May, varies considerably among different *Presbytis* troops (Sugiyama *et al.*, 1965). In Jaipur, North India, there are two seasonal peaks of birth, from January to May, and from November to December (Prakash, 1962).

Seasonality of birth is related in part to environment and food conditions, in part to social conditions and also to physiological conditions of individuals. In *Presbytis entellus* change in leader of troop aroused social and sexual excitement and produced a peak in births (Sugiyama *et al.*, 1965).

Figure 7-7 represents the cycle of growth and breeding in the female and male *Loris tardigradus*.

III. SEXUAL CYCLE

Several techniques have been used to study the sexual cycle of primates: detailed clinical observations; serial vaginal smears stained differentially; sedimentation of specimens obtained by vaginal lavage; and measurements of menstrual flow and blood or urinary gonadotropin levels. In studies where no attempt has been made to determine whether or not ovulation actually occurred in each cycle, the results should be interpreted with caution. Systematic observations should be conducted during the breeding season, allowing males one-half to one hr of access to groups of females each day. Such studies should be combined with sperm data and repetitive laparotomies to inspect the ovaries.

A. Cycle Length

The length of the menstrual cycle is calculated from the first day of bleeding of one cycle to the onset of bleeding in a subsequent cycle. Many Old World primates (*Pan* is one exception) show approximately lunar cycles. In species lacking visible signs of menstruation, the length is estimated less accurately: seven to thirteen days in *Saimiri*, sixteen to twenty days in *Cebus* (capuchin monkey), twenty-one to twenty-six days in *Alouatta* (howler monkey) and *Ateles* (spider monkey).

Cycle length may vary considerably within a species (Table 7-I). Intraspecies variation in cycle length is greater in captive *Papio* than in captive *M. mulatta* or man (Hendrickx, 1967). Varia-

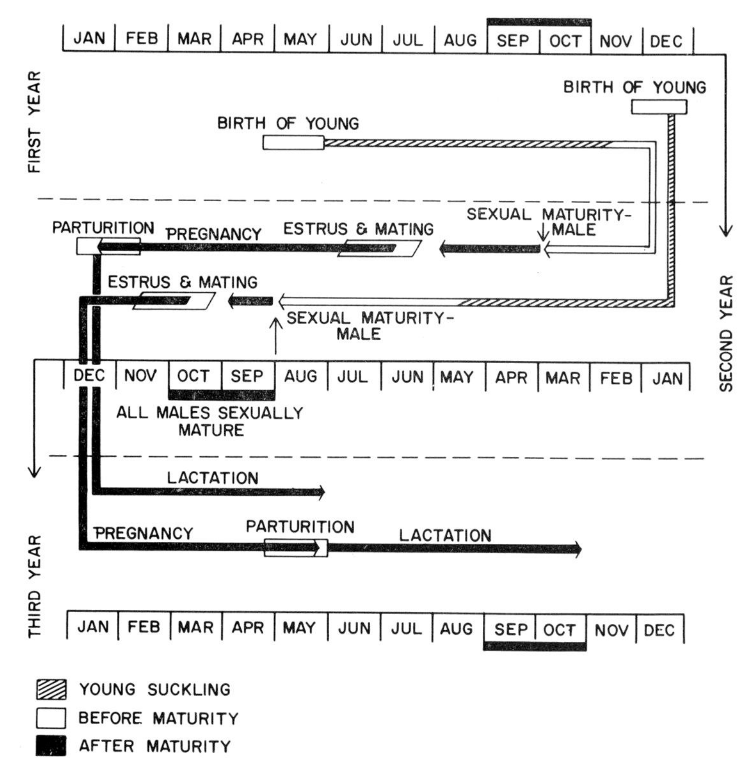

Figure 7-7. Cycle of growth, maturity and breeding in the female and male *Loris tardigradus* (loris) in southern India (12° N). The cycle of growth and maturity of young born in April-May is traced from birth, through suckling and growth to maturity, breeding, pregnancy, and lactation. A similar cycle is traced for young born in November-December. It is presumed that the period of immaturity in the female is 12-15 months. (Ramakrishna and Prasad, 1967 and the literature)

bility is due to illness, abortion, endocrine disturbances, or changes in nutrition, climate, social relations, or frequency of matings (Fig. 7-8).

B. Sexual Receptivity of Females

In most mammals copulation is strictly limited to the period of behavioral estrus, and peak sexual receptivity can be used as an indication of ovulation. In primates, however, some other index of ovulation time is required, because the temporal relationships be-

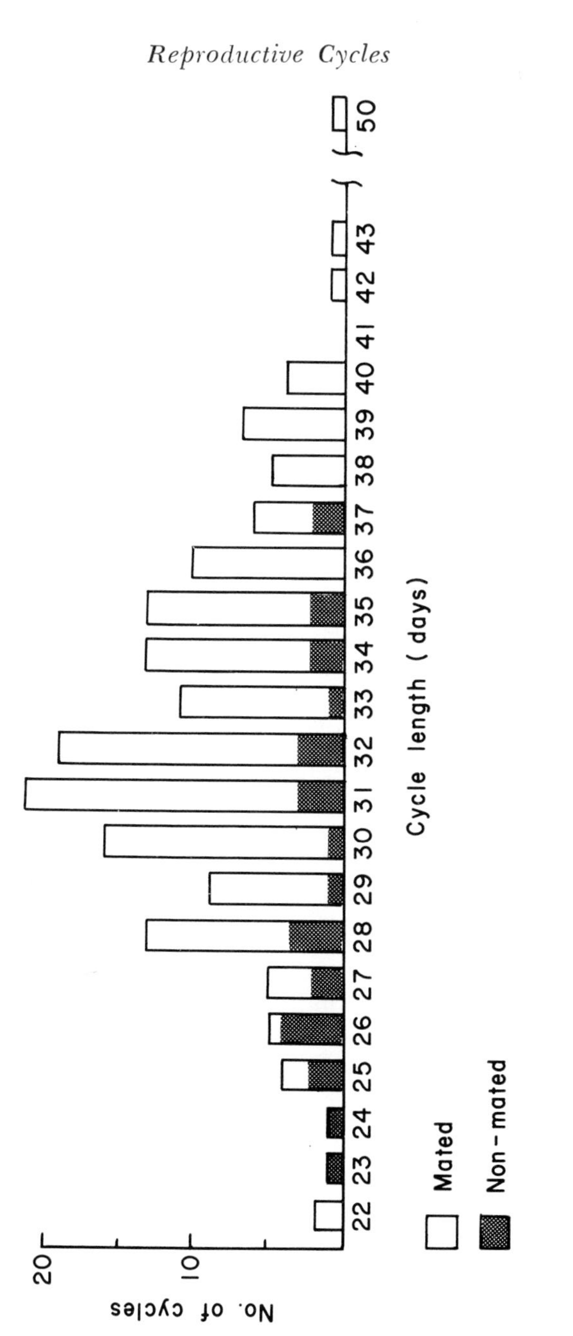

Figure 7-8. Frequency of cycle lengths in mated and nonmated *Papio anubis* (baboon). The cycles in which matings occurred averaged 3 days longer than the nonmated cycles. (Hendrickx and Kraemer, 1969)

tween receptivity and fertility are less distinct. Women and certain nonhuman primates experience no estrus in the strict sense, and sexual cycle is synonymous with menstrual cycle. The copulatory posture varies with the animal species (Fig. 7-9).

Pattern and distribution of primate sexual receptivity depend on the species, the physical and social environment, and the stage of the reproductive cycle (Table 7-II). Sexual receptivity extends for less than one day in *Lemur catta,* two days in *Perodicticus* (potto), three to four days in *Pongo* (orangutan) and *Presbytis entellus,* nine days in *M. mulatta* and *M. fuscata,* and eleven days in *M. fascicularis* (crab-eating macaque).

Major factors in copulation incidence are the social status of the male and the hormonal condition of the female. In species with an elaborate hierarchy status, higher ranking males usually copulate more often than lower-ranked animals, although breeding activity does not decrease with dominance in a regular and predictable manner. Because the dominant male tends to be most frequently associated with the older, and less fertile, females, he may be less effective at producing offspring than some lower-ranking males. Some females copulate infrequently; and females who do not copulate with the more dominant males copulate with the less dominant males.

M. mulatta and *Papio* form temporary consort relationships while the females are in estrus. The female obtains available food and other privileges not otherwise allowed by the male. In caged *M. mulatta,* copulation occurs throughout the cycle, except during and a few days preceding menstruation. However, the frequency of copulation increases steadily from the beginning of the cycle until the sudden drop (Rowell, 1966). Some females allow mounting every day and show peaks of receptivity with complete copulation at intervals; others are less regularly attractive and receptive to the males. The rhythms of mounting behavior in male. *M. mulatta* which are well correlated with the menstrual cycles of their female partners (Fig. 7-10), are abolished by bilateral ovariectomy (Michael *et al.,* 1966).

The female *Pan* copulate mainly during the interval of maximum genital swelling. The male *Presbytis entellus* copulate only with estrous females even if caged with nonestrous females for

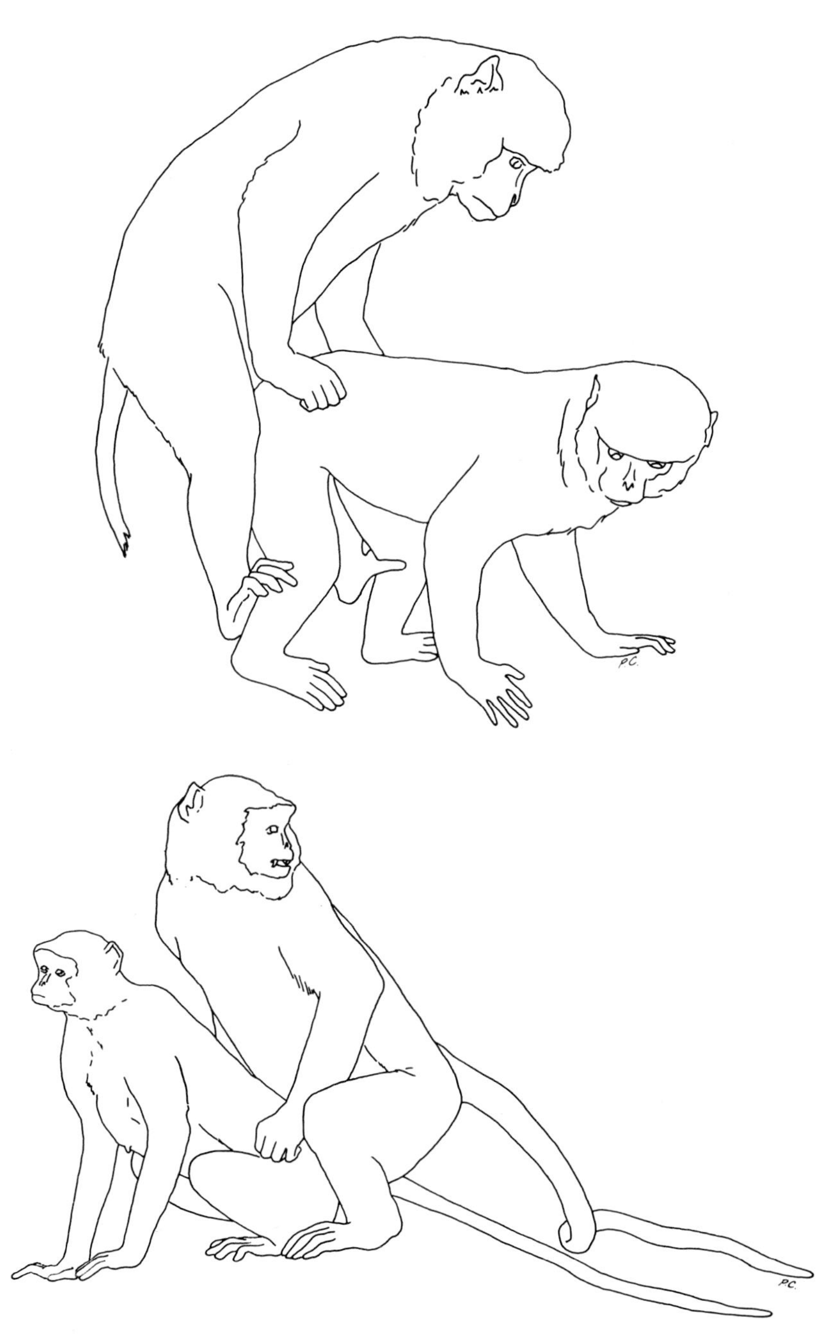

Figure 7-9. Top: Copulatory position for the rhesus monkey. Note that the male grasps the hind legs of the female with his feet.

Bottom: Copulatory position for the langur. Note that the male's hind feet remain on the ground. (From Hendrickx and Kraemer, 1970)

TABLE 7-II

SPECIES DIFFERENCES IN SOME CHARACTERISTICS OF THE REPRODUCTIVE CYCLE[a]

Phenomenon	*Macaca Mulatta*	*Papio*	*Pan*
Mean Cycle Length (Days)	28	32	36
Optimal Period for Conception	11th–14th day	near the end of maximal tumescence	16th–20th day
Signs and Nature of Estrus	consort relationships during distinct estrus; grooming and copulation related to stages of menstrual cycle; presentation to male related to ovulation	estrus during 2nd half of follicular phase is accompanied by maximal perineal swelling	highly receptive during maximal genital swelling or about ovulation time; copulation most frequent during middle third of cycle, least frequent in last third
Estrus During Pregnancy	distinct estrus occurs during early gestation		may accept aggressive males during early gestation
Sexual Skin Swelling	location involves interfemoral membrane, tail root, iliac crest, outer side of thighs	location involves perineum only	enlarged perineum with defined boundary or indistinct hypertrophy involving surrounding areas
Developmental Stage of Occurrence	swelling occurs in pubertal and adolescent animal	swell before fertile	swell when fertile
Hormonal Phase of Occurrence	swelling in young rhesus begins in follicular phase, increases through ovulation to reach a maximum toward end of luteal phase; fades before menstruation	swelling is restricted to follicular phase of cycle	enlarges 10 days after onset of bleeding, reaches a maximum within 7 days and remains maximal for 10 days; detumescence begins on 26th day

[a] Data from Yerkes and Elder, 1936; Rowell, 1966; Kriewaldt and Hendrickx, 1968

TABLE 7-III

CYCLICAL CHANGES IN THE VAGINAL EPITHELIUM, VAGINAL SMEAR AND SEXUAL SKIN OF THE BABOON (*PAPIO PAPIO*)[a]

Phase	*Vaginal Epithelium*	*Vaginal Smear*	*Sexual Skin*
Menstrual	distinct basal and intermediate layers, thin superficial layer	many erythrocytes; cornified and intermediate cells	turgescence begins
Postmenstrual	distinct superficial zone	leucocytes and cornified cells predominate; the rest are mostly intermediate	wrinkles disappear; color changes from dull pink to red
Preovulatory	superficial zone doubles in thickness	epithelial cells with unfolded cytoplasm and edges	turgescent and red
Postovulatory	superficial zone degenerating and sloughing; vacuoles are prevalent	cellular debris; leucocytes; cornified, intermediate parabasal cells	flaccid and pinkish white; wrinkles appear
Luteal	thickness reduced to a few layers of intermediate and basal zone	thin smear; leucocytes, intermediate parabasal cells; cornified cells are rare	pinkish white, wrinkles

[a] From Hendrickx, 1967

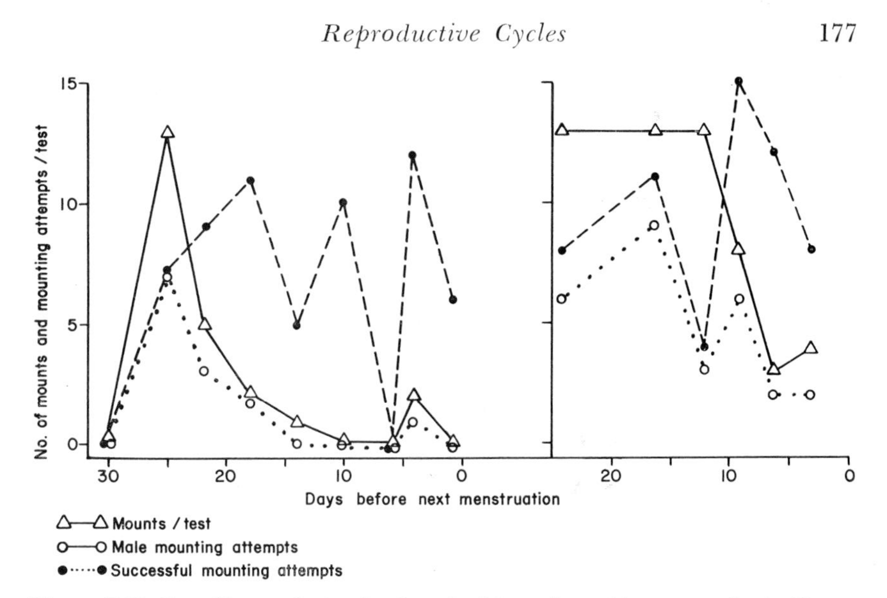

Figure 7-10. Breeding cycle in the female *M. mulatta* (rhesus monkey). Figure illustrates, over 2 cycles, the mounting rhythm resulting from male mounting attempts, female refusals, and female sexual invitations. The female contributed positively, by initiating mounts, during the first parts of the cycles (hatched area), and negatively during the second parts of the cycles by actively refusing (stippled area). Where hatched and stippled areas overlap, the female was inviting and refusing in the same test. ▲——▲, Mounts/test; ●——●, unsuccessful male mounting attempts ○----○, successful attempts. (Michael and Welegalla, 1968)

months. In *Hylobates* copulation occurs throughout the menstrual cycle, even during pregnancy. In some prosimians, copulation takes place at night or, exceptionally, in the morning. In the stumptailed macaque (*M. arctoides*) the male grasps his penis after copulation, pulls out his penis seminal coagulum and devours it (Fig. 7-11).

In certain primates, copulation has also taken on the role of a dominant-submissive behavioral action, and thus may be entirely unrelated to sexual receptivity. In the frequently studied *M. mulatta* and *Papio* mounting occurs in a large variety of social interactions, e.g. dominance, or displacement activity, so that frequency of observed mountings or even fairly complete copulation does not simply reflect sexual interest.

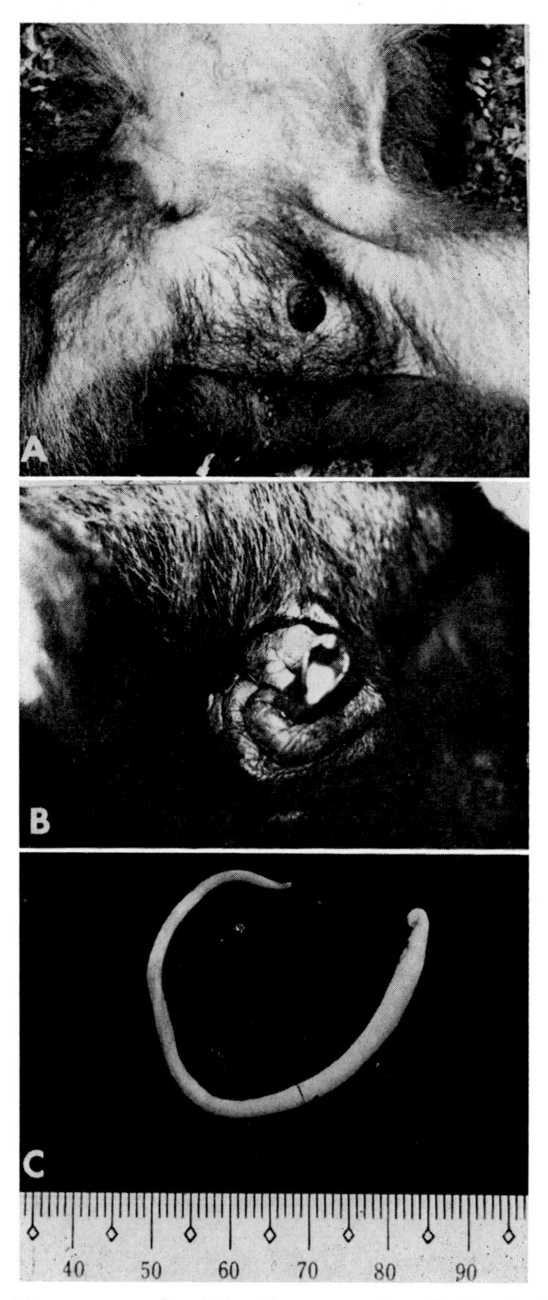

Figure 7-11A. Nonerect penis of the rhesus monkey. B. Penis of stump-tailed monkey (*Macaca arctoides*) immediately after copulation when the male grasps his penis, pulls the semen coagulum (C) left in the penis and devours coagulum.

1. *Phases of Sexual Cycle.* Several classifications have been used to describe the changes occurring during the menstrual cycle: (a) menstruation proper; follicular (estrogenic or proliferative) phase, lasting until about midcycle; and progestational (luteal) phase, lasting the remainder of the cycle; (b) proliferative, ovulatory, luteal, and involutionary phases; (c) menstrual, postmenstrual, tumescent, maximal swelling, detumescent, and premenstrual phases.

The duration and characteristics of these phases have been studied extensively in *M. mulatta* (Zuckerman, 1930; Zuckerman and Fulton, 1934; Zuckerman, 1937; Zuckerman and Parkes, 1952) and *Papio* (Table 7-I); and to a lesser degree in *Perodicticus* (Fig. 7-12).

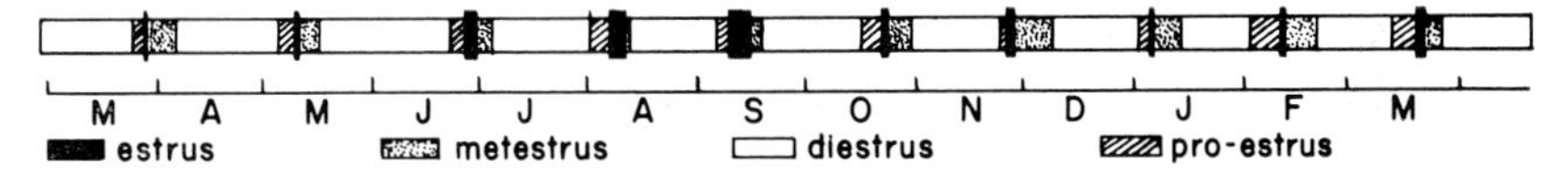

Figure 7-12. Typical estrous cycle of Perodicticus potto (potto). (From Ioannou, 1966)

The sexual cycle in *M. mulatta* may be divided into two phases. (a) the follicular phase, which lasts about thirteen days and may be irregular; and (b) the luteal phase, which lasts about fifteen days and is fairly constant. Progesterone concentration in the blood is maximal during the luteal phase of the cycle and is nil at the onset of menstruation. Ovulation is spontaneous, occurring eight to sixteen days after menstruation. There is a definite period of sexual receptivity beginning around the ninth day of the cycle.

2. *Estrus during pregnancy and lactation.* Following conception periodic menstruation ceases and the cycle of genital swellings generally disappear or become irregular. Copulation decreases or is absent during delivery and early postpartum periods. However, *Pan* in captivity continue full external cycles of swelling throughout pregnancy. *Saimiri* may copulate until the fourth month of pregnancy and during lactation.

Alouatta are sterile during early lactation, but the estrous cycle begins and ovulation occurs before lactation ceases. *Ateles* are sterile, with ovulation apparently completely suppressed, throughout lactation (Dempsey, 1939). Free-ranging lactating *M. mulatta* resume copulatory activities later than nonlactating postpartum females (Vandenbergh and Vessey, 1968). In *Galago* a postpartum estrus occurs only when the neonate is lost or destroyed (Manley, 1966). In undernourished women the menstrual cycles are suspended during lactation.

C. Related Behavioral Patterns

Several behaviors are associated with sexual receptivity of the female, e.g. fighting, grooming, certain copulatory patterns, and scent marking.

In troops of *Papio* fighting among males increases in the presence of an estrous female, and the relative dominance of males may change (Washburn and Hamburg, 1965).

Grooming, as a prelude to, or interlude in, sexual relationships, is an important source of group stability under free-ranging conditions and in captivity (Fig. 7-13). The intensity of social grooming fluctuates with the stage of the sexual cycle. In *M. mulatta,* males groom females most at midcycle, but females groom the males most at the beginning and end of menstrual cycles (Michael *et al.,* 1966). During the late follicular phase, female *Papio* groom males more than females and are groomed more frequently by males. Female *Papio* are groomed more by other females when lactating and less when pregnant and when sexual skin is deflating during early luteal phase (Rowell, 1968).

There are numerous examples of species-specific copulatory patterns in primates. The sexually receptive *Presbytis entellus* female simultaneously shakes her head, drops her tail on the ground, and presents herself with her buttocks shuddering (Jay, 1965; Sugiyama *et al.,* 1965; Dave and Ramaswami, 1969). Clutching syndrome described in the *M. mulatta* female at orgasm is not observed in *Presbytis.*

Scent marking of objects within home range occurs in some species (Fig. 7-14) and involves specialized glands. *Lemur catta* use secretions of the brachial and antebrachial glands on the inner forearms; the latter are both endocrine and exocrine (Montagna, 1962). *Cebus, Aotus, Saimiri,* and many other prosimians wash their hands and feet in urine and rub the perineal region on a

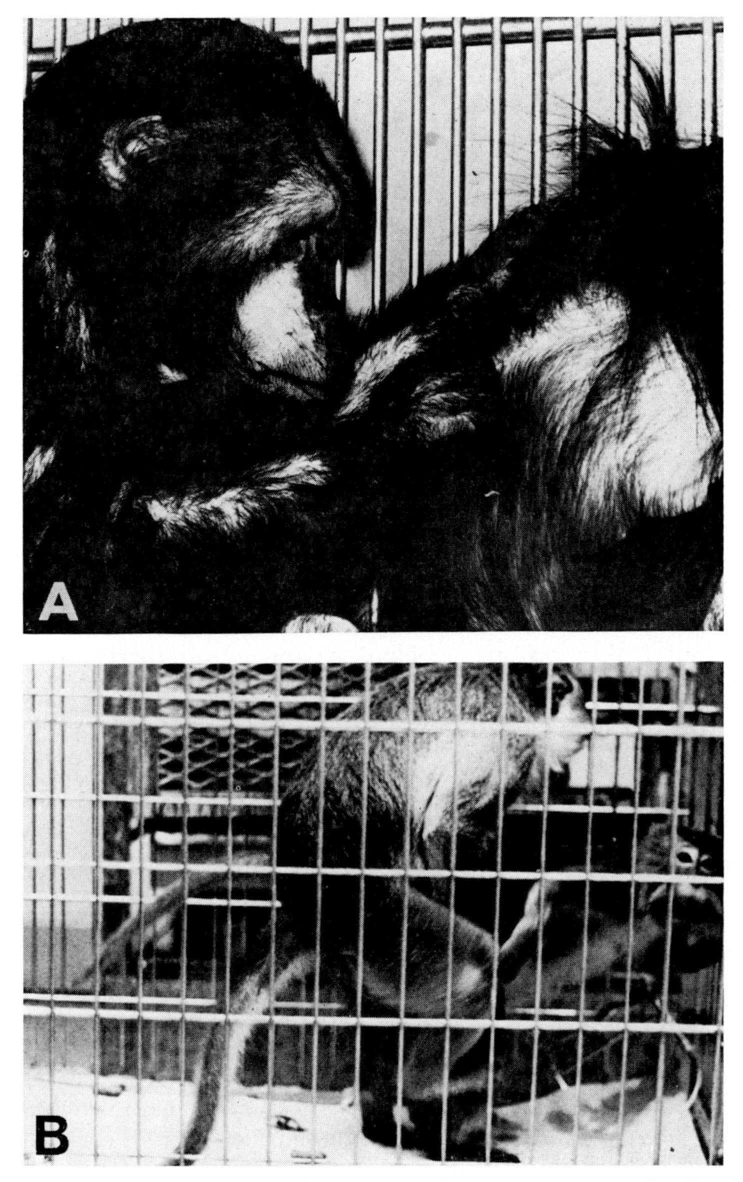

Figure 7-13. Social grooming (A) and copulatory posture (B) in the rhesus monkey.

branch. *Callithrix* use secretions from scrotal and perineal glands. *Propithecus* males rub their neck glands against branches, whereas the females use urine for marking. The relative importance and physiological significance of scent marking in reproduction of primates are not known.

D. Ovulation and Optimal Breeding Time

In species that menstruate, ovulation occurs midway between the beginnings of two consecutive menstrual periods. In *Pan,* ovulation is thought to occur from day sixteen to twenty-eight of a typical thirty-five day cycle. In longer cycles, ovulation occurs proportionately later (Elder and Yerkes, 1936). Ovulation may be accompanied by swelling or color changes of the sexual skin, or by changes in body odor. In *M. mulatta* a few red cells often appear in the vaginal lavage—the so-called midcycle bleeding.

Several methods are used by researchers to predict ovulation time: (a) inspection of corpora lutea during laparotomy; (b) daily recording of body temperature; (c) observation of quantitative and qualitative changes of cervical mucus along with other chemical tests; (d) observations of behavior; and (e) predictions made on the basis of previous regular cycles.

The age of a corpus luteum cannot be estimated from the gross morphology of its ovulation point. Occasionally, corpora lutea persist into succeeding menstrual cycles in forms that could be mistaken for recent ovulation points. The hazards of diagnosing ovulation by examining the ovaries at laparotomy can be reduced by making serial observations and photographic records (Plate 7-I).

»»→

Color Plate I. Morphology of the Ovary of Rhesus Monkey Near the Time of Ovulation. Figures A and B. Graafian follicle on day 14 and the ovulation point on day 16. A one-cell egg in cumulus clot was recovered from the oviduct on day 16. Figures C and D. Ovulation point on day 14 when a one-cell egg in cumulus clot was recovered from the oviduct. Figures E and F. Ovulation point on day 12 when a two-cell egg (E) or one-cell egg (F) was recovered from the oviduct. Figure G. Corpus luteum on day 13, one cycle after its formation. Figure H. Ovary on day 15: the lower structure is a recent ovulation point, but the upper is a Cl formed two cycles proviously. (Betteridge et al., 1970)

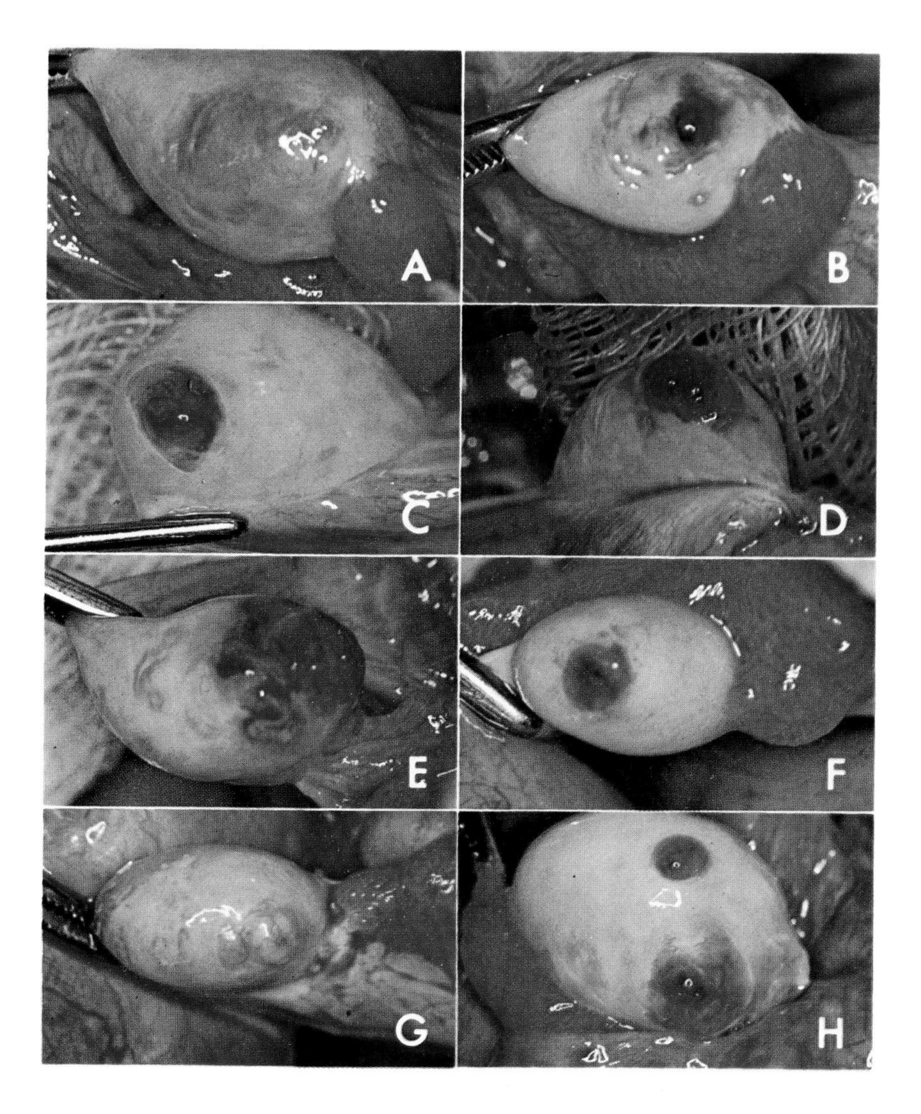
A
B
C
D
E
F
G
H

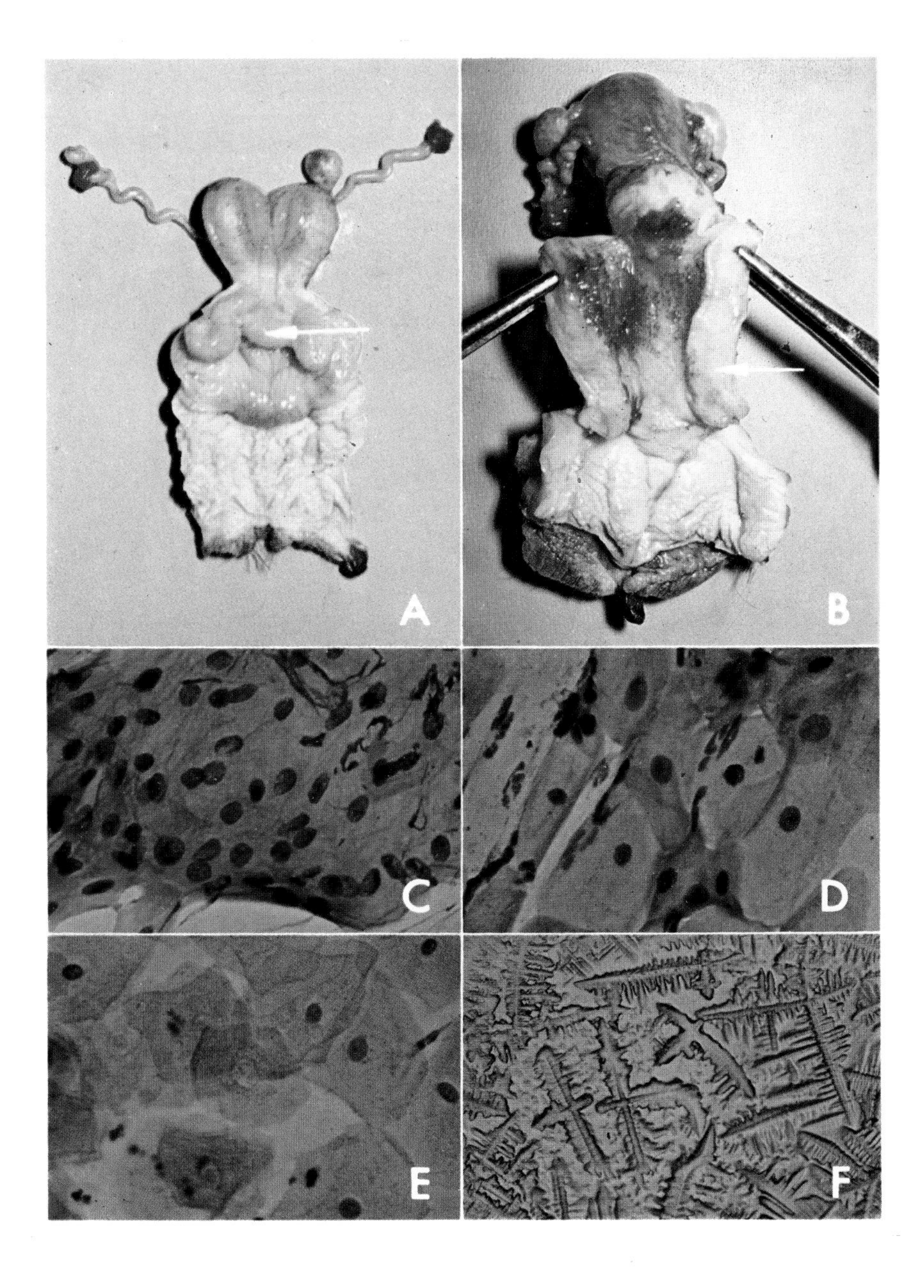
A
B
C
D
E
F

The basal body temperature (BBT), taken in the morning, fluctuates around the normal body temperature. On the day of ovulation BBT rises; it stays slightly above preovulatory temperatures until the next menstrual period. BBT as an indicator of ovulation in women has been controversial (cf. Buxton, 1951; Riley *et al.*, 1955; Garcia and Rock, 1958). The observations of Noyes *et al.* (1950) on dating the endometrial biopsy in nonhuman primates are worth studying.

Intermenstrual bleeding in women frequently indicates anovulatory menstrual cycles (Brown, 1959), although the mechanisms by which endometrial breakdown in such cycles is accomplished is not well understood (Rock, 1959). In certain nonhuman primates, e.g. *Presbytis entellus,* intermenstrual bleeding is common (David and Ramaswami, 1969), but it is not known whether these cycles are anovulatory.

Around the time of ovulation, the cervical mucus is thin and clear and can easily be stretched without breaking. The vaginal lavage from some species crystallize on a microscope slide to form a fern-leaf pattern during the immediate preovulatory, ovulatory, and postovulatory periods (Plate 7-II). This property is not evident during other phases of the cycle.

←

Color Plate II. A. The reproductive organs, cut open, of the rhesus monkey. Note the prominent cervical colliculi (arrow) which results in highly convoluted cervical canal. B. The reproductive organs of the stump-tailed monkey (*Macaca arctoides.*). The vagina is cut open. There are no cervical colliculi whereas the vestibular colliculus (arrow) is prominent. C, D, E. Vaginal smears, stained with Papanicolaou's method, of the crab-eating macaque (*Macaca fascicularis*) during bleeding, postbleeding and midcycle. C. During bleeding the smear shows predominantly rounded or oval cells, relatively small in size and with a large vesicular nucleus. They are usually cyanophilic (staining blue or green) with darkly stained cytoplasm and appear in sheets of large numbers of cells. D. During postbleeding phase the smear contains intermediate eosinophilic exfoliated cells and fewer leukocytes. E. During midcycle the superficial eosinophilic cells are characterized by a large size cell with a small central pyknotic nucleus. The cytoplasm is lightly stained, usually appear as single cells. There are few leukocytes and the slide appears clean. F. Ferning of cervical mucus characterized estrus in several primate species.

Figure 7-14. Illustration of urine marking by male and copulation in *Galago senegalensis*. (Doyle *et al.*, 1967)

More complicated tests for ovulation detect a peak of LH secretion or an increase in urinary pregnanediol excretion or in gonadotropin content of urine. At ovulation in *Presbytis,* albumin content in blood falls significantly; γ-globulin rises and remains elevated for a few days after ovulation (David and Rao, 1969). During the follicular phase in *Papio ursinus* levels of blood albumin and globulins decrease.

Johansson *et al.* (1968) measured peripheral plasma progesterone concentrations, by competitive protein binding analysis, in *M. mulatta* and related them to the day of ovulation as established by direct observation during serial laparotomies. Plasma progesterone concentrations increased abruptly on the day prior to ovulation, reaching maximal values of 4 mμg/ml three to four days after ovulation. On the day of ovulation, plasma progesterone concentration was inconsistent. This provides unequivocal evidence for a peak of preovulatory progesterone secretion, coinciding with secretory changes in the endometrium of *M. mulatta,* three days before ovulation.

The period of greatest fertility may also be estimated from various types of observations: (a) records of isolated fertile matings; (b) behavioral records of maximum percentage of copulations in relation to cycle length; and (c) observation of the rise in intensity of sexual activity preceding ovulation. Conception is most likely to occur on day eleven for *M. mulatta* and days sixteen to twenty for *Pan.*

E. Cyclical Changes

Cyclical changes occur in the sexual skin, external genitalia, vaginal mucosa, cervical mucus, mammary glands, and endometrium.

1. Sexual Skin. The anatomy of the sexual skin varies with the species. Sexual skin is characterized by a thick dermis with a conspicuous edema and an immense vascular supply. It changes color and general conformation during the menstrual cycle.

Swelling of sexual skin results from water deposited in the intercellular spaces and from connective tissue inhibition. The swelling and regression of the sexual skin are associated with a rise and fall in body weight, with cyclical fluctuations in daily water balance, and with concentrations of erythrocytes. For example, the red blood cell count in *M. nemestrina* seems to be lowest during menstruation and highest during maximal genital edema at midcycle.

Location of swelling and its timing in relation to the follicular and luteal phases vary with the species (Table 7-II to 7-IV). The

TABLE 7-IV

SPECIES DIFFERENCES IN THE RATE AND PATTERN OF CYCLICAL CHANGES IN SEXUAL SKIN OF ADULT MACAQUES[a]

Species	*Cyclical Changes in Sexual Skin*
M. assamensis (Assamese)	swelling and redness at estrus may involve thighs, buttocks and hips; present in 50%, pronounced in adolescent
M. cyclopis (Formosan)	conspicuous swelling and reddening at estrus involves root of tail, buttocks and back of thighs
M. fasicularis (crab-eating)	swelling at base of tail is slate-grey
M. fuscata (Japanese)	pink sexual skin becomes red, particularly in adolescent; swelling is less common
M. maurus (Moor)	two types of swelling occur: (a) prominent pink spherical swelling above callosities, concealing tail and involving adjacent furred area of rump; (b) diffuse pink involving only buttocks and sometimes backs of thighs (neither rump nor tail)
M. mulatta (rhesus)	swelling and reddening at estrus involving thighs, buttocks and hips occurs in 50%; pronounced in adolescent
M. nemestrina (pig-tailed)	conspicuous swelling and reddening during estrus involving buttocks and root of tail
M. radiata (bonnet)	sexual skin is bright red or purple throughout cycle
M. silenus (lion-tailed)	conspicuous pink swelling occurs at estrus
M. sinica (toque)	skin is reddish-purple throughout cycle
M. arctoides (stump-tailed)	skin reddens at estrus but swells little
M. sylvanus (Barbary ape)	conspicuous swelling of sexual skin at estrus is blue-grey; adjacent furred area of rump is also involved

[a] Compiled from Rowell, 1966; Napier and Napier, 1967; Hendrickx, 1967

time variation suggests species differences either in cyclical hormonal changes or in the hormonal mechanisms governing the swelling. Cyclic changes also vary among individuals, and even in the same individual during different cycles.

Perineal swelling indicates estrous activity (Figs. 7-15, 7-16, 7-17), but is not correlated with the exact time of ovulation. Ovariectomy during maximal swelling results in prompt subsidence of sexual skin. Injection of estrogen into ovariectomized *Papio, Pan,* and *M. mulatta* will produce enlargement and coloration of sexual skin.

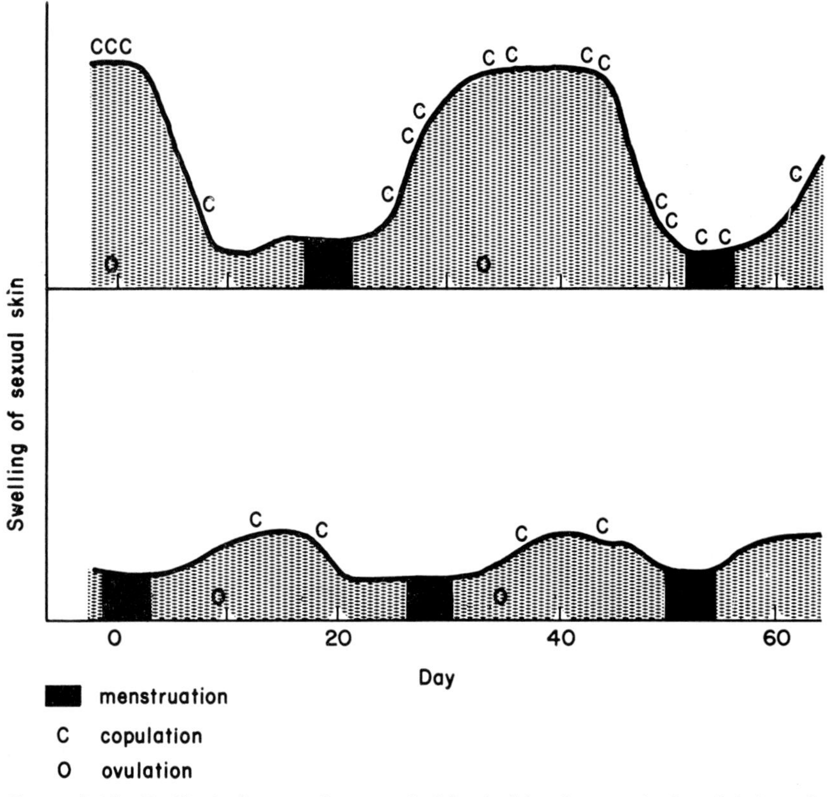

Figure 7-15. Cyclical changes in sexual skin (subjective vertical scale) in relation to menstruation and ovulation in two adolescent female rhesus monkeys, 3 years old. Top female, caged with a male, shows pronounced edema and regular cycles. Swelling begins a few days after menstruation and increases until just before the next menstruation. (Rowell, 1969)

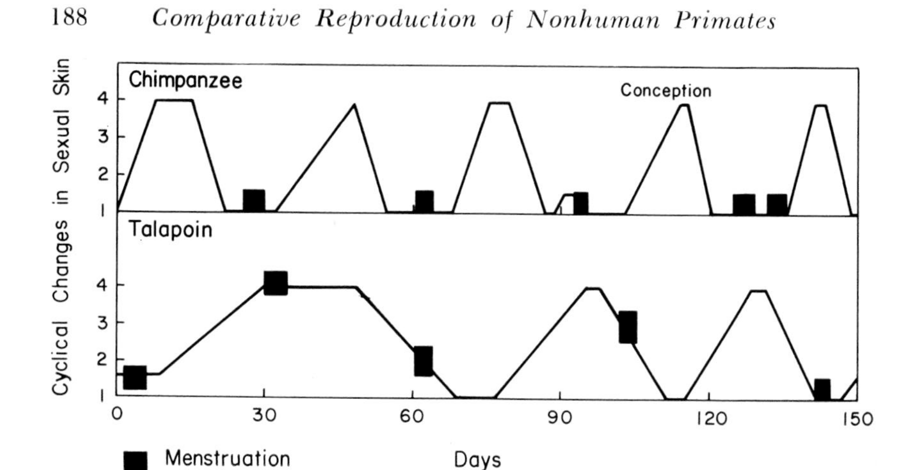

Figure 7-16. Top: The time and extent of sexual skin swelling in relation to onset and duration of menstruation in the chimpanzee. The typical cycle begins with a 3-day menstrual period, followed by 5-6 days during which the sexual skin is quiescent. Enlargement of sexual skin appears 10 days after onset of bleeding, reaches a maximum within a week, and remains for 10-12 days; deturgescence begins on day 26. Bottom: In *Miopithecus (Cercopithecus) talapoin* the fluctuations in the cornification of the perineal region are rather irregular. The time relations of menstruation and swelling of sexual skin vary. (Elder and Yerkes, 1936; Tomilin, 1940)

In *Papio* serum mucoprotein and plasma fibrin levels rise progressively during the turgescence of the perineum and fall with deturgescence. Plasma fibrinolytic activity in the female with regular menstrual cycles increases with the onset of deturgescence and remains elevated until the onset of menstruation, whereafter it falls precipitously (Gillman and Gilbert, 1946; Gillman *et al.,* 1960). Activity of β-glucuronidase and β-acetylglucoaminidase is low during sex-skin turgescence, when hyaluronic acid is accumulating (Naidoo and Baitera, 1970), and high during deturgescence, when hyaluronic acid is mobilized. Estrogen injections in ovariectomized *Papio* lowered enzyme activities whereas their withdrawal produced an excess of activity followed by a gradual return to pre-estrogen levels. When progesterone was injected into estrogen-primed animals, enzyme activities rose earlier and were maintained longer than usual. These enzymes may be involved in the mobilization of hyaluronic acid from *Papio* sex skin during the deturgescent phase of the menstrual cycle.

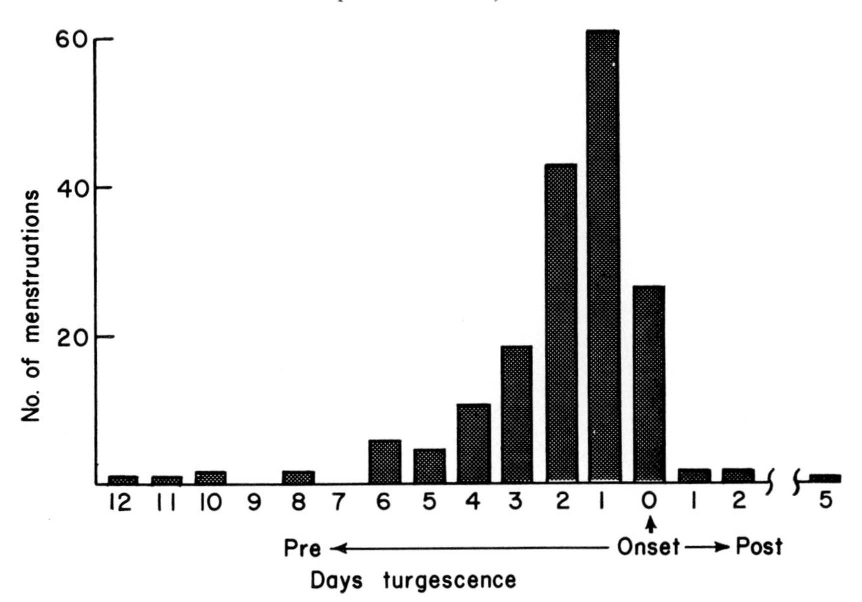

Figure 7-17. Intervals in days, from day 1 menses to perineal turgescence in *Papio cynocephalus* (yellow baboon) and *Papio anubis* (olive baboon). The average interval from day 1 of menstruation to the onset of perineal turgescence was 2.1 days; the average duration of menstrual flow was 2.75 ± 1.44 days. Note the frequencies of occurrence of menstruation on the various days before and after the onset of turgescence. (Hendrickx and Kraemer, 1969)

Cyclic skin changes are pronounced in *M. nemestrina* and *Papio* (Fig. 7-18). In *M. nemestrina* the sexual skin extends from the base of the tail, around the dorsal and lateral margins of the callosities, to the genitalia. The proximal portion of the tail and the areas ventral and medial to the callosities are included. In the quiescent state this region looks much like any other patch of bare skin, except that it may be a deeper red or even have a slightly bluish cast.

In *Papio* perineal deturgescence coincides with the postovulatory and luteal phases. When the estrogen level drops, wrinkles and color changes occur in the region of the anus and vagina and at the outer borders of the skin (Hendrickx, 1967). In some female *Papio* the color changes within a few days from bright red to gray-pink. With pregnancy, the perineum does not swell, but its

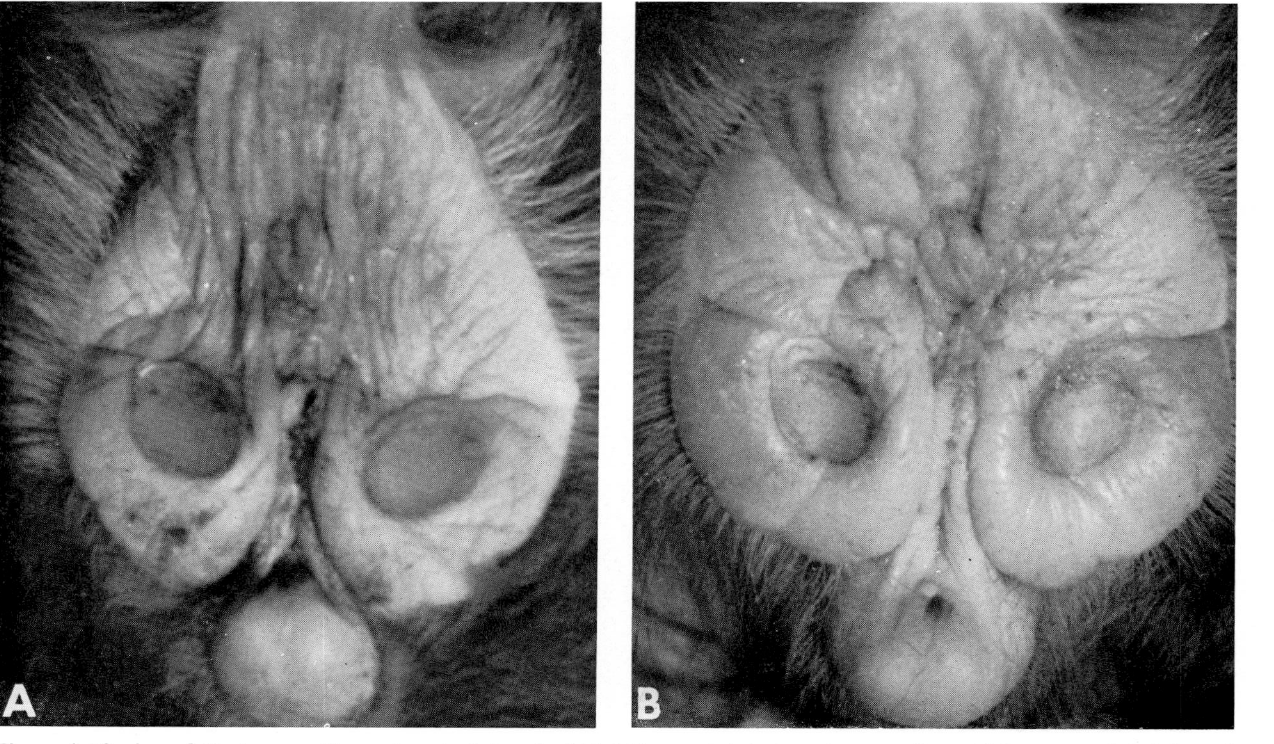

Figure 7-18. A and B. Sex swelling of typical female *Miopithecus talapoin* subgenus *Cercopithecus* on third day of menstruation (A) and near midcycle (B).

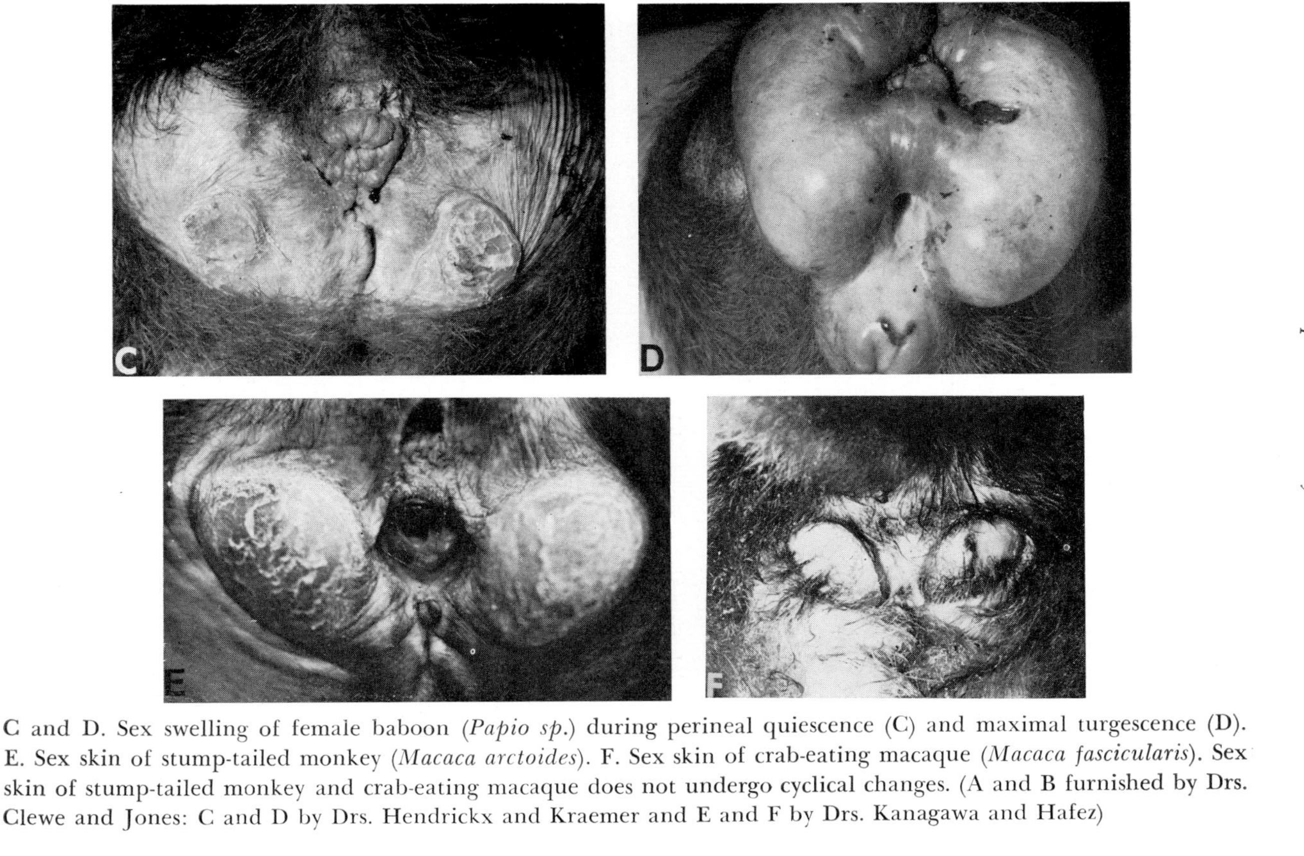

C and D. Sex swelling of female baboon (*Papio sp.*) during perineal quiescence (C) and maximal turgescence (D). E. Sex skin of stump-tailed monkey (*Macaca arctoides*). F. Sex skin of crab-eating macaque (*Macaca fascicularis*). Sex skin of stump-tailed monkey and crab-eating macaque does not undergo cyclical changes. (A and B furnished by Drs. Clewe and Jones: C and D by Drs. Hendrickx and Kraemer and E and F by Drs. Kanagawa and Hafez)

color becomes a deeper red; the bare buttocks become more vascularized and change from black to bright scarlet.

Perineal swelling and coloration occur in approximately 50 percent of *M. mulatta* females in estrus, and facial coloration in about 10 percent. Although the color of the sexual skin does not undergo regular cyclic changes, it usually reaches its maximum intensity about the time of ovulation and fades before menstruation. In young adults, a conspicuous edema affects the thighs, base of tail and back, resulting in a pronounced rugosity of the skin. In older adults, thighs redden without extreme edema. The sexual skin in *Pan* swells during estrus as well as after nursing. In *Presbytis* the sexual skin is underdeveloped in the female, but in the adult male it is present as a distinct large edematous pinkish muscular structure on the rump above the ischial callosities (David and Ramaswami, personal communication). The sexual skin in this species does not show cyclical changes and its development may be under the control of androgens.

The reddish-purple sexual skin of *M. sinica* (toque monkey) and bright red skin of *M. radiata* (bonnet monkey) do not change throughout the sexual cycle. *Theropithecus gelada* (gelada baboon) has a type of skin on the chest and neck which changes in color and size in phase with the perineal sexual skin.

Ischial callosities (the vascular calloused area of the ischium near the sexual skin found in some Old World primates (Fig. 7-19) are not affected by ovarian steroids and do not change during the sexual cycle.

2. *External Genitalia.* The external genitalia of lorisoid primates display clear-cut estrous changes (Fig. 7-20). In the female *Perodicticus* a large mound ("pseudoscrotum") resembling the scrotum of the male appears in the vulval area. It has a surface of highly glandular, closely packed tessellae and is bisected by the rima pudendi. During estrus, "superficial labia" are widely spread and flushed tessellae appear on each side; "deep labia" are separated; the previously closed vagina is open (Manley, 1966).

Miopithecus exhibit well-marked external cyclical changes. The vagina of *Galago senegalensis* changes size considerably during the estrous cycle, and the vaginal orifice opens and closes periodically. The vaginal orifice of *Lemur catta* and *L. fulvus* also opens during

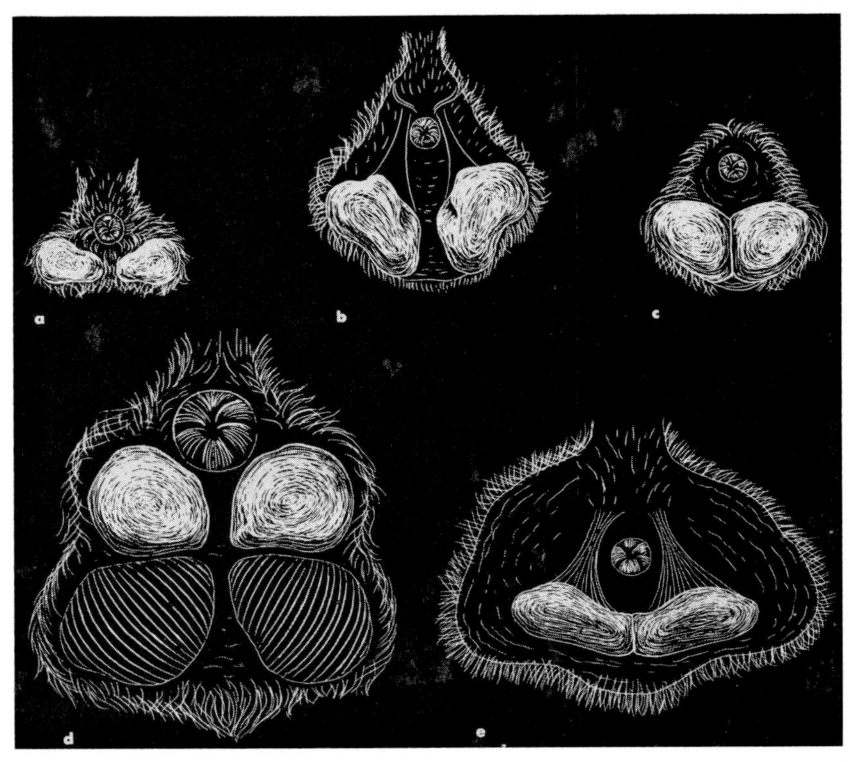

Figure 7-19. Species differences in the gross anatomy of the ischial callosities of male primates: a. *Cercopithecus mona* (mona monkey); b. *Macaca nemestrina* (pigtailed macaque); c. *M. sylvanus* (Barbary ape); d. *Theropithecus gelada* (gelada baboon); e. *Papio papio* (guinea baboon). (Napier and Napier, 1967)

estrus. In the smaller *Lemur, Microcebus* and *Cheirogaleus,* the vagina opens and closes when in and out of estrus (Joly, 1966).

3. *Vaginal Mucosa.* In *M. mulatta* and *Papio* the vaginal mucosa is thickest at ovulation and recedes to the basal zone during the luteal phase. Cyclic desquamation of the extremely thick, cornified epithelium occurs in *Ateles,* whereas *Alouatta* have a less developed vaginal lining that undergoes little cyclic change (Dempsey, 1939).

The vaginal smear is obtained with a cotton swab (Q-tip) moistened in physiological saline, a platinum wire loop, or vaginal lavage with 1 ml distilled water. The smear is fixed in 96 percent alcohol with 4 percent eosin for 1 minute; it is then examined mi-

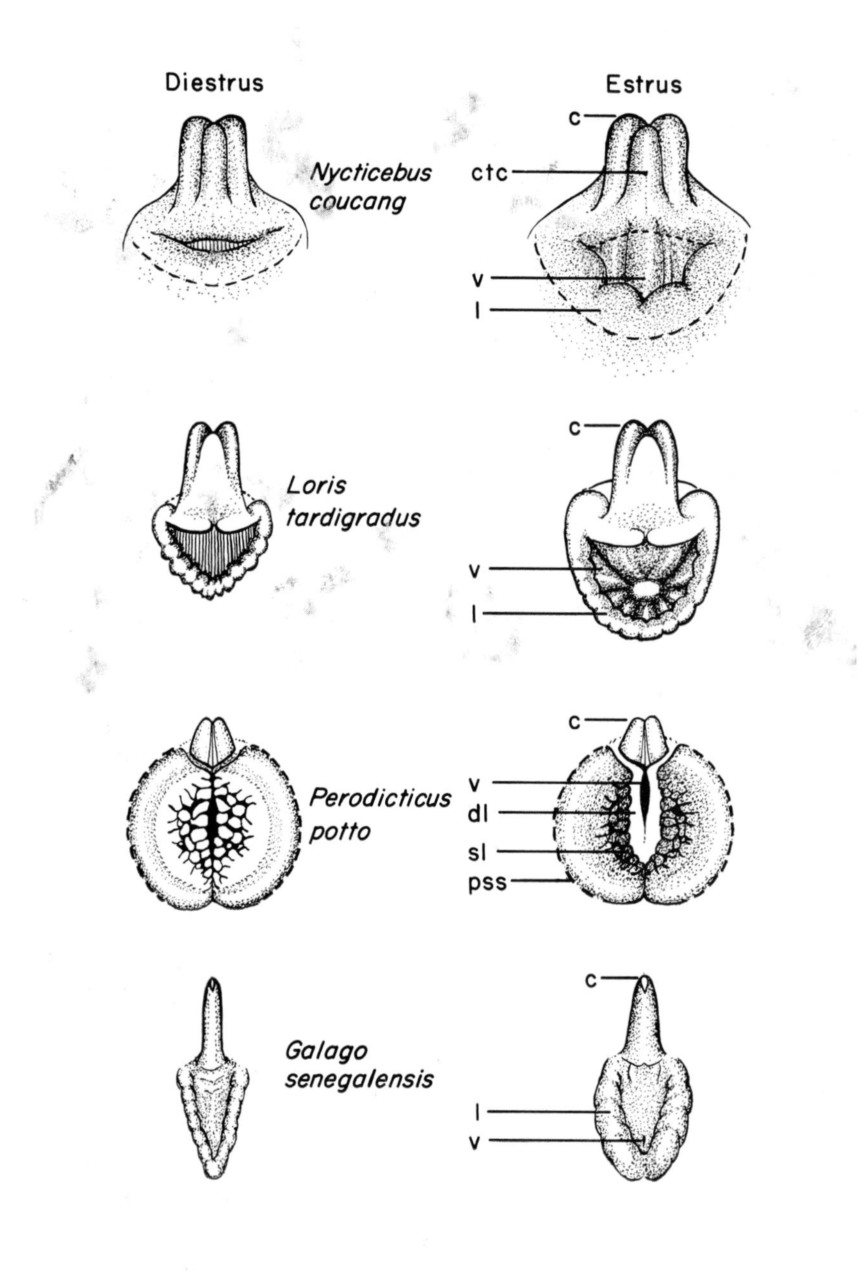

Diestrus
Estrus
Nycticebus coucang
c
ctc
v
l
Loris tardigradus
c
v
l
Perodicticus potto
c
v
dl
sl
pss
Galago senegalensis
c
l
v

croscopically and scored for relative numbers of cornified epithelial cells, young epithelial cells, leukocytes, red blood cells, and spermatozoa. Estrous smears contain maximal numbers of cornified cells but few or no young epithelial cells or leukocytes (Plate II). In *Papio* cytological changes in vaginal smears correlate with concomitant changes in the vaginal epithelium and perineum (Hendrickx, 1967). Such a correlation was not detected in *Saimiri* (Clewe, 1969). Because duration of the ovulatory phase varies, the vaginal smear, though helpful, does not afford absolute diagnosis of ovulation time in many species. For exceptions, see Petter-Rousseau (1962).

4. Cervical Mucus. The cervical mucus changes quantitatively and qualitatively during the sexual cycle (Plate II). In *M. sinica* and *M. radiata,* bad-smelling cervical mucus is discharged from the vagina during estrus. Sanguineous discharge appears in *Loris* during proestrus.

5. Mammary Glands. The mammary glands also change cyclically. During ovulatory cycles of *M. mulatta* lobules begin enlarging seven to ten days before onset of menstruation, attain maximum development about the time of menstruation, and slowly regress during the postmenstrual period. The alveoli enlarge soon after ovulation, persist in this state throughout the menstrual period, and gradually subside during the early part of the next cycle.

Figure 7-20. Semidiagrammatic representation of the female external genitalia during the diestrous interval and at full estrus in several species of lorisoid primates. In *Loris tardigradus* (slender loris) the clitoris surmounts a small triangular vaginal opening, bordered by a labium which is low, narrow, crenated and dark yellow. When fully modified at estrus, however, the vulva is greatly enlarged and the clearly exposed walls of the vaginal passage are turgid and flushed. The labium is markedly turgid and smooth, the crenated effect disappearing, and the earlier pure yellow coloration is suffused with pink. (Manley, 1966)

C clitoris
ctc central tract of clitoris
dl deep labia
l labium
pss pseudoscrotum
sl superficial labia
v vaginal opening

F. Menstruation

Menstruation is apparently absent in lemuriformes and lorisiformes, weak or absent in tarsiiformes, weak in New World monkeys, and clearly defined only in Old World monkeys, apes, and man. The *Cebus* and *Lagothrix* females have a menstrual flow which recurs at specific intervals. *Saimiri* and *Galago* females do not exhibit any menstrual flow.

The duration and intensity of the menstrual flow varies with the species. In *M. mulatta,* menstruation lasts one to ten days, with a 2.6 day mean and a two day median (Kerber and Reese, 1969). A single day of bleeding is quite common. In *Hylobates,* the endometrium remains well-preserved histologically, shows no edema or leukocytic infiltration, and bleeds sparsely. In most species of *Cebidae* menstruation is microscopic in amounts: a few red blood cells are detected every sexual cycle by intravaginal lavage. Only the lining epithelium and superficial stroma are lost. In *Cercopithecus aethiops* "microscopic menstruation" lasts for two to four days (Gartlan, 1969). Cyclical "microscopic menstruation" may be homologous with gross menstruation in other species.

1. Amenorrhea. Amenorrhea, the lack or interruption of menstrual cycles, is of two types: primary, in which menstrual cycles never begin; and secondary, in which the cycles cease to occur. Little is known about primary amenorrhea in nonhuman primates. Secondary amenorrhea is common in all species of primates including man. Pubertal and young mature *M. mulatta* do not ovulate regularly, and in fully adult females the long menstrual cycles of the summer months are considered anovulatory. Even during the breeding season, some 10 to 30 percent of mature *M. mulatta* ovulate so rarely as to be virtually sterile.

Secondary amenorrhea may result from hypothalamic, nutritional, hormonal, or nonspecific causes. Hypothalamic factors involve neural control of pituitary releasing factors. Cessation of menses resulting from malnutrition may be due to hypopituitaryism or stress, e.g. in recently shipped or captive monkeys. A deficiency of high quality protein may lead, in certain cases, to a reduction in the amino acids necessary for synthesis of gonadotropic hormones.

2. *Evolutionary Aspects.* Since *Tupaia* (tree shrew) show many primate as well as insectivore affinities, they used to be classified in the suborder *Prosimii* of the primates rather than within *Insectivora* (Le Gros Clark, 1963). Conaway and Sorenson (1966) hypothesized that the menstrual cycle of primates is derived from modifications that occurred in the *Tupaia* reproductive cycle. However, the uterine structure and placentation of *Tupaia* would seem to contradict this hypothesis.

Tupaia exhibit many unique specializations and such apparently primitive characteristics as urethra and vagina not separate; urogenital sinus present; testes prepenial in male; vagina always open to exterior via urogenital sinus; offspring of nidicolous type; little maternal care; no grooming of the infant; and fast growth rate of infants. Specializations probably unique to *Tupaia* include the following: placentation of obligate bidiscoid, endotheliochorial type; implantation of specialized placentary cushions; and unusual pattern of maternal care, with infants left in separate nest and suckled only rarely (once per forty eight hr. in *Tupaia belangeri*) (R. D. Martin, personal communication).

3. *Cyclical Changes in Endometrium.* A diagrammatic illustration of the estrogenic and luteal phases during the menstrual cycle of primates and the estrous cycle of other mammals is shown in Figure 7-21. The cyclical changes occurring in the endometrium during menstruation are shown in Figure 7-22. Progressive changes occur in the stroma and the uterine gland epithelium and its secretion. Presence and degree of endometrial collapse at menstruation vary with species. The uterine epithelium is restored several days after menstruation. Progestational changes become evident a few days after ovulation.

4. *Physiological Mechanisms.* The physiological mechanisms involved in menstruation are not fully understood and several hypotheses have been developed. Hisaw and Hisaw (1961) summarized one of these hypotheses as follows. Menstruation is associated with extensive and rapid regression of the endometrium due to loss of ground substance from the stroma. The rapid regression causes disproportion between the length of the spiral arteries and the thickness of the endometrium, and coiling increases. The increased coiling shuts off the blood supply to the endometrium, and

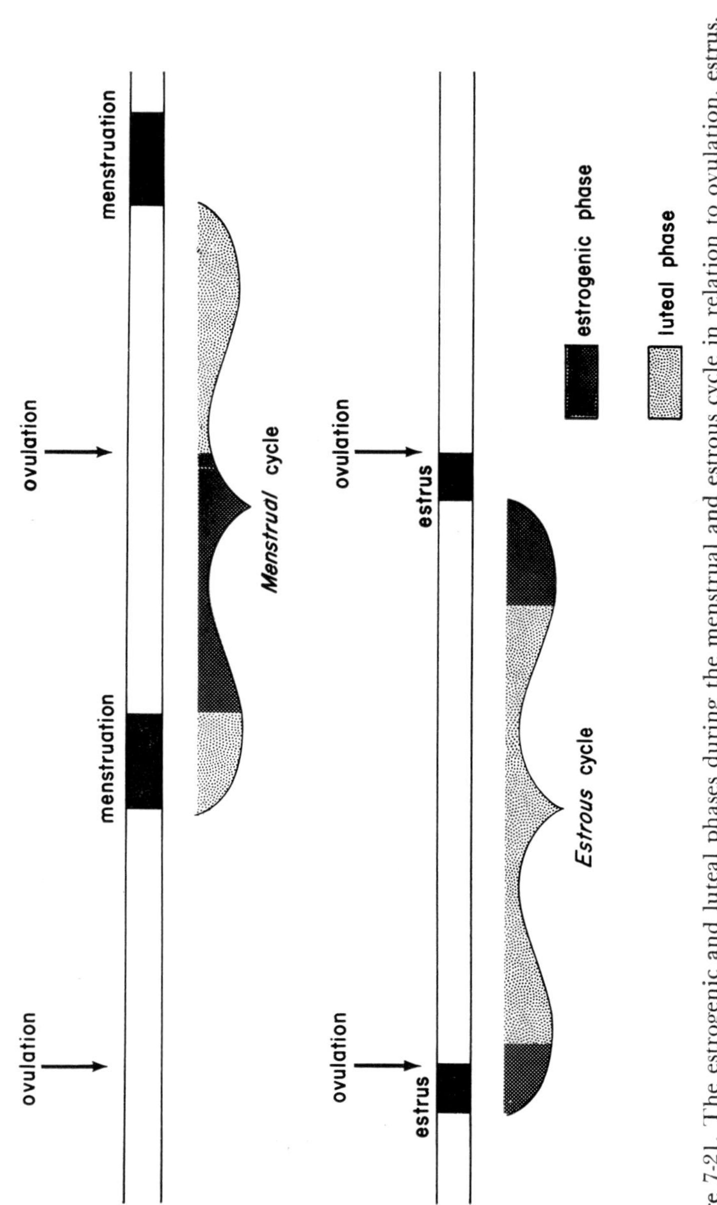

Figure 7-21. The estrogenic and luteal phases during the menstrual and estrous cycle in relation to ovulation, estrus, and menstruation.

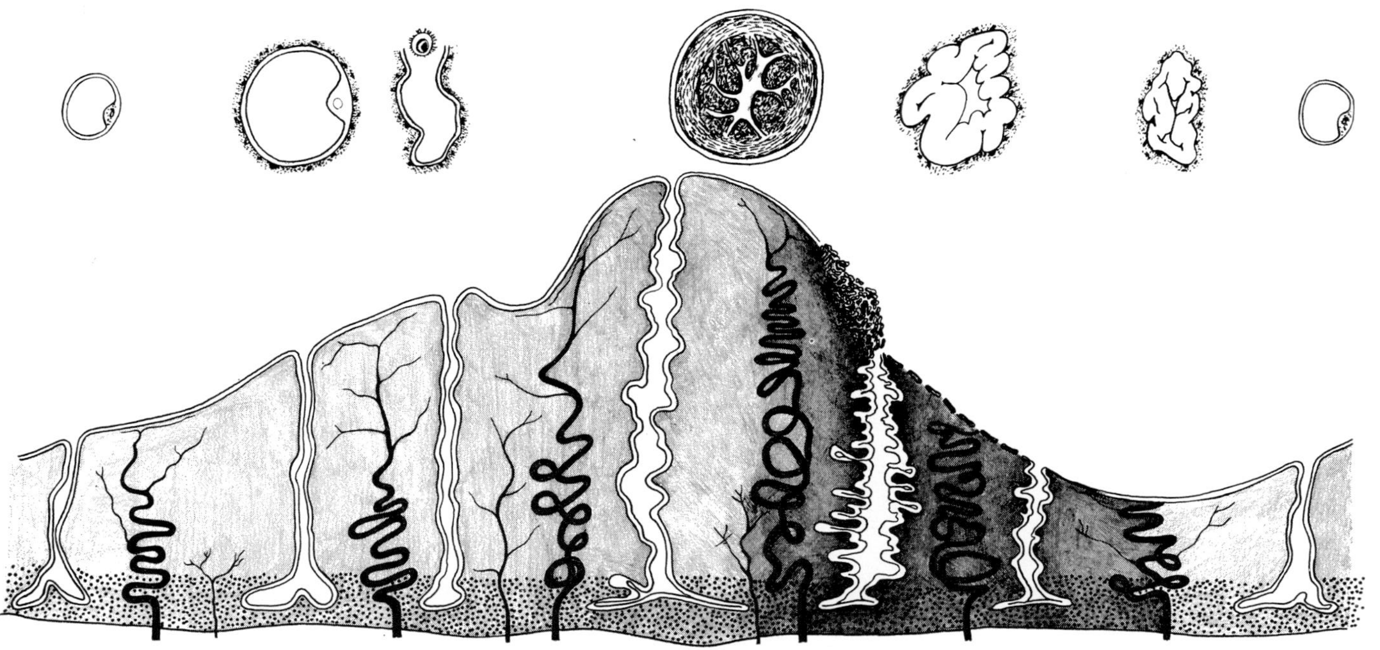

Figure 7-22. A diagram indicating the changes in ovary and endometrium during an ovulatory cycle of rhesus monkey. Thickness of endometrium, density of stroma, form of endometrial gland, and three types of arteries are indicated. Endometrial thickness increases gradually up to the time of ovulation. The progestational phase is followed by loss of ground substance from the stroma, which is the primary cause of premenstrual regression during the ischemic phase. Regression is a prelude to extravasation and shedding of endometrial tissue. During repair, the endometrium thickens due to increase in stromal ground substance and growth of glands. (Adapted from Bartelmez, 1957; Hisaw and Hisaw, 1961)

necrosis of endometrial tissue results. The uterine epithelium is sloughed off and several endometrial layers are shed. The process is set off by the sudden withdrawal of a supporting hormonal stimulus, which in turn causes metabolic changes in the stromal connective tissue of the endometrium.

Markee (1940) transplanted segments of endometrium to the anterior chamber of the eye for direct observation under several hormonal conditions. The spiral arteries coiled one to three days before bleeding. Markee postulated that local anoxemia leads to necrosis of tissue and bleeding. This theory does not explain menstruation in species lacking coiled vessels. Also, experimental ischemia or destruction of coiled vessels does not lead to menstruation.

In menstruating species, the nonpregnant females menstruate when the corpus luteum is regressing and progesterone levels are decreasing. This relationship is referred to as the "estrogen-progesterone withdrawal" theory of menstruation. If estrogen and progesterone are administered to intact females and progesterone is then withdrawn, bleeding follows, even though estrogen given alone prevents uterine bleeding. If estrogen is administered to ovariectomized monkeys and then abruptly discontinued, uterine bleeding ensues. Ovariectomy also precipitates menstrual flow within one to two days. Thus menstruation appears to be caused by the absence of one or both ovarian hormones. If exogenous progesterone or estrogen is withdrawn gradually, however, no bleeding ensues; the endometrium then becomes progestational, to support implantation.

In some species menstruation may be due to the action of catabolites formed when the hormones that support uterine metabolism are withdrawn. In such species, the catabolites cannot be fully eliminated because uterine lymphatic channels are few or absent. Remaining *in situ,* the catabolites continue to cause tissue destruction until the endometrium is shed down to the area maintained by the capillary bed and the basal arterioles. Nonmenstruating primate species have more uterine lymphatic channels than menstruating species, a fact which lends support to this hypothesis.

IV. CONCLUDING REMARKS

It is apparent that detailed information concerning the reproductive cycle of nonhuman primates is very limited for most species and nonexistent for others. Little is known about the extent of male and female breeding seasons in several common laboratory species. Further comparative research is needed to understand the physiological and endocrine mechanisms of menstruation, and the physiological and psychological aspects of primary and secondary amenorrhea under laboratory conditions. Such studies may be relevant to problems of human infertility.

REFERENCES

Bartelmez, G. W. (1957): The phases of the menstrual cycle and their interpretation in terms of the pregnancy cycle. *Amer J Obstet Gynec, 74,* 931-955.

Betteridge, K. J., Kelly, W. A., and Marston, J. H. (1970): Morphology of the Rhesus monkey ovary near the time of ovulation. *J Reprod Fertil, 22,* 453-459.

Brown, J. B. (1959): Estrogen excretion in normal and abnormal menstrual cycles. In Lloyd, C. W. (Ed.): *Endocrinology of Reproduction.* New York, Academic Press, pp. 53-65.

Butler, H. (1967a): Seasonal breeding of the Senegal Galago (*Galago senegalensis senegalensis*) in the Nuba Mountains, Republic of The Sudan. *Folia Primat, 5,* 165-175.

Butler, H. (1967a): The oestrus cycle of the Senegal bush baby (*Galago senegalensis senegalensis*) in the Sudan. *J Zool London, 151,* 143-162.

Buxton, C. L. (1951): Discussion of Seigler, S. L., and Seigler, A. M.: Evaluation of the basal body temperature. An analysis of 1012 basal body temperature recordings. *Fertil Steril, 2,* 287-301.

Clark, W. E. Le Gros (1963): The antecedents of man. Edinburgh, University Press, p. 388.

Clewe, T. H. (1969): Observations on reproduction of squirrel monkeys in captivity. *J Reprod Fertil (Suppl), 6,* 151-156.

Conaway, C. H., and Sorenson, M. W. (1966): Reproduction in tree shrews. In *Comparative Biology of Reproduction in Mammals* (Symposia of the Zoological Society of London, No. 15). London, Academic Press.

David, G. F. X., and Ramaswami, L. S. (1969): Studies on menstrual cycle and other related phenomenon in the langur (*Presbytis entellus entellus*). *Folia Primat, 11,* 300-316.

David, G. F. X., and Rao, C. A. P. (1969): Ovulation and the serum protein changes during ovulation in *Presbytis entellus entellus* Dufresne. *Gen Comp Endocr (Suppl), 2,* 197-202.

Dempsey, E. W. (1939): The reproductive cycle of new world monkeys. *Amer J Anat, 3,* 381-405.

Doyle, G. A.; Pelletier, A., and Bekker, T. (1967): Courtship, mating and parturition in the lesser bushbaby (*Galago senegalensis moholi*) under seminatural conditions. *Folia Primat, 7,* 169-197.

Du Mond, F. V., and Hutchinson, T. C. (1967): Squirrel monkey reproduction: The "Fatted" Male phenomenon and seasonal spermatogenesis. *Science, 158,* 1467-1470.

Elder, J. H., and Yerkes, R. M. (1936): The sexual cycle of the chimpanzee. *Anat Rec, 67,* 119-143.

Garcia, C. R., and Rock, J. (1958): Ovulation. In Veraldo, J. T. (Ed.): *Essentials of Human Reproduction.* New York, Oxford Press, p. 22.

Gartlan, J. S. (1959): Sexual and maternal behaviour of the vervet monkey, *Cercopithecus aethiops. J Reprod Fertil (Suppl), 6,* 137-150.

Gillman, J., and Gilbert, C. (1946): The reproductive cycle of the chacma baboon (*Papio ursinus*) with special reference to the problem of menstrual irregularities as assessed by the behavior of the sex skin. *S Afr J Med Sci, 11,* 1-54.

Gillman, T.; Pillay, R. A., and Naidoo, S. S. (1960): Serum muco-protein, plasma, fibrin and fibrinolytic activity during the menstrual cycle in baboons. *J Endocr, 19,* 303-309.

Hampton, J. K., Jr., and Hampton, S. H. (1965): Marmosets (*Hapalidae*): Breeding seasons, twinning, and sex of offspring. *Science, 150,* 915-917.

Hendrickx, A. G. (1967): The menstrual cycles of the baboon as determined by vaginal smear, vaginal biopsy, and perineal swelling. In Vagtborg, H. (Ed.): *The Baboon in Medical Research,* Austin, University of Texas Press, vol. 2, p. 437.

Hendrickx, A. G., and Kraemer, D. C. (1969): Observations on the menstrual cycle, optimal mating time and pre-implantation embryos of the baboon, *papio anubis* and *papio cynocephalus. J Reprod Fertil (Suppl), 6,* 119-128.

Hendrickx, A. G., and Kraemer, D. C. (1970): Primates. In Hafez, E. S. E. (Ed.): *Reproduction and Breeding Techniques for Laboratory Animals.* Philadelphia, Lea & Febiger, Chapter 18.

Hisaw, F. L., and Hisaw, F. L., Jr. (1961): Action of estrogen and progesterone on the reproductive tract of lower primates. In Young, W. C. (Ed.): *Sex and Internal Secretions.* Baltimore, Williams and Wilkins vol. I, Chapter 18, pp. 556-589.

Ioannou, J. M. (1966): The oestrous cycle of the potto. *J Reprod Fertil, 11,* 455-457.

Jay, P. C. (1963a): The Indian langur monkey (*Presbytis entellus*). In Southwick, C. H. (Ed.): *Primate Social Behavior.* Princeton, Van Nostrand, pp. 114-123.

Jay, P. C. (1963b): Mother-infant relation in free-ranging langurs. In Reingold, H. L. (Ed.): *Maternal Behaviour in Mammals.* New York, John Wiley & Sons, pp. 284-304.

Jay, P. C. (1965): The common langur of North India. In DeVore, I. (Ed.): *Primate Behaviour.* New York, Holt, Rinehart & Winston, pp. 197-249.

Johansson, E. D. B.; Neill, J. D., and Knobil, E. (1968): Periovulatory progesterone concentration in the peripheral plasma of the rhesus monkey with a methodologic note on the detection of ovulation. *Endocrinology, 82,* 143-148.

Joly, A. (1966): *Lemur Behavior, a Madagascar Field Study*. Chicago, University of Chicago Press.

Kawai, M.; Azuma, S., and Yoshiba, K. (1967): Ecological studies of reproduction in Japanese monkeys (*Macaca fuscata*). I. Problems of the birth season. *Primates, 8,* 35-74.

Kerber, W. T., and Reese, W. H. (1969): Comparison of the menstrual cycle of Cynomulgus and Rhesus monkeys. *Fertil Steril, 20,* 975-979.

Kriewaldt, F. H., and Hendrickx, A. G. (1968): Reproductive parameters of the baboon. *Lab Anim Care, 18,* 361-370.

MacRoberts, M., and MacRoberts, B. (1966): The annual reproductive cycle of the barbary apes in Gibraltar. *Amer J Phys Anthro,* p. *25,* 299-303.

Manley, G. H. (1966): Reproduction in lorisoid primates. In *Comparative Biology of Reproduction in Mammals,* Symposia of the Zoological Society of London, No. 15. London, Academic Press.

Markee, J. E. (1940): Menstruation in intraocular endometrial transplants in the rhesus monkey. *Cont Embryol Carnegie Inst Washington, 28,* 219-308.

Michael, R. P.; Herbert, J., and Welegalla, J. (1966): Ovarian hormones and grooming behaviour in the rhesus monkey (*Macaca mulatta*) under laboratory conditions. *J. Endocr, 36,* 263-279.

Michael, R. P., and Welegalla, J. (1968): Ovarian hormones and the sexual behaviour of the female rhesus monkey (*Macaca mulatta*) under laboratory conditions. *J Endocr, 41,* 407-420.

Montagna, W. (1962): The skin of lemurs. *Ann NY Acad Sci, 102,* 190-209.

Naidoo, S. S., and Baitera, B. (1970): Effects of menstrual cycle and sex hormones on γ-glucuronidase and γ-acetylglucosaminidase activities in the baboon sex-skin. *Endocrinology,* in press.

Napier, J. R., and Napier, P. H. (1967): *A Handbook of Living Primates.* New York, Academic Press.

Noyes, R. W.; Hertig, A. T., and Rock, J. (1950): Dating the endometrial biopsy. *Fertil Steril, 1,* 3-25.

Petter-Rousseaux, A. (1962): Recherches sur la biologie des primates inférieurs. *Mammalia, 26 (Suppl),* 1-88.

Petter-Rousseaux, A. (1964): Reproductive physiology and behaviour of the *Lemuroidea.* In Buettner-Janusch, J.: *Evolutionary and Genetic Biology of Primates,* New York, Academic Press, vol. II, pp. 91-132.

Prakash, I. (1962): Group organization, sexual behaviour and breeding season of certain Indian monkeys. *Jap J Ecol, 12,* 83-86.

Ramakrishna, P. A., and Prasad, M. R. N. (1967): Changes in the male reproductive organs of *Loris tardigradus lydekkerianus* (Cabrera). *Folia Primat, 5,* 176-189.

Ramaswami, L. S., and Anand Kumar, T. C. (1962): Reproductive cycle of the slender loris. *Naturwissenschaften, 5,* 115-116.

Ramaswami, L. S., and Anand Kumar, T. C. (1965): Some aspects of reproduction of the female slender loris, *Loris tardigradus lydekkerianus.* Cabr. *Acta Zool, 46,* 257-273.

Riley, G. M.; Dontas, E., and Gill, B. (1955): Use of the serial vaginal smears in detecting the time of ovulation. *Fertil Steril, 6,* 86-102.

Rock, J. (1959): Discussion of Brown, J. B.: Estrogen excretion in normal and abnormal menstrual cycles. In Lloyd, C. W. (Ed.): *Endocrinology of Reproduction,* New York, Academic Press, pp. 53-65.

Rosenblum, L. A. (1969): Some aspects of female reproductive physiology in the squirrel monkey. In Rosenblum, L. A., and Cooper, R. W.: *The Squirrel Monkey*. New York, Academic Press, chap. 5.

Rowell, T. E. (1966): Female reproductive cycles and the behaviour of baboons and rhesus macaques. In Altman, S. (Ed.): *Social Communication in Primates.* Chicago, University Press, pp. 15-32.

Rowell, T. E. (1968): Grooming by adult baboons in relation to reproductive cycles. *Anim Behav, 16,* 585-588.

Rowell, T. E. (1969): Intra-sexual behavior and female reproductive cycles of baboons (*Papio anubis*). *Anim Behav, 17,* 159-167.

Sade, D. St. (1964): Seasonal cycle in size of testis of free ranging *Macaca mulatta. Folio Primat, 2,* 171-180.

Southwick, C. H.; Beg, M. A., and Siddiqi, M. R. (1961): A population survey of rhesus monkeys in Northern India. II. Transportation routes and forest areas. *Ecology, 42,* 699-7.

Sugiyama, Y.; Yoshiba, K., and Parthasarathy, M. D. (1965): Home range, mating season, male group and inter-troop relations in Hanuman langurs (*Presbytis entellus*). *Primates, 6,* 73-106.

Tomlin, M. I. (1940): Menstrual bleeding & genital swelling in *Miopithecus* (*Cercopithecus*) *talapoin. Proc Zool Soc London, 110,* 43-45.

Vandenbergh, J. G., and Vessey, S. (1968): Seasonal breeding of free-ranging rhesus monkeys and related ecological factors. *J Reprod Fertil, 15,* 71-79.

Washburn, S. L., and Hamburg, D. A. (1965): The study of primate behavior. In De Vore, I. (Ed.): *Primate Behavior.* New York, Holt, Rinehart & Winston, pp. 1-15.

Yerkes, R. M., and Elder, J. H. (1936): Oestrus, receptivity and mating in chimpanzee. *Comp Psychol Monogr, 13,* 1-39.

Zuckerman, S. (1930): The menstrual cycle of the primates. I. General nature and homology. *Proc Zool Soc London,* 691-754.

Zuckerman, S. (1937): The duration and phases of the menstrual cycle in primates. *Proc Zool Soc London, 107,* 315-329.

Zuckerman, S., and Fulton, J. F. (1934): The menstrual cycle of the primates. VII. *J Anat London, 69,* 38-46.

Zuckerman, S., and Parkes, S. A. (1952): The menstrual cycle of the primates. V. *Proc Zool Soc London, 102,* 139-191.

Chapter 8

PATTERNS OF REPRODUCTIVE BEHAVIOR

R. P. MICHAEL AND D. ZUMPE

THIS chapter deals with the patterns of copulatory behavior shown by a large range of primate species. There are wide gaps in our knowledge and the picture is necessarily incomplete. Only passing mention is made of primate social organization and of associated behavioral patterns such as mutual grooming and aggression, although reproductive behavior is invariably set in the context of communication with conspecifics. The taxonomy and nomenclature used in this chapter are those of Napier and Napier (1967), and certain familiar species are named accordingly. For instance, *Hapale jacchus* appears as *Callithrix jacchus; Alouatta palliata* appears as *A. villosa; Macaca irus* appears as *M. fascicularis; M. speciosa* appears as *M. arctoides;* and *Miopithecus talapoin* appears as *Cercopithecus talapoin*. Finally, because of the pressing conservation problem now posed by the Great Apes and the need to restrict their use in laboratory work, only passing mention is made of their patterns of reproductive behavior.

I. PROSIMIANS

A. Treeshrews: Tupaiidae

Although recent work questions whether treeshrews should be classified as primates, for the present purpose we are treating them as such: however, their taxonomy remains confused, and some seventy to eighty subspecies are recognized at present. Although widely distributed throughout Southeast Asia, most information on their behavior and social organization has been obtained in the laboratory (Conaway and Sorenson, 1966; Sorenson and Conaway, 1968; Martin, 1968). With the possible exception of the mountain treeshrew, *Tupaia montana,* there is circumstantial evidence that the basic social unit consists of an adult male and female together with their young. In the treeshrew, *T. glis belangeri,* breeding successes are achieved when animals are maintained in a male-female pair in large cages (2 meter^3), each provided with up to four nest boxes. Under optimal conditions of housing and diet, aggression does not present a serious problem, and in both England and Germany females produce up to seven litters a year, each of two young.

Typically, females of this genus exhibit a postpartum estrus lasting from three to twenty-four hours and, as gestation is between forty-five and fifty days, this is approximately the interval between heats. In the few days before parturition, the male shows increased sexual interest, follows the female, nuzzles her and licks her genitalia. At this time the female reacts aggressively to the male's mounting attempts, only becoming fully receptive when parturition has been completed. Receptive females make short, darting runs which maintain a distance of 0.5 to 1.0 meter between her and the pursuing male. The male licks the female's vulva which is exposed by a marked tail deflection, mounts, and takes a grip with his jaws on the fur of the female's neck. The forelimbs are placed round the female's haunches and, following intromission, for which a female lordosis response is necessary, there is a series of pelvic thrusts terminating in ejaculation. After dismounting, each animal grooms its genitalia, and there may be a dozen intromissions, each with ejaculation, during the period of estrus. As estrus terminates and receptivity declines, agonistic exchanges recur, apparently because the female remains attractive to the male for some time. Other reproductive behaviors of treeshrews include a stereotyped courtship "dance" of the predominantly terrestrial *T. tana:* during this the male circles and stamps before the female uttering a characteristic vocalization. In captivity, the estrous females of several species not infrequently mount males and other females and execute pelvic thrusts; the bisexual behavior patterns are reminiscent of those seen in rats and guinea pigs. In the absence of fertile postpartum mating the female of *T. glis longipes,* of *T. tana* and of *T. montana,* shows periods of receptivity at intervals either of none to twelve days which probably represents the basic cycle length, or of twenty to twenty-nine days which possibly corresponds to the duration of pseudopregnancy. There is a further cycle of thirty to forty days which may be related to the period of fetal resorption. Data from animals housed in groups are difficult to interpret because of the high incidence of aggression, pseudopregnancy, embryonic resorption and abortion. It has been suggested that treeshrews ovulate reflexly, but data on this and on the existence of a vaginal cycle are sparse. There is some evidence for a seasonal effect on the breeding of captive treeshrews in the United States, and in both *T. glis* and *T. g. longipes* birth peaks occur in summer: in contrast, no breeding seasonality was observed in *T. g. belangeri* in Germany. In Malaya, mean testicular weights of *T. glis* and *T. minor* are highest in summer: 1.60 g and 0.54 g for April-June compares with 0.81 g and 0.20 g for October-December in these two species respectively (Harrison, 1955).

B. Lemurs: Lemuridae

Field studies in Madagascar, to which the *Lemuridae* are confined (Petter, 1965; Jolly, 1966), have shown that their social organization varies widely with the different genera. *Phaner, Microcebus* and *Cheirogaleus* have a loose organization, *Lemur variegatus* and *Hapalemur griseus* are generally found in family groups, while *L. macaco, L. catta, L. mongoz* and *L. rubiventer* occur in well-organized troops comprising several adult males and females with their young. In captivity, breeding successes are few, but at least thirteen births have been recorded in the mouse lemur, *Microcebus murinus,* in which gestation is from fifty-nine to sixty-two days with usually two young per litter: this compares with a gestation period of at least seventy days in the dwarf lemur, *Cheirogaleus major,* for which there are no data on breeding success. Both forms are seasonally polyestrous, the cycle length is forty-five to fifty-five and thirty days respectively with a one to three day estrus in each case (Petter-Rousseaux, 1964). During estrus the vulva swells, reddens and becomes patent, at other times, closure is complete. There is a vaginal cycle in both forms, with cornified cells predominating during estrus, and a metestrous leucocytic infiltration. There are no good descriptions of the mating behavior of *M. murinus.* In *C. major,* the male mounts the female, which usually lies with her belly to the branch, by holding her with his forelimbs and grasping her ankles with his feet; he waves his tail rapidly, and licks the female's flanks and neck while uttering a warbling vocalization. Mounts last two to three minutes and are repeated several times at ten minute intervals, but the numbers of intromissions and ejaculations have not been reported. Mating in *Microcebus* follows a closely similar pattern to that of *Cheirogaleus* (Martin, personal communication).

Given large cages (3 meter^3) and adequate diet, lemurs breed in captivity without difficulty and over seventy births are on record. Gestation is between 131 to 136 days in the ring-tailed lemur, *L. catta,* and between 120 to 135 days in the black lemur, *L. macaco macaco* and *L. m. fulvus:* in these species, one offspring is produced annually. Captive female ring-tailed lemurs have two estrous cycles of thirty-three to forty-five days duration during the breeding season, and three periods of vaginal estrus lasting three to five days: coincident with maximal cornification, there is a two to ten hr. period of sexual receptivity (Evans and Goy, 1968). As the breeding season approaches there is a marked increase in the aggression between the males of the troop. Whereas intratroop aggression is generally low and restricted to staring and pushing or cuffing with high squeaking "spat" calls, with the approach of mating the frequency and intensity of aggression between males increases. Vigorous chasing and fighting ensues, the males slashing at each other with their canines. Increased aggression is associated with increased marking behavior, particularly with hands and tail: the palms of the hands are rubbed vigorously on branches and the tail is pulled down between the arm and chest, past their brachial and antebrachial glands. Males face each other and wave their scented tails at each other by curving them over their heads; the so-called "stink fights." Both males and females also mark by standing on their hands and rubbing the anogenital region against branches, but there is no apparent increase in marking frequency by females in the breeding season. Females become attractive to males before they become receptive; males follow, investigate and lick the females' genitalia, attempting to mount instead of grooming. Nonreceptive females respond by striking at the male which does not retaliate. Receptive females move only a short distance away from the male, and then adopt one of two receptive postures:

either they present the anogenital region to the male with hind legs fully extended and tail forward, or they crouch and show lordosis. In estrous females, lordosis can be elicited, as in rodents, by manual stimulation of the lumbar region and perineum. The male mounts by wrapping his arms round the female's waist and gripping the female's hind legs with his feet; sometimes the male's feet remain on the ground or branch. There are from two to seven episodes of pelvic thrusting during a mount, each of three to five thrusts, and intromission occurs during the final few episodes of thrusting. Ejaculation is associated with a pause and marked quivering by the male. The mating sequence lasts two to three minutes and thereafter each partner self-grooms intensively, the genital region particularly. Several ejaculations may occur during the several hours that the female is receptive. In the wild, however, males frequently interrupt their copulation in order to chase away other males, and the interacting pair generally tend to become isolated from the rest of the troop, forming a consort pair for a few hours. However, females may mate with several males during the period of estrus. Postcopulatory vaginal plugs have been described in *L. catta, L. m. fulvus* and *L. mongoz.* In the *Lemuridae,* breeding is strictly seasonal: in *M. murinus,* mating occurs from September-February, in *L. m. macaco, L. m. fulvus, L. mongoz, L. rubiventer* and *L. catta,* from April-June, and in the sportive lemur, *Lepilemur mustelinus,* from May-July (Petter-Rousseaux, 1964; Petter, 1965; Jolly, 1966). Transportation to Europe results in a five to six month shift in the mating season in all species studied to date.

C. *Sifakas, Indris, Avahis, Aye-aye: Indridae, Daubentonidae*

The *Indridae* and *Daubentonidae,* like the *Lemuridae,* are restricted to Madagascar: little is known of their reproductive physiology and behavior. The diurnal sifaka, *Propithecus,* and indris, *Indri,* and the nocturnal avahi, *Avahi,* are found either in family groups or in larger territorial troops. The nocturnal aye-aye, *Daubentonia madagascariensis,* is thought to be solitary and territorial (Petter, 1965; Jolly, 1966). In both families, breeding in captivity has not to date been successful. Verreaux's sifaka, *Propithecus verreauxi,* appears to be seasonally polyestrous, with four to six week cycles between January-March, and a gestation period of about five months. In the field, births have been observed in August in both *Avahi* and *Indri*.

D. Bushbabies, Lorises, Pottos, etc.: Lorisidae

The *Lorisidae* are widely distributed: *Galago, Perodicticus* and *Arctocebus* in Africa, *Loris* in Ceylon and South India, and *Nycticebus* in India and Southeast Asia. *Galago* is social, whereas the others are thought to be pair-living or solitary. All lorisoid primates are nocturnal, and most information has come from studies in captivity (Buettner-Janusch, 1964; Manley, 1966, 1967; Ramakrishna and Prasad, 1967; Ioannou, 1966; Butler, 1967; Doyle, Pelletier and Bekker, 1967). For bushbabies, *Galago,* there are well over thirty successful pregnancies on record, generally with one to two young per litter: breeding in captivity is not difficult provided that adequate cages of about 1 meter^3 are used. Gestation is 122 to 125 days in *Galago senegalensis moholi,* 144 to 146 days in *G. s. senegalensis,* and 130 to 135 days in the thick-tailed galago, *G. crassicaudatus.* The estrous cycle is twenty-nine to thirty-nine days in *G. senegalensis;* estrus is marked by swelling and flushing of the external genitalia and vaginal opening, and vaginal smears are fully cornified for seven to ten days in *G. s. senegalensis.* The female *G. s. moholi,* observed under reversed light cycles, is receptive for one to three days; data for the duration of estrus in the other species and subspecies are lacking. In a captive colony of *G. s. moholi* in South Africa, one of three males was dominant, and the females only associated with this male. Males show fairly constant sexual interest in females throughout the year, follow them, and attempt to examine their genitalia. This is frequently associated with marking; the male urinating into his cupped hand and rubbing the foot in the hand. Except during estrus, females do not allow males to make contact with their genitalia, and either jump away or threaten. At the start of estrus, when the vulva opens, there is a white vaginal discharge, and male interest and marking behavior increase conspicuously. The male follows the female closely, making a low clucking call, and mounts by wrapping his arms round her waist, pressing his chin into the nape of her neck, generally keeping his feet on a branch, but sometimes grasping the female's legs with his feet. Mounts may last up to seven minutes, and intromission and ejaculation probably occur only during these long mounts: when mounted and thrusting, the male makes a loud call, terminating in a whistle and, at the termination of the mount, remains motionless for about two minutes before dismounting. There is then a postcopulatory period of genital self-grooming by each animal. Females become receptive and mate from March onwards. In July-September, at the end of the four month gestation period, females commonly exhibit a postpartum estrus, giving birth again in November-January. This second pregnancy of the year is not followed by a postpartum estrus which is delayed until the following March. Breeding is therefore seasonal with two litters a year. In the Sudan, *G. s. senegalensis* has mating peaks in November-January and again in August, with birth peaks in March-June and in December. There is no evidence for seasonal breeding in captive *G. crassicaudatus crassicaudatus* and in *G. c. argentatus* in the northern hemisphere.

Breeding in captivity is difficult in the remaining *Lorisidae,* and only twenty to thirty births are on record for the four genera. On the basis of one to three pregnancies in each case in the London Zoo, gestation is 131 to 136 days in the angwantibo, *Arctocebus calabarensis,* 193 days in the slow loris, *Nycticebus coucang,* and 160 to 166 days in the slender loris, *Loris tardigradus:* that for the potto, *Perdicticus potto,* in Gabon is 193 days. In all genera, one young per litter appears to be the rule. Lorisoid primates are polyestrous. The external genitalia swell and flush at thirty-six to forty-five day intervals in *A. calabarensis,* at thirty-seven to forty-four day intervals in *N. coucang,* and at thrity-four to forty-seven day intervals in *P. potto:* vaginal estrus in this latter species is from 1 to 2.5 days (Ioannou, 1966). The estrous female of the slow-moving lorisoids (slow loris, slender loris, potto, angwantibo) suspends herself upside down beneath a branch; this appears to be the receptive posture because when in this position the male investigates her genitalia, then "mounts" by clambering beneath the female so that copulation takes place with both members of the pair upside down (Manley, personal communication). Behavioral estrus is relatively short, in the case of the angwantibo only a few hours: there is a single ejaculation and a large, visible copulatory plug that rapidly hardens into the consistency of firm wax and may account for the lack of any subsequent intromissions. In the potto, spermatozoa are found almost exclusively in the vaginal smears of estrous females, indicating that in this species, as in *G. s. moholi,* copulation is restricted largely to the female's short period of estrus. There is no clear evidence for seasonal breeding in *Arctocebus, Nycticebus* or *Perodicticus.* However, the female *L. tardigradus* comes into full estrus only twice a year, in the winter and late summer, separated by a 5.5 month period of anestrus. There are no seasonal changes in testicular weight or in seminiferous tubule diameter in male *L. t. lyddekerianus* in India, but there is a peak in the weight of seminal vesicles and accessory glands in May (Ramakrishna and Prasad, 1967).

E. Tarsiers: Tarsiidae

Tarsiers are found, generally in pairs, in Southeast Asia. They are difficult to breed in captivity: one female had two births in twelve years but neither infant survived. Gestation is about six months with one young per litter (Napier and Napier, 1967). The female's external genitalia swell regularly, and about four days after the start of genital swelling there is maximal cornification of the vaginal smear. This lasts twenty-four hours and recurs at a mean interval of 23.5 days (Catchpole and Fulton, 1943). In a pair of captive animals (Harrison, 1963), sexual activity was associated with vocalization and self-grooming by both the male and the female, and with increased urine marking by the male, which repeatedly approached the female from below in attempts to lick her genitalia. The only observed copulation followed after the female had caught some prey. She was chased very rapidly by the male which then approached her from below, wrapped his arms round her waist and copulated for nearly two minutes. The female then jumped away and resumed eating the prey, while the male remained sitting and self-grooming for some time before sleeping for several hours. Little is known about any possible seasonal breeding; however, vaginal cycles are reported to be absent between late August and early November.

II. NEW WORLD MONKEYS

A. Marmosets, Tamarins: Callithricidae

The marmosets and tamarins of South America live in small, territorial family troops. In the wild, the red-handed tamarin, *Sa-*

guinus midas, is found in groups of two to seven individuals showing territorial defence (Thorington, 1968). Within a group of captive animals, a male and female each asserts its dominance over the other adults of its sex, but remains tolerant of juveniles (Epple, 1967, 1970; Christen, 1968). Marmosets breed quite readily in captivity. Gestation is between 140 to 150 days, and there are one to three young per litter. There are no visible external signs of estrus and data on the estrous cycle are lacking, but they are thought to be polyestrous. Captive male common marmosets, *Callithrix jacchus,* follow and show sexual interest in the female three days after parturition, and fertile matings occur when the female is receptive during a period of about ten days starting seven to ten days after parturition. Fertile matings have been described in captive female pygmy marmosets, *Cebuella pygmaea,* within three months of parturition, when they are still lactating. In groups containing more than one adult of each sex, all the adults mate, but most copulations are between the dominant pair. The two dominant animals frequently interfere when the partner attempts to copulate with a subordinate. In the common marmoset, copulation is preceded by a courtship display in which the male and female follow one another with backs arched and arms and legs fully extended; this activity is associated with marked piloerection. The display is frequently interrupted by scent marking when both the male and the female drag their glandular anogenital regions along a branch and deposit a few drops of urine. The male approaches the female, lip smacking and rapidly moving the tongue in and out of his mouth. The receptive female crouches and makes identical tongue movements at the male, their tongues frequently make contact. The animals rapidly lick each other's faces and genitalia, the male then mounts the crouching female, grasps the hair of her waist and makes seven to ten rapid, intromitted pelvic thrusts terminating in ejaculation; the lingual gestures are continued throughout. In Geoffroy's tamarin, *Saguinus geoffroyi,* neither the arched back display nor the extensive licking is seen. Instead, the female wipes her tightly curled tail several times across her genitalia, and the male takes it in both hands and sniffs it intensively. Rapid tongue movements are regarded as female sexual invitations in *C. jacchus,* in *S. geoffroyi,* in the Pinché, *S. oedipus,* in the golden lion tamarin, *Leontideus rosalia,* and in Goeldi's marmoset, *Callimico goeldii.* Birth peaks have been noted in January-March in captive *S. oedipus* (Hampton, Hampton and Landwehr, 1966), but there are no data suggesting seasonal breeding in any other species of the *Callithricidae.*

B. Capuchins, Squirrel and Howler Monkeys, etc.: Cebidae

These Central and South American forms are familiar in zoos, and several species breed freely in captivity; all *Cebidae* generally have one young per litter. The black-capped capuchin. *Cebus apella,* is found in groups of eight to thirty or more individuals: they breed well in captivity, and gestation is about 180 days. There is a vaginal cycle of sixteen to twenty-three days, no regular external menstruation, but irregular vaginal bleeding can be detected by lavage. Copulation occurs during the three days prior to maximum vaginal cornification which lasts twenty-four hours and coincides with ovulation, and a vaginal plug is described (Hamlett, 1939). Ovulatory cycles continue for at least nine months of the year, but there are doubts about the remaining three months. Birth peaks occur, however, in May-June and again in October-November in the Goyaz district of Brazil. In the white-fronted capuchin, *Cebus albifrons,* vaginal bleeding can be detected by lavage at fifteen to twenty-one day intervals, and maximal vaginal cornification lasting twenty-four hours occurs between days six to eight of the cycle; it is associated with swelling of the female's external genitalia (Castellanos and McCombs, 1968). There are no good descriptions of reproductive behavior in this genus. In the woolly monkey, *Lagothrix lagotrichia,* a species that has rarely bred in captivity, vaginal bleeding can be detected at twenty-three to twenty-six day intervals in over half the cases. Where it occurs, there is maximal vaginal cornification, not associated with any swelling of the external genitalia, between days six to eight of the cycle. Copulation in captive night monkeys, *Aotus trivirgatus,* and dusky titis, *Callicebus moloch,* is not preceded by a display, but there is increasingly frequent inspection and manipulation by the male of the partner's genitalia; in the night monkey, ejaculation typically occurs during the first mount after only three to four thrusts (Moynihan, 1964, 1966; Mason, 1966).

The squirrel monkey, *Saimiri sciureus,* is extensively used in the laboratory and breeds successfully in captivity although neonatal mortality is rather high. Gestation is about 168 days (Hopf, 1967). The cycle, assessed by the interval between successive periods of vaginal cornification and receptivity, and the appearance of sperm in smears, is variously reported as having a mean duration of between seven to thirteen days, but its length appears sensitive to environmental factors such as housing animals in smaller or larger groups (Rosenblum *et al.,* 1967; Latta *et al.,* 1967; Castellanos and McCombs, 1968; Clewe, 1969; Hutchinson, 1970). Receptivity varies from a few hours to two days while vaginal cornification, sometimes associated with swelling of the external genitalia, lasts from one to three days. Precopulatory activity in free-ranging male squirrel monkeys includes leaping backwards and forwards between branches around the female and "silent vocalization," whereby the male opens his mouth and contracts the abdominal muscles, although no sound can be detected at twenty feet (Baldwin, 1968). In captivity, males chase the female, bite her tail and inspect her genitalia prior to copulation. Receptive females make frequent genital displays directed at the male partner: they face the male, abduct one thigh and display the erect clitoris, sometimes emitting a few drops of urine as they do so. Females initiate mounting by presenting the anogenital region to the male, standing with arms and legs braced and tail deflected, looking backwards over their shoulder towards him. The sexually interacting pair form temporary consort bonds, following, sitting near and continually looking at each other. The male mounts by grasping the female's waist with his hands and her legs with his feet. Several rapid, small amplitude pelvic thrusts are made and there follow from one to fifteen slower, deeper thrusts. Ejaculation occcurs during the last of a series of ten to twenty-five mounts; thereafter, each animal inspects and cleans its genitalia. Nonreceptive females move quietly away from males showing sexual interest, generally without any agonistic behavior. In both wild and captive squirrel monkeys there is a three-month mating season with a birth season some six months later; their timing depends upon geographical location. Thus, mating occurs in July-September in Peru, in December-March in Florida, in February-March in Tennessee, in March-

July in New York, and also in spring and summer in Munich (DuMond and Hutchinson, 1967; Latta *et al.,* 1967; Rosenblum *et al.,* 1967; Clewe, 1969). Some of the seasonal differences have been attributed to differences in precipitation, since mating occurs in the dry seasons in Peru and Florida, and animals transported from the former location to the latter, experience a six-month shift in mating season. There are marked physiological and behavioral changes in males which become "fatted," spermatogenic, aggressive and excitable during the mating season; these phenomena do not occur in Munich where males appear to remain sexually active throughout the year.

The mantled howler monkey, *Alouatta villosa* (formerly *A. palliata*), is found in groups of up to forty-five individuals. To date, this species has been found unsuited to captivity and our information comes from field studies (Carpenter, 1934; Altmann, 1959; Bernstein, 1964). A sexually interacting pair spends a number of hours together, apart from the group. The female incites the male to mount by rapidly moving the tongue in and out of the mouth and by crouching in a copulatory posture. The male also initiates sexual interaction by means of the lingual gesture, and mounts by grasping the female's waist with his hands. There is a series of mounts, each with from eight to twenty-eight pelvic thrusts, but it is not clearly established how many ejaculations occur. During copulation, the female occasionally looks back at the male and may reach back to touch him with her hand. At the end of a mating sequence, females are often observed to roll on their backs. In the female, the period of maximum receptivity lasts from three to four days. There is no evidence of a mating season, but there may be a winter peak in the frequency of births.

The black-handed spider monkey, *Ateles geoffroyi,* occurs in groups of up to more than forty individuals. Spider monkeys breed quite readily in captivity, gestation is about 139 days with one young per litter, and bleeding is detectable in the vaginal lavage at twenty-four to twenty-seven day intervals. There is no description of copulatory behavior, however, a female *A. geoffroyi,* observed being embraced by a male, was found on autopsy to have an enlarged vagina containing a recently formed vaginal plug (Carpenter, 1935).

III. OLD WORLD MONKEYS

A. Macaques, Baboons, Mangabeys, Langurs etc.: Cercopithecidae

1. Macaques. The macaques have been extensively studied, and a great deal of information is available on their reproductive behavior, particularly that of the rhesus monkey, *Macaca mulatta.* Many of the basic observations were made in field studies on a free-ranging colony on Cayo Santiago (Carpenter, 1942a, b). Rhesus monkeys are widely distributed in India and Southeast Asia, where they are found in groups of up to one hundred or more individuals of all ages. Given adequate diet and vitamin supplements, they breed readily in captivity, gestation is about 164 days with one young per litter; twins occur very rarely. There is a twenty-eight day menstrual cycle with a visible, external menstrual flow lasting two to seven days. Unless interrupted by pregnancy, in most situations cycles continue for nine months of the year, and from June-September there is a period of summer amenorrhoea (Corner, 1945; van Wagenen, 1945; and Keverne and Michael, 1970). Ovulation occurs between days nine to sixteen of the cycle and is associated with increased sexual activity and vaginal cornification. Ripe follicles can be detected by rectal palpation of ovaries (Hartman, 1932). At puberty and at the time of ovulation in some cycles thereafter, there may be marked reddening and edema of the sexual skin, extending up to the hips and down the backs of the legs: however, these changes are quite inconspicuous in fully mature females in which they are no longer a useful indication of the ovarian condition.

In the wild as females become receptive their aggressivity increases and they actively approach, at first, the lower-ranking males with which they mate. At the height of receptivity, however, they form a consort pair with a dominant male (Altmann, 1962; Southwick, Beg and Siddiqi, 1965). The male mounts the female by grasping her waist with his hands and the backs of her legs with his feet. Copulation consists of a series of one to twenty mounts, initiated by either sex, each associated with one to fifteen rapid pelvic thrusts. The mounting series terminates in an ejaculatory mount, sometimes characterized by deeper, faster thrusting and, at the moment of ejaculation, a pause accompanied by rhythmic contractions of the thigh muscles. During standardized one-hour tests, from zero to seven ejaculations occur, depending on the potency of the male and the identity of the partner. Many aspects of reproductive behavior can be studied quantitatively in the laboratory by observing oppositely-sexed pairs under standardized test conditions. More detailed consideration is now given to these behavioral parameters.

a. *Male sexual behavior (M. mulatta):* The *number of mounts per test* is an easily observed indication of male sexual activity. A distinction is made between mounts with intromission and those without, the latter and also those occurring haphazardly (not in a mounting sequence) are more related to dominance than to sex. *Number of male mounting attempts per test* provides an indication of male sexual motivation. If a mounting attempt is "successful," it results in a mount; if the female prevents mounting, the attempt is "unsuccessful" (see female refusals) (Michael *et al.*, 1967). *Male success ratio,* the number of successful male mounting attempts expressed as a percentage of total male mounting attempts, is a useful index of female receptivity. *Mounting rate* is the number of mounts to ejaculation × 60, divided by ejaculation time (see below) (Michael and Saayman, 1967a). This index of male sexual performance is used in the evaluation of hormone treatments. *Sexual performance index (SPI)* is the total number of thrusts to ejaculation × 60, divided by ejaculation time. This depends on the stimulus properties of the partner (Michael and Saayman, 1967b). *Number of ejaculations per test and ejaculation time*: the latter is the time in minutes between the first and the final ejaculatory mount. Both indices vary widely and depend on the identity of the male. The number of ejaculations tends to increase with females near midcycle, when ejaculation times decrease. *Male grooming time per test,* the number of minutes spent by the male grooming the female, is a sensitive index and increases when females are attractive to the male near midcycle (Michael, Herbert and Welegalla, 1966).

b. *Female sexual behavior (M. mulatta):* There are four types of invitational gesture: (i) presentation: while standing on all fours, the female directs her anogenital region towards the male;

(ii) hand-reach: the female sits with her back to the male, rapidly extends an arm to place her hand on the ground and then withdraws it; (iii) head-duck: the female sits with her back to the male and rapidly ducks her head and (iv) head-bob: while sitting, the female rapidly jerks her head upwards and backwards. The numbers of these gestures provide an indication of the female's sexual motivation (Michael and Welegalla, 1968; Michael and Zumpe, 1970a). *Female success ratio:* female sexual invitations may either be successful or unsuccessful in initiating a mount. The success ratio is the number of successful invitations expressed as a percentage of the total number of invitations, and provides an indication of the female's value as a sexual stimulus (i.e. her attractiveness) (Michael, 1968). *Number of female refusals per test* is the number of times the female refuses male mounting attempts. This provides a direct measure of female receptivity or lack of it. Refusals increase after ovariectomy and sometimes in the luteal phase of the cycle. Clutching at the moment of ejaculation, the female twists backwards, clutches the male's fur with one hand and lipsmacks vigorously at his face. This behavior is most marked in fully receptive females and its incidence declines after ovariectomy (Zumpe and Michael, 1968). *Withdrawal reaction* also occurs at ejaculation. The female vigorously pulls away from the male before ejaculation is completed (Michael and Saayman, 1968).

c. *Rhythmic changes in behavior:* Divergent reports concerning rhythmic changes in the sexual activity of rhesus monkeys are in part due to marked differences in the behavior of individual pairs; this makes generalizations difficult. Changes in the male's mounting activity in relation to the menstrual cycle of the female partner are of four main types (Fig. 8-1): (a) those with well-defined maxima near midcycle, sharp declines early in the luteal phase and secondary rises immediately before menstruation; (b) those with sustained high levels of activity throughout the follicular phase, sharp declines early in the luteal phase with low levels persisting for the rest of the cycle; (c) cycles without evidence of rhythmic changes but with fairly high levels of mounting throughout; (d) also cycles without any rhythmic changes but with generally low levels of interaction throughout. About 50 percent of the pairs and cycles studied show clear evidence of rhythmicity (Michael, 1971). The

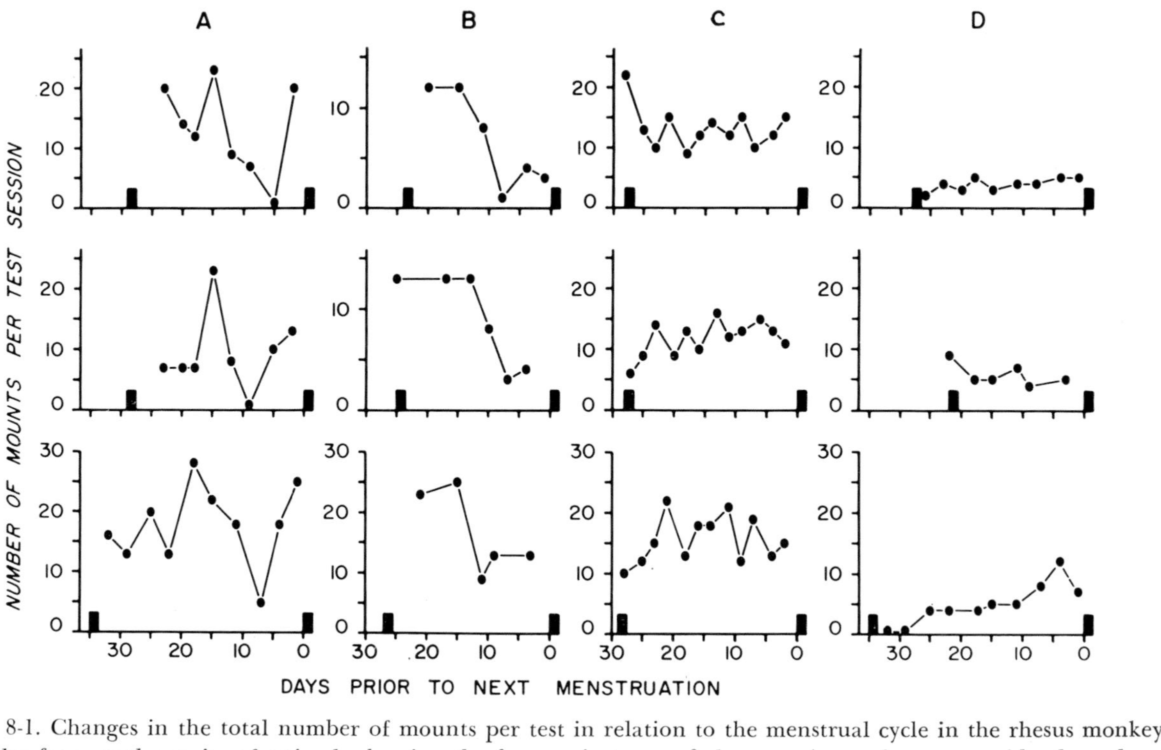

Figure 8-1. Changes in the total number of mounts per test in relation to the menstrual cycle in the rhesus monkey. Examples from twelve pairs of animals showing the four main types of changes: A, maxima near midcycle and secondary rises immediately before menstruation; B, high levels of mounting during follicular phases and low levels during luteal phases; C, fairly high levels of mounting throughout the cycles; D, low levels of interaction throughout the cycles. Types A and B show rhythmicity. Solid rectangles indicate vaginal bleeding.

existence of rhythmic changes in sexual activity in a rhesus monkey population has been confirmed by considering the changes in the frequency of ejaculation during all seventy-five menstrual cycles observed in thirty-two pairs of animals over a period of years (Michael and Zumpe, 1970b). The mean number of ejaculations during the follicular phase is significantly greater than that for the luteal phase and comparisons with some human data are shown in Figure 8-2.

The effect of the hormonal status of the female on the pattern of sexual interaction of the pair is confirmed by ovariectomy and hormone replacement treatment. Generally, but not always, ovariectomizing the female results in decreased sexual interaction and increased aggression between the pair (Michael, 1965; Michael and Zumpe, 1970c). Daily s.c. injections of 5-10 μg oestradiol monobenzoate rapidly restore copulatory activity, and the subsequent administration of 10-25 mg progesterone s.c. per day depresses mounting and ejaculation. In some cases, treating the female with progesterone increases the number of refusals, making her unreceptive, but in other cases, males simply cease making mounting attempts (Fig. 8-3). In these latter females, progesterone treatment makes them unattractive to males (Michael, Saayman and Zumpe, 1968). There is now evidence that the stimulus properties of the female depend very considerably upon the presence, in vaginal secretions, of a substance or substances with the properties of a releaser pheromone (Michael and Keverne, 1968, 1970). These substances so powerfully stimulate males that they mount and ejaculate with totally unreceptive, ovariectomized females when secretions containing pheromones are applied to the latters' sexual skin (Fig. 8-4). They act via the olfactory sense and are entirely without effect on the behavior of males that have been rendered anosmic.

In India, most matings occur in October-November with a major birth peak in the following March-April (Southwick *et al.*, 1961, 1965; Prakash, 1962); similar peaks have been reported in the laboratory (Hartman, 1932), although not all authors agree. The existence of an annual rhythm in sexual performance and motivation has been difficult to establish because of the seasonal disturbance caused by pregnancy and by the birth of young. This

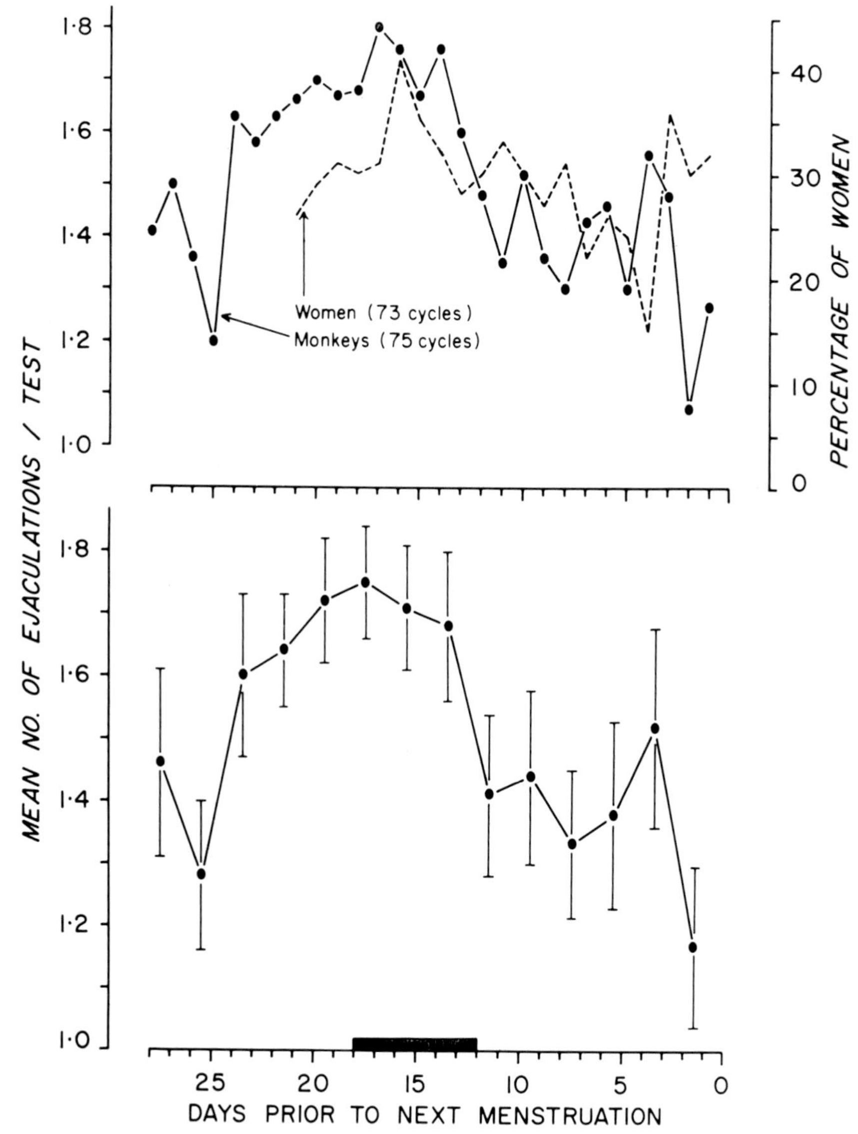

Figure 8-2. Upper part: comparison of the copulatory activity of rhesus monkey and man in relation to the menstrual cycle. ●———●, mean number of ejaculations per test (32 pairs rhesus monkeys); - - - - - -, percentage of women reporting sexual intercourse (40 women, Udry and Morris, 1968). Lower part: rhesus monkey data smoothed by plotting means of two consecutive days. Vertical bars give standard errors of means. Horizontal bar gives expected time of ovulation (Hartman, 1932). (From Michael and Zumpe, 1970b)

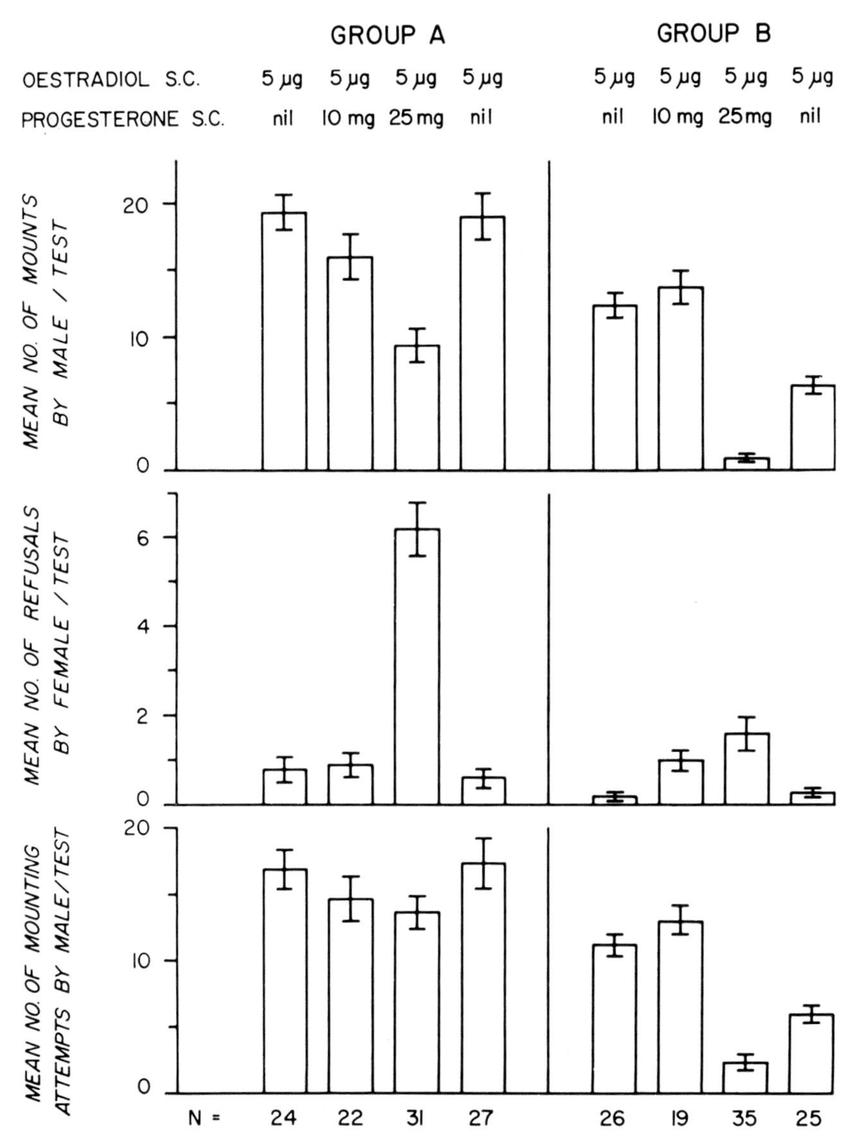

Figure 8-3. Two mechanisms responsible for the suppression of male mounting activity when progesterone is administered to their female partners: group A, three pairs with a marked increase in female refusals; group B, three pairs with a marked decrease in male mounting attempts. In both groups, a decline in the number of mounts results (upper part). Vertical bars give S.E.'s of means. N = number of tests. (From Michael, Saayman and Zumpe, 1968)

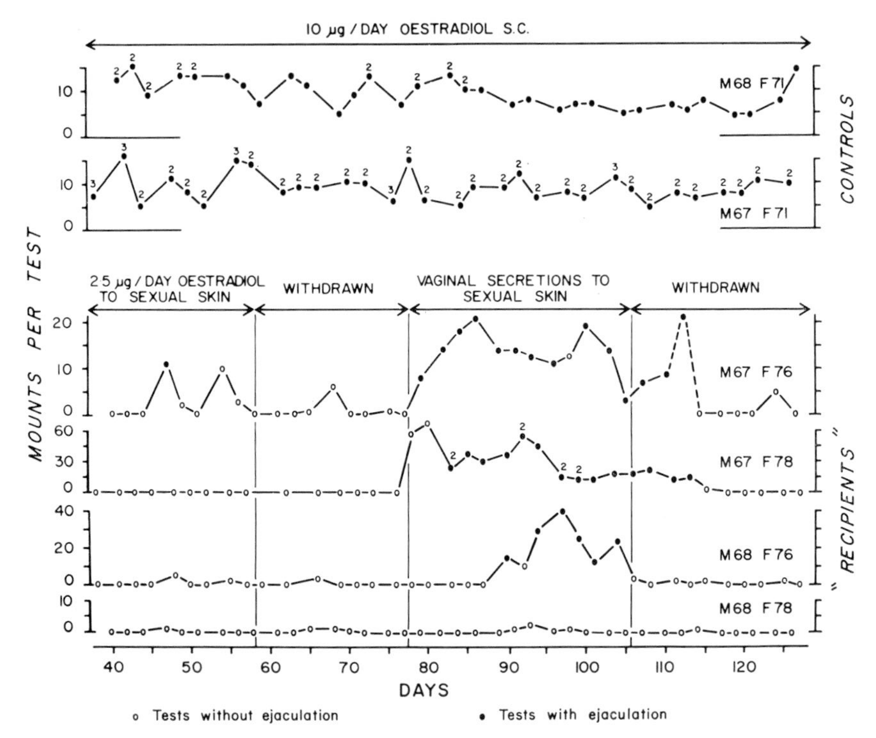

Figure 8-4. Stimulation of sexual behaviour in male rhesus monkeys by vaginal secretions (6 pairs). Effects on mounting and ejaculation by males when their ovariectomized female partners are treated (a) with s.c. injections 10 µg/day estradiol (controls), (b) by applying 2.5 µg/day estradiol to the sexual skin, and (c) by applying vaginal secretions to the sexual skin: these were obtained from estrogen-treated donors. Applications of vaginal secretions, but not of estradiol, to recipients resulted in increased mounting and ejaculation in three of four pairs. Thirty-five days of pretreatment baseline are not illustrated. Small numbers near tests give number of ejaculations when more than one occurred. Animal pairs are given on the right side (from Michael and Keverne, 1970).

problem has recently been resolved by studying the changes in the ejaculatory activity of males paired with intact females whose oviducts were ligated to prevent pregnancy (Michael and Keverne, 1971). All thirty animals were housed together under controlled environmental conditions, and a well-marked maximum in ejaculatory activity is seen during December, contrasting with the low level during February-May (Fig. 8-5): these laboratory findings agree fairly well with those of field studies (Conaway and Koford,

1964; Vandenbergh and Vessey, 1968). The decline in male sexual activity in the period February-May occurs although reproductively active females with regular menstrual cycles are available as partners (Keverne and Michael, 1970) (Fig. 8-6). This period coincides with, but clearly cannot be due to, the birth season and period of gestation in feral rhesus monkeys, shown as hatched columns in Figure 8-5. Testicular regression in rhesus monkeys on Cayo Santiago is maximal between February and May, and an increase in tubular diameter and testicular size occurs between September-December (Conaway and Sade, 1965); it is possible that the gonadal changes account for these annual fluctuations in male sexual activity.

The Japanese macaque, *M. fuscata,* occurs now in groups of up to two hundred individuals as the result of artificial provisioning. It breeds readily in captivity, and gestation is 150 to 170 days with generally one young per litter. As in *M. mulatta,* the modal menstrual cycle length is twenty-eight days, and there are periods of heightened receptivity of about nine days near midcycle which are not reliably associated with any swelling of the sex skin. During their period of receptivity, females consort with several males and copulation consists of eight to thirty mounts each with one to eight intromitted pelvic thrusts, and at ejaculation the female reaches back with one hand to grasp at the male (Imanishi, 1957; Tokuda, 1961-62). Receptive females emit a characteristic explosive call, and mounts are initiated either by the male or by the female's presentation posture. There is a distinct mating season in December-March and a corresponding May-August birth season. Thus there are many close similarities to *M. mulatta.*

The pig-tailed macaque, *M. nemestrina,* occurs in Malaysia and Southeast Asia in groups of up to fifty individuals. This macaque also breeds freely in captivity; gestation is between 167 to 179 days with one young per litter. There is a menstrual cycle of thirty-two days and, unlike the rhesus monkey, there is conspicuous sexual skin swelling for twenty-one days of the cycle and this is maximal for the twelve days about midcycle (Zuckerman, 1937; Bernstein, 1967; Tokuda, Simons and Jensen, 1968). Mounting is most frequent during the period of sexual skin swelling when females copulate with several males. There is a mounting series of eight to

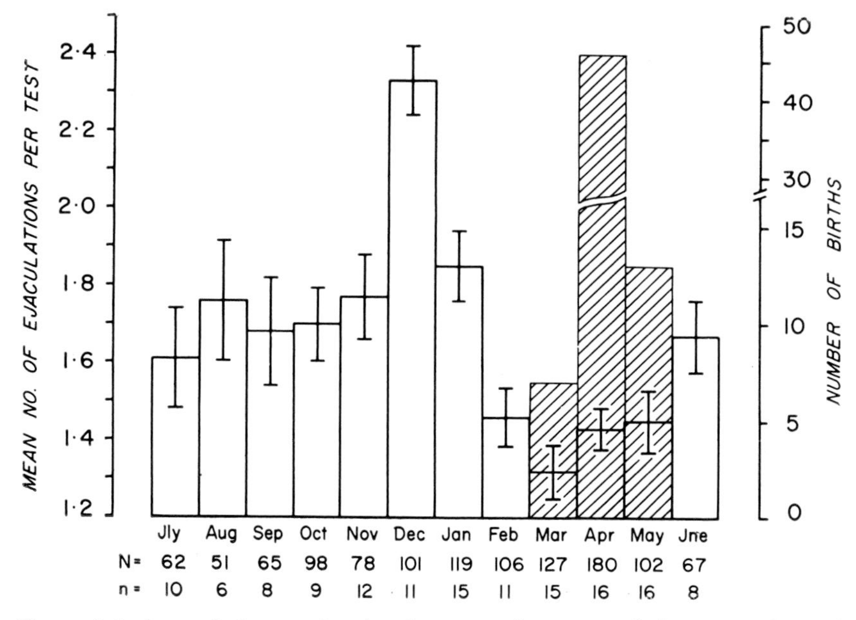

Figure 8-5. Annual changes in ejaculatory performance of rhesus monkeys. A well-marked maximum in the number of ejaculations per test occurs in December. Low levels between February and May coincide with the natural birth season in northern India (hatched columns, Southwick *et al.,* 1961). Births cannot account for the decline in the sexual activity of males in the London colony as the Fallopian tubes of females were ligated to prevent pregnancy. N = number of tests (1,156). n = number of pairs. Vertical bars give S.E.'s of means. Gestation = 5½ months. (Michael and Keverne, unpublished observations)

twenty-three mounts at approximately three minute intervals, each mount being associated with some twelve intromitted thrusts. Females sometimes reach back and grasp the male's leg during a mount. At ejaculation, the male often grimaces and utters a high-pitched cry. Mounts may be initiated either by the male's courtship approach, during which the ears are retracted and the lips pushed forward and everted in the "Flehmen" face (van Hooff, 1962), or by the female adopting a typical presentation posture. There is no good evidence for a birth season in this species.

The bonnet macaque, *M. radiata,* is found in Southern India in groups of up to sixty individuals. This macaque breeds readily in captivity, and gestation is 153 to 169 days with generally one

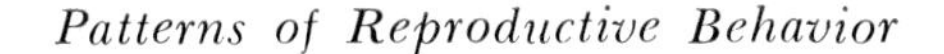

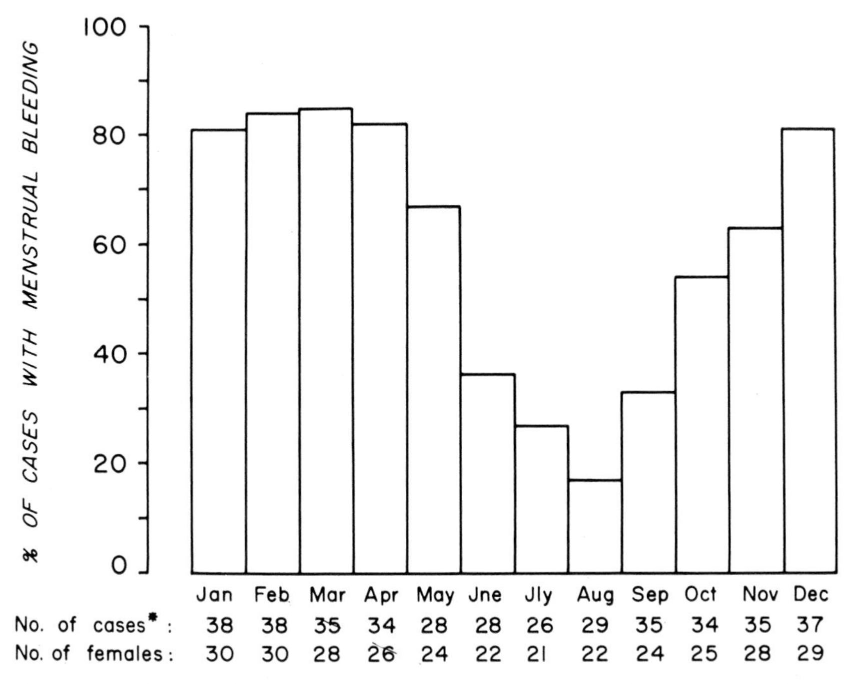

Figure 8-6. Annual changes in the incidence of menstrual bleeding in rhesus monkeys. In the period February-May, when male sexual activity is at a low level, females are generally showing regular menstrual cycles. Summer amenorrhea does not become marked until June and reaches a maximum in August. Case * = a female observed daily from one month. (from Keverne and Michael, 1970)

young per litter. The duration of the menstrual cycle is twenty-five to thirty-six days and the menstrual flow may last up to ten days: there are no cyclic changes in the appearance of the external genitalia. Spermatozoa are found almost exclusively in midcycle vaginal smears (Hartman, 1938) and there is a copious, strong-smelling vaginal discharge occurring intermittently during the cycle. Unlike other macaques (except *M. arctoides*), copulation is generally completed in a single mount of five to thirty pelvic thrusts terminating in ejaculation. Mounts are usually initiated by the male which approaches the female, flips aside her tail and mounts without further ado. As in other macaques, the female reaches back with one hand to clasp the male at ejaculation; but there appears to be no consort pair formation during the period of maximal receptivity as in the rhesus monkey. There is a mating peak in October-November and a birth peak in the following February-March (Simonds, 1965; Kaufman and Rosenblum, 1966; Rahaman and Parthasarathy, 1969).

In the stump-tailed macaque, *M. arctoides,* gestation is thought to be about 170 days and it breeds in captivity. The menstrual cycle is twenty-eight days, but the menses are scarcely visible and there is no swelling of the sex skin. As in the bonnet macaque, copulation consists of a single mount with many intromitted thrusts terminating in ejaculation. While mounted and thrusting, the male lipsmacks in a way that exposes the teeth, making first a chattering and then a barking vocalization. Early in the mount, the female reaches back with one hand to grasp the male and, at ejaculation, the male mouths the female's back strongly but without completing the bite; nevertheless, the skin of the female's back may be damaged. Mounts are generally initiated by the male's approach: he flips aside her tail and may place a finger in the vagina, sniffing at the finger before mounting. Females occasionally initiate mounts by adopting the presentation posture (Blurton Jones and Trollope, 1968).

In the common macaque, *M. fascicularis,* gestation is 153-179 days with generally one young per litter. The modal cycle length is twenty-eight days and the menstrual flow lasts two to seven days. Only at puberty is there midcycle swelling and reddening of the sexual skin. Descriptions of behavior are poor, but copulation is reported mainly during the follicular phase (Eckstein and Zuckerman, 1956).

While many New World monkeys have cyclic uterine bleeding, it tends to be irregular and only detectable by vaginal lavage: in contrast, the macaques have a regular twenty-eight to thirty-two day menstrual cycle with visible menses. Ovulation occurs near midcycle at which time, in the female rhesus monkey, there are detectable changes in basal body temperature. Figure 8-7 shows the combined data from all temperature recordings obtained by telemetry during five menstrual cycles, each point being the mean of between nineteen to twenty-eight temperature readings (Michael, Weller and Zumpe, unpublished data). In *M. mulatta, M. fuscata* and *M. nemestrina,* there are consort bonds with receptive

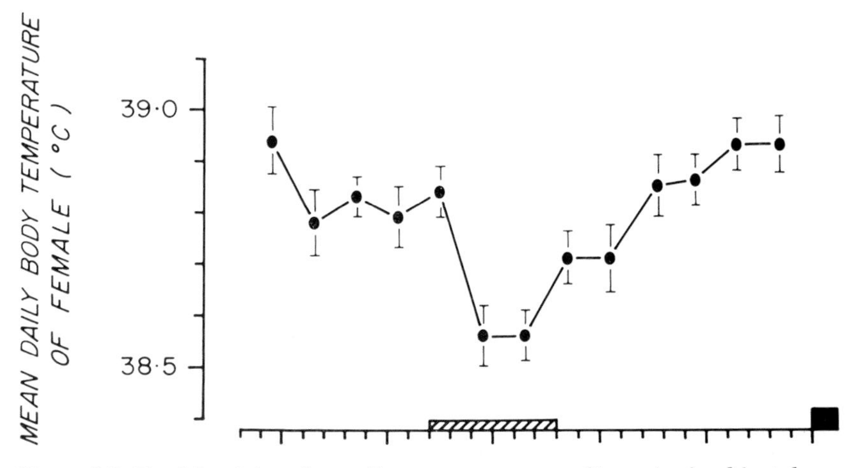

Figure 8-7. Combined data from all temperature recordings obtained by telemetry during five menstrual cycles. Each point is the mean of from 19-28 readings; vertical bars give standard errors of means. There is a significant drop in temperature at the expected time of ovulation (hatched bar). Abscissa gives days of menstrual cycle, solid rectangle gives first day of menstruation (Michael, Weller and Zumpe, unpublished observations).

females of a few hours' or days' duration, generally with a sequence of different males and, at the height of receptivity, with a highly dominant male. In these species, copulation consists of a series of mounts, each with a number of intromitted thrusts, culminating in an ejaculatory mount, but in *M. radiata* and *M. arctoides,* there is characteristically a single mount with ejaculation; in the two latter species, consort bonds are less well-marked. In most macaques there are rhythms of sexual activity related to the female's menstrual cycle, most extensively studied in *M. mulatta.* In species with a mounting series, both males and females initiate mounting, whereas in those with a single mount, it is generally initiated by the male. Only *M. nemestrina* among macaques exhibits conspicuous sexual skin swelling during midcycle. Heterosexual grooming is closely associated with sexual behavior and, in the rhesus monkey, grooming times change with the female's cycle (Fig. 8-8) (Michael, Herbert and Welegalla, 1966). Homosexual mounting and masturbation by males and mounting by females constitute other easily observable aspects of the behavioral repertoire.

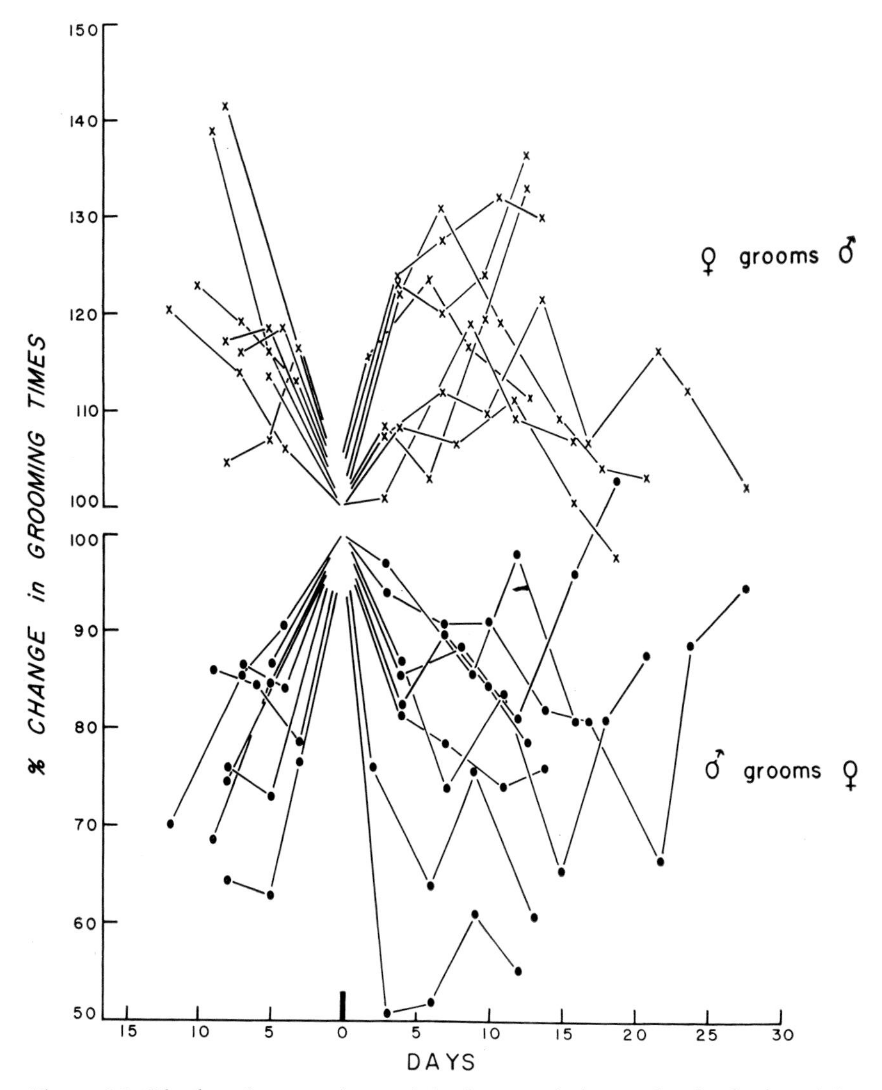

Figure 8-8. Rhythms in grooming activity in oppositely sexed pairs during eight menstrual cycles calculated as a percentage of the maximum grooming times of males (lower part) and minimum grooming times of females (upper part). Data from different cycles are arranged about day 0, the day when maximum changes occur (Michael, Herbert and Welegalla, 1966).

2. *Baboons.* The baboons of Africa, the olive baboon, *Papio anubis,* the yellow baboon, *P. cynocephalus,* the chacma baboon, *P. ursinus,* the guinea baboon, *P. papio,* and the sacred baboon, *P. hamadryas,* are found in troops of up to two hundred individuals. They breed in captivity and gestation is between 173 to 193 days with one young per litter. There is a thirty-one to thirty-five day menstrual cycle and a menstrual flow of about three days. In contrast to most macaques, swelling of the sexual skin is conspicuous in all species. Tumescence starts a few days after the onset of menstruation and is maximal for three to nine days about midcycle; ovulation is thought to occur two to three days prior to the onset of the abrupt detumescence (Zuckerman, 1937, 1953; Gillman and Gilbert, 1946; Gilbert and Gillman, 1951; Hendrickx and Kraemer, 1969). In London, the modal length of eighty-five menstrual cycles of captive *P. anubis,* isolated from males, is thirty-one days (Michael and Evans, unpublished data): for a given female, the onset of tumescence and detumescence is remarkably constant from cycle to cycle.

In the chacma baboon, copulation consists of a series of mounts, each with one to twenty intromitted thrusts, terminating in an ejaculatory mount. As in the rhesus monkey, the male mounts by grasping the female's waist with his hands and her legs with his feet. While thrusting, the male makes a facial grimace and the female emits a characteristic copulation call consisting of a series of sharp barks: as thrusting terminates, the female rapidly withdraws from the male and forcefully bounds away (Saayman, 1970). Mounts may be initiated by either sex and the female's presentation posture is similar to that of macaques. Presentations, copulation calls and withdrawals are more frequent in females with sexual skin swelling and, at the height of receptivity, when mounting and ejaculation reach their maxima, females consort almost exclusively with a dominant male. Between mounts, either partner may groom the other (Hall, 1962; Saayman, 1970). Captive female olive and yellow baboons are groomed by males more near midcycle than near menstruation; this is similar to the grooming pattern of rhesus monkeys (Rowell, 1968). Reproductive behavior of olive and chacma baboons differ in the following respects: in the former, ejaculation typically occurs during a single mount with a mean of six intromitted thrusts, males rarely grimace during mounts and females do not give copulation calls, neither do they withdraw from the male as he dismounts (Hall and DeVore, 1965). Within a troop of sacred baboons, the permanent social unit is a one-male group consisting of an adult male with one to nine females and their young; the male copulates exclusively with the females of his harem, and only with those with sexual skin swelling. Copulation is closely similar to that described for the chacma baboon: there is a series of mounts, initiated by either male or female, with mutual grooming between mounts (Kummer, 1968). There is no good description of the reproductive behavior of the gelada baboon, *Theropithecus gelada,* but its social organization and displays are similar in many respects to those of the sacred baboon (Spivak, 1968). There is no obvious seasonality in breeding among baboons: however, an October-December birth peak occurs in the olive baboon of Kenya, and in the sacred baboon in Ethiopia there is a peak in both mating and births in May-July and probably therefore a second peak six months later (Hall and DeVore, 1965; Kummer, 1968).

3. Mangabeys. The arboreal, grey-cheeked mangabey, *Cercocebus albigena,* and the white-collared mangabey, *C. torquatus,* of Africa occur in groups of nine to twenty-three individuals comprising adult males and females with their young. They breed well in captivity, gestation is 174 to 179 days with one young per litter. The menstrual cycle modal length is thirty days, but external bleeding is rarely visible. Near midcycle, swelling of the sexual skin is at its height for about five days, and copulations are generally restricted to periods of sexual skin swelling (Chalmers, 1968; Jones and Sabater Pi, 1968; Rowell and Chalmers, 1970). There is a mounting series terminating in ejaculation closely similar to that described for the rhesus monkey. Mounts may be initiated either by the male or by the female and, at ejaculation, the female reaches backwards to grasp the male. Females make a typical presentation posture but its frequency does not increase at midcycle. Neither is there any evidence for a breeding season in this genus which reproduces throughout the year.

4. Guenons. Arboreal species of *Cercopithecus* are found in Africa generally in groups of up to twenty-nine individuals containing only one adult male (Struhsaker, 1969). The terrestrial vervet monkey, *C. aethiops,* occurs in groups of seven to fifty-three individuals containing several adult males and females with their young. Vervet monkeys maintained in groups breed readily in captivity, gestation is 165 days and the menstrual cycle modal length is thirty-three days. Menses are not visible externally, nor are there any external genital changes. There appears to be a leucocytic infiltration in the vaginal smear, maximal about day sixteen, but spermatozoa can be found throughout most of the cycle (Rowell, 1970). Copulation consists of a single mount in which the male grasps the female's waist with his hands and her legs with his feet, and makes a few shallow, rapid pelvic thrusts, then intromits and ejaculates after making up to twenty-five deeper, slower thrusts. At ejaculation, the female may glance back and grasp at the male. Mounts may be initiated either by the male or female which presents by adopting a crouching posture, deflecting the tail and looking over her shoulder at the male (Struhsaker, 1967; Gartlan, 1969). Most other *Cercopithecus* monkeys do not breed very readily in captivity. In the Sykes monkey, *C. mitis,* gestation is 140 days, the modal cycle length is thirty days, and menses are not visible externally, nor are there any external genital changes. There is no clear cycle of vaginal cornification, but a marked leucocytic infiltration in the smear near midcycle, and spermatozoa are found mainly in follicular and midcycle smears (Rowell, 1970). In contrast, Booth (1962) found no relation between the stage of the menstrual cycle and frequency of copulation in *C. mitis, C. aethiops* and *C. neglectus.* The talapoin monkey, *C. talapoin,* stands in marked contrast to the above species in that it exhibits a midcycle swelling of the sexual skin. There is a thirty-three day menstrual cycle, with maximum cornification of the smear near midcycle, at which time mounting by males and presentations by females are increased: ten to twelve copulations occur during the period of maximum swelling (Gautier-Hion, personal communication; Herbert, 1970). Breeding seasons in guenons vary with the geographical location and with local climatic factors: in the vervet monkeys of Amboseli, mating occurs from May-October and births from October-March; on Lolui Island in Lake Victoria, mating occurs from October-May and births from April-September. On the West

Indian island of St. Kitts, where vervets were introduced in the seventeenth century, the testis size of male *C. aethiops sabaeus* is greatest during the winter mating season, indicating that spermatogenesis may be seasonal (Sade and Hildrech, 1965). Further, male talapoins in Gabon are "fatted" during the May-August mating season and are slim during the December-March birth season (Gautier-Hion, personal communication).

The patas monkey, *Erythrocebus patas,* of Africa occurs in groups of up to thirty individuals containing one adult male together with adult females and their young; there are also all-male groups. They breed in captivity, but not very freely, gestation is about 170 days, and the menstrual cycle lasts approximately thirty days. There are no cyclic changes in the female's external genitalia. In captivity, copulation is restricted to a few days near midcycle, and consists of a series of mounts, each with intromission, terminating in ejaculation. During mounts, the male grasps the female's waist with his hands, his feet remaining on the ground or a branch. Mounts may be initiated by either sex: the female solicits mounting by making a cringing half-run towards the male with her tail drooping, eyebrows lowered and tightly-closed lips protruding; accompanying this facial gesture is a vocalization produced by inflating and deflating the cheek-pouches. In the wild, mounting by males and soliciting by females is seen between July-September, indicating that breeding may be seasonal in this species (Hall, 1965; Hall, Boelkins and Goswell, 1965).

5. *Langurs.* The Hanuman langur, *Presbytis entellus,* the John's langur, *P. johnii,* and the silver leaf-monkey, *P. cristatus,* of India and Asia all occur in groups of up to 120 individuals. In northern and central India, the larger troops of Hanuman langurs contain several adult males, but in the south, the smaller troops of all three species generally contain only one adult male. Langurs breed in captivity, gestation is thought to be about six months, and there is one young per litter. The mean cycle length in *P. entellus* is twenty-seven days and the menstrual flow lasts two to four days. The vaginal smear becomes cornified about day seven of the menstrual cycle, and cornification persists until a few days after ovulation (David and Ramaswami, 1969). Cornification coincides with the five to seven day period of receptivity about midcycle to which

copulations are confined. There is no cyclic swelling of the external genitalia. Reproductive behavior is similar in all three species: copulation generally consists of a series of mounts during which the male grasps the female's waist with his hands, but his feet remain on the ground. All mounts are initiated by the female which solicits mounting by presenting her anogenital region to the male and simultaneously dropping her tail to the ground and shaking her head from side to side. Sexually excited males sometimes make repeated low-pitched vocalizations (Jay, 1965; Sugiyama, Yoshiba and Parthasarathy, 1965; Bernstein, 1968; Poirier, 1969). As in the guenons, breeding seasons vary with the geographical location of troops: thus, the birth season for *P. entellus* is November-March in southern India but April-May in central India.

C. Apes

Chimpanzee, Orang-utan, Gorilla: Pongidae. The Great Apes present at this time a pressing conservation problem. This is particularly the case for the orang-utan, *Pongo,* and for the mountain and lowland gorillas, *Gorilla,* none of which should now be regarded as appropriate genera for laboratory studies unconnected with their conservation. The situation is also rapidly deteriorating for the chimpanzee, *Pan.* However, all three genera breed in captivity and the chimpanzee, whose gestation is 227 days, does so quite readily. In the chimpanzees studied in captivity by Yerkes and Elder (1936), the modal length of the menstrual cycle was thirty-five days with an external menstrual flow of three days. There is marked swelling of the sexual skin and this is maximal for about eighteen days in the middle part of the menstrual cycle (Young and Yerkes, 1943). Females are most attractive and receptive to males during the period of maximal sexual skin swelling. In the wild, copulation typically consists of a single mount during which the male holds the back of the crouching female with one hand and an overhanging branch with the other. While in a squatting position behind the female, the male performs from five to twenty intromitted thrusts culminating in ejaculation. Females may initiate mounting by presenting their anogenital region to the male in a crouching posture and, during a mount, the female often looks back at the male and makes a squealing or even a screaming vocalization (van Lawick-Goodall, 1968). There is no evidence that breeding is seasonal. While copulation by the Great Apes under natural conditions is generally ventro-dorsal, ventro-ventral copulation has been described in captive pygmy chimpanzees, *Pan paniscus Schwarz* (Kirchshofer, 1962), in captive orang-utans, *Pongo pygmaeus* (Fox, 1929), and in captive gorillas, *Gorilla gorilla* (Schaller, 1963).

REFERENCES

Atlmann, S. A. (1959): Field observations on a howling monkey society. *J Mammal, 40,* 317-330.

Altmann, S. A. (1962): A field study of the sociobiology of rhesus monkeys (*Macaca mulatta*). *Ann NY Acad Sci, 102,* 338-435.

Baldwin, J. D. (1968): The social behavior of adult male squirrel monkeys (*Saimiri sciureus*) in a seminatural environment. *Folia Primat, 9,* 281-314.

Bernstein, I. S. (1964): A field study of the activities of howler monkeys. *Anim Behav, 12,* 92-97.

Bernstein, I. S. (1967): A field study of the pigtail monkey (*Macaca nemestrina*). *Primates, 8,* 217-228.

Bernstein, I. S. (1968): The Lutong of Kuala Selangor. *Behavior, 32,* 1-16.

Blurton Jones, N. G., and Trollope, J. (1968): Social behaviour of stump-tailed macaques in captivity. *Primates, 9,* 365-394.

Booth, C. (1962): Some observations on behaviour of Cercopithecus monkeys. *Ann NY Acad Sci, 102,* 477-487.

Buettner-Janusch, J. (1964): The breeding of Galagos in captivity and some notes on their behavior. *Folia Primat, 2,* 93-110.

Butler, H. (1967): Seasonal breeding of the Senegal Galago (*Galago senegalensis senegalensis*) in the Nuba Mountains, Republic of the Sudan, *Folia Primat, 5,* 165-175.

Carpenter, C. R. (1934): A field study in Siam of the behavior and social relations of howling monkeys (*Alouatta palliata*). *Comp Psychol Monogr, 10,* 1-168.

Carpenter, C. R. (1935): Behavior of red spider monkeys in Panama. *J Mammal, 16,* 171-180.

Carpenter, C. R. (1942a): Sexual behavior of free ranging rhesus monkeys (*Macaca mulatta*). I. Specimens, procedures and behavioral characteristics of estrus. *J Comp Psychol, 33,* 113-142.

Carpenter, C. R. (1942b): Sexual behavior of free ranging rhesus monkeys (*Macaca mulatta*). II. Periodicity of estrus, homosexual, autoerotic and non-conformist behavior. *J Comp Psychol, 33,* 143-162.

Castellanos, H., and McCombs, H. L. (1968): The reproductive cycle of the New World monkey. *Fertil Steril, 19,* 213-227.

Catchpole, H. R., and Fulton, J. F. (1943): The oestrous cycle in *Tarsius:* Observations on a captive pair. *J Mammal, 24,* 90-93.

Christen, A. (1968): Haltung und Brutbiologie von *Cebuella. Folia Primat, 8,* 41-49.

Clewe, T. H. (1969): Observations on reproduction of squirrel monkeys in captivity. *J Reprod Fertil (Suppl.), 6,* 151-156.

Chalmers, N. R. (1968): The social behaviour of free living mangabeys in Uganda. *Folia Primat, 8,* 263-281.

Conaway, C. H., and Koford, C. B. (1964): Estrous cycles and mating behavior in a free-ranging band of rhesus monkeys. *J Mammal, 45,* 577-588.

Conaway, C. H., and Sade, D. S. (1965): The seasonal spermatogenic cycle in free ranging rhesus monkeys. *Folia Primat, 3,* 1-12.

Conaway, C. H., and Sorenson, N. W. (1966): Reproduction in tree shrews. *Symp Zool Soc London, 15,* 471-492.

Corner, G. W. (1945): Development, organization and breakdown of the corpus luteum in the rhesus monkey. *Contr Embryol (Washington, D.C.), 31,* 117-146.

David, G. F. X., and Ramaswami, L. S. (1969): Studies on menstrual cycles and other related phenomena in the langur (*Presbytis entellus*). *Folia Primat, 11,* 300-316.

Doyle, G. A.; Pelletier, A., and Bekker, T. (1967): Courtship, mating and parturition in the lesser bushbaby (*Galago senegalensis moholi*) under semi-natural conditions. *Folia Primat, 7,* 169-197.

DuMond, F. V., and Hutchinson, T. C. (1967): Squirrel monkey reproduction: The "fatted" male phenomenon and seasonal spermatogenesis. *Science, 158,* 1467-1470.

Eckstein, P., and Zuckerman, S. (1956): The oestrous cycle in the *Mammalia.* In Parkes, A. S. (Ed.): *Marshall's Physiology of Reproduction.* London, Longmans Green, pp. 328-359.

Epple, G. (1967): Vergleichende Untersuchungen über Sexual- und Sozialverhalten der Krallenaffen (*Hapalidae*). *Folia Primat, 7,* 36-65.

Epple, G. (1970): Maintenance, breeding, and development of marmoset monkeys (*Callithricidae*) in captivity. *Folia Primat, 12,* 56-76.

Evans, C. S., and Goy, R. W. (1968): Social behaviour and reproductive cycles in captive ring-tailed lemurs (*Lemur catta*). *J Zool London, 156,* 181-197.

Fox, H. (1929): The birth of two anthropoid apes. *J Mammal, 10,* 37-51.

Gartlan, J. S. (1969): Sexual and maternal behavior of the vervet monkey, *Cercopithecus aethiops. J Reprod Fert (Suppl), 6,* 137-150.

Gilbert, C., and Gillman, J. (1951): Pregnancy in the baboon (*Papio ursinus*). *S Afr J Med Sci, 16,* 115-124.

Gillman, J., and Gilbert, C. (1946): The reproductive cycle of the chacma baboon (*Papio ursinus*) with special reference to the problems of menstrual irregularities as assessed by the behaviour of the sex skin. *S Afr J Med Sci, 11,* 1-54.

Hall, K. R. L. (1962): The sexual, agonistic and derived social behaviour patterns of the wild chacma baboon, *Papio ursinus. Proc Zool Soc London, 139,* 283-327.

Hall, K. R. L. (1965): The behaviour and ecology of the wild patas monkey, *Erythrocebus patas,* in Uganda. *J Zool London, 148,* 15-87.

Hall, K. R. L., and Devore, I. (1965): Baboon social behavior. In DeVore, I. (Ed.): *Primate Behavior.* New York, Holt, Rinehart and Winston, pp. 53-110.

Hall, K. R. L.; Boelkins, R. C., and Goswell, M. J. (1965): Behaviour of patas monkeys, *Erythrocebus patas,* in captivity, with notes on the natural habitat. *Folia Primat, 3,* 22-49.

Hamlett, G. W. D. (1939): Reproduction in American monkeys. I. estrous cycle, ovulation and menstruation in cebus. *Anat Rec, 73,* 171-187.

Hampton, J. K.; Hampton, S. H., and Landwehr, B. T. (1966): Observations on a successful breeding colony of the marmoset, *Oedipomidas oedipus. Folia Primat, 4,* 265-287.

Harrison, B. (1963): Trying to breed *Tarsius. Malay Nat J, 17,* 218-231.

Harrison, J. L. (1955): Data on the reproduction of some Malayan mammals. *Proc Zool Soc London, 125,* 445-460.

Hartman, C. G. (1932): Studies in the reproduction of the monkey *Macacus (Pithecus) rhesus,* with special reference to menstruation and pregnancy. *Contr Embryol* (Washington, D.C.), *23,* 1-161.

Hartman, C. G. (1938): Some observations on the bonnet macaque. *J Mammal, 19,* 468-474.

Henrickx, A. G., and Kraemer, D. C. (1969): Observations on the menstrual cycle, optimal mating time and pre-implantation embryos of the baboon, *Papio anubis* and *Papio cynocephalus. J Reprod Fertil (Suppl.), 6,* 119-128.

Herbert, J. (1970): Hormones and reproductive behaviour in rhesus and talapoin monkeys. *J Reprod Fertil (Suppl.) 11,* 119-140.

Hooff, J. A. R. A. M. van (1962): Facial expressions in higher primates. *Symp Zool Soc London, 8,* 97-125.

Hopf, S. (1967): Notes on pregnancy, delivery, and infant survival in captive squirrel monkeys. *Primates, 8,* 323-332.

Hutchinson, T. C. (1970): Vaginal cytology and reproduction in the squirrel monkey (*Saimiri sciureus*). *Folia Primat, 12,* 212-223.

Imanishi, K. (1957): Social behaviour in Japanese monkeys, *Macaca fuscata. Psychologia, 1,* 47-54.

Ioannou, J. M. (1966): The oestrous cycle of the Potto. *J Reprod Fertil, 11,* 455-457.

Jay, P. (1965): The common langur of North India. In DeVore, I. (Ed.): *Primate Behavior.* New York, Holt, Rinehart & Winston, pp. 197-249.

Jolly, A. (1966): *Lemur Behavior: A Madagascar Field Study.* Chicago, University of Chicago Press.

Jones, C., and Sabater Pi, J. (1968): Comparative ecology of *Cercocebus albigena* and *Cercocebus torquatus* in Rio Muni, West Africa. *Folia Primat, 9,* 99-113.

Kaufman, I. C., and Rosenblum, L. A. (1966): A behavioral taxonomy for *Macaca nemestrina* and *Macaca radiata:* Based on longitudinal observation of family groups in the laboratory. *Primates, 7,* 205-258.

Keverne, E. B., and Michael, R. P. (1970): Annual changes in the menstruation of rhesus monkeys. *J Endocr, 48,* 669-670.

Kirchshofer, R. (1962): Beobachtungen bei der Geburt eines Zwergschimpansen (*Pan paniscus Schwarz 1929*) und einige Bemerkungen zum Paarungsverhalten. *Z Tierpsychol, 19,* 597-606.

Kummer, H. (1968): *Social Organization of Hamadryas Baboons.* Chicago, University of Chicago Press.

Latta, J.; Hopf, S., and Ploog, D. (1967): Observation on mating behavior and sexual play in the squirrel monkey (*Saimiri sciureus*). *Primates, 8,* 229-246.

Lawick-Goodall, J. van (1968): The behaviour of free-living chimpanzees in the Gombe Stream Reserve. *Anim Behav Monogr, 1,* 161-311.

Manley, G. H. (1966): Reproduction in Lorisoid primates. *Symp Zool Soc London, 15,* 493-509.

Manley, G. H. (1967): Gestation periods in the *Lorisidae. Inter Zoo Year Book, 7,* 80-81.

Martin, R. D. (1968): Reproduction and ontogeny in tree-shrews (*Tupaia belangeri*), with reference to their general behaviour and taxonomic relationships. *Z Tierpsychol,* 25, 409-495 and 505-532.

Mason, W. A. (1966): Social organization of the South American monkey, *Callicebus moloch:* A preliminary report. *Tulane Studies in Zoology, 13,* 23-28.

Michael, R. P. (1965): Some aspects of the endocrine control of sexual activity in primates. *Proc Roy Soc Med, 58,* 595-598.

Michael, R. P. (1968): Gonadal hormones and the control of primate behaviour. In Michael, R. P. (Ed.): *Endocrinology and Human Behaviour.* London, Oxford University Press, pp. 69-93.

Michael R. P. (1971): Neuroendocrine factors regulating primate behavior. In Martini, L., and Ganong, W. F. (Eds.): *Frontiers in Neuroendocrinology, 1971.* New York, Oxford University Press.

Michael, R. P., and Keverne, E. B. (1968): Pheromones in the communication of sexual status in primates. *Nature* (*London*), *218,* 746-749.

Michael, R. P., and Keverne, E. B. (1970): Primate sexual pheromones of vaginal origin. *Nature* (*London*), *225,* 84-85.

Michael, R. P., and Keverne, E. B. (1971): An annual rhythm in the sexual activity of the male rhesus monkey (*Macaca mulatta*) in the laboratory. *J Reprod Fertil* (in press).

Michael, R. P., and Saayman, G. (1967a): Individual differences in the sexual behaviour of male rhesus monkeys (*Macaca mulatta*) under laboratory conditions. *Anim Behav, 15,* 460-466.

Michael, R. P., and Saayman, G. (1967b): Sexual performance and the timing of ejaculation in male rhesus monkeys (*Macaca mulatta*). *J Comp Physiol, Psychol, 64,* 213-218.

Michael, R. P., and Saayman, G. (1968): Differential effects on behaviour of the subcutaneous and intravaginal administration of oestrogen in the rhesus monkey (*Macaca mulatta*). *J Endocr, 41,* 231-246.

Michael, R. P., and Welegalla, J. (1968): Ovarian hormones and the sexual behaviour of the female rhesus monkey (*Macaca mulatta*) under laboratory conditions. *J Endocr, 41,* 407-420.

Michael, R. P., and Zumpe, D. (1970a): Sexual initiating behaviour by female rhesus monkeys (*Macaca mulatta*) under laboratory conditions. *Behaviour, 36,* 168-186.

Michael, R. P., and Zumpe, D. (1970b): Rhythmic changes in the copulatory frequency of rhesus monkeys (*Macaca mulatta*) in relation to the menstrual cycle and a comparison with the human cycle. *J Reprod Fertil, 21,* 199-201.

Michael, R. P. and Zumpe, D. (1970c). Aggression and gonadal hormones in captive rhesus monkeys (*Macaca mulatta*). *Anim Behav, 18,* 1-10.

Michael, R. P.; Herbert, J., and Welegalla, J. (1966): Ovarian hormones and grooming behaviour in the rhesus monkey (*Macaca mulatta*) under laboratory conditions, *J Endocr, 36,* 263-279.

Michael, R. P.; Herbert, J., and Welegalla, J. (1967): Ovarian hormones and the sexual behaviour of the male rhesus monkey (*Macaca mulatta*) under laboratory conditions. *J Endocr, 39,* 81-98.

Michael, R. P.; Saayman, G., and Zumpe, D. (1968): The suppression of mounting behaviour and ejaculation in male rhesus monkeys (*Macaca mulatta*) by administering progesterone to their female partners. *J Endocr, 41,* 421-431.

Moynihan, M. (1964): Some behavior patterns of Platyrrhine monkeys. I. The night monkey (*Aotus trivirgatus*). *Smithson Misc Coll, (Washington, D.C.), 146,* 1-84.

Moynihan, M. (1966): Communication in the Titi monkey, *Callicebus. J Zool London, 150,* 77-127.

Napier, J. R., and Napier, P. H. (1967): *A Handbook of Living Primates.* London, Academic Press.

Petter, J. J. (1965): The lemurs of Madagascar. In DeVore, I. (Ed.): *Primate Behavior.* New York, Holt, Rinehart & Winston, pp. 292-319.

Petter-Rousseaux, A. (1964): Reproductive physiology and behavior of the *Lemuroidea.* In Buettner-Janusch, J. (Ed.): *Evolutionary and Genetic Biology of Primates.* New York, Academic Press, pp. 91-132.

Poirier, F. E. (1969): Behavioral flexibility and intertroop variation among Nilgiri langurs (*Presbytis johnii*) of South India. *Folia Primat, 11,* 119-133.

Prakash, I. (1962): Group organization, sexual behavior and breeding season of certain Indian monkeys. *Jap J Ecol, 12,* 83-86.

Rahaman, H., and Parthasarathy, M. D. (1969): Studies on the social behaviour of bonnet monkeys. *Primates, 10,* 149-162.

Ramakrishna, P. A., and Prasad, M. R. N. (1967): Changes in the male reproductive organs of *Loris tardigradus lydekkerianus. Folia Primat, 5,* 176-189.

Rosenblum, L. A.; Nathan, T.; Nelson, J., and Kaufman, I. C. (1967): Vaginal cornification cycles in the squirrel monkey *(Saimiri sciureus). Folia Primat, 6,* 83-91.

Rowell, T. E. (1968): Grooming by adult baboons in relation to reproductive cycles. *Anim Behav, 16,* 585-588.

Rowell, T. E. (1970): Reproductive cycles of two *Cercopithecus* monkeys. *J Reprod Fertil, 22,* 321-338.

Rowell, T. E., and Chalmers, N. R. (1970): Reproductive cycles of the mangabey *Cercocebus albigena. Folia Primat, 12,* 264-272.

Saayman, G. S. (1970): The menstrual cycle and sexual behaviour in a troop of free ranging chacma baboons *(Papio ursinus). Folia Primat, 12,* 81-110.

Sade, D. S., and Hildrech, R. W. (1965): Notes of the green monkey (*Cercopithecus aethiops sabaeus*) on St. Kitts, West Indies. *Carib J Sci, 5,* 67-79.

Schaller, G. B. (1963): *The Mountain Gorilla.* Chicago, University of Chicago Press.

Simonds, P. E. (1965): The bonnet macaque in South India. In DeVore, I. (Ed.): *Primate Behavior.* New York, Holt, Rinehart & Winston, pp. 175-196.

Sorenson, M. W., and Conaway, C. H. (1968): The social and reproductive behavior of *Tupaia montana* in captivity. *J Mammal, 49,* 502-512.

Southwick, C. H.; Beg, M. A., and Siddiqi, M. R. (1961): A population survey of rhesus monkeys in Northern India: II. Transportation routes and forest areas. *Ecology, 42,* 698-710.

Southwick, C. H.: Beg, M. A., and Siddiqi, M. R. (1965): Rhesus monkeys in North India. In DeVore, I. (Ed.): *Primate Behavior.* New York, Holt, Rinehart & Winston, pp. 111-159.

Spivak, H. (1968): *Ausdrucksformen und soziale Beziehungen in einer Dschelada-Gruppe (Theropithecus gelada) im Zoo.* Zurich, Juris Druck + Verlag.

Struhsaker, T. T. (1967): Behavior of vervet monkeys *(Cercopithecus aethiops). Univ Calif Publ Zool, 82,* 1-74.

Struhsaker, T. T. (1969): Correlates of ecology and social organization among African Cercopithecines. *Folia Primat, 11,* 80-118.

Sugiyama, Y.; Yoshiba, K., and Parthasarathy, M. D. (1965): Home range, mating season, male group and inter-troop relations in Hanuman langurs (*Presbytis entellus*). *Primates, 6,* 73-106.

Thorington, R. W. (1968): Observations of the tamarin *Saguinus midas. Folia Primat, 9,* 95-98.

Tokuda, K. (1961-62): A study on the sexual behavior in the Japanese monkey troop. *Primates, 3,* 1-40.

Tokuda, K.; Simons, R. C., and Jensen, G. D. (1968): Sexual behavior in a captive group of pigtailed monkeys (*Macaca nemestrina*). *Primates, 9,* 283-294.

Udry, J. R., and Morris, N. M. (1968): Distribution of coitus in the menstrual cycle. *Nature (London), 220,* 593-596.

Vandenbergh, J. G., and Vessey, S. (1968): Seasonal breeding of free-ranging rhesus monkeys and related ecological factors. *J Reprod Fertil, 15,* 71-79.

Wagenen, G. van (1945): Optimal mating time for pregnancy in the monkey. *Endocrinology, 37,* 307-312.

Yerkes, R. M., and Elder, J. H. (1936): Oestrus, receptivity, and mating in chimpanzees. *Comp Psychol Monogr, 13* (No. 5).

Young, W. C., and Yerkes, R. M. (1943): Factors influencing the reproductive cycle in the chimpanzee; the period of adolescent sterility and related problems. *Endocrinology, 33,* 121-154.

Zuckerman, S. (1937): The duration and phases of the menstrual cycle in primates. *Proc. Zool Soc London, 107* (A), 315-329.

Zuckerman, S. (1953): The breeding seasons of mammals in captivity. *Proc Zool Soc London, 122,* 827-950.

Zumpe, D., and Michael, R. P. (1968): The clutching reaction and orgasm in the female rhesus monkey *(Macaca mulatta). J Endocr, 40,* 117-123.

Chapter 9

OOGENESIS AND FOLLICULOGENESIS

H. BUTLER

I. OOGENESIS

A. Primordial Germ Cells

Origin and Migration. It is generally agreed that the primordial germ cells of vertebrates have an extragonadal origin in the endoderm of the yolk sac. A full account of the origin and subsequent migration of the primordial germ cells of primates is only available for man (Witschi, 1948). In the Senegal galago migrating primordial germ cells are found in the dorsal mesentery and the beginning genital ridge when the embryo is 3.6 mm greatest length (Fig. 9-1). The primordial germ cells are large and have vesicular nuclei with one or more nucleoli. Primordial germ cells have entered the genital ridge of a rhesus monkey embryo of thirty-three days conception age (van Wagenen and Simpson, 1965).

Fate. When the primordial germ cells arrive in the genital ridge there is an increase in its prominence and proliferation of its covering coelomic epithelium to form the germinal cords. This occurs in approximately forty-day embryos of the rhesus monkey and man. At the same time, however, the primordial germ cells lose all or most of their distinguishing characters and become lost among the proliferating epithelial cells. It is uncertain whether the presence of primordial germ cells is necessary for the formation of the genital ridges, but experimental evidence indicates that their absence leads to the development of sterile gonads (Franchi *et al.*, 1962).

B. Ovarian Differentiation

For a period of time following the arrival of the primordial germ cells and the commencement of epithelial proliferation, the

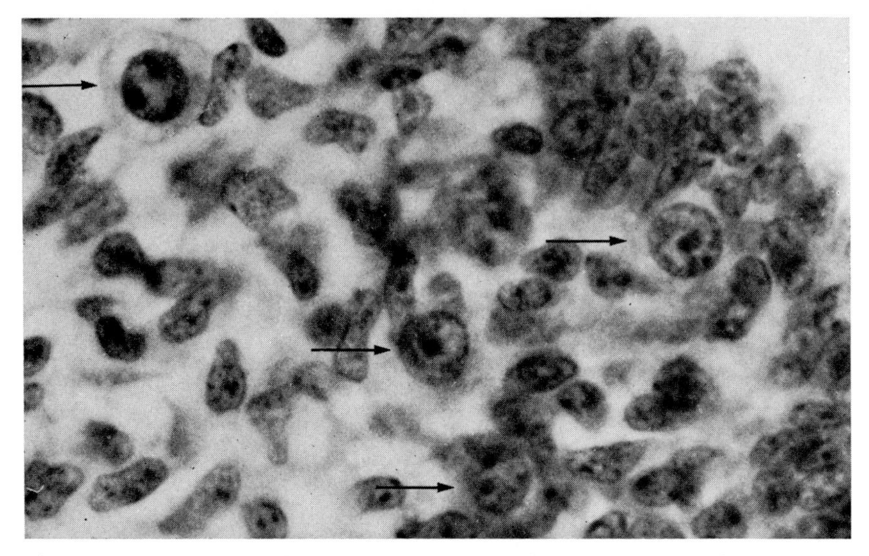

Figure 9-1. Four primordial germ cells (arrowed) in the genital ridge of a 3.5 mm greatest length embryo of the Senegal galago. Note the proximity of one of them to the proliferating germinal epithelium.

male and female gonads are indistinguishable. Primates follow the general rule that histological differentiation of the testis precedes that of the ovary. The definitive ovary is recognizable in the forty-six-day-old rhesus monkey embryo. Epithelial cells continue to proliferate in the peripheral zone of the developing ovary and have formed the definitive ovarian cortex in fifty to sixty-day-old rhesus monkey embryos. Some of the cells of the ovarian cortex enlarge to form the definitive germ cells or oogonia which begin to proliferate by mitotic division. This process begins close to the cortico-medullary junction and spreads outwards to the surface of the ovary. Smaller epithelial cells intermingled with the oogonia are the somatic or pregranulosa cells destined to form the granulosa cells which will eventually cover the primary oocytes. At the same time the ovarian cortex is invaded by connective tissue and blood vessels growing outwards from the medulla which break it up into irregular masses or germinal cords. This is a critical but still ill-understood phase of ovarian development because the apparent disappearance of the primordial germ cells amongst the proliferating epithelial cells obscures the origin and relationship of the definitive oogonia and pregranulosa cells. Some believe that the primordial germ cells give rise to the definitive oogonia and the epithelial cells become the pregranulosa cells, and others believe that the primordial germ cells disappear and that both the definitive oogonia and pregranulosa cells are derived from the epithelial cells.

C. *Prepuberal Oogenesis*

Histological Characteristics. In the majority of Eutherian mammals that have been investigated, oogenesis is completed before birth or during the first few weeks of postnatal life. In this context oogenesis is defined as the mitotic proliferation of oogonia followed by the formation of primordial follicles consisting of primary oocytes in the arrested diplotene stage of miosis and surrounded by a single layer of flattened granulosa cells. These female mammals have, therefore, acquired their entire stock of primordial follicles before or very shortly after birth, and, consequently, the proliferation of oogonia and the formation of new primordial follicles does not occur when they become sexually mature. Thus oogenesis differs sharply from spermatogenesis which does not commence until just prior to puberty and then remains a continuous process throughout the life of the adult male mammal. Oogenesis occurs in this manner in the rhesus monkey and man and most probably in the baboon and anthropoid apes.

Oogenesis is fully documented for the rhesus monkey (van Wagenen and Simpson, 1965). Following mitotic proliferation the oogonia enter the prophase of miosis and become primary oocytes. This occurs first at the cortico-medullary junction and steadily spreads outwards towards the surface of the ovary. Miosis proceeds to the diplotene stage where it becomes arrested and does not resume until immediately prior to ovulation. Primary oocytes in arrested diplotene become surrounded by a single layer of flattened granulosa cells forming primordial follicles. The first formed primordial follicles are at the cortico-medullary junction and the process spreads centrifugally until practically all the germinal cords are replaced by them. The last signs of oogenesis are seen in the form of small germinal cords in the ovarian cortex immediately subjacent to the misnamed germinal epithelium covering the surface of the ovary. They have completely disappeared from the ovary by nine months to one year after birth, i.e. well

TABLE 9-I

TIMETABLE OF MAJOR EVENTS OF OOGENESIS IN RHESUS MONKEY AND HUMAN FETUSES*

	Rhesus Monkey	*Man*
	Conception Age in Lunar Months	*Menstrual Age in Lunar Months*
Enlarged Oogonia First Appear	2.5–2.8	2.5–3.0
Miosis First Appears	2.5–2.8	3.0–3.5
First Primordial Follicles	4.0–4.5	4.5–5.5
Cuboidal Granulosa Cells in Primordial Follicles	4.0–4.5	5.5–6.0
Enlarged Primary Oocytes in Multilaminar Follicles	5.0–5.5	7.5–9.0
Birth	6	10

* Data from van Wagenen and Simpson, 1965

before puberty which occurs between 3.0 to 4.5 years of age. A similar sequence of events occurs somewhat later (Table 9-I) in the human ovary (van Wagenen and Simpson, 1965) and this is in accord with the difference in length of gestation, ten lunar months in man as compared to six lunar months in the rhesus monkey. Also, in man all histological appearances suggestive of the new formation of oocytes have disappeared by the fourth month of postnatal life.

Quantitative Aspects. Counts of the total germ cell population of fetal and postnatal rhesus monkey ovaries completely substantiate the histological evidence that oogenesis ceases shortly after birth (Baker, 1963, 1966b). These counts also indicate the extent to which germ cells are destroyed by atresia (Table 9-II). Quantitative analysis of the different kinds of germ cells shows that at two months postcoitus oogonia form over 90 percent of the total population of germ cells and no primary oocytes in the diplotene stage of miosis are present. In full term fetuses and neonates, there are only 4 to 5 percent oogonia, but primary oocytes in diplotene, normal and atretic, form over 80 percent of the total population of germ cells.

D. Postpuberal Oogenesis

Histological Characteristics. Gérard (1920, 1932) first described germinal cords, showing all the histological features of oogenesis,

TABLE 9-II

TOTAL POPULATION OF GERM CELLS, NORMAL AND ATRETIC, IN ONE OVARY OF FETAL, PREPUBERAL AND ADULT RHESUS MONKEYS*

Age	*Germ Cells Per Ovary*		
	Normal	*Atretic*	*Total*
2 Months Postcoitum	148,600	6,400	155,000
3 Months Postcoitum	692,000	104,500	796,500
4 Months Postcoitum	874,900	210,500	1,085,400
5 Months Postcoitum	1,098,200	660,800	1,759,000
Full-term Fetuses and Neonates	267,200	187,800	455,000
Prepuberal (1.5–3.0 years)	—	—	162,000
Old Multiparous Females	—	—	20,000

* Based on data from Baker, 1966b

in the ovary of an adult Moholi bush baby. He believed that the new germ cells in these cords were derived from the germinal epithelium. Since then similar germinal cords have been found in the ovarian cortex of several adult prosimians: *Daubentonia madagascariensis, Loris tardigradus, Nycticebus coucang, Perodicticus potto, Galago demidovii, Galago senegalensis senegalensis and Galago senegalensis braccatus.*

Examination of many pairs of ovaries from adult Senegal galagos shows that varying quantities of germinal cords are always present in the cortex (Butler, 1964, 1969). The cords of germinal cells are surrounded by a connective tissue capsule which separates them from the ovarian stroma and the germinal epithelium (Fig. 9-2A). They contain oogonia, primary oocytes in the prophase of miosis and somatic or pregranulosa cells. Oogonia in mitotic metaphase are only occasionally seen. Some germinal cords contain very large and peripherally situated cells surrounded by a single layer of pregranulosa cells (Fig. 9-2B). They are about twice the size of oogonia and have a large spherical nucleus which appears to be structurally identical with the dictyotene (arrested diplotene) nucleus of the primary oocytes in the primordial follicles lying within the ovarian stroma. Germinal cords have been found containing primary oocytes ranging in size from 50 to 96μ in diameter. The largest of these oocytes is the same size as the fully grown primary oocyte at the time of ovulation and has a zona pellucida

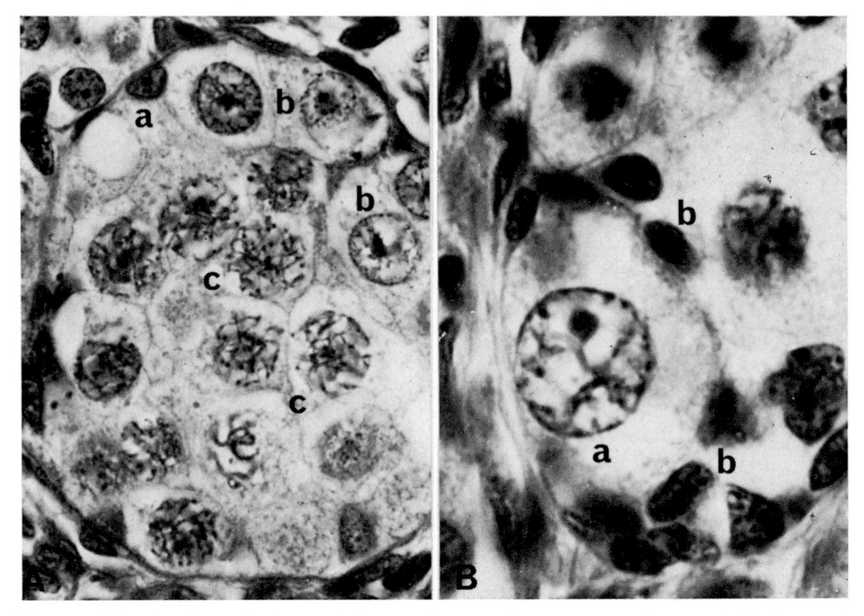

Figure 9-2. A. Germinal cord from the ovarian cortex of an adult Senegal galago showing a pregranulosa cell (a), oogonia (b) and oocytes in the prophase of miosis (c). B. A large oocyte (a), with a dictyate nucleus and a single layer of granulosa cells (b), lying within a germinal cord.

(Fig. 9-3A). It is surrounded by two or three layers of regularly arranged granulosa cells. Oogonia and primary oocytes in the prophase of miosis are present in the same germinal cord. These findings support the view that new primary oocytes are being formed in the adult Senegal galago and indicate the manner in which polyovular follicles are formed. They also raise the possibility that the newly formed primary oocytes may not be liberated from the germinal cords, and therefore, do not add to the total stock of primordial follicles.

The ovary of the newborn Senegal bushbaby has a thick cortical zone of germinal cords with primordial follicles situated at the cortico-medullary junction. It is not yet known when oogenesis commences in the fetus. Prepuberal animals have a similar thick cortical zone of germinal cords. In postpuberal animals the quantity of germinal cords varies greatly suggesting that their activity may be influenced by cyclic fluctuations of the sex hormones and/or age. Germinal cords were very small and scanty in a yellow-thighed gal-

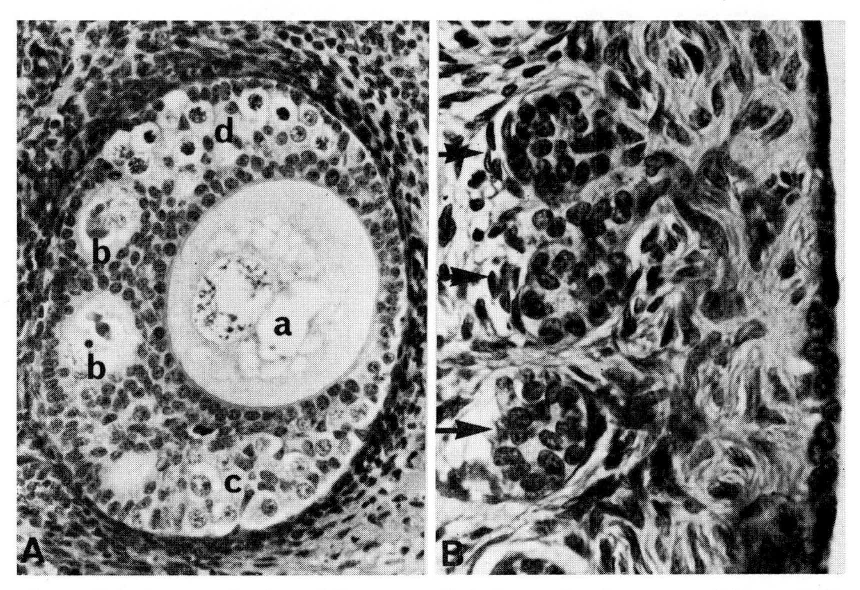

Figure 9-3. A. Germinal cord from an adult Senegal galago containing a fully grown primary oocyte (a) with a zona pellucida and surrounded by granulosa cells. Two smaller primary oocytes (b) are undergoing atresia. There are also oogonia (c) and oocytes (d) in the prophase of miosis. B. The ovarian cortex of a yellow-thighed galago aged 5 years and 10 months. The cords of cells (arrowed) contain neither oogonia nor oocytes in the prophase of miosis.

ago aged five years and ten months which had been showing regular sex cycles for four years and five months. The ovarian cortex contained numerous cords of small cells resembling pregranulosa cells (Fig. 9-3B).

Ultrastructural Studies. Electron microscopic preparations of the ovarian cortex of the adult Senegal galago (Butler, 1969) show that the germinal cords consist of large round cells surrounded by a connective tissue capsule (Fig. 9-4A). Many of the large round cells (Fig. 9-4B) have all the ultrastructural features found in the oogonia of embryonic mammalian ovaries (Franchi and Mandl, 1963). These include a relatively large nucleus with a granular matrix which is more electron dense than the cytoplasm; one or more nucleoli showing a coarse irregular network of finely particulate material; large oval mitochondria and continuity of cytoplasm between adjacent cells across cell bridges.

Other cells have tripartite cords or synaptinemal cores (Fig. 9-

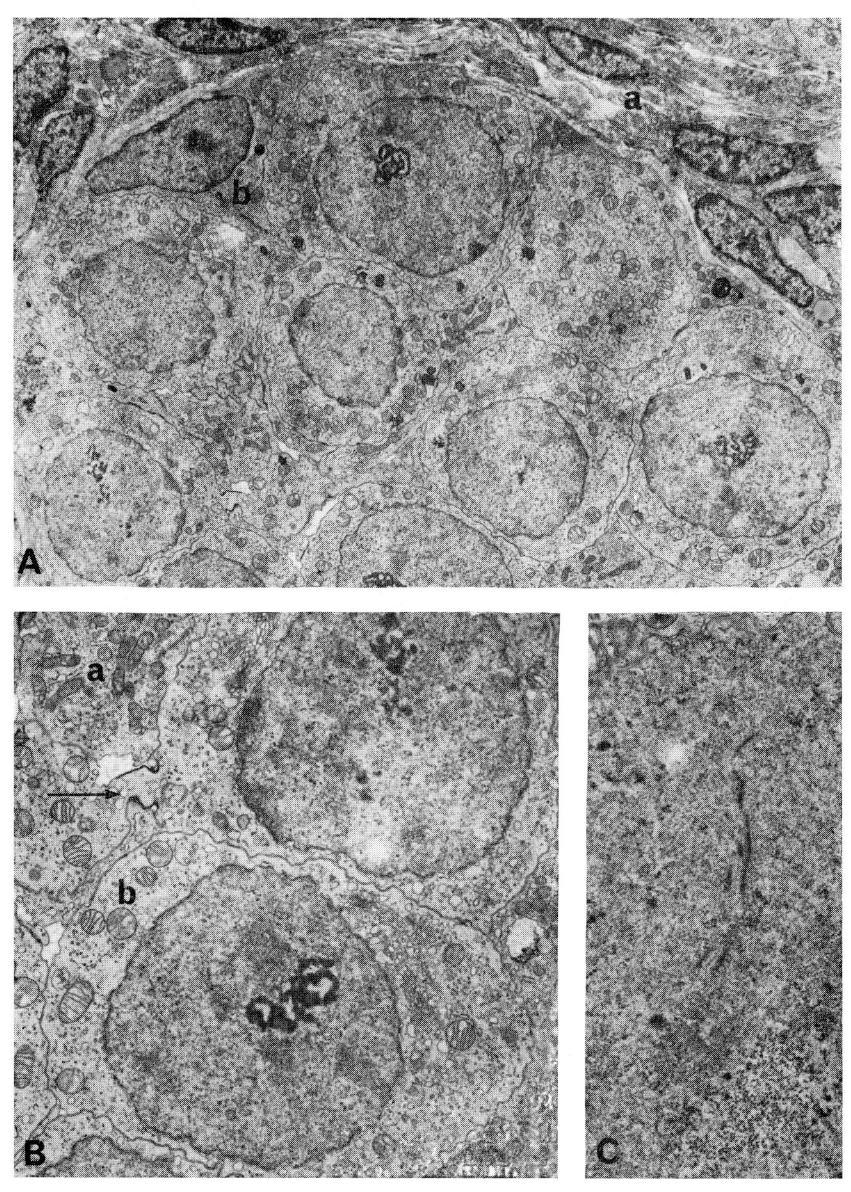

Figure 9-4. A. EM section of part of a germinal cord from an adult Senegal galago showing the connective tissue capsule (a) and a pregranulosa cell (b). The other cells within the germinal cord are oogonia. B. Two oogonia showing the characteristic nucleolus and an intercellular bridge (arrow). Note the different shape and size of the mitochondria of the pregranulosa cell (a) and the oogonium (b). C. A tripartite core, characteristic of the pachytene stage of miosis, in the nucleus of an oocyte from an adult Senegal galago.

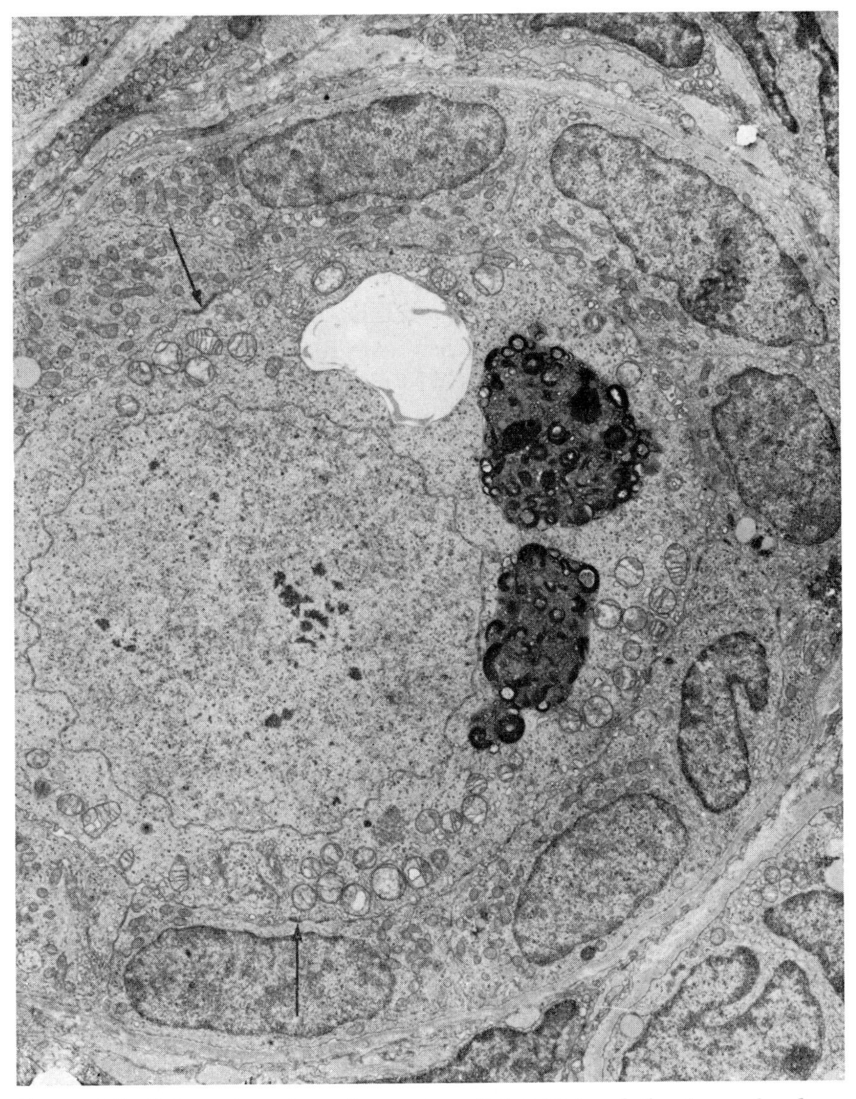

Figure 9-5. EM section through a primordial follicle of the Senegal galago. The oocyte has no zona pellucida and its cell membrane is in close contact with those of the granulosa cells. The arrows indicate junctional complexes. Compare the nuclei and mitochondria of the granulosa cells with those of the pregranulosa cells in Figure 9-4 A and B.

4C) which are characteristic of the pachytene stage of miosis (Moses, 1958) and, therefore, are primary oocytes. The pregranulosa cells completely line the connective tissue capsule and have irregular centrally directed cytoplasmic processes which form an incomplete network amongst the oogonia. The pregranulosa cells closely resemble the granulosa cells of the primordial follicles (Fig. 9-5). The main differences are the more regular shape and presence of lipid deposits in the granulosa cells.

Radioautographic Studies. Radioautographs of the ovarian cortex were made at four hours and at ten days after the injection of 250 μc of H^3-thymidine into adult Senegal galagos (Butler and Juma, 1970). At four hours the germinal tubes show numerous heavily labelled oogonia. At ten days there are very few labelled cells in the germinal cords. Some are oogonia with a greatly reduced label indicating that there has been mitotic proliferation of oogonia since injection of the H^3-thymidine. Others are heavily labelled primary oocytes with a zygotene/pachytene nucleus (Fig. 9-6). Prophase of miosis in these oocytes is, therefore, a slow process and requires

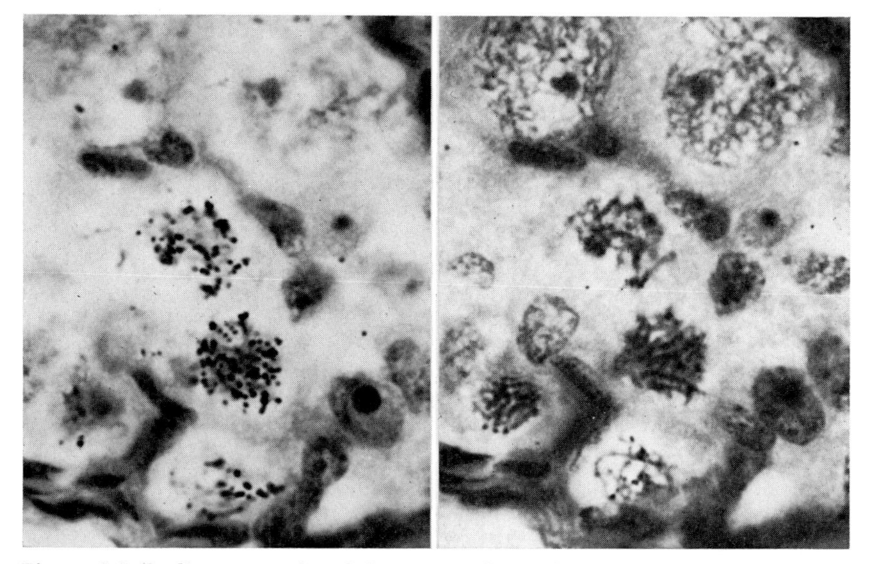

Figure 9-6. Radioautographs of the ovary of an adult Senegal galago removed 10 days after exposure to H^3-thymidine. The labelled nuclei are at the zygotene/pachytene stage of miosis.

TABLE 9-III

EFFECT OF GONADAL HORMONES ON THE PRIMORDIAL GERM CELL POPULATIONS IN LORIS*

Group	*Percentage Distribution of*		
	Oogonia	*Primordial Oocytes*	*Atretic Germ Cells*
Control	5.1	5.4	9.4
Estrogen	4.7	6.3	10.9
Progesterone	5.6	2.7	11.0
Testosterone	8.8	5.9	7.9

* Based on data from Anand Kumar, 1968b

upwards of ten days to proceed from the premiotic DNA synthesis to the zygotene/pachytene stage.

Quantitative Aspects. Counts of the primordial germ cell population in ovaries from postnatal slender lorises indicate that they decrease from birth to puberty (Anand Kumar, 1968a). There is some indication that, in adults, oogenesis varies in relation to the sexual cycle and might be under endocrine control. He suggests that most of the newly formed germ cells perish as a result of atresia and could not decide whether the newly formed oocytes do actually add to the total stock of primordial follicles. He tested the possibility of endocrine control of oogenesis in the slender loris by studying the effects of 17-β estradiol, progesterone and testosterone on the primordial germ cells (Anand Kumar, 1968b). The results (Table 9-III) show an increase of the total number of primordial germ cells in all the treated lorises, but in estrogen-treated animals the percentage of primordial oocytes is greater than that of oogonia.

II. FOLLICULOGENESIS

A. The Ovarian Follicle

Number and Kind. Counts of the total population of ovarian follicles, both normal and atretic, in mature rhesus monkeys show an average of 54,650 per ovary (Green and Zuckerman, 1951). They can be classified into seven size groups ranging from primary oocytes, surrounded by a single layer of flattened granulosa cells, to follicles with an antrum. At least 90 to 95 percent of the follicle population consists of primary oocytes surrounded by a single

TABLE 9-IV

DIAMETER OF FULLY GROWN PRIMARY OOCYTES OF VARIOUS PRIMATES

Species	*Oocyte Diameter* (μ)
Tarsius sp.	90–100
Loris tardigradus	90–100
Galago senegalensis senegalensis	95
Callithrix sp.	80–100
Macaca mulatta	110–120
Hylobates sp.	110–120
Gorilla sp.	130–140
Homo sapiens	130–150

layer of flattened or cuboidal granulosa cells. The number of larger follicles decreases inversely with their size and the maximum number averaged 149 per ovary on day nine of the menstrual cycle of a rhesus monkey whose average cycle length was 28.2 days (Koering, 1969). Thus only about 0.25 percent of the total number of follicles have antra at the peak of follicular growth in a cycle, a number too insignificant to affect the *total* count. Earlier workers (Evans and Swezy, 1931) did not make total counts and were misled by the cyclic fluctuations of the very small number of growing follicles into believing that oogenesis was a continuous process in the adult rhesus monkey.

Primary Oocytes. The size of the primary oocytes varies greatly in relation to their stage of growth. Those in primordial follicles of the Senegal galago are 15 to 20μ in diameter but in the preovulatory follicle they are 95μ in diameter. The fully grown primary oocytes of primates fall into the general range for Eutherian mammals, i.e. 80 to 150μ in diameter (Table 9-IV). Large lipid droplets occur in the ooplasm of the primary oocytes of the Senegal galago and slender loris (Rao, 1927). A single large droplet is seen in the smallest primordial follicles, but as the oocyte grows they become smaller and more numerous and are widely dispersed in the ooplasm (Fig. 9-7A and B). The fully grown oocytes of the rhesus monkey (Hartman and Corner, 1941) and the baboon (Katzberg, 1967) have fine yolk granules, of unspecified nature, uniformly dispersed in the ooplasm.

The nuclei of oocytes in primordial follicles are generally re-

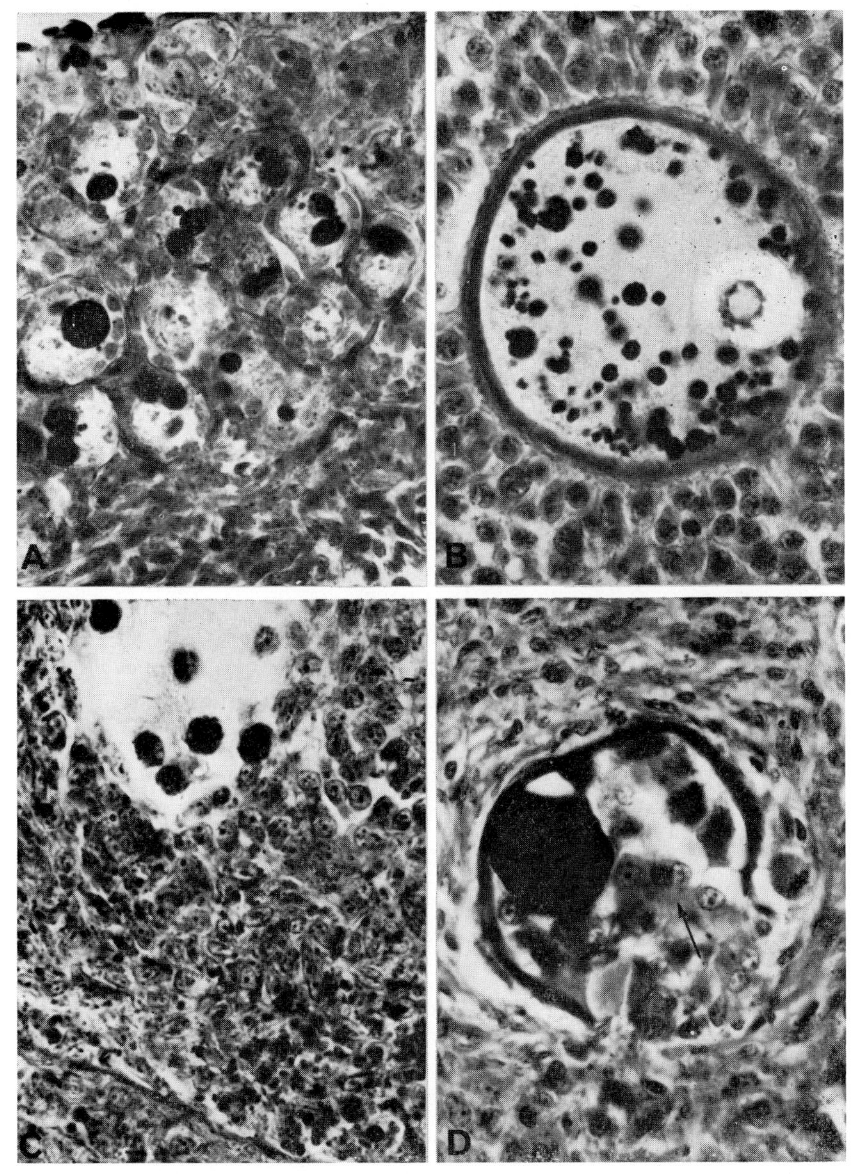

Figure 9-7. A. Primordial follicles from an adult Senegal galago showing one or two large lipid droplets in the oocyte. Compare with Figure 9-5. B. Fully grown oocyte showing the numerous lipid droplets scattered throughout the ooplasm. C. Part of the granulosa of a vesicular follicle in early atresia. The atretic granulosa cells contain lipid droplets and large cells, full of lipid, are floating in the follicular fluid. D. A very late stage of atresia of the oocyte. The thickened zona pellucida is ruptured and contains a large lipid droplet and numerous invading cells (? macrophages) (arrowed). All sections are from ovaries fixed in Fleming's solution.

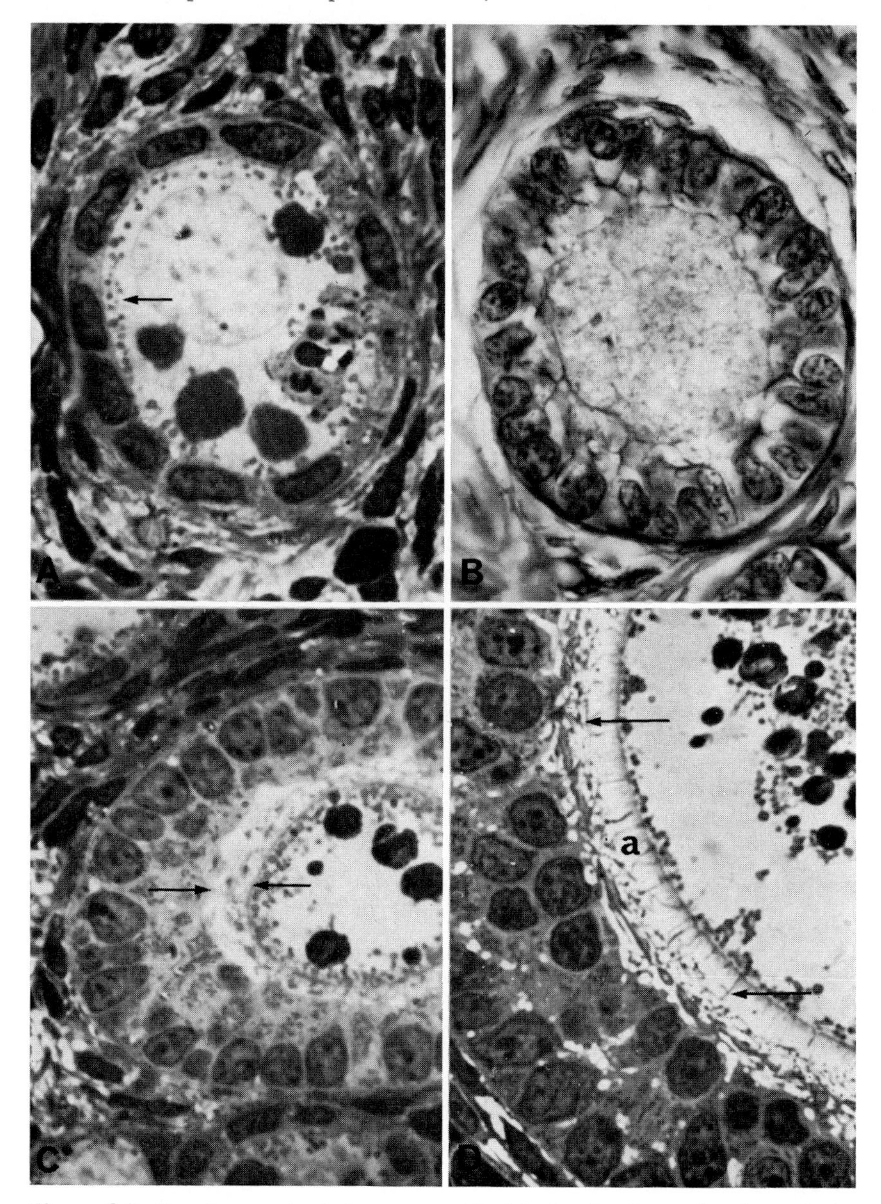

Figure 9-8. Development of the zona pellucida in the Senegal galago. A. In the smallest primordial follicles there is close contact between the flattened granulosa cells and the cell membrane of the oocyte. Compare with Figure 9-5. Note the zone of mitochondria (arrow) close to cell membrane of the oocyte. B. A slightly larger primordial follicle has cuboidal granulosa cells

garded as being in a prolonged "resting" or dictyate phase which intervenes between diplotene and preovulatory maturation (Franchi *et al.,* 1962). However, Baker (1966a) and Baker and Franchi (1966, 1967) believe that the oocytes in the primordial follicles of man, rhesus monkey, loris and galago remain at the diplotene stage. Histologically their nuclei contain well-defined deeply basophilic chromosomes bearing faint lateral projections which are larger in oocytes within multilaminar follicles. Electron microscopy shows that these chromosomes have an electron-dense axis or "core," a surrounding sheath of fibrillar material and clusters of granules at the outer limits of the sheath. These features are interpreted as indicating that these are "lampbrush" chromosomes, hitherto only found in invertebrates and nonmammalian vertebrates. Recent investigations into the uptake of tritiated uridine and phenylalanine by the ovaries of the rhesus monkey show a heavy label associated with the chromosomes and nucleoli and most of the extranucleolar silver grains are associated with condensed fibrillar material thought to represent part of the lateral component of "lampbrush" chromosomes (Baker *et al.,* 1969).

The fully grown oocyte of the Senegal galago is surrounded by a zona pellucida, some 7 to 8μ thick, which is strongly PAS positive and stains metachromatically with toluidine blue indicating the presence of acid mucopolysaccharides and polysaccharide proteins. The oocytes of primordial follicles with a single layer of flattened granulosa cells do not have a zona pellucida (Fig. 9-8A). The granulosa cells are in close contact with the surface of the oocyte and junctional complexes are seen (Fig. 9-5). Slightly larger follicles with a single layer of cuboidal granulosa cells have an irregular

---

←

with irregular thread-like deposits of PAS positive material between them and the oocyte. C. A one micron thick section reveals an irregular space (between arrows) separating the granulosa cells and oocyte. It contains microvilli arising from the granulosa cells and presumably the PAS positive material. D. The zone pellucida (a) is in close contact with the oocyte but an irregular space separates it from the granulosa cells. Granulosa cell microvilli cross this space and penetrate the zona pellucida. Many terminate in the outer half of the zona pellucida (upper arrow) but others make contact with the ovum (lower arrow).

space which completely surrounds the oocyte and separates it from the granulosa cells (Fig. 9-8C). This space contains numerous microvilli which arise from the granulosa cells and irregularly dispersed strands of PAS positive material (Fig. 9-8B). By the time growing follicles are on the verge of antrum formation the zona pellucida is fully formed (Fig. 9-8D). It is closely adherent to the oocyte, but a narrow space separates it from the irregular surfaces of the innermost layer of granulosa cells. The latter give rise to numerous stout microvilli which penetrate the zona pellucida. Some end in the outer half of the zona pellucida, but others penetrate completely and make contact with the surface of the ovum. Similar appearances are seen during the development of the zona pellucida of the baboon (Katzberg, 1967). The development of the zona pellucida in primates is very similar to that seen in other mammals (Chiquoine, 1960). The granulosa cells play an active part in the formation of the zona pellucida (Nørrevang, 1968), but there is controversy as to the part played by the oocyte. It is noteworthy that, at all stages of the development of the zona pellucida in the Senegal galago, there is a well marked zone of mitochondria immediately adjacent to the cell membrane (Fig. 9-8).

Little is known concerning the influence of sex hormones on the zona pellucida, but Katzberg (1967) has shown that gonadotrophins, which produce superovulation and multiple births in sterile women, profoundly affect the zona pellucida of the baboon. The zona pellucida of the oocytes of growing follicles becomes thickened and filled with enlarged vacuoles that disrupt it. The zona pellucida may disappear completely from the majority of the growing oocytes, but it is not clear whether gonadotrophins cause failure of development of the zona pellucida or destroy it by lysis similar to the action of hydrogen peroxide or hyaluronidase.

Follicular Growth. The growth of the follicle relative to the contained oocyte can be divided into two phases (Brambell, 1956). During the first phase the growth of the oocyte is rapid and correlated with follicular growth. During the second phase there is very considerable increase in follicular size, mainly due to antrum formation, but there is no significant correlated increase in oocyte diameter (Fig. 9-9). At the beginning of the second growth phase the solid follicle has about twenty layers of granulosa cells, and al-

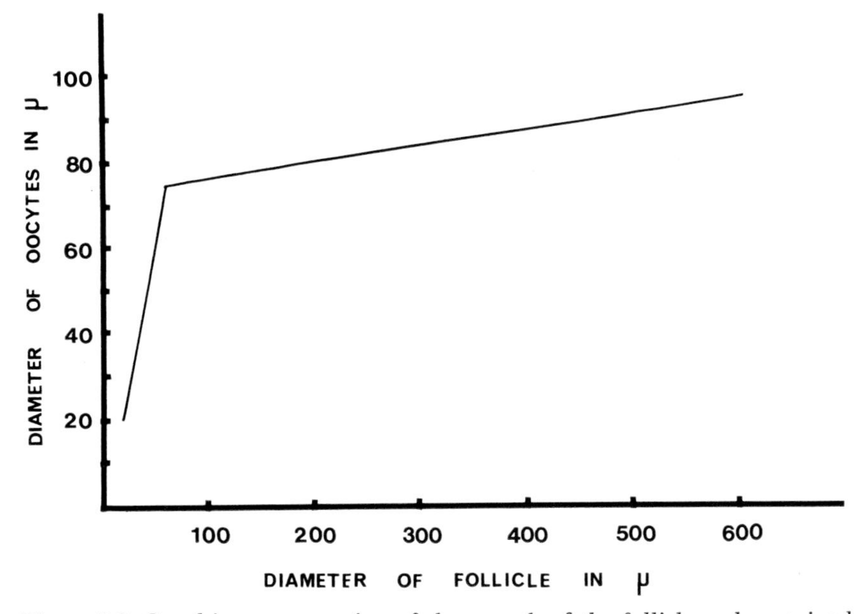

Figure 9-9. Graphic representation of the growth of the follicle and contained oocyte of the Senegal galago. During the first phase the growth of the oocyte and follicle is correlated. During the second phase the oocyte does not grow as fast as the follicle.

most immediately antra begin to appear and rapidly coalesce to form a vesicular (Graafian) follicle. Folliculogenesis begins in the rhesus monkey when the corpus luteum of the nonpregnant cycle commences to show signs of degeneration (Koering, 1969). Many of the follicles undergo atresia before attaining a diameter of 1.0 mm and all, except the one destined to ovulate, become atretic by the time they have reached 3.0 in diameter. The preovulatory follicle is about 6.0 mm in diameter. Mitosis has ceased in the granulosa cells which are now separated by accumulations of intercellular fluid.

The Preovulatory Follicle. Direct observation at laparotomy indicates that the Graafian follicle of the rhesus monkey reaches a maximum diameter of 8 to 10 mm immediately prior to ovulation (Betteridge *et al.*, 1970). The average size of the ovum is 110 × 100 × 80μ with a nucleus some 26μ in diameter. The zona pellucida is 5μ thick. The granulosa cells are four to eight cells deep and the position of the compact cumulus oophorus bears no relationship to the probable site of follicular rupture. The liquor folliculi is granular, but has not yet reached its maximum density. The theca interna is generally sparse in the rhesus monkey, and is usually unevenly distributed but well vascularized (Koering, 1969). In the baboon the theca interna cells undergo enlargement immediately prior to ovulation (Zuckerman and Parkes, 1932). The follicle destined for ovulation is detectable in the rhesus monkey ovary between days nine and eleven of the menstrual cycle (Koering, 1969).

Ovulation. The rhesus monkey is like the great majority of mammals in that the first maturation division occurs within the Graafian follicle immediately prior to its rupture (Hartman and Corner, 1941). The heavy precipitate seen in preovulatory follicles suggests that the liquor folliculi reaches its maximum viscosity at ovulation. This viscosity accounts for the slow "oozing out" of the secondary oocyte at ovulation (Koering, 1969). Serial laparotomies, timed to permit observations of the ovaries of individual rhesus monkeys before, during and after ovulation, have provided a photographic record of the events of ovulation (Johansson *et al.*, 1968). The appearance of the stigma, which is found within two days prior to ovulation, varies considerably from follicle to follicle. It commonly appears as a raised hyperemic area and may be either opaque or translucent. Follicular fluid, tinged with blood to a varying degree, oozes out of the stigma at ovulation. Luteal tissue becomes visible near the edge of the stigma on the second day after ovulation. In most instances the formed corpus luteum bulges above the surface of the ovary.

However, Betteridge *et al.* (1970) using a similar technique did not observe any changes in mature Graafian follicles which might indicate the imminent occurrence of ovulation and suggest that Johansson *et al.* (1968) had mistakenly identified fresh ovulation points as preovulatory stigmata. In the nonprimates in which the time interval between ovulation and stigma formation is known, it is invariably short. For instance, in the rat the stigma grows and ruptures within three to five minutes (Blandau, 1955). Ovulation is spontaneous and almost all ovulations occur between days ten and sixteen of the cycle, and most between the eleventh to fourteenth days (Hartman, 1932). On the basis of timed laparotomies in *Papio hamadryas,* Zuckerman (1930, 1937) and Zuckerman and Parkes (1932) concluded that ovulation coincides with sexual skin subsidence. Ovulation is probably spontaneous in all primates.

In Vitro Culture of Ovarian Oocytes. Edwards (1962, 1965) studied the *in vitro* maturation of follicular oocytes of the rhesus monkey and showed that extrusion of the first polar body occurred after approximately thirty hours culture. Suzuki and Mastroianni (1966) showed that the time required for maturation to reach polar body extrusion was variable. After forty-six to forty-eight hours of culture 80 percent of the oocytes were in postdictyate stages of miosis, and twenty-six out of forty-seven oocytes showed a polar body. Follicular oocytes, returned to the uterine tubes following forty-eight hours culture, could not be fertilized (Suzuki and Mastroianni, 1968).

Atresia. The ultimate fate of the vast majority of oocytes and their follicles is atresia and this may occur at any stage of oogenesis and folliculogenesis. Atresia is a complex series of degenerative processes whose causes are unknown. The gross histological features of advanced atresia are readily recognizable in medium or large vesicular follicles, but the early stages are difficult to detect, particularly in primordial follicles (Ingram, 1962). Three stages of atresia have been defined in the large follicles of the rhesus monkey by Sturgis (1949) who attempted to time the process on the premise that the cytological changes in the luteal cells of atretic follicles occur at the same speed as they do in the formation of the normal corpus luteum. The major feature of stage I is the complete dissolution of the granulosa which may occur in twenty-four to forty-eight hours, but is certainly over in five days. Stage II, which is well under way on the sixth day after the process is assumed to have begun, is characterized by degeneration of the oocyte, development of the hyaloid membrane and subsidence of theca interna activity. The hyaloid membrane is deposited within the theca interna. Stage III commences some three weeks after the process has begun and is complete in five weeks or less. At the end of this stage all that remains is a shrunken and infolded hyaloid membrane with occasionally a small clear space containing the calcified remnant of an oocyte.

A similar sequence of events occurs when large vesicular follicles of the Senegal galago undergo atresia. Lipid droplets accumulate within the granulosa cells which are eventually shed into the follicular fluid (Fig. 9-7C). With increasing dissolution of the granulosa degenerative changes become apparent in the oocytes including shrinkage, nuclear pyknosis and thickening of the zona pellucida. Fully grown oocytes frequently proceed into the spindle stage of the first miotic division and then disintegrate. Occasionally, the first polar body is formed and both it and the secondary oocyte progress to the spindle stage for the second miotic division before disintegrating (Fig. 9-10A). Later stages include disappearance of the follicular cavity and formation of a hyaloid membrane. Thickened and collapsed zona pellucidas containing lipid droplets and large cells which may be macrophages are a common end result of atresia (Fig. 9-7D).

Effects of X-irradiation. Studies of the effects of X-irradiation on the mammalian ovary have shown that: (a) there is considerable species difference in the dosage required to destroy all germinal elements, and (b) the radiosensitivity of oocytes depends on the stage of follicular growth (Lacassagne *et al.*, 1962; Mandl, 1964). All the oocytes in multilayered follicles are destroyed in the rhesus monkey seven days after exposure to 1200r (600 r/day on consecutive days), but many primordial oocytes survive (Vermande-Van Eck, 1959) and exposure to 100r is sufficient to cause atresia in all follicles with three or more layers of granulosa cells (Vermande-Van Eck, 1959). However, atresia of large oocytes in growing follicles is a natural phenomenon whose incidence varies with the phases of the sexual cycle. Baker (1966a) exposed one ovary of postpuberal rhesus monkey to X-irradiation and used the opposite ovary as a control. The dose of X-rays required to destroy 50 percent or 100 percent of the oocytes in the rhesus monkey ovary is higher than that for other mammals. Also, oocytes in primordial follicles of the rhesus monkeys are less susceptible to the effects of X-irradiation than those in growing follicles, and it is suggested (Baker, 1966a) that this may be related to the presence of lampbrush chromosomes in the oocytes of primordial follicles.

Polyovular Follicles. Some of the lower primates (*Lemur macaco, Saimiri sciureus*) show frequent polyovular follicles (Harrison, 1949). Polyovular follicles are uncommon in the Senegal galago, but the presence of growing occytes in germinal cords (Fig. 9-3A) indicates the manner by which they may be formed.

B. The Corpus Luteum

Corpus Luteum of Estrous Cycle. In the rhesus monkey capillaries from the vascular net of the theca interna grow into the granulosa on day two after ovulation and transformation of the granulosa cells into lutein cells is complete by day four (Corner, 1945). The corpus luteum is regarded as attaining maturity between days seven to nine after ovulation by which time connective tissue is appearing in the central cavity. The modal sexual cycle is twenty-eight days with ovulation occurring on or about day thirteen, hence the corpus luteum reaches maturity some six to eight days before the onset of the next menstruation. It is noteworthy that the blastocyst begins to attach to the endometrium between eight to nine days after ovulation. If there is no pregnancy degenerative changes in the form of increasing vacuolization appear in the luteal cells about thirteen days after ovulation or some two days before the expected onset of menstruation. By the time menstruation commences, the luteal cells show nuclear pyknosis and fragmentation, cell shrinkage and cytolysis. The mature luteal cells contain lipid droplets, but as degeneration increases they are replaced by increasing quantities of a substance called *luteolipin* by Rossman (1942). Luteolipin stains brilliantly with Sudan III and related lipid soluble dyes but defies extraction by lipid solvents. On the basis of the relative quantities of lipid and luteolipin, he recognized three well defined stages in the regression of the corpus luteum. Remnants of the corpus luteum were recognizable up to seventeen weeks after ovulation. The corpus luteum of the Senegal galago also shows cytoplasmic vacuolation as the first sign of degeneration and this is first seen twenty-six days after ovulation. By the onset of the next ovulation there is still a moderate sized corpus luteum with more marked signs of degeneration. Tiny remnants of the corpus luteum are frequently found in ovaries at all stages of the sexual cycle.

Theca Interna Cells. In the chimpanzee and man, the theca interna cells persist as distinct epithelioid elements forming either a continuous zone or separate groups around the periphery of the

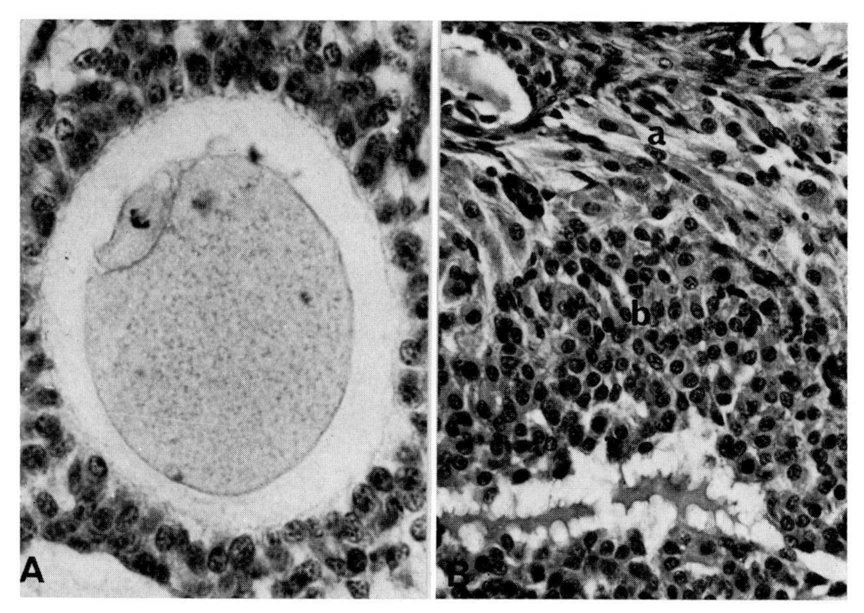

Figure 9-10. A. Atretic oocyte in a large vesicular follicle from a Senegal galago in late proestrus. The first miotic division has occurred and the secondary oocyte and first polar body are in metaphase of the second miotic division. B. The wall of a recently ruptured Graafian follicle of the Senegal galago showing theca interna cells (a) and luteinizing granulosa cells (b). The uterine tube contained an ovum with male and female pronuclei.

corpus luteum (Corner, 1945). In the rhesus monkey, the theca interna is small in the mature follicle and only under and around the cumulus oophoricus is it more than one or two cells thick. At this stage the theca interna cells are clearly distinguishable from the granulosa cells by reason of their larger size, vesicular nucleus and lipid filled cytoplasm. By the fourth day after ovulation the epithelioid changes in the granulosa cells have made them indistinguishable from the theca lutein cells. By the tenth to eleventh days the granulosa lutein cells are larger than the theca interna cells and their irregular cytoplasmic vacuoles are quite distinct from the smaller, more regular vacuoles, of the theca interna cells.

Preovulatory follicles of the Senegal galago have a distinct theca interna, some four cells deep, all around the follicle. The theca interna cells are readily seen in a recently ruptured follicle (fertilized ovum with pronuclei in uterine tube) (Fig. 9-10B). Examination of numerous corpora lutea of nonpregnant cycles and of pregnancy reveals no theca lutein cells, so they have either become indistinguishable from granulosa lutein cells or disappeared.

Corpus Luteum of Pregnancy. Up until the twelfth day after ovulation it is not possible to distinguish the corpus luteum of pregnancy in the rhesus monkey (Corner, 1945). Instead of degenerating on the thirteenth day, it persists unchanged until around the nineteenth to twenty-second days when the granulosa lutein cells lose their lipid vacuoles and become reduced in size. The theca lutein cells do not change in size and retain their lipid vacuoles, consequently they are readily visible. This typical pregnancy state of the corpus luteum persists until degenerative changes appear some two weeks before parturition. Despite the long life of the corpus luteum it can be removed as early as the twenty-fifth day of pregnancy without resulting in abortion (Hartman, 1941). The corpus luteum of pregnancy of the Senegal galago, which is frequently pedunculated, disappears by about the end of the first third of pregnancy (Butler, 1960).

Atypical Corpora Lutea. Corpora lutea atretica or accessory corpora lutea are frequent in the rhesus monkey (Corner, Bartelmez and Hartman, 1936), gorilla, gibbon, spider and howler monkeys (Săglick, 1938) and baboons (Zuckerman and Parkes, 1932). They are recognized by the presence of an atretic ovum and are regarded as a form of follicular atresia in which luteinized theca interna cells have invaded the antrum. They are frequently associated with pregnancy.

REFERENCES

Anand Kumar, T. C. (1968a): Oogenesis in lorises; *Loris tardigradus lydekkerianus* and *Nycticebus coucang*. *Proc Roy Soc (Biol), 169,* 167-176.

Anand Kumar, T. C. (1968b): The effects of gonadal hormones on primordial germ cell populations in the slender loris. *J Reprod Fertil, 16,* 322-323.

Baker, T. G. (1963): A quantitative and cytological study of germ cells in human ovaries. *Proc Roy Soc (Biol), 158,* 417-433.

Baker, T. G. (1966a): The sensitivity of oocytes in postnatal rhesus monkeys to X-irradiation. *J Reprod Fertil, 12,* 183-192.

Baker, T. G. (1966b): A quantitative and cytological study of oogenesis in the rhesus monkey. *J Anat, 100,* 761-776.

Baker, T. G., and Franchi, L. L. (1966): Fine structure of the nucleus in the primordial oocyte of primates. *J Anat, 100,* 697-699.

Baker, T. G. and Franchi, L. L. (1967): The structure of the chromosomes in human primordial oocytes. *Chromosoma, 22,* 358-377.

Baker, T. G.; Beaumont, H. M., and Franchi, L. L. (1969): The uptake of tritiated uridine and phenylalanine by the ovaries of rats and monkeys. *J Cell Sci, 4,* 655-675.

Betteridge, K. J.; Kelly, W. A., and Marston, J. H. (1970): Morphology of the rhesus monkey ovary near the time of ovulation. *J Reprod Fertil* (in press).

Blandau, R. J. (1955): Ovulation in the living albino rat. *Fertil Steril, 6,* 391-404.

Brambell, F. W. R. (1956): Ovarian changes. In Parkes, A. S. (Ed.): *Marshall's Physiology of Reproduction.* London, Longmans, Green and Co., chap. 5, p. 397.

Butler, H. (1960): Some notes on the breeding cycle of the Senegal galago (*Galago senegalensis senegalensis*) in the Sudan. *Proc Zool Soc London, 135,* 423-430.

Butler, H. (1964): The reproductive biology of a strepsirhine (*Galago senegalensis senegalensis*). *Int Rev Gen Exp Zool, 1,* 241-296.

Butler, H. (1969): Post puberal oogenesis in Prosimiae. In Hofer, H. O. (Ed.): *Int Cong Primat, Atlanta, Ga. 1968.* Basel, Karger, vol. 2, pp. 15-21.

Butler, H., and Juma, M. B. (1970): Oogenesis in an adult Prosimian. *Nature (Lond), 226,* 552-553.

Chiquoine, A. D. (1960): The development of the zona pellucida of the mammalian ovary. *Amer J Anat, 106,* 149-170.

Corner, G. W. (1945): Development, organisation and breakdown of the corpus luteum in the rhesus monkey. *Contr Embryol Carneg Inst, Wash., D.C., 31,* 117-146.

Corner, G. W.; Bartelmez, G. W., and Hartman, C. G. (1936): On normal and aberrant corpora lutea of the rhesus monkey. *Amer J Anat, 59,* 433-443.

Edwards, R. G. (1962): Meiosis of ovarian oocytes in adult mammals. *Nature, (London), 196,* 446.

Edwards, R. G. (1965): Maturation *in vitro* of mouse, sheep, cow, pig, rhesus monkey and human ovarian oocytes. *Nature (London), 208,* 349.

Evans, H. M., and Swezy, O. (1931): Oogenesis and the normal follicular cycle in adult mammalia. *Mem Univ Calif, 9,* 119-188.

Franchi, L. L., and Mandl, A. M. (1963): The ultrastructure of oogonia and oocytes in the foetal and neonatal rat. *Proc Roy Soc London B, 157,* 99-114.

Franchi, L. L.; Mandl, A. M., and Zuckerman, S. (1962): The development of the ovary and the process of oogenesis. In Zuckerman, S. (Ed.): *The Ovary,* New York, Academic Press, Chap. 1, p. 1.

Gérard, P. (1920): Contribution à l'étude de l'ovaire des Mammifères: L'ovaire de *Galago mossambicus* Young. *Arch Biol (Paris), 30,* 357-391.

Gérard, P. (1932): Etude sur l'ovogénèse et l'ontogénèse chez les Lemuriens adultes. *Arch Biol (Paris), 64,* 97-111.

Green, S. H., and Zuckerman, S. (1951): The number of oocytes in the mature rhesus monkey (*Macaca mulatta*). *J Endoc, 7,* 194-202.

Harrison, R. H. (1949): Multiovular follicles in the ovaries of lower primates. *Nature (Lond), 164,* 409.

Hartman, C. G. (1932): Studies in the reproduction of the monkey *Macacus (Pithecus) rhesus,* with special reference to menstruation and pregnancy. *Contr Embryol Carneg Inst (Wash., D.C.), 23,* 1-161.

Hartman, C. G. (1941): Non-effect of ovariectomy on the twenty-fifth day of pregnancy in the rhesus monkey. *Proc Soc Exp Biol Med, 48,* 221-223.

Hartman, C. G., and Corner, G. W. (1941): The first maturation division of the macaque ovum. *Contr Embryol Carneg Inst (Wash., D.C.), 29,* 1-161.

Ingram, D. L. (1962): Atresia. In Zuckerman, S. (Ed.): *The Ovary*. New York, Academic Press, p. 247.

Johansson, E. D. B.; Neill, J. D., and Knobil, E. (1968): Periovulatory progesterone concentration in the peripheral plasma of the rhesus monkey with a methodologic note on the detection of ovulation. *Endocrinology, 82,* 143-143.

Katzberg, A. A. (1967): The developing ovum in the baboon. In Vagtborg, H. (Ed.): *The Baboon in Medical Research.* Austin, University of Texas Press, vol. II, pp. 216-231.

Koering, M. J. (1969): Cyclic changes in ovarian morphology during the menstrual cycle in *Macaca mulatta. Amer J Anat, 126,* 73-101.

Lacassagne, A.; Duplan, J. F.; Marcovitch, H., and Raynaud, A. (1962): The action of ionizing radiations on the mammalian ovary. In Zuckerman, S. (Ed.): *The Ovary*. New York, Academic Press, p. 463.

Mandl, A. M. (1964): The radiosensitivity of germ cells. *Biol Rev, 39,* 288-371.

Moses, M. J. (1958): The relation between the axial complex of meiotic prophase chromosomes are chromosome pairing in a Salamander (*Plethodus cinereus*). *J Biophys Biochem Cytol, 4,* 633-638.

Nørrevang, A. (1968): Electron microscopic morphology of oogenesis. *Int Rev Cytol, 23,* 113-186.

Rao, C. R. N. (1927): On the structure of the ovary and ovarian ovum of *Loris lydekkeriannus Cabr. Quart J Micr Sci, 71,* 57-73.

Rossman, I. (1942): On the lipin and pigment in the corpus luteum of the rhesus monkey. *Contr Embryol Carneg Inst (Wash., D.C.), 30,* 97-109.

Săglick, S. (1938): Ovaries of gorilla, chimpanzee, orang-utan and gibbon. *Contr Embryol Carneg Inst (Wash., D.C.), 27,* 179-189.

Sturgis, S. H. (1949): Rate and significance of atresia of the ovarian follicles of the rhesus monkey. *Contr Embryol Carneg Inst (Wash., D.C.), 33,* 67-80.

Suzuki, S., and Mastroianni, L. (1966): Maturation of monkey ovarian follicular oocytes in vitro. *Amer J Obstet Gynec, 96,* 723-731.

Suzuki, S., and Mastroianni, L. (1968): The fertilisation of *in vitro* cultured ovarian follicular oocytes. *Fertil Steril, 19,* 500-508.

Vermande-Van Eck, G. J. (1959): Effect of low-dosage of X-irradiation upon pituitary gland and ovaries of the rhesus monkey. *Fertil Steril, 10,* 190-202.

van Wagenen, G., and Simpson, M. E. (1965): Embryology of the ovary and testis of *Homo sapiens* and *Macaca mulatta*. New Haven, Yale University Press.

Witschi, E. (1948). Migration of the germ cells of human embryos from the yolk sac to the primitive gonadal folds. *Contr Embryol Carneg (Wash., D.C.), 32,* 67-80.

Zuckerman, S. (1930): The menstrual cycle of the primates. I. General nature and homology. *Proc Zool Soc London, 1930,* 691-754.

Zuckerman, S. (1937): The duration and phases of the menstrual cycle in primates. *Proc Zool Soc London A, 1937,* 315-329.

Zuckerman, S., and Parkes, A. D. (1932): The menstrual cycle of the primates. V. The cycle of the baboon. *Proc Zool Soc London,* part 1, 138-191.

Chapter 10

GESTATION

A. G. HENDRICKX AND M. L. HOUSTON

THE maintenance of pregnancy is a complex phenomenon requiring certain events to occur in a proper sequence. Physiological changes which accompany gestation include the increase of blood supply to the uterus, a rise in overall metabolism of the mother, the development of a functional placenta which enables the uptake of nutrients and excretion of metabolic wastes by the conceptus, and changes in the materno-fetal fluid compartments. The variation in species appears to be considerable.

In this chapter the discussion will deal with duration and hormonal requirements of pregnancy, uterine growth, placental function, materno-fetal fluid, dynamics and pregnancy diagnosis.

I. PHENOMENA OF PREGNANCY

A. Duration of Pregnancy

The length of gestation varies considerably between species but appears to be rather constant for each species (Table 10-I). One of the difficulties in determining the duration of pregnancy is obtaining accurate observations on conceptual mating. This difficulty has been overcome to a large extent in many of the Old World monkeys with the establishment of timed breeding programs in which the female is exposed to the male for limited periods of time (several hours to 5 days). In general, the longer the gestation, the more self-sufficient are the young at the time of birth, although this is not true in all instances. The newborn chimpanzee is helpless even though the gestation period is approximately 7½ months.

Both genetic and environmental factors influence the duration of pregnancy in laboratory animals and have some bearing on the length of gestation in the primates. The sex of the fetus is known to be a factor in determining gestation time in several nonprimate species, however, it does not appear to be a significant factor in the primate.

Age, weight and general physiological condition of the mother and the size and the weight of the fetus, as well as the number of offspring are environmental factors which have an effect on the gestation period. There is a direct correlation between size and weight of the fetus and gestation length in the baboon. Mothers with multiple births tend to have shorter gestation periods than those with single births.

B. Growth of the Gravid Uterus

The uterus during pregnancy must be able to expand many times beyond it's nongravid size in order to accommodate the growing conceptus(es). However, this is not entirely a matter of being stretched by the growing fetus since, in species with bicornate uteri, a uterine horn rendered sterile will more than triple in size during the course of pregnancy in the other horn. Three phases of uterine adaptation to pregnancy are recognized in the period of gestation. The duration of each phase varies with the species.

Endometrial Proliferation. The embryo of most primate species spends from five to nine days free in the oviducts and uterine cavity before implantation begins. During this time the endometrium, under progestational stimulation from the corpus luteum, undergoes characteristic changes in preparation for implantation. These changes include a general increase in thickness along with increased vascularity, growth and coiling of the uterine glands, and leukocytic infiltration.

General Uterine Growth. Both endometrial and myometrial tissue increase rapidly after implantation. Muscular hypertrophy occurs as well as extensive increases in the connective tissue, fibrillar elements, and collagen, adding to the actual tissue content of the uterus. In addition, increases in the vascularity of the tissue and the amount of intercellular fluids account for an appreciable amount of size increase.

Uterine Stretching. During the latter portion of gestation, actual addition of tissue to the uterine wall is minimal but the actual volume of the uterus is increased by the rapidly growing fetal con-

TABLE 10-I

LENGTH OF GESTATION AND NUMBER OF YOUNG/LITTER FOR SOME COMMONLY USED PRIMATES

Animals	*Gestation Period (Days)*	*Young/ Litter*	*Animal*	*Gestation Period (Days)*	*Young/ Litter*
Prosimians			*Old World Monkeys*		
Cheirogaleus	70	—	*Cercocebus*		1
Galago (Senegal)	144–146		*Cercopithecus*	150–210	1
Lemur	120–135	1–2	*Erythrocebus*	150–270	1–2
Lepilemur	120–150	1	*Macaca*		
Loris	160–174	1–2	*M. fuscata*		1
Microcebus	59–62	1–3	*M. irus*	167–170	1
Nycticebus	193	—	*M. mulatta*	163–173	1
Tupaia	46–50	1–2	*M. nemestrina*	162–186	1
			M. radiata		1
			M. speciosa		1
New World Monkeys			*M. sylvana*	210*	
Alouatta	140*	1	*Miopithecus*	150–210	1
Aotus	140–180	1	*Presbytis*	196	1–2
Ateles	139	1	Baboons		
Callithrix	142–150	1–3	*Mandrillus*	220–270	1
Cebus	180*	1	*Papio*	164–186	1
Lagothrix	130–150	1	*Theropithecus*		1
Saimiri	165–170	1			
Saquinus	120*	1–2	*The Greater Apes*		
			Gorilla	270	1
			Hylobates	210*	1
			Pan	216–260	1
			Pongo	240–270	1

* Approximate gestation period

tents. The fetal tissues undergo the period of their most rapid growth during this period.

Primates, with predominently simple types of uteri, tend to give birth to a set number (usually 1) of offspring at each pregnancy and the amount of uterine growth is highly regular. Very little expansion occurs during the first trimester of gestation, but the uterus increases rapidly throughout the remainder of pregnancy. The rate of growth for the baboon is shown in Figure 10-1. The relative rates are similar in other animals with simplex uteri such as man and the rhesus monkey although the actual measurements differ. The rate of uterine expansion and the actual size of the uterus at particular stages of pregnancy increase somewhat with increased parity.

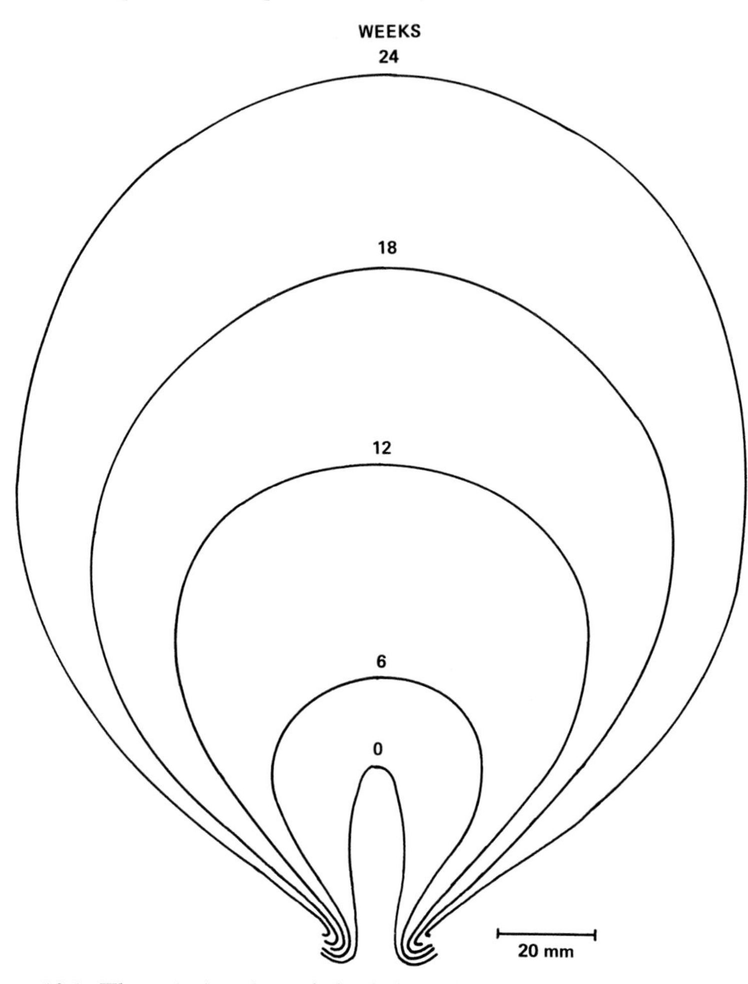

Figure 10-1. The relative sizes of the baboon simplex uterus at various stages of pregnancy. The increase in size is due to continued muscular hypertrophy, increase in vascularity and accumulation of intercellular fluids. (From Hendrickx and Houston, 1970)

C. Estrus and Ovulation During Pregnancy

The cessation of estrus or menses after breeding is a good indication that pregnancy has occurred. However there are notable exceptions to this. Female squirrel monkeys *Saimiri scuireus,* known to be pregnant, mate. Similar behavior is seen in marmosets. Solicitation of the attention of the males by presenting, and copulation also has been observed in the green monkey, *Cercopithecus aethiops sabeus.*

Postconception periods of sexual receptivity have been observed in free-ranging rhesus monkeys (Conaway and Koford, 1965). Most of the postconception cycles began three to four weeks after the end of the apparent estrus of conception. In one instance copulation was last seen only six weeks before parturition.

Vaginal flow has been observed repeatedly in the captive pregnant rhesus monkey (Hartman, 1932; Pickering, 1966). Wislocki and Hartman (1929) found that the dilated uterine glands peripheral to the placenta in the pregnant rhesus monkey were filled with maternal blood which drained into the uterine cavity and was then recovered in the vaginal fluid. The presence of blood in the vaginal fluid constitutes the *placental sign* in the monkey. Conception is followed by the regular onset of a subsequent period of vaginal flow (placental sign) at the expected time of approximately twenty-eight days in a high percentage of cases. In contrast to the normal menstrual cycle, however, the duration of flow is much more variable. Vaginal bleeding following conception is common to most of the other macaque species but rarely occurs in the baboon. It also is uncommon to observe turgescence of the sex skin in the baboon, although it occurs quite frequently in the chimpanzee. Both menstrual bleeding and copulation have been observed in the pregnant chimpanzee. Enlargement of the sex skin has been observed in a pregnant orangutan (Graham-Jones and Dill, 1962).

There is no evidence that ovulation occurs during pregnancy, and superfetation, which is two simultaneous pregnancies with young of different ages in the same female, has not yet been reported.

The occurrence of estrus during pregnancy is of practical importance. Females which have normal estrous cycles after breeding and are hard to settle should be checked for pregnancy when possible before they are culled and sold.

D. Hormonal Requirements of Pregnancy

A balance of certain maternal hormones is necessary for the development and maintentenance of a successful pregnancy. With the development of the placenta and the fetal endocrine glands, an interplay of hormones occurs between the placenta, fetus and mother. Estrogen and progesterone from the ovary and placenta, and gonadotropins from the anterior pituitary are necessary for the maintenance of pregnancy.

Progesterone is essential for maintaining the embryos before and after implantation. Meyer *et al.* (1969) have shown that in the ovariectomized rhesus monkey implantation occurs in the presence of progesterone alone and in the absence of ovarian estrogen. Although ovarian estrogen is not required for implantation in the monkey, it is possible that the adrenal cortex provides sufficient estrogen for implantation to occur. It is also possible that the uterus becomes sensitized by the ovarian estrogen at an early stage of pregnancy (i.e. before ovariectomy). The ovary, the main source of progesterone, is probably essential up to day twenty-one of pregnancy in the rhesus monkey. Ovariectomy after day twenty-one of pregnancy has no effect (Tullner and Hertz 1960). It is inferred that the placenta produces sufficient progesterone to maintain pregnancy. Pregnancy can be maintained until parturition in animals ovariectomized between the second and sixth day after ovulation by the administration of progesterone.

In the nonovariectomized pregnant rhesus monkey there is a sharp but short rise in plasma progesterone concentration at a time when progesterone is falling in the nonpregnant menstrual cycle. This sharp rise occurs on days twenty-two to twenty-four of the cycle or days nine to eleven of pregnancy (Neill *et al.,* 1969), the time of implantation and formation of the syncytiotrophoblast, which is the source of chorionic gonadotropin in man and probably also in the monkey. Gonadotropic activity, possibly of chorionic origin has been detected in urine as early as the twelfth day of pregnancy (Arslan, *et al.,* 1967). Maximum levels were detected between days eighteen and twenty-eight of pregnancy which coincides fairly well with the findings of Tullner and Hertz (1966), Tullner (1968) and Wilson *et al.* (1970).

Excretion of chorionic gonadotropin during pregnancy in the baboon is similar to that of the rhesus monkey and has been detected in the urine of gorillas (Tullner and Gray, 1968). Like man the gorilla appears to produce chorionic gonadotropin throughout pregnancy. Urinary estrogens, particularly estrone, 17β-estradiol and estriol gradually increase as parturition approaches in the rhesus monkey (Hooper and Tullner, 1967). Hopper *et al.*, (1968) found that the urinary estrogen levels in the lowland gorilla increased throughout pregnancy (9 to 35 weeks). Estriol showed a marked elevation similar to that found in pregnant women. A sharp decline was noted after parturition.

E. Functions of the Placenta

The placenta is the only adequate source of exchange between mother and fetus and, as such, must serve as a substitute for the fetal gastrointestinal tract, kidney, liver, lung, and various endocrine organs during gestation. The majority of transfer in most primates takes place across the placenta between the maternal intervillous space and the fetal capillary bed through the chorion frondosum. Of course, in species such as the Galago where a chorio-vitelline placenta is active for some time there is a great deal of transfer at this point.

Transmission of materials across the placenta is accomplished by several means, depending primarily on the nature of the material being transferred. The main categories of these mechanisms are listed below.

1. *Simple diffusion* is the movement of a certain material in response to either a chemical or electrochemical gradient, i.e. the movement of a solute from a point of higher concentration to one of lower concentration. No energy is expended in this process.

2. *Facilitated diffusion* is a term used to define the process by which solute materials are able to move with a concentration gradient but at a rate higher than what would be expected of simple diffusion. It is probable that these materials combine with some sort of a chemical receptor in the placental membrane which renders it more soluble in the lipid of the membrane and which would allow passage without a chemical alteration of the carrier requiring energy or another type of endergonic reaction as occurs in active transport. Glucose crosses the membrane of red blood cells in this manner (Seeds, 1968).

3. *Active transport* is a mechanism by which materials can move "uphill" against a concentration gradient. This "pumping" is the

major mechanism by which molecules are transferred across the placental barrier (Dancis, 1964). Energy and the involvement of some enzyme system is required, and the reaction involves the chemical alteration of a membrane carrier.

4. *Miscellaneous* mechanisms such as solvent drag, phagocytosis and pinocytosis are also involved in placental transfer. The process of pinocytosis has been cited as important in the transfer of large molecular weight substances such as albumens, gamma globulins, etc.

Transport of Gases. The only source of oxygen uptake and release of carbon dioxide for the fetus is through the placental barrier. The passage of these gases across the barrier is by the process of dissociation from the hemoglobin of one blood, diffusion across the membrane, and association with hemoglobin of the other blood system. For this exchange to take place several physiological mechanisms must be involved and must be in the proper mode of activity for exchange to occur.

In both the human (Eastman *et al.,* 1933; Hellegers and Schruefer, 1961) and monkey (Parer, 1967; Behrman *et al.,* 1963) the fetal blood has a higher affinity for oxygen than does maternal blood. Closely associated with this phenomenon may be the fact that, at least in the human, the hemoglobin concentration of maternal blood is decreased during pregnancy ("physiological anemia of pregnancy") falling below that of fetal blood. Thus human maternal blood has been found to have an oxygen capacity of 15.5 vol percent (ml/100 ml) with a hemoglobin concentration of 11.6 g/100 ml, while fetal blood has an oxygen capacity of 20 vol percent with a higher hemoglobin concentration of 14.9 g/100 ml (Stenger *et al.,* 1965). Similar values have been reported in *Macaca mulatta* by Hellegers *et al.,* 1964 and Dawes *et al.,* 1960. Other factors such as low pH in the placenta which readily dissociates oxyhemoglobin in maternal blood, and a higher partial pressure of oxygen on the maternal side of the placental barrier are important. In addition, phenomena such as the effects of carbon dioxide transfer on the position of the maternal and fetal blood oxygen dissociation curves, the rates of uterine and umbilical blood flow and the pattern of blood flow distribution within the uterus are all important in regulating the transmission of oxygen across the placenta.

As with oxygen, the transfer of carbon dioxide across the placenta is a matter of diffusion and the actual process is inseparable from the transfer of oxygen. As would be expected there, the mechanisms controlling this diffusion are very similar to those of oxygen transfer. These include a higher carbon dioxide tension in fetal blood than in maternal blood due to the fact that women hyperventilate during pregnancy (Loeschcke and Sommer, 1944), a lower carbon dioxide dissociation curve for fetal than maternal blood (Eastman *et al.*, 1933) as well as the other factors of blood flow and distribution (Metcalf *et al.*, 1967).

Transport of Inorganic Materials. Inorganic ions vary greatly in their relative concentrations and transmissions across the placental barrier. It is well known that in cases of dietary deficiencies of calcium, this ion will be transported from maternal to fetal blood (McDonald *et al.*, 1965) against a concentration gradient to the extent that maternal supplies will be depleted. In all primates studied, sodium is in complete equilibrium between maternal and fetal bloods, but the transfer does not seem to be one of simple diffusion (Battaglia *et al.*, 1968). Huggett and Hammond (1964), in studying the comparative transmission of sodium in many species, reported the permeability of the placenta to this ion to be inversely proportional to the number of tissue layers in the placental barrier.

Iron is absorbed from maternal to fetal tissue in the rhesus monkey (Cotes *et al.*, 1966) as well as in man (Huggett and Hammond, 1964), and the rate of this absorption seems to increase markedly in later stages of pregnancy.

Transport of Organic Materials. Glucose concentrations are higher in human maternal than fetal blood, and glucose readily crosses the placental barrier at a rate higher than would be expected of simple diffusion. Transfer against a concentration has not been observed, perhaps because three other monosaccharides; fructose, sorbitol and inositol, which are of almost equal molecular weight as glucose are present in fetal blood in much greater quantities (Adamson, 1965; Battaglia *et al.*, 1964a). A good deal of this difference may also be attributed to placental metabolic utilization of the glucose which is taken up. Studies of human and rhesus monkey chorion show no significant differences in permeability to different pentoses and hexoses (Battaglia *et al.*, 1964b;

Chinard *et al.*, 1956). Other *in vitro* permeability studies show some correlation between molecular weight and passage across the placenta.

Proteinaceous materials most readily pass the placental barrier in the form of free amino acids. It is conveniently shown that labeled amino acids cross the placenta from maternal to fetal bloods and are incorporated into fetal tissues (Adamson, 1965; Kerr and Waisman, 1967). Many of the essential amino acids are found in higher concentrations on the fetal side of the barrier indicating that active transport is involved (Seeds, 1968).

The proteinaceous hormones are rarely transported across the placenta in primates and when transported they move very slowly. Some large molecule proteins such as gamma globulin, albumin and fibrinogen have been shown to be selectively transferred. In monkeys it has been shown that all of the serum proteins are capable of being selectively transferred by the placenta (Bangham, 1960).

Only minor amounts of intact lipids cross the placenta, but the fetal requirements are also very small because of the affinity of the fetus for lipid synthesis. However, free fatty acids and glycerol cross the placenta readily (Wirtschaffer, 1958) and certain evidence exists which would indicate a break-down, transmission and resynthesis of certain fats by placental tissue (Popjak, 1954).

The fat soluble vitamins (A and E) seem to be held up by the primate placenta as they are found at much lower concentrations in fetal blood than maternal levels. This is somewhat surprising since other lipid soluble materials are known to cross the placenta readily. Water soluble vitamins, however, are transferred in large quantities and appear in fetal blood in much higher concentrations than in maternal blood. However, it has been suggested (Seeds, 1968) that these vitamins probably undergo some sort of transformation during passage because of their frequent participation as coenzymes.

Transport of Water. The human conceptus is approximately 90 percent water by weight in early pregnancy and still some 70 percent water at birth (Seeds, 1968). During this time there is a net increase of almost 4 l of water within the fetus and fetal membranes, an amount which far exceeds what is available from fetal metabolic sources and must therefore be transferred from the mother.

The primate placental membrane conforms to the definition of other mammalian cellular semipermeable membranes in that water and many small solutes cross the layers rapidly whereas most proteins and other macromolecules do not pass. However, the transfer of water is to a much greater extent than would be possible by simple diffusion. Therefore the passage of water across the membrane is by a process known as *bulk flow,* or transfer of a given volume of solvent water in response to either a hydrostatic concentration gradient force or an osmotic force. Although the experimental evidence for the primate is sparce in this regard, it is evident that at least the human placental membrane conforms to two important properties of porous, partially semipermeable membranes in the passage of water, namely: (a) transfer of water in response to gradients in chemical potential by bulk flow, and (b) transfer of water in response to gradients in solute concentration in proportion to the ability of the membrane to discriminate between solute and water (Bruns *et al.,* 1964; Seeds, 1968).

The pathway of water transfer is probably via the chorion frondosum from maternal to fetal blood. This is supported by evidence from tracer experiments, whereas similar experiments indicate there is no significant flow through the chorioamnion (Scoggins *et al.,* 1964).

Biosynthesis. Two basic types of hormones are required during the course of primate gestation which are produced by the placental tissue, namely pituitary-like hormones and steroid hormones.

Of the pituitary-like hormones, chorionic gonadotropin was the first to be recognized as a placental derivative. The origin of chorionic gonadotropin is probably from the syncytiotrophoblast (Midgley and Pierce, 1962; Dreskin *et al.* 1970), although there is some evidence that it is elaborated from the cytotrophoblastic cells of the chorion frondosum (Weber, 1963) and, at least in the human serves to prolong the life span of the corpus luteum during the early stages of gestation (Jones, 1968) and possibly has some function in regulating the production of placental progesterone in later pregnancy (Villee, 1966).

Placental lactogen was first reported by Ito and Higashi (1961) and has been carefully studied in primates by Friesen *et al.,* 1969. It has been shown to have properties similar to those of pituitary prolactin as well as some somatotropic properties (Greenwood *et al.,* 1964) and is thought to be produced in the syncytiotrophoblast of the placenta (Kaplan and Grumbach, 1964) and probably functions both to promote mammary growth and suppress pituitary gonadotropic hormones (Jones & Greep, 1950).

Steroid hormones, namely estrogen and progesterone are produced within the placental tissue of most mammals, including primates (Ainsworth *et al.,* 1969). These important hormones are elaborated from the syncytiotrophoblast (Lobel *et al.,* 1962) and function in the growth of the uterus and mammary glands and in the maintenance of a proper vascular bed for placental function. Progesterone is also thought to be active in maintaining the quiescence of the uterine musculature during pregnancy (Csapo, 1959).

F. Hematological Changes

During pregnancy there is an increase in the blood volume of approximately 30 percent in *Macaca mulatta* (Allen and Ahlgren, 1968). The increase in blood volume has a diluting effect on other blood constituents, including the red blood cells, hemoglobin, total plasma protein and plasma albumin. The total amount of these constituents in the blood increases, but because of the diluting effect of the plasma the amounts per unit volume of blood decrease. Total plasma protein and albumin concentrations decline progressively throughout pregnancy and reach their lowest level just prior to delivery (Fig. 10-2). The fibrinogen level increases progressively throughout pregnancy and drops to nonpregnant levels five-six days postpartum. Both alpha-1 and alpha-2 globulins increase slightly during pregnancy, and the peak is attained just prior to delivery. The beta globulin concentration is elevated 18 percent during pregnancy but falls below the nonpregnant level within a week postpartum. The gamma globulins increase during pregnancy, attaining maximum levels at 100 to 120 days of gestation (Fig. 10-3). The concentration in the blood returns to the nonpregnant value within five weeks following delivery. The sedi-

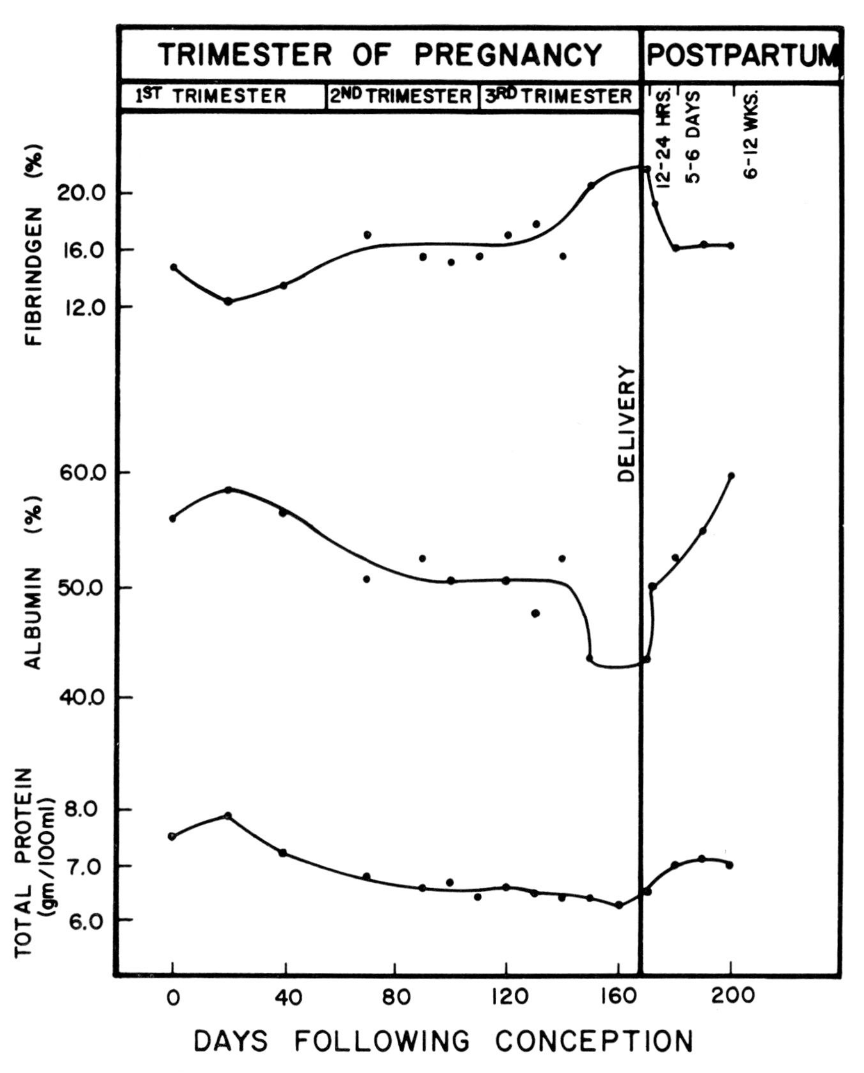

Figure 10-2. Changes in total protein, albumin, and fibrinogen in the *Macaca mulatta* female. (From Allen and Ahlgren, 1968)

mentation rate of the red blood cells in the pregnant *Macaca mulatta* starts to increase between the 110th and 120th days of pregnancy and reaches a peak just prior to delivery.

The red blood cell and white blood cell count declines progres-

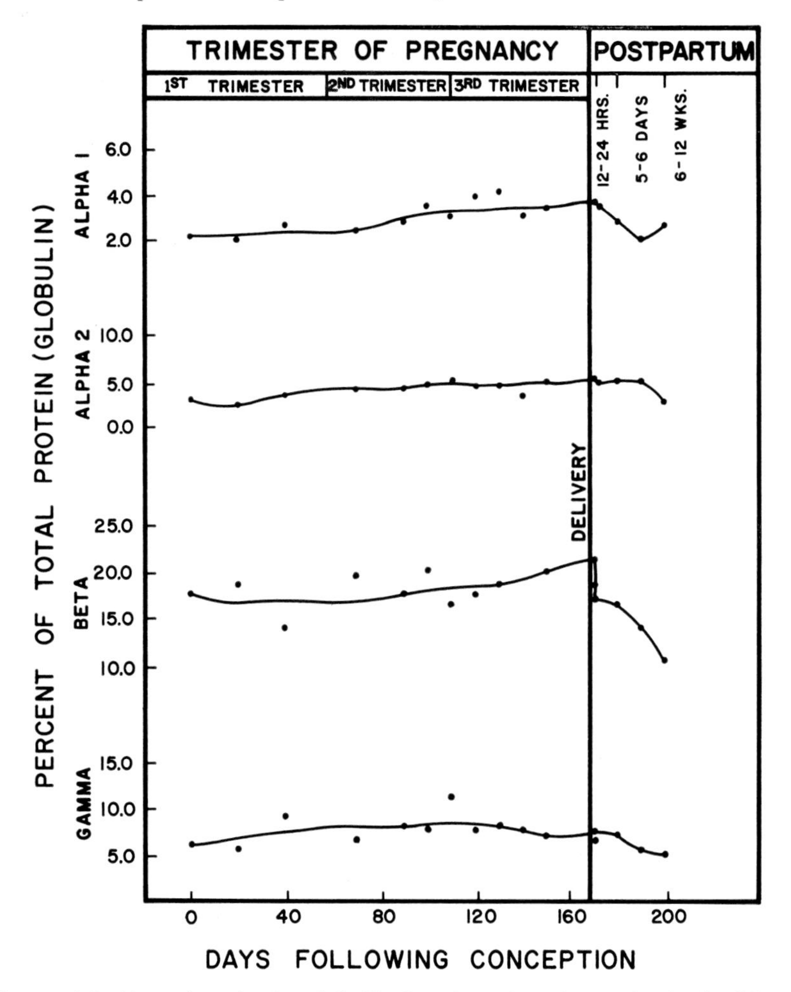

Figure 10-3. Alterations in the globulin fraction of total proteins in the *Macaca mulatta* female during pregnancy. (From Allen and Ahlgren, 1968)

sively throughout pregnancy. There is a 29 percent decrease in the white blood cells, although the circulating neutrophils increase in number.

In contrast to most other values the cholesterol concentration decreases gradually throughout pregnancy with an overall decrease of 50 percent (Fig. 10-4). The hemoglobin and hematocrit levels

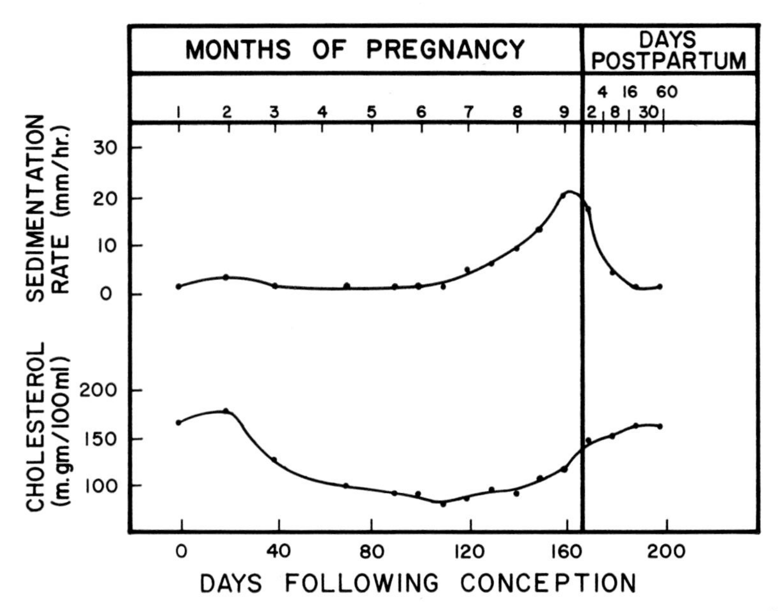

Figure 10-4. Changes in the sedimentation rate and the plasma cholesterol during pregnancy in the *Macaca mulatta* female. (From Allen and Ahlgren, 1968)

also decrease. The decrease in hemoglobin concentration is approximately 13 percent (Fig. 10-5).

A clear understanding of the increases in protein fractions is lacking, for the most part; however, there are some possible explanations. The increased sedimentation rate of the red blood cells is due to the increase in the number of red blood cells per unit volume of blood. The reason for the increase in polymorphonuclear leukocytes is not apparent; however, the reaction of the maternal system to excretions by the fetus must be considered.

G. Alterations in the Amniotic Fluid

The amniotic fluid is a transudate of the maternal plasma during the first ninety days of gestation. After this time it more closely resembles a transudate of fetal body fluids (Behrman *et al.,* 1964 and 1967). The amnion itself is capable of secreting a fluid into the amniotic space. Evidence for a contribution to the amniotic fluid from fetal excretions is suggested by the clinical association

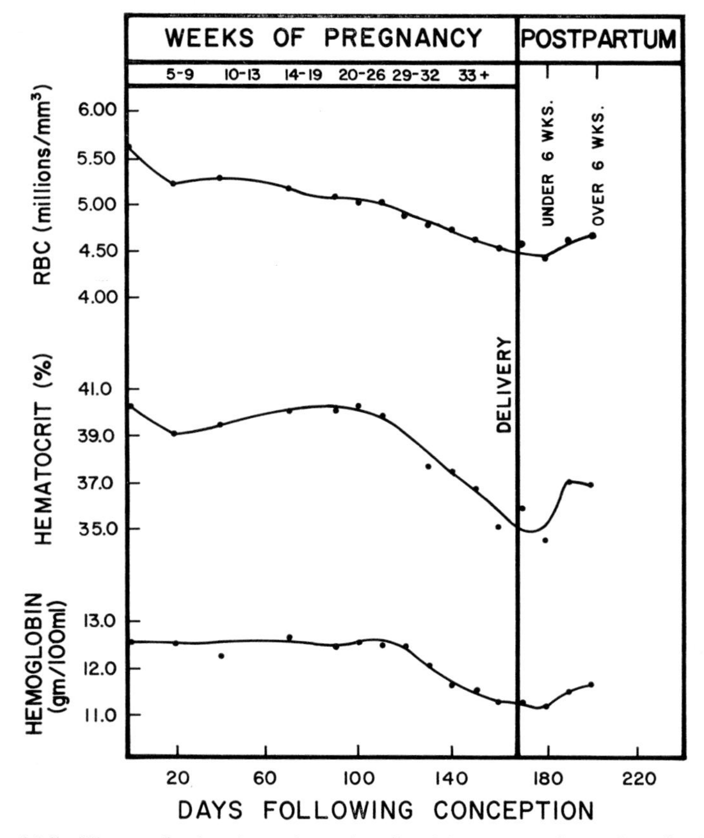

Figure 10-5. Hematologic alterations in the *Macaca mulatta* female during pregnancy. (From Allen and Ahlgren, 1968)

of renal agenesis or congenital urinary tract obstruction with oligohydramnios (Jeffcoat and Scott, 1959). The fetus itself contributes hypotonic urine and other body secretions to the amniotic fluid (Chez *et al.*, 1964; Behrman *et al.*, 1967; Pitkin *et al.*, 1968). Experiments in which radioactive materials (Diodrast I^{131}) are injected into the circulation of fetal *Macaca mulatta* demonstrate that the radioactivity appears promptly in the amniotic fluid (Fig. 10-6). With a dead fetus there is virtually no transfer of radioactivity from the fetus to the amniotic fluid (Fig. 10-7).

Changes in amniotic fluid carbon dioxide tension and pH provide a rapid and accurate indication of changes in fetal plasma pCO_2

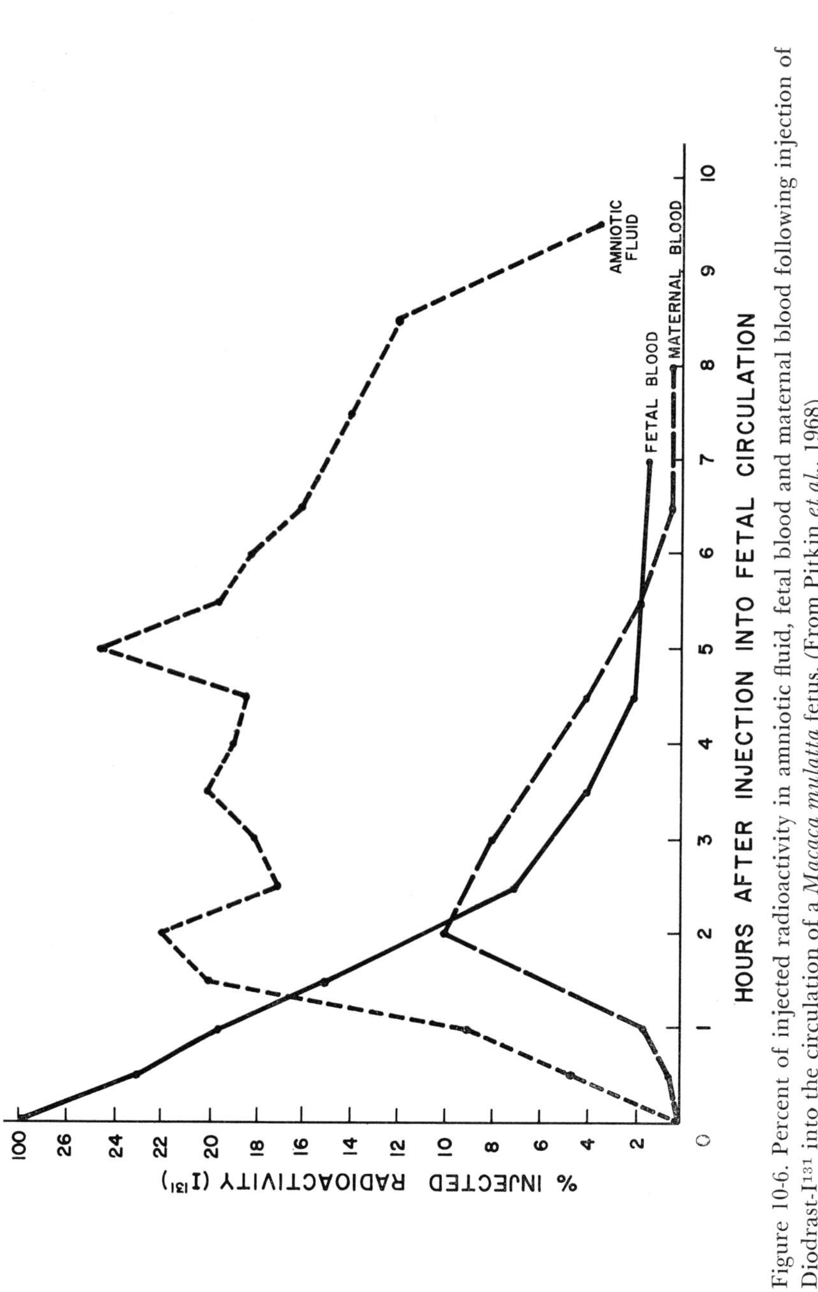

Figure 10-6. Percent of injected radioactivity in amniotic fluid, fetal blood and maternal blood following injection of Diodrast-I^{131} into the circulation of a *Macaca mulatta* fetus. (From Pitkin *et al.*, 1968)

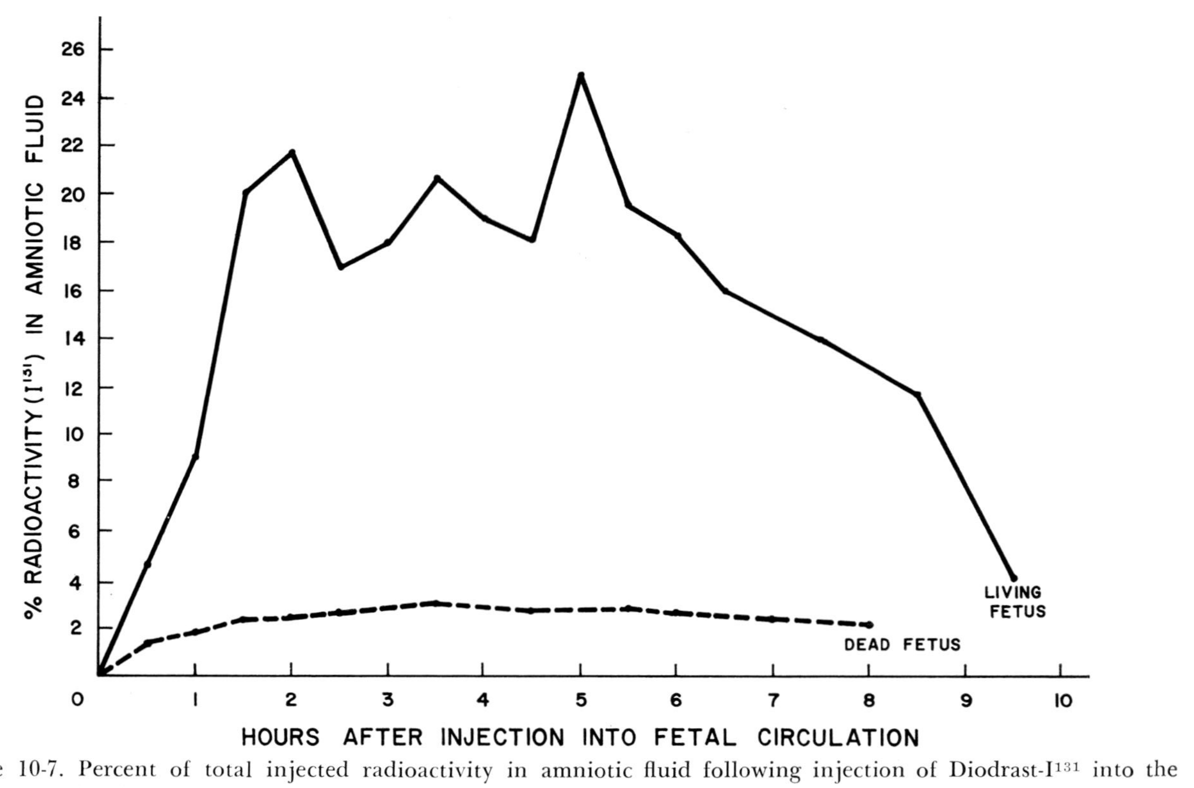

Figure 10-7. Percent of total injected radioactivity in amniotic fluid following injection of Diodrast-I^{131} into the circulation of living and dead *Macaca mulatta* fetuses. (From Pitkin *et al.,* 1968)

and pH because of their similarity (Seeds *et al.,* 1967). Thus, analysis of amniotic fluid is of diagnostic value during pregnancy, particularly when a detailed confirmation of fetal status is required. This may be due to the ability of carbon dioxide to diffuse between the fetal and amniotic fluid compartments or equilibration with the amniotic fluid and the maternal blood perfusing the uterus, or a combination of the two events. During normal pregnancy there is an increase in pCO_2, a decrease in pH levels and a decrease in the bicarbonate concentration of the amniotic fluid with increasing gestational age. Induction of maternal respiratory acidosis by inhalation of a 10 percent CO_2 in air causes a corresponding rise in pCO_2 and decrease in pH in the amniotic fluid, which may continue long after the maternal uterine venous blood pCO_2 and pH levels return to baseline values. A marked increase in pCO_2 and decrease in pH is found in amniotic fluid following surgery, indicating an acute fetal acidosis. This is primarily due to a decreased bicarbonate concentration. With time these changes become more pronounced. In one instance of premature placental separation, elevated levels of pCO_2 and reduced levels of pH develop in the amniotic fluid as the hemorrhagic site enlarges (Fig. 10-8).

Significant changes occur in these levels following fetal death *in utero* (Fig. 10-9). The pCO_2 levels rise after fetal death to levels over 100 mm and decrease very slowly. The pH drops and bicarbonate levels decrease markedly. The pH levels associated with fetal death *in utero* are below normal values for corresponding stages in pregnancy. The changes persist for a prolonged period because of the relative inability of carbon dioxide and bicarbonate to equilibrate with the maternal system in the absence of the fetal circulation.

In the experiments briefly described, fetal distress was accompanied by and may have been due to a reduction in uterine blood flow, as indicated by the difference in O_2 and CO_2 of uterine arteriovenous blood. The elevated pCO_2 and decreased pH uterine blood values were similar to fetal and amniotic fluid values. An elevation of pCO_2 in the amniotic fluid could result from direct diffusion from maternal venous blood across the chorioamnion. When the uterine venous pH and pCO_2 return to baseline levels

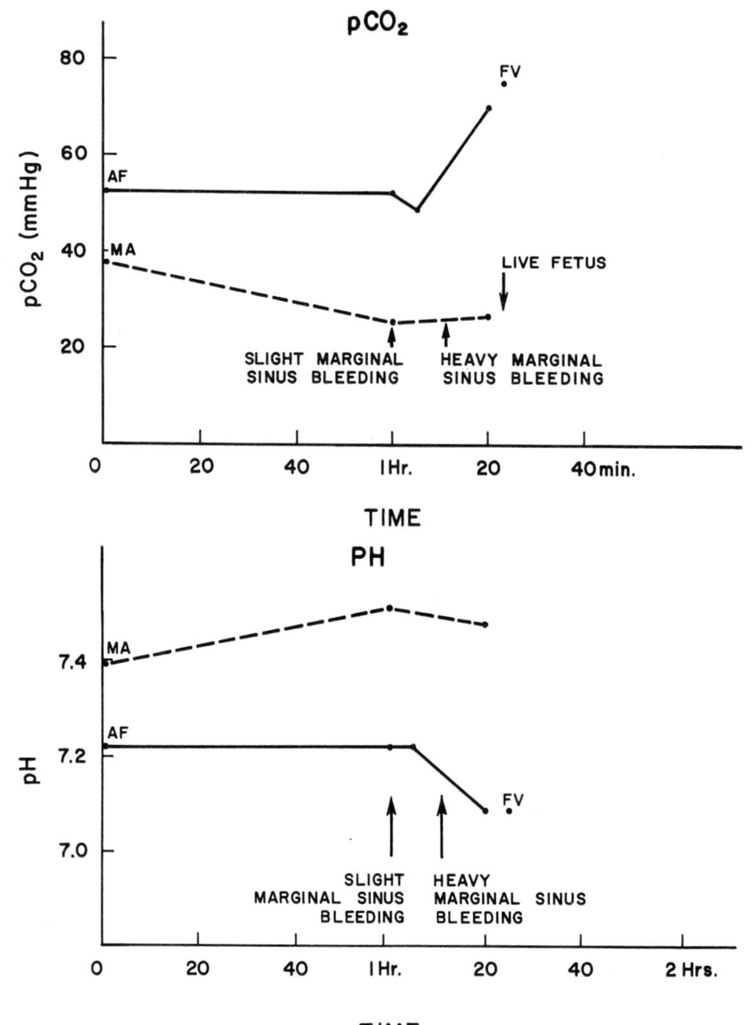

Figure 10-8. Changes in pCO_2 and pH following a large hemorrhage from a premature placental separation in *Macaca mulatta.* A depressed fetus was delivered after collection of the last sample. *AF,* amniotic fluid; *FV,* fetal vein; *MA,* maternal artery. (From Seeds *et al.,* 1967)

after the initial stress and the fetal and amniotic fluid levels remain abnormal the exchanges between the fetal and amniotic fluids may determine amniotic fluid pCO_2, as well as account for the return to baseline values of abnormal levels of pCO_2 and pH in the amniotic fluid and fetal vein (Fig. 10-10).

II. TECHNIQUES OF STUDY

A. Diagnosis of Pregnancy

A sign of pregnancy in the baboon and, to a lesser extent, the rhesus monkey is the color of the buttocks. In most instances the hairless area around the external genitalia becomes a deep red color during pregnancy. In addition, at least three major methods are used for diagnosing pregnancy: (a) clinical diagnosis (palpation), (b) biological diagnosis (bio-assay) and (c) chemical diagnosis (chemo-assay).

Clinical Diagnosis (Palpation). Abdominal palpation of the uterus containing the fetus(es) is a reliable way of detecting pregnancy. In the smaller species the head and shoulders are held in one hand; the other hand is placed on the abdomen between the hind legs and slightly in front of the pelvis; the thumb is placed on the right side and the fingers on the left side of the uterus or uterine horns in order to palpate the enlarged portions (s) containing the fetus(es). The elongate-shaped fetus(es) are distinguished as they slip between the thumb and fingers when they are gently moved back and forth with slight pressure. The uterus of the *Galago* is extremely thin and resembles a fluid-filled balloon during early pregnancy which makes it difficult to distinguish it from the urinary bladder.

In the larger species the animal is placed in a prone position, the middle finger of the right hand is inserted into the rectum and pressed forward until it rests upon the cervix uteri; the left hand is placed on the abdomen and the uterus is gently grasped between the fingers and thumb of the left hand while the middle finger of the right hand guides the uterus from above (Fig. 10-11). At twenty-three to twenty-four days of pregnancy in the rhesus monkey and baboon the uterus is sufficiently enlarged for the experienced investigator to confirm pregnancy. In doubtful cases, the palpation is repeated several days later. It is more difficult to con-

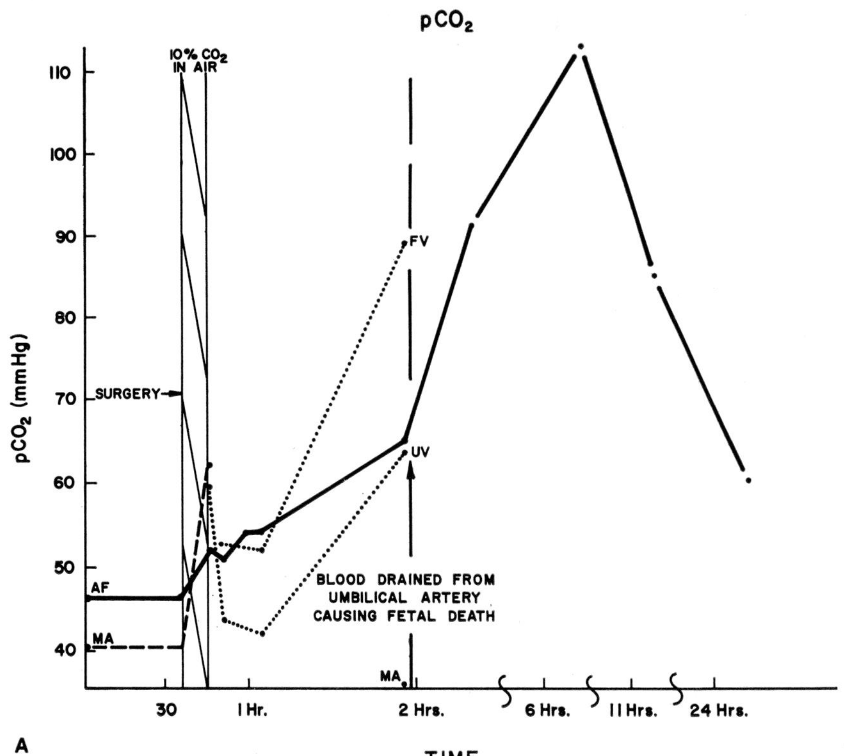
pCO2
10% CO2 IN AIR
110
100
90
80
70
60
50
40
pCO2 (mmHg)
SURGERY
FV
UV
AF
MA
BLOOD DRAINED FROM UMBILICAL ARTERY CAUSING FETAL DEATH
MA
30
1 Hr.
2 Hrs.
6 Hrs.
11 Hrs.
24 Hrs.
A

TIME

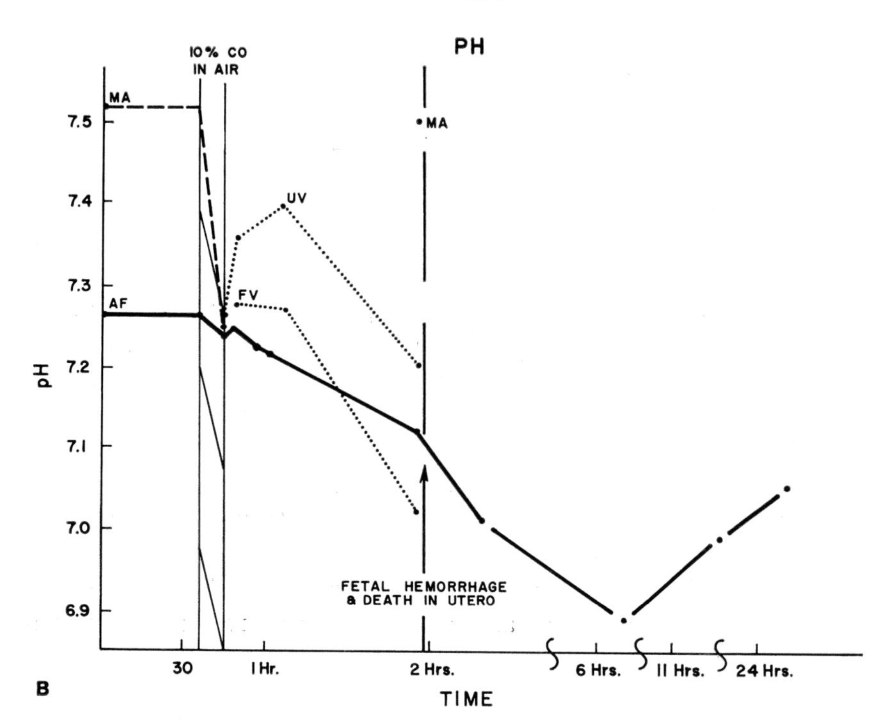
PH
10% CO IN AIR
MA
MA
UV
FV
AF
7.5
7.4
7.3
7.2
7.1
7.0
6.9
pH
FETAL HEMORRHAGE & DEATH IN UTERO
30
1 Hr.
2 Hrs.
6 Hrs.
11 Hrs.
24 Hrs.
B
TIME

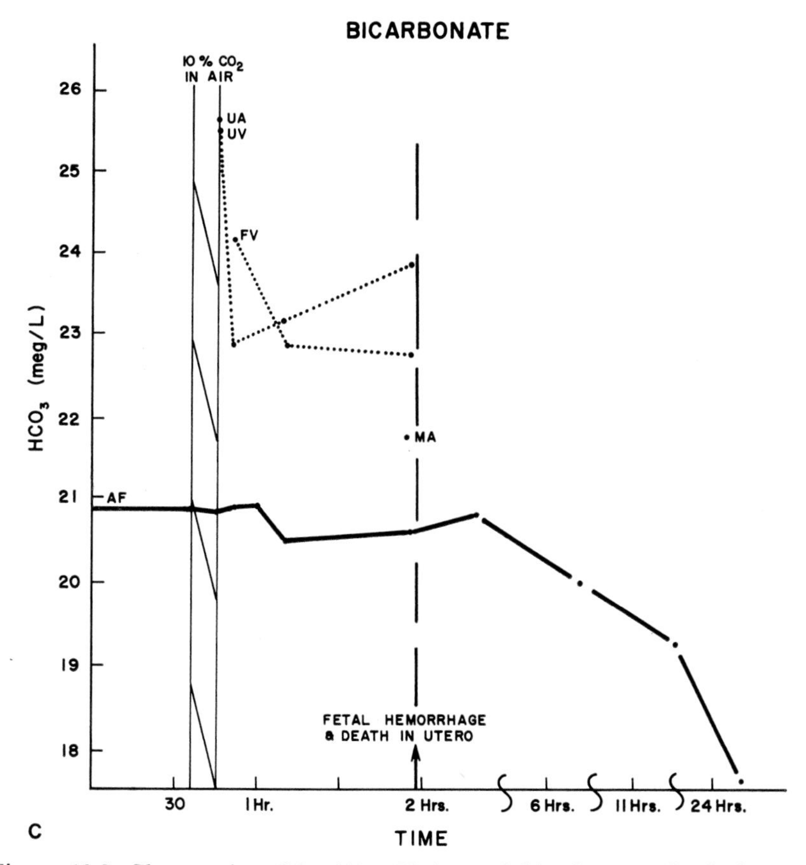

Figure 10-9. Changes in pCO_2 (A), pH (B) and bicarbonate (C) during and following carbon dioxide administration to a *Macaca mulatta* female at 130 days gestational age. Amniotic fluid values are shown after known fetal death *in utero*. *AF,* amniotic fluid; *FV,* fetal vein; *MA,* maternal artery; *UV,* uterine vein. (Seeds *et al.*, 1967)

firm pregnancy in the baboon between fifty and seventy days of pregnancy because the amnionic fluid is increasing in quantity and the fetal skeleton is not well formed. If too much pressure is exerted, the tissues may be bruised or torn loose from the walls of the uterus and a toxic condition or abortion may result.

The rhesus monkey is restrained similar to the smaller primates, but the baboon and chimpanzee should be lightly anesthetized before palpating for pregnancy. The breeder may develop the technique by palpating at thirty to thirty-two days of pregnancy, and

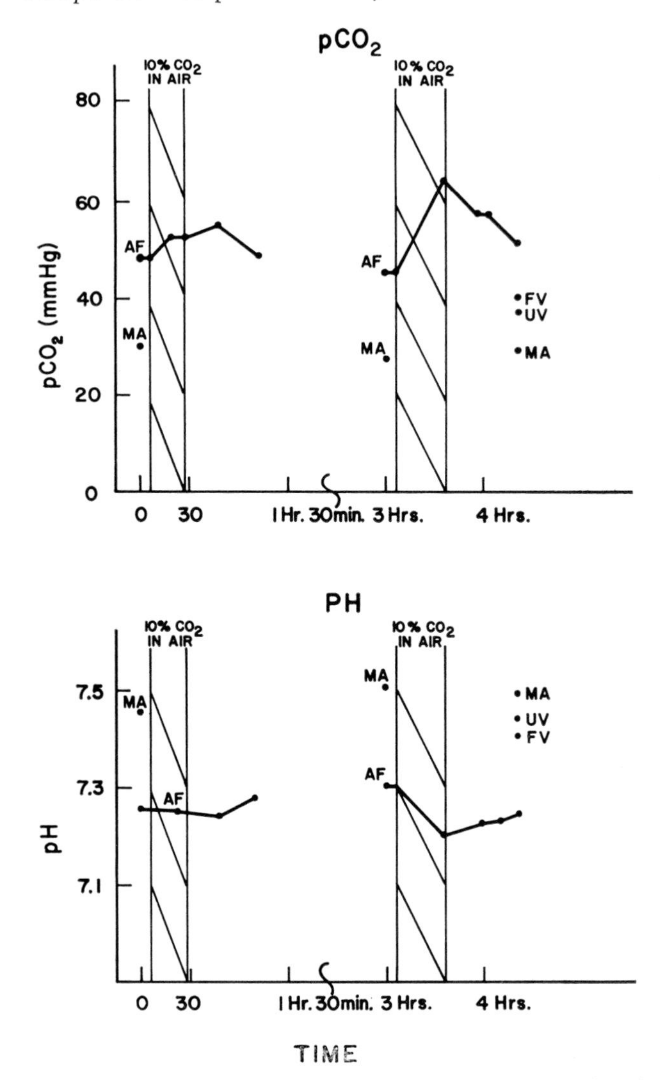

Figure 10-10. Changes in pCO_2 and pH during and following administration of 10 percent CO_2 in air to a *Macaca mulatta* female at 131 days gestational age. No intrauterine surgery was performed prior to carbon dioxide inhalation, and amniotic fluid pCO_2 and pH changes toward base-line levels were observed when the female was allowed to rebreathe room air. A valid indication of improvement in fetal status was provided by delivery of a normal, nondepressed fetus with normal acid-base levels at the conclusion of the experiment. *AF,* amniotic fluid; *FV,* fetal vein; *MA,* maternal artery; *UV,* uterine vein. (Seeds *et al.,* 1967)

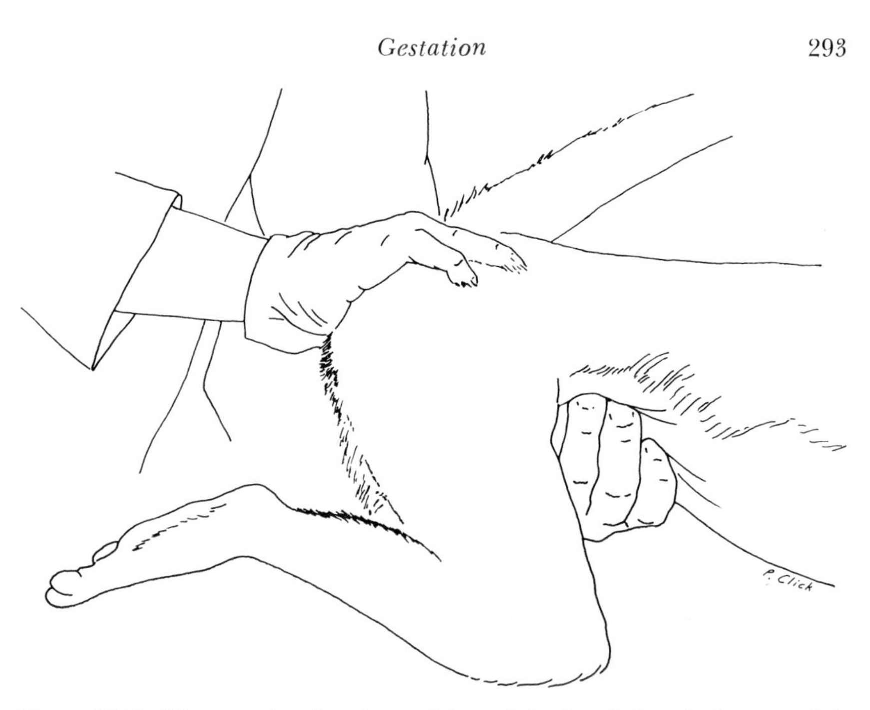

Figure 10-11. Diagram showing the position of the hands in relation to pelvic organs of the female monkey during bimanual palpation of the uterus per rectum. (From Hendrickx and Kraemer, 1970)

with experience should be able to check for pregnancy with this procedure at twenty-two to twenty-four days. Measurements of the gravid uterus taken at the time of Cesarean section (hysterotomy) are helpful in confirming the size of the uterus at different stages of pregnancy.

A set of gauges that cover the range of uterine sizes felt during bimanual palpation at different functional states from preadolescence through approximately day forty of pregnancy is helpful to confirm size, shape and consistency of the uterus. One of the greatest uses for palpation of the uterus is in diagnosing early abortion. The maintenance of systematic weight charts along with visual and palpatory examinations is usually a reliable way to detect pregnancy after the sixth or eighth week of gestation in the primate. These methods may not be useful for all primates but X-ray films or detection of the fetus by ultrasonic methods during the second half of gestation are useful.

Biological Assay (Bio-assay). Bio-assay has proven to be of value for diagnosis of pregnancy in primates. This diagnosis is dependent on detection of chorionic gonadotropin in the urine or serum by injection of urine or serum into immature female rats, mice or rabbits. Formation of ovarian follicles, ovarian hyperemia or an increase in uterine weight of these test animals assure the diagnosis of pregnancy. This approach seems reliable after about three weeks gestation in the squirrel monkey (Rosenblum, 1968) and rhesus monkey (Tullner and Hertz, 1966). The disadvantage of this assay is that it requires several days for its completion. Wilson *et al.,* (1970) has developed a method for early diagnosis of pregnancy which is based on chorionic gonadotropin assay in the mouse uterus. Pregnancy can be established within twenty-four hours of collecting the serum, sometimes as early as day sixteen of gestation and with a high degree of certainty by day twenty.

Chemical Diagnosis (Chemo-assay). Detection of progesterone in the plasma of the rhesus monkey by the *competitive protein binding technique* signals pregnancy. Surges of progesterone occur at the time of implantation and again approximately twenty days later, otherwise it remains low during gestation and falls abruptly after parturition (Neill *et al.,* 1969).

B. Collection of Embryos

Embryos can be obtained either at autopsy, hysterectomy or by *in vivo* surgical procedures. Collection at autopsy or by hysterectomy is rather inefficient from the standpoint of animal utilization since it limits the number of collections to one per animal. *In vivo* collection procedures have been developed which allow repeated use of the same animal. The total number of collections from a given animal depends upon the stage of pregnancy and the amount of adhesion which develops between the uterine tube, ovary and uterus. Usually a maximum of four preimplantation embryo collections can be made before the adhesions are severe enough to markedly affect ovum pick-up by the fimbriae of the uterine tube. Handling of the uterine tubes and ovaries in the flushing procedure increases the chances for adhesions and decreases the number of successful collections that can be made. On the other hand as many as eight operations may be performed for postimplantation embryos before sufficient adhesions result to severely affect fertility.

Preimplantation Embryos. The collection procedure varies slightly depending upon the species, expected location of the embryo and the necessity of establishing its location. In the rhesus it is difficult to force fluid from the uterine cavity retrograde through the uterotubal junction. For this reason oviductal rhesus embryos are collected by irrigating the oviducts with fluid introduced retrograde into the oviductal lumen at a point as close to the uterotubal junction as possible using a 25-30 gauge hypodermic needle. This same procedure is used for collecting baboon oviductal embryos when it is necessary to establish that the embryo was in fact located in the oviduct at the time of collection. If establishing location is not important, baboon tubal embryos can be obtained by clamping the cervix, introducing the flushing fluid into the uterus and forcing it retrograde through the utero tubal junction and out the oviduct. The flushing fluid can be either collected at the fimbriae or transported to a receptacle via a fluted plastic cannula which is inserted approximately 3 mm into the infundibular ostium of the oviduct and held in place by a ligature of a clamp (Fig. 10-12).

Uterine embryos are recovered by inserting a needle or intravenous catheter through the fundus, anchoring it with a pursestring suture, and forcing fluid through the uterine lumen and out the cervix. In the baboon, fluid will usually flow out the oviducts as well as the cervix. This fluid should also be collected since a uterine embryo is occasionally forced out the oviducts instead of the cervix. A speculum is placed in the vagina, which has been thoroughly irrigated with saline, and held firmly around the cervical os to conduct the washings to a collecting vessel. The fluid is examined for location of the embryo using a stereoscopic microscope. The embryos settle rapidly in physiological saline and are therefore usually located at the bottom of the collecting vessel. Recovery rates are usually around 50 percent.

Postimplantation Embryos. Once implantation has taken place the embryo or fetus may be collected free of artifact by incising the endometrial sac containing the embryo, placenta and membranes. The collection procedure is similar in all species. The only

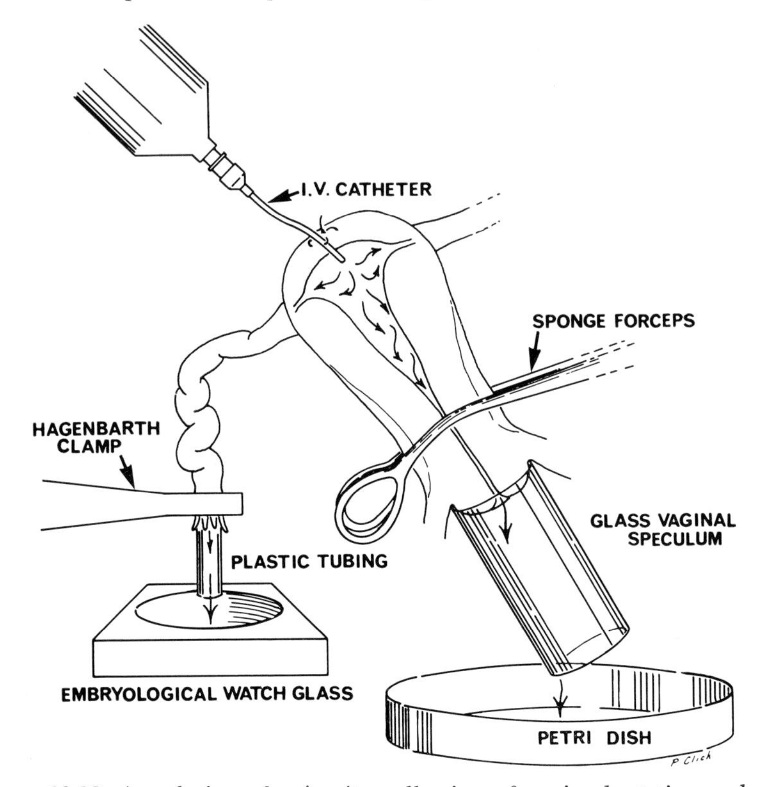

Figure 10-12. A technique for *in situ* collection of preimplantation embryos. Fluid is forced through the uterus and out the oviducts and cervix. It may be necessary to clamp the cervix to obtain sufficient flow through the oviducts. (From Hendrickx and Kraemer, 1970)

variation is the number of placental lobes which may be present. A ventral midline incision is made to expose the gravid uterus, which is delivered manually through the incision. In species with a monodiscoid placenta the implantation site can be recognized in an increased area of myometrial vascularity with reasonable success as early as the twentieth day of pregnancy. In species with a bidiscoid placenta both placental lobes usually can be recognized at a slightly older age. The initial uterine incision is made opposite the implantation site in those animals with monodiscoid placentae and between placental lobes in those with bidiscoid placentae. A sponge forceps or similar instrument placed at the cervix uteri is helpful in restricting uterine blood supply.

Once the endometrium is exposed the incision is slowly enlarged while the incised edges of the myometrium are held in apposition with allis tissue forceps to avoid pressure and the possibility of rupture of the chorionic sac. The endometrium, which varies in thickness from 8 mm during the third week to 5 mm during the eighth week of pregnancy in the baboon, is removed as an intact sac by separating the decidual layers from the basal layer with scissors and a spatula. During the final stages of excision, digital pressure applied to the outside of the uterus at the implantation site aids in excision by partially everting the uterus and exposing the base of the vascular placental attachment.

The early implantation stages are the most difficult to obtain in a condition free of artifact, therefore it is sometimes necessary to resort to hysterectomy to get the necessary specimens. The most frequent artifact occurring in the early implantation period is a disruption of the placental surface, destroying normal relationships. Maternal blood also engulfs the embryo and fills the amniotic and vitelline cavity.

REFERENCES

Arslan, M.; Meyer, R. K., and Wolf, R. C. (1967): Chorionic gonadotrophin in the blood and urine of pregnant rhesus monkeys (Macaca mulatta). *Proc Soc Exp Biol Med, 125,* 349-352.

Adamsons, K., Jr. (1965): Transport of organic substances and oxygen across the placenta. In Bergsma, D. (Ed.): *Symposium on the Placenta.* New York, The National Foundation—March of Dimes.

Ainsworth, L.; Daenen, M., and Ryan, K. J. (1969): Steroid hormone transformations by endocrine organs from pregnant mammals. IV. Biosynthesis and metabolism of estrogens and progesterones by primate placental preparations *in vitro. Endocrinology, 84,* 1421-1429.

Allen, J. R., and Ahlgren, S. A. (1968): A comparative study of the hematologic changes in pregnancy in the *Macaca mulatta* monkey and the human female. *A J Obstet Gynec, 100,* 894-903.

Bangham, D. R. (1960): The transmission of homologous serum proteins to the fetus and to the amniotic fluid in the rhesus monkey. *J Physiol, 153,* 265-271.

Battaglia, F. C.; Hellegers, A. E.; Heller, C. J., and Behrman, R. E. (1964): Glucose concentration gradients across the maternal surface, the placenta, and the amnion of the rhesus monkey (*Macaca mulatta*). *A J Obstet Gynec, 88,* 32-37.

Battaglia, F. C., and Hellegers, A. E. (1964): Permeability to carbohydrates of human chorion levae *in vitro. Amer J Obstet Gynec, 89,* 771-783.

Battaglia, F. C.; Behrman, R. E.; Meschia, G.; Seeds, A. E., and Bruns, P. D. (1968): Clearance of inert molecules, Na and Cl ions across the primate placenta. *A J Obstet Gynec, 102,* 1135-1143.

Behrman, R. E.; Heller, C. J.; Battaglia, F. C., and Hellegers, A. E. (1963): A comparison of the oxygen affinity of maternal and fetal blood of the *Macaca mulatta. Quart J Exp Physiol, 48,* 258-264.

Behrman, R. E.; Seeds, A. E.; Battaglia, F. C.; Hellegers, A. E., and Bruns, P. D. (1964): *J Pediat, 65,* 38-44.

Behrman, R. E.; Parer, J. T., and de Lannoy, C. W. (1967): Placental growth and the formation of amniotic fluid. *Nature, 214 (5089)*:678-680.

Bruns, P. D.; Hellegers, A. E.; Seeds, A. E.; Behrman, R. E., and Battaglia, F. C. (1964): Effects of osmotic gradients across the primate placenta upon fetal and placental water contents. *Pediatrics, 34,* 407-411.

Chez, R. A.; Smith, F. G., and Hutchinson, D. L. (1964): Renal function in the intrauterine primate fetus. *Am J Obstet Gynec, 90,* 128-131.

Chinard, F. P.; Danesino, V.; Hartmann, W. L.; Huggett, A. St. G.; Paul, W., and Reynolds, S. R. M. (1956): The transmission of hexoses across the placenta in the human and the rhesus monkey (*Macaca mulatta*). *J Physiol, 132,* 289-303.

Conaway, C. H., and Koford, C. B. (1965): Estrous cycles and mating behavior in a free-ranging band of rhesus monkeys. *J Mammal, 45,* 577-588.

Csapo, A. (1959): Function and regulation of the myometrium. *Ann Acad Sci, 75,* 790-797.

Cotes, P. M.; Moss, G. F.; Muir, A. R., and Scheuer, P. J. (1966): Distribution of iron in maternal and fetal tissues from pregnant rhesus monkeys treated with a single intravenous infusion of ^{59}Fe iron destian. *Brit J Pharmacol, 26,* 633-648.

Dancis, J. (1964): The perfusion of the guinea pig placenta *in situ. Fed Proc, 23,* 781-784.

Dawes, G. S.; Jacobson, H. N.; Mott, J. C., and Shelley, H. J. (1960): Some observations on foetal and newborn rhesus monkeys. *J Physiol (London), 152,* 271-298.

Dreskin, R. B.; Spicer, S. S., and Greene, W. B. (1970): Ultrastructural localization of chorionic gonadotropin in human term placenta. *J Histochem Cytochem, 18,* 862-874.

Eastman, N. J.; Geiling, E. M. K., and DeLawder, A. M. (1933): Foetal blood studies. IV. The oxygen and carbon dioxide dissociation curves of foetal blood. *Bull Hopkins Hosp, 53,* 246-254.

Friesen, H. G.; Suwa, S., and Parc, P. (1969): Synthesis and secretion of placental lactogen and other proteins by the placenta. *Recent Progr Hormone Res, 25,* 161-205.

Graham-Jones, O., and Hill, W. C. O. (1962): Pregnancy and parturition in a Bornean orang. *Proc Zool Soc London, 139,* 503-510.

Greenwood, F. C.; Hunter, W. M., and Klopper, A. (1964): Assay of human growth hormone in pregnancy, at parturition and in lactation. *Brit Med J, 1,* 22-35.

Hartman, C. G. (1932): Studies in the reproduction of the monkey macacus (Pithecus) rhesus, with special reference to menstruation and pregnancy. *Contrib Embryol Carnegie Inst Washington, 23,* 1-161.

Hellegers, A. E., and Schruefer, J. J. P. (1961): Nomograms and empirical equations relating oxygen tension, percentage saturation and pH in maternal and fetal blood. *Amer J Obstet Gynec, 81,* 377-384.

Hellegers, A. E.; Heller, C. J.; Behrman, R. E., and Battaglia, F. C. (1964): Oxygen and carbon dioxide transfer across the rhesus monkey placenta *(Macaca mulatta). Amer J Obstet Gynec, 88,* 22-31.

Hendrickx, A. G., and Houston, M. L. (1970): Gestation. In Hafez, E. S. E. (Ed.): *Reproduction and Breeding Techniques in Laboratory Animals.* Philadelphia, Lea & Febiger, pp. 157-176.

Hendrickx, A. G., and Kraemer, D. C. (1970): Primates. In Hafez, E. S. E. (Ed.): *Reproduction and Breeding Techniques in Laboratory Animals.* Philadelphia, Lea & Febiger, pp. 316-335.

Hopper, B. R.; Tullner, W. W., and Gray, C. W. (1968): Urinary estrogen excretion during pregnancy in a gorilla (*Gorilla gorilla*). *Proc Soc Exp Biol Med, 129,* 213-214.

Hopper, B. R., and Tullner, W. W. (1967): Urinary estrogen excretion patterns in pregnant rhesus monkeys. *Steroids, 9,* 517-527.

Huggett, A. S. G., and Hammond, J. (1964): Physiology of the placenta. In Parkes, A. S. (Ed.): *Marshall's Physiology of Reproduction.* Longmans, Green, London, vol. II, chap. 16.

Ito, Y., and Higashi, K. (1961): Studies on the prolactin-like substance in the human placenta. *Endoc Jap, 8,* 279-300.

Jeffecoate, T. N. A., and Scott, J. S. (1959): Polyhydramnios and Oligohydramnios. *Canad Med Ass J, 80,* 77-86.

Jones, G. E. S. (1968): Endocrine functions of the placenta. In Barnes, A. C. (Ed.): *Intra-Uterine Development.* Lea & Febiger, Philadelphia.

Jones, C. I., and Greep, R. (1950): *Rec Prog Hormone Res.* G. Pincus (Ed.), *5,* 197-208. New York, Academic Press.

Kaplan, S. L., and Grumbach, M. M. (1964): Studies of a human and simian placental hormone with growth hormone-like and prolactin-like activities. *J Clin Endocr, 24,* 80-97.

Kerr, G. R., and Waisman, H. A. (1967): Transplacental ratios of serum free amino acids during pregnancy in the rhesus monkey. In Nyhan, W. L. (Ed.): *Amino Acid Metabolism and Genetic Variation.* New York, McGraw-Hill, Chap. 31.

Lobel, B. L.; Deane, H. W., and Romney, S. L. (1962): Enzymatic histo-chemistry of the villous portion of the human placenta from six weeks of gestation to term. *A J Obstet Gynec, 83,* 295-311.

Loeschcke, H. H., and Sommer, K. H. (1944): Über Atmungserregbaukeit in der Schwangerschaft. *Arch Gen Physiol, 248,* 405-425.

McDonald, N. S.; Hutchinson, D. L.; Hepler, M., and Flynn, E. (1965): Movement of calcium in both directions across the primate placenta. *Proc Soc Exp Biol Med, 119,* 476-481.

Metcalfe, J.; Bartels, H., and Moll, W. (1967): Gas exchange in the pregnant uterus. *Physiol Rev, 47,* 782-838.

Meyer, R. K.; Wolf, R. C., and Arslan, M. (1969): Implantation and maintenance of pregnancy in progesterone treated ovariectomized monkeys (*Macaca mulatta*) *Proc 2nd Int Congr Primat, 2,* 30-35.

Midgley, A. R., and Pierce, G. B. (1963): Immunohistochemical localization of human chorionic gonadotropin. *J Exp Med, 115,* 289-294.

Neill, J. D.; Johansson, E. D. B., and Knobil, E. (1969): Patterns of circulating progesterone concentrations during the fertile menstrual cycle and the remainder of gestation in the rhesus monkey. *Endocrinology, 84,* 45-48.

Pickering, D. E. (1966): The Laboratory confined Mulatta macaque monkey: *Reproduction characteristics.* In Miller, C. O. (Ed.): *Proc Conf Nonhuman Prim Toxicol.* Washington, D.C. Food & Drug Admin.

Parer, J. T. (1967): The O_2 dissociation curve of blood of the rhesus monkey (*Macaca mulatta*). *Resp Physiol, 2,* 168-172.

Pitkin, R. M.; Reynolds, W. A., and Burchell, R. C. (1968): Fetal contributions to amniotic fluid. *Am J Obstet Gynec, 100,* 834-838.

Popjak, G. (1954): The origin of fetal lipids. *Cold Spring Harbor Symposium, 19,* 200-227.

Rosenblum, L. A. (1968): In Rosenblum & Cooper, R. W. (Eds.): *Some Aspects of Female Reproductive Physiology in the Squirrel Monkey.* New York, Academic Press, chap. 5, p. 147.

Scoggins, W. A.; Herbert, G. M.; Anslow, W. P.; Van't Riet, B., and McGaughey, H. S. (1964): Feto-maternal exchange of water at term. *A J Obstet Gynec., 90,* 7-21.

Seeds, A. E., Jr. (1968): Placental Transfer. In Barnes, A. C. (Ed.): *Intra-Uterine Development.* Philadelphia, Lea & Febiger, chap. 5.

Seeds, A. E., Jr. (1968): Amnionic fluid and fetal water metabolism. In Barnes, A. C. (Ed.): *Intra-Uterine Development.* Philadelphia, Lea & Febiger, chap. 6.

Seeds, A. E.; Kock, H. C.; Myers, R. E.; Stolte, L. A. M., and Hellegers, A. E. (1967): Changes in rhesus monkey amniotic fluid pH, pCO_2 and bicarbonate concentration following maternal and fetal hypercarbia and fetal death in utero. *A J Obstet Gynec, 97,* 67-75.

Stenger, V.; Eitzman, D.; Andersen, T.; Cotter, J., and Prystowsky, H. (1965): A study of the oxygenation of the fetus and newborn and its relation to that of the mother. *A J Obstet Gynec, 93,* 376-385.

Tullner, W. W., and Hertz, R. (1966): Chorionic gonadotropin levels in the rhesus monkey during early pregnancy. *Endocrinology, 78,* 204-207.

Tullner, W. W., and Hertz, R. (1966): Normal gestation and gonadotropin levels in the monkey after ovariectomy in early pregnancy. *Endocrinology, 78,* 1076-1078.

Tullner, W. W. (1968): Urinary chorionic gonadotropin excretion in the monkey (*Macaca mulatta*) early phase. *Endocrinology, 82,* 874-875.

Tullner, W. W., and Gray, C. W. (1968): Chorionic gonadotropin excretion during pregnancy in a gorilla. *Proc Soc Exp Biol Med, 128,* 954-956.

Villee, C. A. (1966): In Weber, G. (Ed.): Advances in Enzyme Regulation. Pergamon, New York.

Weber, J. (1963): Histochemical studies of the production of gonadotropin in the placenta and foetal membranes. *Acta Obstet Gynec Scand (Suppl), 2,* 82.

Wilson, J. G.; Fradkin, R., and Hardman, A. (1970): Breeding and pregnancy in rhesus monkeys used for teratological testing. *Teratology, 3,* 59-61.

Wirtschafter, Z. T. (1958): Free amino acids in human amniotic fluid, fetal and maternal serum. *Amer J Obstet Gynec, 76,* 1219-1222.

Wislocki, G. B., and Hartman, C. G. (1929): On the placentation of a macaque (*M.* rhesus) with observations on the origin of the blood constituting the placental sign. *Johns Hopkins Hosp Bull, 44,* 165-185.

Chapter 11

PARTURITION

W. J. BO

I. MECHANISMS INVOLVED

PARTURITION consists of a series of events that are concerned with the expulsion from the uterus of the products of conception. The time parturition begins varies with the species. Despite the attention that this field of research has received, the mechanism by which parturition is initiated is still unclear. Since morphological, mechanical, nutritional, hormonal, circulatory and nervous factors are involved in maintaining pregnancy, it is unlikely that only one factor is responsible for parturition. Normal parturition requires the synchronization of many events.

Information from a variety of species helps clarify the process of parturition. Because complete data concerning the mechanism of parturition are lacking on the nonhuman primates, observations from other species will be presented. The differences in endocrine control of parturition among the different species may be the result of a difference in hormone production instead of in the controlling mechanisms.

A. Hormonal Mechanisms

Oxytocin, progesterone and estrogen affect the contractility of the myometrium and have a role in parturition. Oxytocin is produced in the supraoptic and paraventricular nuclei of the hypothalamus and passes within the axons to the posterior pituitary. After being stored in the gland it is released into the blood as required, bound to plasma protein and transported to the target organs. The hormone stimulates uterine contractions, but whether or not it is responsible for initiating parturition is not clear. If the maternal or fetal pituitary gland is removed from the rhesus monkey, pregnancy or parturition is unaltered (Hutchinson *et al.*, 1962). Residual neurohypophyseal tissue may have remained after surgery and undergone hypertrophy resulting in secretion of oxytocin. The importance of the hormone in initiating parturition is supported by the studies of Caldeyro-Barcia and Poseiro (1959). The characteristic contractions of the human uterus that result when oxytocin is infused cannot be distinguished from the contractions of spontaneous parturition. During the last four to eight weeks of pregnancy spontaneous activity of the uterus increases, although it is no more sensitive to oxytocin than before. This indicates that the increase in activity is the result of an increased release of oxytocin from the posterior pituitary. The concept that maternal oxytocin is not essential for the initiation of parturition, but has a stimulatory effect on the myometrium after contractions have started, is supported by the investigation of Csapo and Wood (1968). In the rabbit the hormone appears only a few minutes before the first fetus is delivered, even though the spontaneous activity has been in progress for several days. If oxytocin is given more than forty-eight hours before expected time of delivery it is ineffective. In the human the blood concentration of the hormone is increased only after the first stage of parturition is well advanced.

Unlike estrogen, progesterone does not stimulate contractions of the myometrium. During pregnancy the uterus is dominated by progesterone, which is important in maintaining and terminating pregnancy. The corpus luteum is more essential for the maintenance of pregnancy in the rat, rabbit and golden hamster than it is in primates.

In the human the site of synthesis of progesterone shifts, early in pregnancy, from the corpus luteum to the placenta. Urinary excretion of pregnanediol by the human increases during pregnancy, decreasing sharply after parturition. During late pregnancy the concentration of the hormone is highest in the placenta, with gradually lesser amounts being found in fetal membranes, myometrium, amniotic fluid and peripheral vein plasma (Csapo and Wood, 1968). These findings, along with those that have shown the concentration of the hormone at the anti-implantation site to be lower than at the placental site, support the concept of a direct local block of uterine smooth muscle activity by progesterone

(Csapo, 1956). According to this concept the hormone reaches the myometrium directly from the placenta, not from the general circulation. The concentration of progesterone alters the activity of the myometrium at the placental site by inhibiting the propagation of a stimulus. As the uterus is increasingly distended and continuously stimulated by estrogen during gestation, the contractile elements of the organ increase.

Uterine contractions cannot be intensified until the progesterone block is removed. Following removal of the block the uterine muscle is predominately under the influence of estrogen, stimuli are propagated and uterine contractions increase. Destruction of the placenta, which produces progesterone, increases myometrial activity, resulting in abortion. In women destruction of the placental function by intra-amniotic injection of formalin induces abortion (Bengtsson, 1962). Intra-amniotic injections of saline into all the placental sites of the rabbit result in abortion of all the fetuses in about fifty-six hours. In these studies abortion apparently was the result of an interruption of the luteotrophic function of the placenta, which caused a loss of essential luteal function (Porter *et al.,* 1968).

The nonpregnant woman primarily synthesizes estrogen in the ovaries, but during pregnancy it is predominantly made in the placenta. Estrogen stimulates growth of the myometrium and also enhances glycogen synthesis. Under its influence contractile elements increase, and there is rapid propagation of contraction and improved coordination between different parts of the myometrium. These effects are essentially the same in women and experimental animals. It is not clear whether the increase in uterine contractions is produced by the changes in circulatory estrogen concentration or progesterone concentration. Fetal death triggers uterine activity, and parturition occurs after a variably latent period. Because this phenomenon is followed by a drop in placental estrogen, the hormone may not be essential for the initiation of parturition (Csapo and Wood, 1968).

B. Mechanical Mechanisms

Mechanical factors affect the initiation of parturition. A decreased uterine volume affected by withdrawing 500 to 1000 ml of

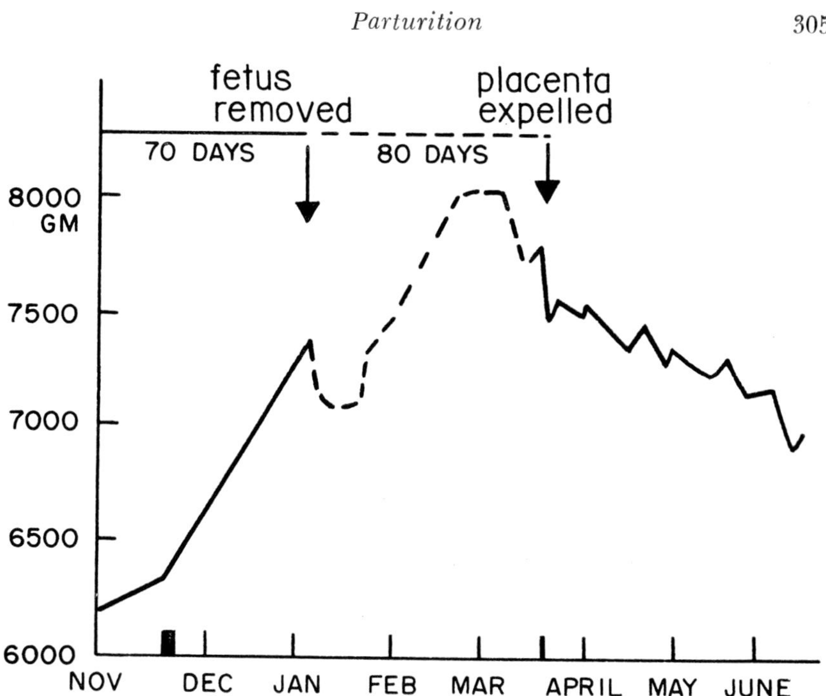

Figure 11-1. Body weight curve of a rhesus monkey from day of fertilization through pregnancy and postpartum period. The broken lines represent the time after the fetus was removed but the placenta remained in place. The placenta was expelled spontaneously approximately seventeen days before the estimated time of delivery. (From van Wagenen and Newton, 1943)

amniotic fluid from normal women at term did not precipitate parturition (Csapo and Lloyd-Jacob, 1963). If the fetus were removed from the rhesus monkey (*Macaca mulatta*) on day seventy of gestation, leaving the placenta behind, pregnancy continued with respect to body weight increments as in normal pregnancy (van Wagenen and Newton, 1943). Besides the increase in body weight, other characteristics were evident: sex-skin color intensified, generalized edema and physical inactivity of the monkey (Fig. 11-1). The typical signs of impending parturition were present, and it consisted of the first and third stages. The increase in uterine activity after rupture of the membranes may not be caused by a decrease in uterine volume, but more likely by an alteration in the transfer of progesterone to the myometrium (Csapo and Wood, 1968). Increase in uterine volume precipitates parturition, as demonstrated both clinically and in experimental animals (Csapo and Lloyd-Jacob, 1963).

C. Neural Mechanisms

After withdrawal of the progesterone block at the end of gestation, uterine contractions become more pronounced in the estrogen-dominated uterus, starting at the fundus of the uterus and forcing the fetus towards the cervix. Stimulation of the cervix elicits a nervous reflect to the neurohypophysis, increasing the rate of oxytocin secretion, which in turn increases and intensifies uterine contractions. The nervous elements (sensory mechanisms, spinal cord, brain stem, forebrain) which are involved between a stimulus such as irritation or stretching of the cervix and the output of oxytocin are not clear (Cross, 1959; Powell and Rorie, 1967). The final common pathway for all the neural influences is the supraoptic and paraventricular nuclei and their projections to the neurohypophysis. In addition to eliciting a nervous reflex to the neurohypophysis, stimulation of the cervix by the fetus can produce a reflex increase in uterine contractions. With each uterine contraction the fetus stretches the cervix and initiates still further intensity of contractions. The fetus is, therefore, pushed further down the cervical canal. The above process repeats itself until delivery of the fetus is complete (Guyton, 1966) (Fig. 11-2).

II. NORMAL COURSE OF PARTURITION

A. Signs, Stages and Duration of Parturition

The most reliable sign of oncoming parturition in woman is the presence of the cervical plug which indicates that delivery will probably occur within twenty-four hours. It is difficult to ascertain approaching parturition with certainty in the nonhuman primates. Various changes in behavior such as restlessness, eating and sleeping habits, frequency of urination, intensified grooming and manipulation of the genitalia occur to variable degrees in the nonhuman primates; however, *Gorrilla* (Gorilla) and *Hylobates* (gibbon) become less active, and the gorilla withdraws from the other animals when parturition is near (Rumbaugh, 1967; Ibscher, 1967).

The process of parturition is classified into three stages which

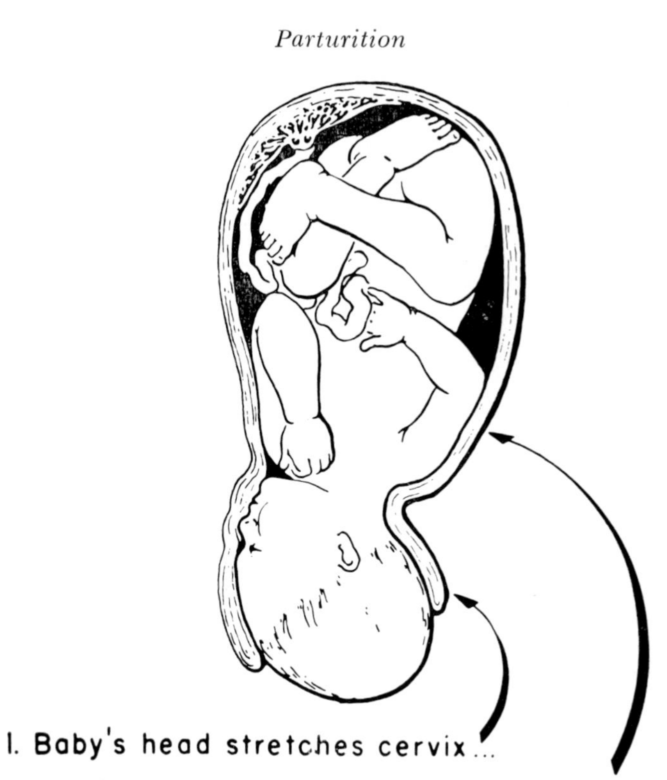

Figure 11-2. A suggestive mechanism for the initiation of parturition. (From Guyton, 1966)

are well defined in the human. Stage I begins with labor pains and ends with complete dilatation of the cervix; stage II begins with complete dilatation of the cervix and ends with the delivery of the infant; stage III begins with the delivery of the infant and ends with the expulsion of the placenta (Eastman and Hellman, 1961). Although different stages can be observed in nonhuman primates, they are not precisely defined as in the human; therefore, different criteria are used for the stages, particularly the first. The literature contains several reports on the events which take place during par-

TABLE 11-I

SOME COMPARATIVE EVENTS AT DIFFERENT STAGES OF PARTURITION[a]

Genus	*Stage I*	*Stage II*	*Stage III*
Cercopithecus[1]	excretion of feces and urine; feels pubis; mucus from vagina; abdominal contractions; lies down and stretches; on all fours; duration 4 minutes	feels pubis; large amount of mucus; vertex appears; holds baby with both hands; pulls at the baby and licks its face carefully; complete appearance of baby; duration 3 minutes	licks infant's face and her own body which is wet with perspiration; placenta comes out; licks pubis; eats the placenta; duration 55 minutes
Erthrocepus[2]	very restless; does a lot of crouching; contractions of abdominal wall; vagina opens; duration approximately 45 minutes	much straining; strong contractions; some mucus discharge; head of fetus shows; mother grasps infant and pulls at it; marked contraction and infant is expelled; approximate duration 15 minutes	licks infant's face; supports infant; licks umbilical cord; pulls placenta out; consumes placenta but does not ignore infant; approximately 3 hours duration
Galago[3]	hyperactivity starts during day; carries nesting material but no nests are made	begins intense grooming of herself and others; very restless; examines genitalia for first time; does not drink or eat	infant appears; expelled in about 30 seconds; mother handles infant and examines her genitalia frequently; this continues until last delivery which requires one to two hours; placenta expelled and consumed
Hylobates[a,4]	several contractions at 8–12 minute intervals; animal lies on side; palpates the genitalia; licks fluid around pubis; vomits violently; contractions closer together; duration about 9 hours	head visible; strong uterine contractions; assumes sitting position; grasps infant by head; stands erect and pulls infant out; approximately 10 minutes duration	takes young and licks it and fluid; afterbirth expelled 30 minutes after infant; eats most of afterbirth
Macaca[a,5]	squats on floor; breath labored; face flushed; grunts loudly; hyperactive; duration approximately 2 hours	places hand in vagina; fluid passes; licks hands; crown of head visible; licks fluid avidly; head of infant emerges and mother grasps head and pulls it out; duration approximately 12 minutes	licks infant; placenta is expelled; mother continues to lick infant and then starts to eat placenta; ignores infant while eating placenta; duration 45 minutes
Pam[a,6]	several contractions; straining and grunting; unusually restless; examines vagina; duration approximately 1 hour, 15 minutes	assumes squatting position; small amount of fluid expelled; crown of infant's head appears; head delivered; mother on her left side supports head of infant, but does not aid delivery; body delivered after single contraction; duration about 4 minutes	placenta expelled three minutes later; picks up infant; afterbirth only half consumed within an hour after birth
Pongo[7]	vaginal discharge; indicates pain by raising arms; very active; duration approximately 10 minutes	examines vulva; signs of severe pain; assumes a right lateral or dorsal decubitus position; contractions increase; head appears; female rests on right knee and forearm; left forearm free to grasp the infant; expulsion of infant; duration approximately 13 minutes	fetal membranes delivered; mother licks but does not consume them; licks the infant; duration approximately 90 minutes
Saimiri[1]	hyperactive; feels pubis; several abdominal contractions; some crying; mucus discharge from vagina; head of infant is visible; duration 63 minutes	on all fours; licks mucus; licks infant continuously as expelled; duration 16 minutes	placenta expelled with aid of mother; eats the placenta completely; duration 9 minutes

TABLE 11-I (Continued)

Genus	*Stage I*	*Stage II*	*Stage III*
Saimiri[8]	one animal showed some genital inspection; little mucus present; little licking of perineum; in second animal more mucus was expelled and more licking of perineum; severe uterine contractions in both animals; vocalization; duration 42 minutes	assumes a squatting position; licks infant as it comes out; does not assist in delivery; second animal pulled infant's tail during delivery; duration 63 seconds	supports infant for a short time; placenta emerges; duration 11 minutes *Stage IV* efforts of mother to eat placenta; duration 10 minutes

[a] Separate stages not indicated specifically by the authors.
[1] Takeshita 1961-62; [2] Goswell and Gartlan, 1965; [3] Doyle *et al.*, 1967; [4] Ibscher, 1967; [5] Hartman, 1928; [6] Elder and Yerkes, 1936; [7] Graham-Jones and Hill, 1962; [8] Bowden *et al.*, 1967.

turition (Table 11-I), but there are relatively few which give precise documentations of the specific events at the different stages.

The time of the day parturition occurs is not only variable in the different species but also in the same species (Table 11-II).

Behavioral Patterns of Mother. The posture of the mothers during uterine contractions and expulsion of the infants is variable. However, most of the primates, except modern man, assume a posture resembling the squatting position. In *Pongo* (orangutan) a right lateral or a dorsal decubitus position is assumed just prior to parturition (Graham-Jones and Hill, 1962). *Hylobates* (gibbon) lie on their side during early stages and assume the sitting position at the time of expulsion of the infant (Ibscher, 1967). *Gorrilla* (gorilla) lie prone with knees parallel to the body and the face buried in their palms (Rumbaugh, 1967). A pattern observed in *Pan* (chimpanzee) was a quick run followed by a squat and a grunt (Nissen and Yerkes, 1943). The squatting position predominates in *Macaca* (rhesus monkey) (Tinklepaugh and Hartman, 1930-31) and in *Saimiri* (squirrel monkey) (Bowden *et al.*, 1967). In *Lagothrix* (woolly monkey) the female stands on all fours (Williams, 1967), while in *Cercopithecus* (mona monkey) the sitting and standing positions are assumed (Takeshita, 1961-62).

Manual aid by the mother during delivery is a phenomenon which is characteristic of nonhuman primates. Intense manipulation of the perineum prior to presentation of the infant's head occurs in many species; however, the degree of aid given by the mother is variable. After the head appears the mother will support

TABLE 11-II

DURATION OF PARTURITION, TIME OF DAY BIRTH OCCURS AND PRESENTATION OF FETUS IN SEVERAL SPECIES OF NONHUMAN PRIMATES

Species	*Duration of Parturition (Hrs.)*	*Time of Birth*	*Presentation*
Cercopthecus mona[1]	1.03	4:25 A.M.	vertex
Erythrocepus patas[2]	1.4	7:32 A.M.	—
Galago senegalensis moholi[3]	3–4	—	—
Gorilla gorilla[4]	—	9:58 A.M.	—
Hylobates lar[5]	10	midnight	—
Macaca mulatta[6]	1–2	4:10 A.M.	vertical axis
Macaca mulatta[7]	—	—	face meno-anterior
Macaca mulatta[8]	4–5	11:28 A.M.	—
	0.4	afternoon	—
Pan[9]	3–4	10:10 A.M.	—
Pan[10]	2–3	11:15 A.M.	vertex, occiput posterior
Pan[11]	—	—	vertex, occiput posterior
Pan[12]	6–8	6:00 A.M.–6:00 P.M. 23 deliveries 6:00 P.M.–6:00 A.M. 26 deliveries	—
Pan[13]	4–5	7:15 P.M.	—
Pan[14]	—	—	4 animals, vertex 2 occiput posterior 1 occiput anterior 1 uncertain
Pongo pygmaeus[10]	—	during the night	—
Pongo pygmaeus[15]	1.4	12:38 P.M.	vertex, right occiput posterior
Saimiri sciureus[16]	1.07	early morning	vertex, occiputs posterior
Saimiri sciureus[1]	1.5	1:43 A.M.	—

[1] Takeshita, 1961-62.
[2] Goswell and Gartlan, 1965.
[3] Doyle, *et al.*, 1967.
[4] Rumbaugh, 1967.
[5] Ibscher, 1967.
[6] Hartman, 1928.
[7] Hill, 1962.
[8] Tinklepaugh and Hartman, 1931.
[9] Budd, *et al.*, 1943.
[10] Fox, 1929.
[11] Elder and Yerkes, 1936.
[12] Nissen and Yerkes, 1943.
[13] Wyatt and Vevers, 1935.
[14] Yerkes and Elder, 1937.
[15] Graham-Jones and Hill, 1962.
[16] Bowden, *et al.*, 1967.

and grasp it in order to pull out the infant. The help given by the mother speeds up stage II of parturition. This has been observed in such species as the rhesus monkey (Hartman, 1928), chimpanzee (Fox, 1929), orangutan (Graham-Jones and Hill, 1962), mona monkey (Takeshita, 1961-62) and patas monkey (Goswell and Gartlan, 1965). In the squirrel monkey the pulling of the half-exposed infant is a weaker phenomenon than in other infraprimates (Bowden *et al.,* 1967). No assistance by the mother occurs in *Galago* (Doyle *et al.,* 1967).

Vocalization during parturition is not a universal phenomenon among the subhuman primates. The rhesus monkey (Tinklepaugh and Hartman, 1930-31), orangutan (Graham-Jones and Hill, 1962) and chimpanzee (Nissen and Yerkes, 1943; Budd *et al.,* 1943) give an occasional grunt during the process of parturition. The chimpanzee (Fox, 1929) also gives and occasional howl. Using spectrograms four sounds were identified as characteristic of the parturition period (Stages I and II) in the squirrel monkey (Bowden *et al.,* 1967). They were classified as "labor squeak," "labor grunt," "labor growl" and "labor groan." As the mother went from the first stage of parturition to that of protecting her infant a shift in vocalization from excitement to aggression occurred.

B. Presentation

The fetus develops in breach presentation and during late pregnancy it changes to a cephalic presentation. This change occurs in the squirrel monkey twenty-three to sixty-five days before delivery, four to eighty hours in the rhesus monkey, and in the baboon it was noted several times within the last twenty-four hours prior to delivery (Bowden *et al.,* 1967). Vertex presentation is more common in the human than face presentation, and the fetus emerges occiput anterior more frequently than occiput posterior. The manner of presentation in several species of primates is indicated in Table 11-II. Occiput posterior is more common in apes and monkeys than in the human (Bowden *et al.,* 1967).

C. Consumption of the Placenta

Complete or partial consumption of the placenta is very common in several species, e.g. *Galgo* (Doyle *et al.,* 1927), marmosets (Hampton, personal communication), mona monkeys (Bowden *et al.,* 1967), squirrel monkeys (Takeshita, 1961-62; Bowden *et al.,* 1967), patas monkeys (Goswell and Gartlan, 1965), and orangutans (Nissen and Yerkes, 1943). Of seventeen parturitions in rhesus monkeys, twelve mothers consumed the placenta, two partially ate it and three did not (Tinklepaugh and Hartman, 1931). The woolly monkey does not consume the placenta (Williams, 1967).

III. BEHAVIOR OF MOTHER AND NEONATE

The mother's behavior to the neonate varies greatly. Cleaning of the infant occurs in most of the animals, and it appears to be a continuation of the licking process of the fetal fluids. The orangutan demonstrates great care for the infant by licking and sucking it, breathes into its mouth, examines it carefully and cuddles it between her legs. The infant orangutan begins to breathe within thirty seconds after birth, blinks and stares normally, feels for the mother's nipple and clings to her hair with hands and feet. Hair is present on the extensor side of the arms and legs, and within four hours the infant is sucking (Graham-Jones and Hill, 1962). The gibbon infant with his eyes closed clings to the mother immediately (Ibscher, 1967).

The primiparous chimpanzee appears confused towards the infant, and her behavior is less appropriate than in the multiparous animal (Yerkes and Elder, 1937). Within six hours after birth the mother takes the baby's head and places its mouth to her nipple, and the infant grasps and sucks. The mother continues cuddling, licking and cleaning of the afterbirth for approximately forty-five minutes. The infant has the capability to cling to the mother's hair without assistance (Elder and Yerkes, 1936). The chimpanzee infant's eyes are open (Budd *et al.,* 1943); the head, back and extensor surfaces of the extremities are covered with hair, skin of the palms of the feet is dull red, no teeth are present and gums and tongue are a healthy pink (Fox, 1929). With some support from the mother the infant gorilla has the strength to cling to her (Rumbaugh, 1967).

Licking of the infant rhesus monkey takes place postpartum, but it is ignored while the mother eats the placenta (Hartman, 1928). On the other hand, the infant mona monkey is on the mother's breast while she handles and eats the placenta (Takeshita, 1961-62). In the rhesus monkey the eyes are open slightly within two hours after birth and are wide open at eight hours; no sucking was observed during the first night (Hartman, 1929). The eyes are open as soon as the woolly monkey is born, and within two hours after birth it is sucking (Williams, 1967). The mother squirrel monkey supports the infant very briefly; it climbs immediately to the mother's back; its eyes are open three minutes after birth, and it sucks within one hour after birth (Bowden *et al.*, 1967). The patas monkey supports the infant while it is clinging and does not ignore the infant while eating the placenta (Goswell and Gartlan, 1965). The infant galago receives little assistance from the mother; the eyes are closed but it can grip strongly to the mother (Doyle *et al.*, 1967).

REFERENCES

Bengtsson, L. Ph. (1962): Endocrine factors in labour. *Acta Obstet Gynec Scand* (Suppl. 1), *41*, 87-116.

Bowden, D.; Winter, P., and Ploog, D. (1967): Pregnancy and delivery behavior in the squirrel monkey (Saimiri Sciureus) and other primates. *Folia Primat, 5,* 1-42.

Budd, A.; Smith, L. G., and Shelley, F. W. (1943): On the birth and upbringing of the female chimpanzee. *Proc Zool Garden London, 113,* 1-21.

Caldeyro-Barcia, R., and Poseiro, J. J. (1959): Oxytocin and contractility of the pregnant human uterus. *Ann NY Acad Sci, 75,* 813-830.

Cross, B. A. (1959): Neurohypophyseal control of parturition. In Lloyd, C. W. (Ed.): *Recent Progress in the Endocrinology of Reproduction.* N.Y., Academic Press, pp. 441-455.

Csapo, A. I. (1956): Progesterone "block." *A J Anat, 98,* 273.

Csapo, A. I., and Lloyd-Jacob, M. A. (1963): Effect of uterine volume on parturition. *A J Obstet Gynec, 85,* 806-812.

Csapo, A. I., and Wood, C. (1968): The endocrine control of the initiation of labour in the human. In James, V. H. T. (Ed.): *Recent Advances in Endocrinology*. Boston, Little, Brown, chap. 7, pp. 207-239.

Doyle, G. A.; Pelletier, A., and Bekker, T. (1967): Courtship, mating and parturition in the lesser bushbaby (*Galago senegalensis moholi*) under semi-natural conditions. *Folia Primat, 7,* 169-197.

Eastman, N. J., and Hellman, L. M. (1961): The forces concerned with labor. In *Williams Obstetrics,* 12th ed. New York, Appleton-Century-Crofts, pp. 373-403.

Elder, J. H., and Yerkes, R. M. (1936): The sexual cycle of the chimpanzee. *Anat Rec, 67,* 119-143.

Fox, H. (1929): The birth of two anthropoid apes. *J Mamm, 10,* 37-51.

Goswell, M. J., and Gartlan, J. S. (1965): Pregnancy, birth and early infant behavior in the captive Patas monkey Erythrocepus Patas. *Folia Primat, 3,* 189-200.

Graham-Jones, O., and Hill, W. C. O. (1962): Pregnancy and parturition in a Bornean orangutan. *Proc Zool Soc London, 139 (3),* 403-410.

Guyton, A. (1966): Part XI. Endocrinology and Reproduction. In *Textbook of Medical Physiology,* 3rd ed., chap. 7, pp. 1035-1182.

Hartman, C. (1928): The period of gestation in the monkey, macacus rhesus, first description of parturition in monkeys, size and behavior of the young. *J Mamm, 9,* 181-194.

Hill, W. C. Osman (1955): *Primates.* Edinburgh University Press, vol. 2, pp. 1-102.

Hutchinson, D. L.; Westover, J. L., and Will, D. W. (1962): The destruction of the maternal and fetal pituitary glands in subhuman primates. *Amer J Obstet Gynec, 83,* 857-865.

Ibscher, L. (1967): Geburt and Fruhe Entwicklung Zweier Gibbons (Hylobates Lar L.). *Folia Primat, 5,* 43-69.

Nissen, H. W., and Yerkes, R. M. (1943): Reproduction in the chimpanzee: Report on forty-nine births. *Anat Rec, 86,* 567-578.

Porter, D. G.; Becker, R., and Csapo, A. (1968): On the mechanism of action of intra-amniotic hypertonic saline treatment in rabbits. *J Reprod Fertil, 17,* 433-442.

Powell, E. W., and Rorie, D. K. (1967): Septal projections to nuclei functioning in oxytocin release. *Amer J Anat, 120,* 605-610.

Rumbaugh, D. M. (1967): 'Alvila'—San Diego captive—born gorilla, Gorilla g. gorilla. In Jarvis, C. (Ed.): *International Zoo Yearbook.* London, Zool Soc London, vol. VII, pp. 98-107.

Takeshita, H. (1961-62): On the delivery behavior of squirrel monkeys (Saimiri sciurea) and a mona monkey (Cercopithecus mona). *Primates, 3,* 59-72.

Tinklepaugh, O. L., and Hartman, C. G. (1930-31): Behavioral aspects of parturition in the monkey (Macacus rhesus). *J Comp Psychol, 2,* 63-98

Van Wagenen, G., and Newton, W. H. (1943): Pregnancy in the monkey after removal of the fetus. *Surg Gynec Obstet, 77,* 539-543.

Williams, L. (1967): Breeding Humboldt's woolly monkey (Lagothrix lagotricha) at Murraytown Woolly Monkey Sanctuary. In Jarvis, C. (Ed.): *International Zoo Yearbook.* London, Zool Soc London, vol. VII, pp. 86-89.

Wyatt, J. M., and Vevers, G. M. (1935): On the birth of a chimpanzee recently born in the Society's Garden. *Proc Zool Soc London,* 195-197.

Yerkes, R. N., and Elder, J. H. (1937): Concerning reproduction in the chimpanzee. *Yale J Biol Med, 10,* 41-48.

Chapter 12

MAMMARY GLANDS AND LACTATION

D. H. BUSS

I. MAMMARY GLANDS

A. Morphology

1. Gross Morphology. The great apes, Old-World and New World monkeys normally have one pair of pectoral mammary glands. Because these glands are sheets of tissue only a few millimeters thick, they are barely visible under the chest hair. They are palpable only with difficulty, except towards the end of pregnancy and during lactation. At this time the glands are enlarged more in area than thickness, and are kept well-drained by the infants, so do not become especially prominent (although exceptions include the apes, especially *Pongo,* some *Macaca mulatta,* and *Arctocebus*). The mammary glands of males resemble those of virgin females.

There is more variation in the number and position of mammary glands in prosimians, both between species and within a species, as judged by the location of the nipples (Schultz, 1948). There may be one or two pectoral (including axillary and thoracic) pairs, with or without an abdominal (or inguinal) pair. *Daubentonia* and *Dendrogale* are unusual in having only one abdominal pair. The literature data are summarized in Table 12-I; some of the variations may be because small nipples are difficult to find in the dense chest hair. Some of this hair is lost, however, during lactation in *Loris* and *Nycticebus* to give "lacteal tracts" about 5 cm × 1 cm.

The mammary area of *Theropithecus gelada* is unique in having a large bare patch shaped like an inverted heart. In mature females, it is surrounded by a "necklace" of fleshy lumps, and its

TABLE 12-I

NUMBER AND GENERAL POSITION* OF PROSIMIAN NIPPLES†

Genus	*Number*	*Positions*
Anathana	6	
Arctocebus	6	4 Pectoral & 2 abdominal
Avahi	2	Pectoral
Cheirogaleus	2, 4 or 6	2 Pectoral; 4 pectoral; 2 pectoral & 2 abdominal; or 4 pectoral & 2 abdominal
Daubentonia	2	Abdominal
Dendrogale	2	Abdominal
Galago	4 or 6	4 Pectoral; 2 pectoral & 2 abdominal; 4 pectoral & 2 abdominal; or 2 pectoral & 4 abdominal
Hapalemur	4	4 Pectoral; or 2 pectoral & 2 abdominal
Indri	2	Pectoral
Lemur	2, 4 or 6	2 Pectoral; 4 pectoral; 2 pectoral & 2 abdominal; or 4 pectoral & 2 abdominal
Lepilemur	2	Pectoral
Loris	2 or 4	2 Pectoral; 4 pectoral; or 2 pectoral & 2 abdominal
Microcebus	4 or 6	2 Pectoral & 2 abdominal; or 4 pectoral & 2 abdominal
Nycticebus	4 or 6	4 Pectoral; or 4 pectoral & 2 abdominal
Perodicticus	4 or 6	2 Pectoral & 2 abdominal; or 4 pectoral & 2 abdominal
Propithecus	2	Pectoral
Ptilocercus	4	
Tarsius	4 or 6	2 Pectoral & 2 abdominal; or 4 pectoral & 2 abdominal
Tupaia	2, 4 or 6	4 Pectoral (*T. glis*); 4 pectoral & 2 abdominal (*T. belangeri*)
Urogale	4	

* "Pectoral" also includes the axillary and thoracic areas, and "abdominal" includes the inguinal area.

† Data from Hill, 1953; Napier and Napier, 1967; Schultz, 1948; and others.

red color intensifies during the follicular phase of the menstrual cycle (Hill, 1970).

The nipples are normally away from the centers of the glands. They can be so close together that the infant will nurse on both simultaneously (*Cercopithecus aethiops* and *Theropithecus gelada*) or so far apart as to be axillary (*Alouatta, Lagothrix,* and some marmosets and sakis) or on the shoulder (*Hapalemur,* and male *Cheirogaleus*). *Galago senegalensis* has three pairs of nipples on glands extending without obvious subdivisions from clavicle to groin (Butler, 1967)

The nipples are proportionately much longer in nonhuman primates than in man. During lactation they become pendulous (Fig. 12-1) and one may be twice the length of the other, depending on the traction exerted by the nursing infant. *Macaca mulatta* infants

Figure 12-1. *Papio cynocephalus* after 4 months lactation, partially shaved to show the flat mammary glands and pendulous nipples. The left nipple has been slightly deformed from the nursing of the infant.

develop a pronounced preference for one nipple, and when one infant is born to a prosimian with four or six nipples, it may nurse from all (*Loris, Perodicticus*) or just one pair (*Lemur, Tarsius*); in this case the other nipples can involute completely and be used by the infant solely for anchorage.

The nipples of mature female *Macaca mulatta* vary in color, from pink to bright red, and size through the menstrual cycles and pregnancy. They average 9-12 mm long and 5-6 mm wide, and have between two and ten ducts—commonly a central duct within a circle of four or five others (Speert, 1948). The nipples of lactating *Papio cynocephalus* are usually pink, but may be purplish-black all over or just on the anterior surface. They are 10-30 mm long, and 10-15 mm wide at the base; those of a *Pan* were black, and 15 mm long and 4 mm wide, with eight or nine ducts (Hill, 1951); of a *Pongo pygmaeus,* 40 mm long; of a *Galago senegalensis,* 4 mm long with two ducts; and of a *Nycticebus coucang,* 7-10 mm long with seven to ten ducts (Ahmed and Kanagasuntheram, 1965). The nipples of *Alouatta seniculus* are black with white tips.

The areolae, or slightly-raised pigmented areas around the nipples, of nonhuman primates are insignifiant, except during pregnancy in the great apes.

2. *Histogenesis.* Mammary gland development has been described in detail for only one species of nonhuman primate—*Macaca mulatta*—and the following account is taken almost entirely from the monumental work of Speert (1948). The few observations which have been made on other primates are summarized in the following section, and can be compared with the extensive information on nonprimates (Kon and Cowie, 1961).

Mammary lines, from which the glands develop, are first found along the ventral surface of five week embryos (crown-rump length, 11-12 mm), and are best-developed in the thoracic region. By the time of birth, there are two small pink nipples and areolae almost flush with the skin. The glands are then less than 2 mm in diameter and consist only of a few poorly-branched ducts. These ducts are lined with four to six layers of epithelial cells, which later decrease to one to two layers.

By adolescence, the ducts have extended and branched, and lobules of alveoli may be present. These glands have an area of about 4 cm^2, and are extremely thin. A period of accelerated growth then occurs until the glands reach an area of about 100 cm^2, during which time the body weight increases from about 2.5 kg to 5 kg.

The glands of adult females lie in flat sheets of connective tissue between the pectoral muscles and the skin, and can extend into the axilla and down to the costal margin. The many lobules of alveoli are associated with the repeatedly branching ducts which radiate from the nipple, and are separated by connective-tissue stroma. The alveoli are supplied by capillaries from the one or more arteries supplying each lobule.

The mammary glands of both males and females vary enormously in size and development from one *M. mulatta* to the next, except in late pregnancy and lactation when the glands are always well-developed. Some alveolar-lobular enlargement also occurs during ovulatory cycles. Adult male glands can vary from a few unbranched ducts not even extending to the base of the nipple to extremely branched systems with lobules of alveoli and a diameter of 3 cm.

During the first half of pregnancy there is little increase in the size of the gland or lobules, although the latter become denser as a result of some proliferation of the alveoli. During the third month there is a great increase in the size and especially the number of alveoli, and colostrum is present in them. The lobules therefore grow progressively larger, and reduce the interlobular stroma. Some mitotic figures are present. The cells and their nuclei also become larger, but as the alveoli fill with colostrum their walls become thinner. All these changes continue until the end of pregnancy.

After birth, the mammary glands rapidly enlarge and are no longer flat. The alveoli are greatly distended, and the lobules are so large that almost no stroma remains. The septa between the alveoli are often ruptured. Milk is actively secreted from the epithelial linings of the alveoli within two days of birth, and at the height of lactation some secretion also occurs from the lining of the ducts. The cell nuclei are large and some are double or lobulated, but few mitoses occur after two days postpartum. The glands are, of course, extensively vascularized.

Involution of the mammary glands occurs at different rates, even in different lobules of the same animal. It is most rapid in the first three weeks after weaning, although the alveoli remain engorged with secretion for about two weeks. They then atrophy, and some of their cells are resorbed and some sloughed off into the ducts, as is much of the ductal epithelium. Involution is slower after a stillbirth, but is complete within 3½ months unless an ovulatory cycle or pregnancy intervenes.

3. Comparative Anatomy. Of the few other primates whose mammary glands have been investigated, *Papio hamadryas* and *P. ursinus* (Zuckerman and Parkes, 1932) grossly and histologically

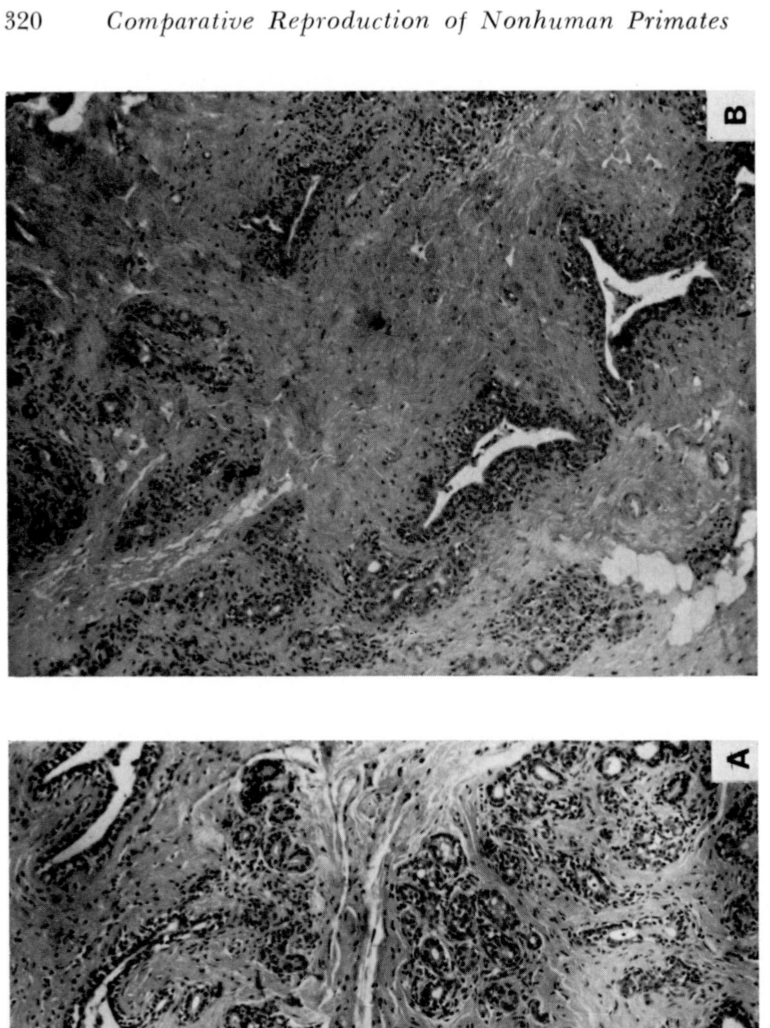

Figure 12-2. Mammary gland sections from mature female *Papio cynocephalus*, stained with hematoxylin and eosin, x 125. A, quiescent; B. 50 days pregnant.

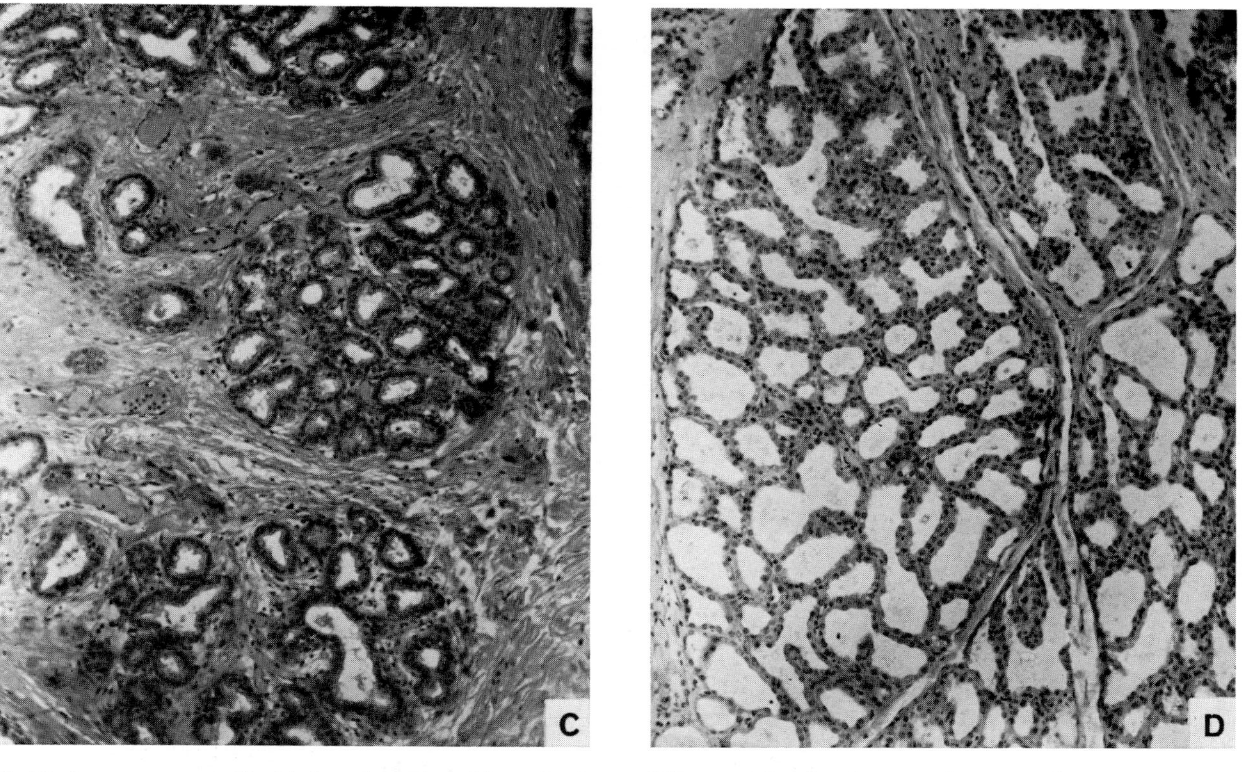

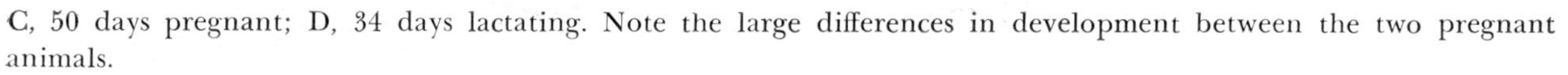
C, 50 days pregnant; D, 34 days lactating. Note the large differences in development between the two pregnant animals.

closely resemble *Macaca mulatta* (see Fig. 12-2). Little change occurs in their mammary glands through the menstrual cycles and early pregnancy, but by the end of pregnancy, the thin (0.5 cm) disks of tissue have extensive alveolar-lobular development which is similar to that of *M. mulatta.* The glands enlarge immediately after parturition presumably because of engorgement with secretion, and atrophy rapidly when lactation ceases. The nipples of *Papio papio* have a circulatory system and erectile tissues as in man. The mammary glands of *Macaca irus* also appear to resemble those of *M. mulatta* (Zuckerman, 1931), and, as in the other species, the functional state of the glands of adult female *Cercopithecus sabaeus* can be better determined from their alveolar development than their area (20-45 cm^2).

The mammary glands of pregnant *Pan* are flat disks, little larger than the 50 cm^2 of the virgin female. Those of the male do not even extend to the edge of the areola (Hill, 1951).

Histologically, the mammary glands of lactating *Galago senegalensis* differ from those of *M. mulatta* in that striped muscle fibers are found between the lobules; this is not so in glands from *Nycticebus coucang* (Ahmed and Kanagasuntheram, 1965). The abdominal glands of *Cheirogaleus major* are the largest, and all are larger than the partially described glands of Lemurinae (Petter-Rousseaux, 1965).

B. Hormonal Responses

Studies of the hormonal control of mammary gland development and lactation of nonhuman primates have been confined almost entirely to *Macaca mulatta* (Speert, 1948).

Mammary development occurring before puberty is mainly ductal; alveoli develop only after ovulation and luteinization are well established, and removal of the corpus luteum five days after ovulation causes rapid atrophy of the lobules. Yet almost complete growth of both the ducts and alveolar-lobular system can be induced in prepubertal or ovariectomized *M. mulatta* with estrogen alone. There is little synergism with progesterone, although very large doses of this hormone alone will cause development of both ducts and alveoli. The female gland is more responsive than the male to both hormones. Androgens, corticosteroids, and gonadotrophins also stimulate mammary growth in ovariectomized animals.

The nipples of mature female *Loris tardigradus* increase in width with estrogens, and in length with androgens, but the mammary glands are apparently little affected by either hormone.

Removal of the ovaries after the first month of pregnancy has no effect on mammary development or lactation in *M. mulatta* (Speert, 1948). Hypophysectomy after the first month of pregnancy has little effect on mammary development, and lactation is initiated but cannot be maintained (Agate, 1952).

After birth, lactation presumably starts because the mammary gland and prolactin synthesis are no longer inhibited by placental estrogen and progesterone, as for other species (Kon and Cowie, 1961).

Prolactin from *M. mulatta* is different from the prolactins of several other species, including man.

The milk ejection response to oxytocin in the anesthetized *M. mulatta* occurs after a 12-45 second latent period and lasts from 1½-5 minutes. The threshold dose is 0.75 mU. With doses of 10 mU, the normal monophasic response changes to triphasic (Bissett, 1968).

Through much of lactation the ovaries, uterus, and sex-skin (if present) of most primates are quiescent. There may then be one or two nonovulatory cycles before the first ovulation. It is not unusual for conception to occur during lactation, and the first infant may still be nursing when the next is born. This period of infertility is considerably reduced by removal of the infants.

Tupaiinae exhibit estrus even during parturition, and lactation is unimpaired. Other prosimians, including *Galago crassicaudatus, G. senegalensis, Loris tardigradus, Microcebus murinus,* and *Nycticebus coucang,* ovulate three to twelve days postpartum only if the infants are not nursing. Several species of marmosets also exhibit postpartum estrus, but it is probably nonovulatory (Epple, 1970).

C. Abnormal Development

Supernumerary Nipples. Supernumerary nipples are known in *Callithrix,* three species of *Cebus* monkeys, *Cercopithecus ascan-*

ius, Erythrocebus patas, Hylobytes lar, four species of macaque, *Pan troglodytes, Papio ursinus, Pongo pygmaeus, Symphalangus syndactylus* (Schultz, 1948), and in *Galago senegalensis* (Ahmed and Kanagasuntheram, 1965). Usually one extra nipple is present, below one of the normal pair; occasionally two extra nipples occur and an instance of four has been reported. Such nipples may be associated with the normal or with an extra mammary gland. A *Pan* has successfully lactated through four nipples connected with two glands (Matthews and Baxter, 1948).

The incidence of such nipples is difficult to determine because they may be overlooked in the thick hair, and because occasional groups of primates have a hereditary tendency to supernumerary nipples. In *Pan, Macaca mulatta,* and *Papio cynocephalus,* it appears to be 1 to 1½ percent, as in man.

Gynecomastia. The mammary glands of an adult male *Macaca nemestrina* were 20 cm^2 in area, consisting solely of ducts without alveolae, and another example may have occurred in an *M. mulatta* (Folley *et al.,* 1939). However, these could have been within the great range of sizes which occurs normally (Speert, 1948).

Cancer. Because nonhuman primates have rarely developed cancer, very few mammary tumors are known. One of these—a noninvasive ductal carcinoma—was induced in a seven year old virgin female *Macaca mulatta* by proton irradiation. A carcinosarcoma has been induced with radioactive silver after estrogen priming, but estrogen treatment alone has never induced cancerous changes in the mammary gland of a nonhuman primate.

Of the spontaneous tumors, that in a *Pongo pygmaeus* (Brack, 1966) closely resembled a human carcinoma. The animal was at least fifteen years old, had been pregnant three times and had successfully nursed an infant. The well-differentiated primary tumor of the mammary gland had invaded the intercostal muscles. Metastases were found throughout the body, including an axillary lymph node, the lungs, pleura, pericardium, liver, a kidney, bladder, uterus, thyroid, and the air-sac; there was, however, no involvement of the skeleton or central nervous system.

A mammary adenocarcinoma which occurred spontaneously in an eight year old virgin female *M. mulatta* was associated with C-type "virus" particles. Nodes were also found in the axilla and thorax, and extensive metastases were found, including in the other mammary gland (Mason *et al.,* 1970).

Mammary adenocarcinomas have also occurred in one elderly male and two elderly multiparous female *M. mulatta* (Ruch, 1959). The latter tumors were small nodules near the nipple; both had invaded the surrounding fibrous stroma, but no metastases were observed.

A mammary fibrosarcoma has also been found in a *Cercopithecus sabaeus.*

II. LACTATION

A. Length of Lactation

The infants of nonhuman primates nurse almost immediately after they have been cleaned by the mother, usually within a few minutes or hours of birth. Occasionally the infants of captive great apes will not nurse until the day after birth if they have difficulty finding the nipple.

Because there is a very gradual change from the infant's complete dependence on milk to its complete dietary independence, it is difficult to determine exactly when lactation ceases. For example, *Macaca mulatta* and *Papio cynocephalus* infants often "mouth" pieces of food from one month, yet rarely eat more than fragments until two to three months old. Solid food then becomes more and more important, and the frequent suckling gradually changes from a nutritive to non-nutritive mode, until at some time between six months and one year the infants no longer obtain milk. But even later they occasionally suck the nipple at times of stress. These timings are further affected by the birth of another infant, by the mother's nutritional status, and even by changes in climate.

Under nursery conditions, *M. mulatta* and *P. cynocephalus* infants will take fruit or solid food, well-soaked in formula, from about one month, and can be successfully weaned as early as three months.

Weaning of *Presbytis entellus* infants is easily timed, for it is an especially traumatic experience as the mother prevents her infant from nursing. But lactation could well have ceased earlier.

Because of all these variations in conditions, and the difficulties

TABLE 12-II

LENGTH OF PRIMATE LACTATION*

Species	*Age Infant First Eats Solid Food (Mo.)*	*Age of Weaning (Mo.)*
Alouatta palliata		18–24
Arctocebus calabarensis	1	2–3
Avahi laniger		5
Callimico goeldii	1	2½
Callithrix sp.	1	2–6
Cebuella pygmaea	1½–2	3
Cercopithecus aethiops	2	6
Cercopithecus (Miopithecus) talapoin	½–1	2–6
Cheirogaleus major	1	1½
Galago crassicaudatus	½–1	3–5
Galago demidovii	½–1½	1–1½
Galago senegalensis	½–1	1½–3½
Gorilla gorilla beringei	2½–3	12–24
Hapalemur sp.		1½
Hylobytes sp.	6	24
Indri sp.		4
Lagothrix sp.		12
Lemur sp.	1	5–6
Leontideus sp.		2–4
Lepilemur mustelinus	1½	2½–4
Loris tardigradus	1–1½	6
Macaca fascicularis (= *M. irus*)	1	12–18
Macaca fuscata	1½	6–8
Macaca mulatta	1½–3	7–14
Macaca nemestrina	1	8–12
Macaca radiata	1	8–12
Microcebus murinus	½–1	1½–5
Nycticebus coucang	½–2	3–6
Pan troglodytes	4–6	18–42
Papio anubis, *P. cynocephalus*, and *P. ursinus*	3–6	6–15
Papio hamadryas		12
Perodicticus potto		5
Pongo pygmaeus	6	24–36
Propithecus verreauxi		3–7
Presbytis entellus	3	10–15
Saguinus geoffroyi	1–1½	
Saguinus (Oedipomidas) oedipus	1–1½	2–3
Saimiri sciureus	1–1½	6
Tupaia sp.	1	1
Urogale everetti	1	

* Data from DeVore, 1965; Napier and Napier, 1967; Petter-Rousseaux, 1965; and others.

of accurate observation, the true length of lactation of nonhuman primates can only be inferred as being close to the ages given for weaning in Table 12-II (which includes data obtained with both wild and captive animals).

B. Milk Composition

1. Colostrum. When nonhuman primate infants nurse vigorously within a few hours of birth, the secretion they obtain is presumably colostrum. It has, however, been described in few species: in *Pan,* colostrum is whitish, opalescent, and stringy (Yerkes, 1943), in *Papio cynocephalus,* colostrum is a thin opalescent liquid (Buss, 1968), but in *Saimiri sciureus,* colostrum is orange.

Precolostrum can sometimes be expressed from *Pan* after four months of pregnancy, and from *Gorilla* after five to six months of pregnancy. A few drops of colostrum can usually be expressed from *P. cynocephalus* after a cesarean-section two weeks before full-term, if oxytocin is given. It can also be obtained for up to twenty-four hours after a normal birth.

Colostrum from *P. cynocephalus,* like the colostrum from other mammals (Kon and Cowie, 1961), is low in lactose and fat, and contains more protein and ash than the later milk (Buss, 1968). This protein is very rich in immunoglobulin A and poor in casein. Colostrum from *Macaca mulatta* also contains more immunoglobulins than the milk (Eitzman, 1970), but the contribution made by colostrum to the passive immunity of nonhuman primate infants is, by analogy with man, probably small. Milk globulins cannot be absorbed intact by infant *M. mulatta* three days postpartum (Quinlivan, 1967).

2. Milk. After the colostrum has been replaced by milk, there are only slight changes in composition until weaning occurs. The gross composition of mature milk from three apes, five Old-World monkeys, two New-World monkeys, and three prosimians is summarized in Table 12-III. With the exception of *Tupaia belangeri* these primates have a higher proportion of the calories in their milk as lactose, and a lower proportion as protein and fat, than nearly all other mammals (Ben Shaul, 1963); this is especially marked in apes (as in man). Milk from *Cercocebus torquatus, Macaca fascicularis, M. nemestrina, M. radiata,* and *M. speciosa*

TABLE 12-III

GROSS COMPOSITION (G/100 ML) OF MILK FROM SOME PRIMATES[a]

Species	*Fat*	*Protein*	*Lactose*	*Ash*
Cercocebus sp.	1.5	2.3	7.0	0.1
Cercopithecus (*Miopithecus*) *talapoin*	2.9	2.1	7.2	0.28
Cercopithecus sabaeus	4.0	3.1	10.2	0.6
Galago crassicaudatus	3.7	5.3	5.0	—
Gorilla gorilla	2.2	1.1	—	—
Macaca mulatta	3.9	2.1	5.9	0.26
Nycticebus coucang	11.8	3.6	6.2	—
Pan troglodytes	3.0	1.0	7.1	0.21
Papio cynocephalus	5.0	1.6	7.3	0.26
Pongo pygmaeus	4.7	2.0	6.4	0.30
Saguinus (*Oedipomidas*) *oedipus*	3.1	3.8	5.8	0.4
Saimiri sciureus	4.6	3.4	6.4	0.30
Tupaia belangeri	25.6	10.4	1.5	2.9

[a] From the literature, and D. H. Buss, N. B. Guilloud, and R. Jenness (unpublished).

appears similar in composition to milk from other Old-World primates (L. M. Smith, unpublished). The differences in composition between some of these milks must account in part for the difficulty of bottle-raising infant New-World monkeys and prosimians with formulas designed for human infants.

Milk from *Pan* (as from humans) has a blue-white color, while milk from the other species examined has a very slight yellow cast.

The milk fat exists as small globules (about 5μ mean diameter for *Papio cynocephalus*) which slowly separate on standing. The total lipid content is very variable, even in samples from each breast of the same animal, but tends to increase as lactation progresses. This fat is almost entirely triglycerides, whose fatty acids are predominantly palmitic, oleic, and linoleic acids, in proportions reflecting those in the diet. However, the mammary glands of nonhuman primates other than the great apes synthesize considerable amounts of the readily digestible fatty acids with eight to fourteen carbon atoms, in proportions varying considerably from Old-World monkeys to New-World monkeys to prosimians.

Milk from *M. mulatta* contains about 40 mg cholesterol/100 ml, twice that of milk from *Papio ursinus* or humans. Yet their infants have less plasma cholesterol when nursing than when raised on cholesterol-free formulas.

The caseins of primate milk can be precipitated at about pH

4.6. There is about twice as much casein as residual whey proteins in milk from *Papio cynocephalus, Cercopithecus (Miopithecus) talapoin* and *Pongo,* but milk from *Saimiri sciureus* and *Pan,* as from humans, has less casein than whey proteins. There are considerable electrophoretic differences, both in number and mobility of the components, between the whey proteins of these species, although the total amino acid compositions appear similar. The caseins, however, differ little in their three major components.

All primate milks examined contain large amounts of lysozyme. In *Papio cynocephalus,* this bacteriolytic enzyme does not appear to affect the infant's resistance to disease, so may play a role in protecting the mother's mammary glands from infection. Both mumps virus and Kyasanur forest disease virus can pass into the milk of some infected Old-World monkeys.

TABLE 12-IV

CONCENTRATION OF MAJOR MINERALS (G/LITER) IN MILK FROM SOME PRIMATES[a]

Species	*Calcium*	*Chloride*	*Phosphorus*	*Potassium*	*Sodium*
Cercopithecus (Miopithecus) talapoin	0.4	0.7	0.2	0.3	0.4
Gorilla gorilla	0.3	0.3	0.2	0.4	0.1
Pan troglodytes	0.4	—	0.2	0.3	0.2
Papio cynocephalus	0.4	0.2	0.3	0.4	0.1
Pongo pygmaeus	0.6	0.9	—	0.5	—
Saimiri sciureus	0.5	—	0.3	0.4	0.2

[a] From the literature; and D. H. Buss (unpublished).

The only carbohydrate detected in nonhuman primate milk is lactose. A report that *Saimiri sciureus* milk contains approximately equal amounts of lactose, glucose, and galactose, has not been substantiated.

The major minerals of some primate milks are shown in Table 12-IV. One sample of *Pongo* milk also contained (per liter): 4 mg cobalt, 1 mg copper, 23 mg iron, 41 mg magnesium, 1 mg manganese, and 6 mg zinc (N. B. Guilloud, unpublished). Milk from *Galago crassicaudatus* contains 0.3 g/liter chloride (Pilson and Cooper, 1967). Strontium-90 is passed from mother to infant through the milk in *Macaca mulatta.*

The vitamins of nonhuman primate milk have never been investigated, but there is an implication that milk from *M. mulatta* contains very little folic acid.

As the milk supply dries up at the end of lactation, the lipid, protein, and ash contents of the milk increase to as much as three times their normal values, while the lactose and water contents drop markedly.

C. Milk Yield

Direct measurement of the daily milk yield of nonhuman primates is difficult. The mammary glands have a low capacity for storing milk, and the infants (except for *Tupaiinae*) nurse frequently—especially Old-World primate infants which are carried by their mothers in a ventral-ventral position. Hence the animals cannot be milked manually throughout a day for measurement of the milk obtained, nor can the infants be weighed before and after each feeding without considerable likelihood of their rejection as a result of the frequent disturbances (except *Tupaia* sp., which were found by this method to average 5-10 g milk/day (Martin, 1968)). Manual milking rarely gives more than 5 ml, except from apes, where over 20 ml can be expressed. If sedation is necessary before the animal can be handled, the milk yield is depressed.

The milk yield of *Papio cynocephalus* has been accurately determined (Buss and Voss, 1971) from the dilution of tritiated water in nursing infants by the nonradioactive milk they drink, and from comparing the growth rates of nursing infants and infants drinking known amounts of milk from a bottle. The yield rises rapidly to about 200 ml/day when lactation is fully established (one week postpartum), then rises more gradually to about 400 ml/day by the time the infants are four months old. Similar amounts of formula are drunk by *M. mulatta* infants (Kerr and Waisman, 1968).

From the very few data available, it appears that the milk intake by infants of Old-World and New-World monkeys is about 200-400 kcal/kg/day, but is possibly twice this for prosimians. The milk intake of the great apes appears close to the human intake of 120-140 kcal/kg/day.

D. Problems of Lactation

Captive primates, especially primiparae, may prevent their newborn infants from nursing. This can be from inexperience, or because the mother is upset by other members of the group or by humans, or, with some prosimians and marmosets, because there are too many infants. If isolation of the mother with her infant(s) does not help, or is impossible, the infant must be bottle-raised. The composition data in Tables 12-III and 12-IV may be helpful for the preparation of suitable substitute formulas. In contrast to infants of *Papio* sp. and *Macaca nemestrina,* those of *M. mulatta, M. radiata* and *Saimiri sciureus* can sometimes be fostered by another mother of the same species. This may also be possible in Lemurinae, for mothers will often change infants for nursing in the wild (Hill, 1953). *Arctocebus* infants have even been fostered by a lactating *Perodicticus* (Jewell and Oates, 1969).

Because of the frequent sucking (both nutritive and non-nutritive) by the infants of *Papio* sp., and the long lactation period, the mothers' nipples can become badly deformed or lacerated. Mastitis, both micrococcal and streptococcal, has been found in *P. cynocephalus;* it responds to antibiotic therapy. Changes in milk composition suggesting breast infection (increased chloride and sodium, and reduced lactose concentrations) have also occurred in *Galago crassicaudatus* (Pilson and Cooper, 1967) and *Cercopithecus talapoin* (Buss and Cooper, 1970).

The loss of large amounts of essential nutrients through the milk means that any inadequacies in the diets of laboratory primates are most likely to be seen during lactation. Provision of more food is advisable at this time, but nutritional tetany can still occur; it has responded to vitamin D in *Papio* sp. (Ruch, 1959) and to calcium in *Cercopithecus talapoin* and *Saimiri sciureus* (R. W. Cooper, unpublished) and *Tupaia belangeri* (Martin, 1968). A poor diet can also affect the milk: for example, a low-protein diet fed to *Papio cynocephalus* during late pregnancy and lactation reduces the protein concentration in the milk, and substantially lowers the milk yield (Buss and Reed, 1970).

REFERENCES

Agate, F. J. (1952): The growth and secretory activity of the mammary glands of the pregnant rhesus monkey (Macaca mulatta) following hypophysectomy. *Amer J Anat, 90,* 257-283.

Ahmed, M. M. U., and Kanagasuntheram, R. (1965): A note on the mammary glands in the lesser bush baby (*Galago senegalensis senegalensis*). *Acta Anat (Basel), 60,* 253-261.

Ben Shaul, D. M. (1963): The composition of the milk of wild animals. In Jarvis, C., and Morris, D. (Eds.): *The International Zoo Yearbook*. London, Hutchinson, vol. 4, pp. 333-342.

Bissett, G. W. (1968): The milk ejection reflex and the actions of oxytocin, vasopressin and synthetic analogues on the mammary gland. In Berde, B. (Ed.): *Handbuch der Experimentellen Pharmakologie,* vol. 23: *Neurohypophysial Hormones and Similar Polypeptides.* New York, Springer-Verlag, pp. 475-544.

Brack, M. (1966): Carcinoma solidum simplex mammae bei einem Orang-Utan (Pongo pygmaeus). *Zbl Allg Path, 109,* 474-480.

Buss, D. H. (1968): Gross composition and variation of the components of baboon milk during natural lactation. *J Nutr, 96,* 421-426.

Buss, D. H., and Cooper, R. W. (1970): Composition of milk from talapoin monkeys. *Folia Primat, 13,* 196-206.

Buss, D. H., and Reed, O. M. (1970): Lactation of baboons fed a low protein maintenance diet. *Lab Anim Care, 20,* 709-712.

Buss, D. H., and Voss, W. R. (1971): Evaluation of four methods for estimating the milk yield of baboons. *J Nutr* (In press).

Butler, H. (1967): Seasonal breeding of the Senegal Galago (*Galago senegalensis senegalensis*) in the Nuba Mountains, Republic of the Sudan. *Folia Primat, 5,* 165-175.

DeVore, I. (1965): *Primate Behavior.* New York, Holt, Rinehart & Winston.

Eitzman, D. V. (1970): Immunoglobulin levels in the *Macaca mulatta. Folia Primat, 12,* 313-316.

Epple, G. (1970): Maintenance, breeding, and development of marmoset monkeys (Callithricidae) in captivity. *Folia Primat, 12,* 56-76.

Folley, S. J.; Guthkelch, A. N., and Zuckerman, S. (1939): The mammary gland of the rhesus monkey under normal and experimental conditions. *Proc Roy Soc London, B., 126,* 469-491.

Hill, W. C. O. (1951): The external genitalia of the female chimpanzee, with observations on the mammary apparatus. *Proc Zool Soc London, 121,* 133-145.

Hill, W. C. O. (1953): *Primates. Comparative Anatomy and Taxonomy. Strepsirrhini.* Edinburgh, University Press, vol. 1.

Hill, W. C. O. (1970): *Primates. Comparative Anatomy and Taxonomy. Cynopithecinae.* New York, Wiley-Interscience, vol. 8.

Jewell, P. A., and Oates, J. F. (1969): Breeding activity in prosimians and small rodents in West Africa. *J Reprod Fertil (Suppl.), 6,* 23-38.

Kerr, G. R., and Waisman, H. A. (1968): The use of the rhesus monkey in the experimental production of "inborn errors of metabolism." In Vagtborg, H. (Ed.): *Use of Nonhuman Primates in Drug Evaluation.* Austin, University of Texas Press, pp. 51-66.

Kon, S. K., and Cowie, A. T. (1961): *Milk: The Mammary Gland and Its Secretion.* New York, Academic Press.

Martin, R. D. (1968): Reproduction and ontogeny in tree-shrews (*Tupaia belangeri*), with reference to their general behaviour and taxonomic relationships. *Z Tierpsychol, 25,* 409-532.

Mason, M. M.; Baker, J. R., and Ilievski, V. R. (1970): Histopathology of a spontaneous tumor in a Macaca mulatta in which RNA virus particles were found. *Proc Amer Ass Cancer Res, 11,* 53.

Matthews, L. H., and Baxter, J. S. (1948): Polythelia in a chimpanzee. *Proc Zool Soc London, 118,* 144-145.

Napier, J. R., and Napier, P. H. (1967): *A Handbook of Living Primates.* New York, Academic Press.

Petter-Rousseaux, A. (1965): Reproductive physiology and behavior of the Lemuroidea. In Buettner-Janusch, J. (Ed.): *Evolutionary and Genetic Biology of Primates.* New York, Academic Press, vol. 2, pp. 91-132.

Pilson, M. E. Q., and Cooper, R. W. (1967): Composition of milk from *Galago crassicaudatus. Folia Primat, 5,* 88-91.

Quinlivan, W. L. G. (1967): Gamma globulin-^{131}I transfer between mother and offspring in the rhesus monkey. *Amer J Physiol, 212,* 324-328.

Ruch, T. C. (1959): *Diseases of Laboratory Primates.* Philadelphia, Saunders.

Schultz, A. H. (1948): The number of young at a birth and the number of nipples in primates. *Amer J Phys Anthrop, 6,* 1-23.

Speert, H. (1948): The normal and experimental development of the mammary gland of the rhesus monkey, with some pathological correlations. *Contr Embryol (Carnegie Inst of Washington, Baltimore), 32,* 9-65.

Yerkes, R. M. (1943): *Chimpanzees, A Laboratory Colony.* New Haven, Yale University Press.

Zuckerman, S. (1931): The menstrual cycle of primates—Part IV. Observations on the lactation period. *Proc Zool Soc London,* pp. 593-602.

Zuckerman, S., and Parkes, A. S. (1932): The menstrual cycle of the primates—Part V. The cycle of the baboon. *Proc Zool Soc London,* pp. 139-191.

Chapter 13

PRENATAL AND POSTNATAL DEVELOPMENT

A. G. HENDRICKX and M. L. HOUSTON

PRENATAL development begins with the fertilization of the ovum and ends with the explusion of the fetus at birth. The orderly series of events which transform a single-celled ovum into an organism typical of the species includes five phases of development: fertilization, cleavage, gastrulation, organogenesis, differentiation and growth.

I. FERTILIZATION

Fertilization consists essentially of the fusion of male and female gametes to form a single cell, the zygote or embryo as it should be called once development has started. Fertilization begins with the entry of the sperm into the cytoplasm of the ovum and ends with the formation of the metaphase plate of the first cleavage division. As an *embryological* event fertilization involves activation of the ovum by the sperm in a series of precisely timed steps. As a *genetical* event, fertilization involves the introduction into the zygote of hereditary material from the sire. The haploid number of chromosomes from the male parent are brought together with the haploid number from the female parent to form a single diploid group of chromosomes which are characteristic for the species.

Much of the detailed and exact information about fertilization and cleavage in mammals is derived from laboratory animals. The general comments are largely based on these studies. Data are available on the rate of development for the rhesus monkey and baboon. The site of fertilization is the oviduct, probably the lower portion of the ampulla. The ovum is still surrounded, at least partially, with granulosa cells, often called cumulus cells, which were shed with it from the ovarian follicle.

The number of sperm which enter the oviduct is relatively small despite the millions contained in an ejaculate. Marston and Kelly (1968) estimated that less than fifty spermatozoa were flushed from the oviduct of the rhesus monkey following insemination directly into the uterus and after natural mating. Although there is no direct evidence that capacitation, the physiological change undergone by spermatozoa which enables it to pass through the cumulus cells and zona pellucida, occurs in the nonhuman primate, indirect evidence suggests that rhesus monkey spermatozoa require capacitation before they are capable of fertilizing an ovum (Dukelow and Chernoff, 1969). Based on the time of sperm penetration the sperm of rhesus monkeys require three to four hours for capacitation (Marston and Kelly, 1968). After the spermatozoan penetrates the ovum the latter finishes its second maturation division and both the female and male pronuclei are formed. Rhesus monkey ova with well formed pronuclei were found and examined within 6.5 hours after insemination and baboon ova in the pronuclear stage were found and examined within twenty-four hours of ovulation. The fertile life of ova and sperm is unknown but it is fairly short as in other mammals. Possibly sperm may lose their ability to induce viable embryos before they lose their ability to fertilize. The relatively brief fertile life of both sperm and ovum makes the time of mating a matter of utmost importance.

Both the head and the tail of the spermatozoan enter the ovum. Once the spermatozoan has penetrated the zona pellucida and vitelline membrane, and lies inside the vitellus, the sperm head swells and the tail drops off, forming the *male pronucleus.* The second polar body probably is extruded from the ovum soon after sperm entry, and formation of the *female pronucleus* begins. Little is known of the constituents of the pronuclei, however numerous nucleoli are present. The male and female pronuclei come into contact, combine, the nuclear membranes disappear and the pronuclei can no longer be seen. Thus, the process of *syngamy* is completed. The total time interval from the penetration of sperm to the time of first cleavage is not known, but is is unlikely to exceed twenty-four hours. In the cases in which the time of insemination is known pronuclear stages were found in the rhesus monkey (Marston and Kelly, 1968) within six hours after insemination and a baboon embryo in the syngamy stage occurred one day after insemination (Hendrickx and Kraemer, 1968).

II. CLEAVAGE

After syngamy is completed, there is a period of several days during which the embryo leads a free-living existence in the oviducts and uterus of the mother. During the latter part of this period, the embryo may be nourished by uterine secretions; but not until implantation has taken place does the embryo derive any direct nourishment from the maternal organism.

At the beginning of the free-living period, the embryo is a single cell, much larger in volume than other cells of the body, with a very large ratio of cytoplasm to nuclear material. Cleavage of the embryo is relatively slow mitotic divisions and results in progressively smaller cells. There is little increase in cell mass until the blastocyst is implanted, by which time the size of the cell is characteristic for the species.

In most mammals the plane of the first cleavage division is not related to the plane of symmetry of the ovum. It passes through the area where the male and female pronuclei were situated at the beginning of syngamy. The normal course of cleavage has not been studied extensively in primates, however, it appears that the process is similar to other mammalian species. The second cleavage divisions occur at right angles to the first, the third approximately at right angles to the second. Cleavage divisions are not synchronized, so that three, five, six, seven-cell stages etc. may be found.

Cleavage is probably of the *indeterminate* type, i.e. the differentiation of any given cell(s) into particular organs of the body is unknown until a later stage of development, and any cell would be capable of giving rise to an entire new embryo if the environmental conditions were suitable.

A. Cleavage Rates

Approximate estimates of the cleavage rates for embryos of the rhesus monkey and baboon are as follows: 2-4 cells = 1-2 days; 8 cells = 2.5-3 days; 16 cells = 3.5-4.5 days; 16-60 cells (blastocoele) = 5-6 days; 60-130 cells (blastocyst) = 6.5-8 days (Lewis and Hartman, 1941; Hendrickx and Kraemer, 1968). All of the primate species that have been studied ovulate spontaneously and little specific information is available concerning the time of ovulation. Estimates of cleavage rate and other aspects of development are based on palpation of the ruptured follicle (Hartman, 1933) or on matings of short duration at a time during the menstrual cycle when ovulation is most likely to occur (Hendrickx and Kraemer, 1968). Consequently, the developmental rate is subject to an error of unknown magnitude. In addition, the developmental rate will be subject to considerable real variation, both among individuals, species, and, probably, subspecies. Transport of the embryos down the oviduct is vague. In both the rhesus monkey and baboon the embryo has reached at least the 16-cell stage by the time it enters the uterus. *Tupaia javanica* embryos were found in the uterus in the 64-128 cell stage (Starck, 1956). Differences in the cleavage stage at which the embryos reach the uterus may be due to differences in either the rate of cleavage or in rate of tubal transport.

B. Blastocyst

The first sign of cellular differentiation in *Tupaia javanica* and *Tarsius* embryos occurs at the sixteen cell stage (Starck, 1956). At this stage the embryoblast, cells which will form the embryo, consists of large centrally located blastomeres surrounded by smaller trophoblast cells, cells which will form the placenta. Cellular differentiation begins at the same time for rhesus monkey and baboon embryos. As the cells differentiate the blastocoele develops by coalescence of the intercellular spaces. The blastocyst becomes a thin-walled fluid filled sac by the fifth or sixth day after fertilization in the rhesus monkey and baboon. The zona pellucida is shed on the sixth or seventh day in both these species (Fig. 13-1).

The rate of transport of embryos through the oviduct is not influenced by the intrauterine device in spontaneously ovulated rhesus monkeys; however the rate of transport increases in animals with intrauterine devices and superovulated with gonadotropins (Mastroianni, 1967).

III. IMPLANTATION

Implantation occurs during the blastocyst stage of embryonic development when the zona pellucida is shed and the outer trophoblast is allowed direct contact with the uterine epithelium.

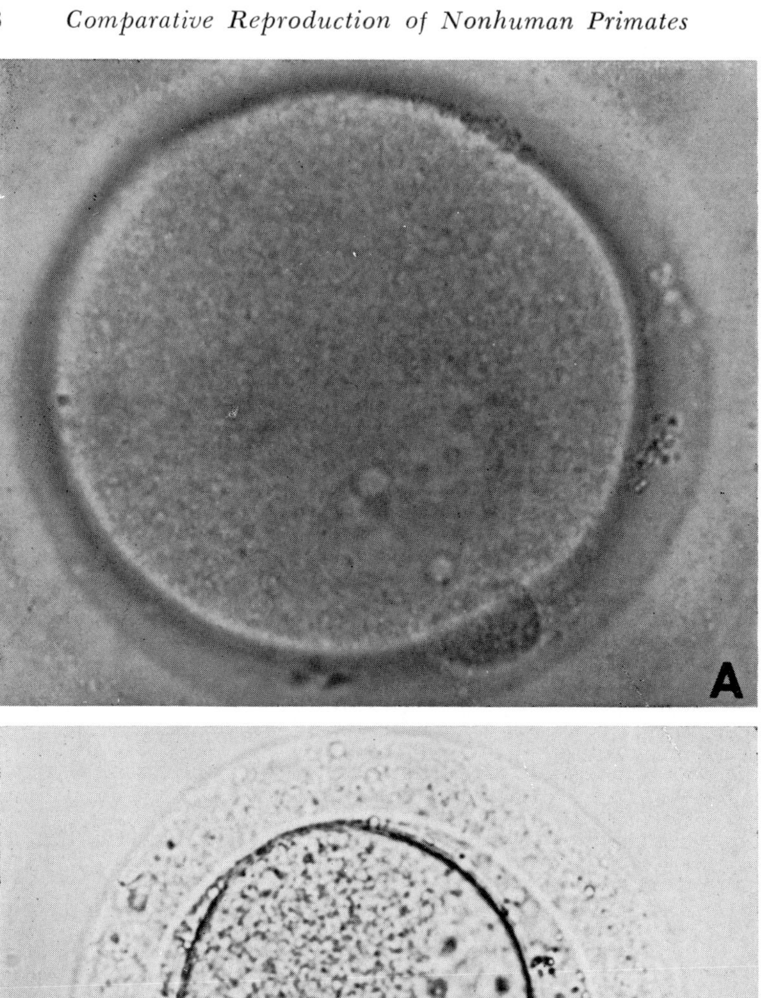

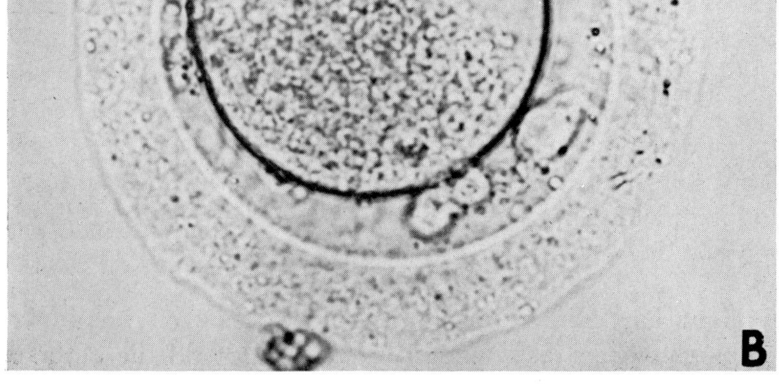

Figure 13-1. (Legend appears on page 341)

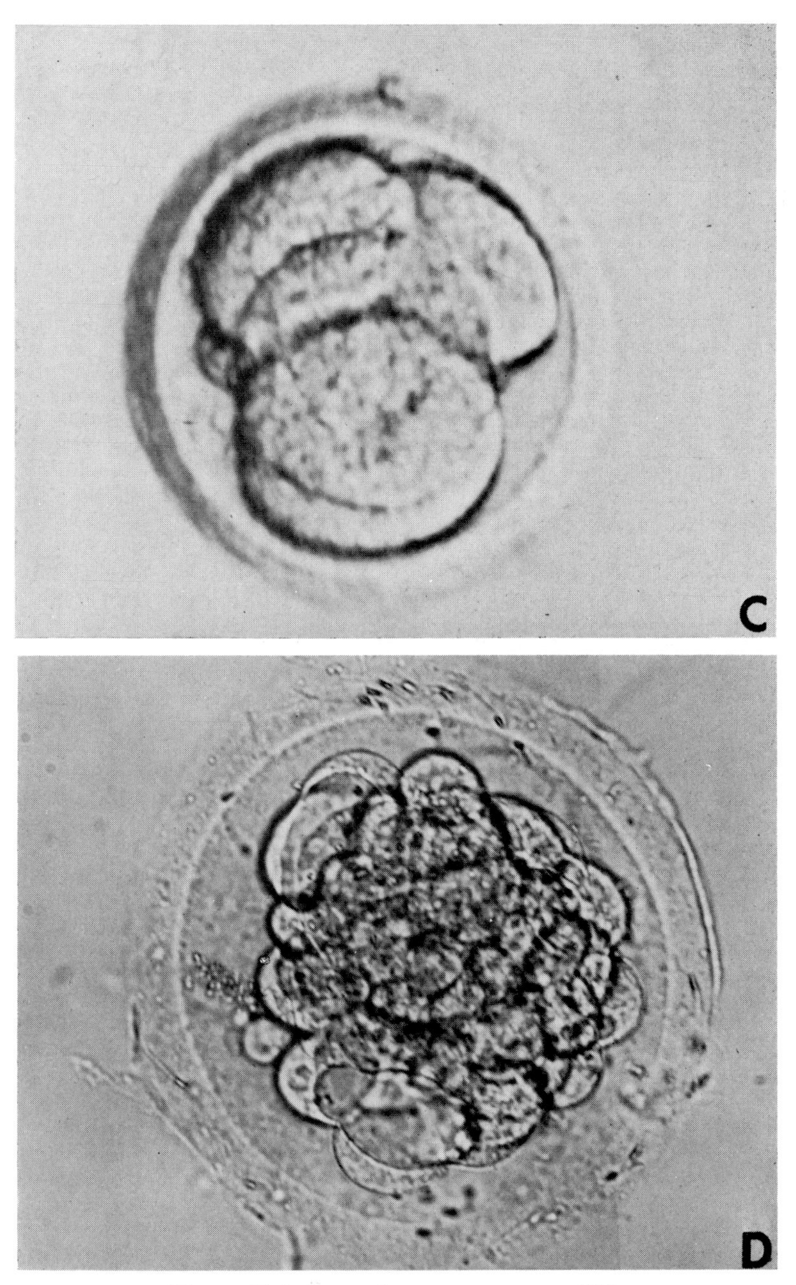

Figure 13-1. (Legend appears on page 341)

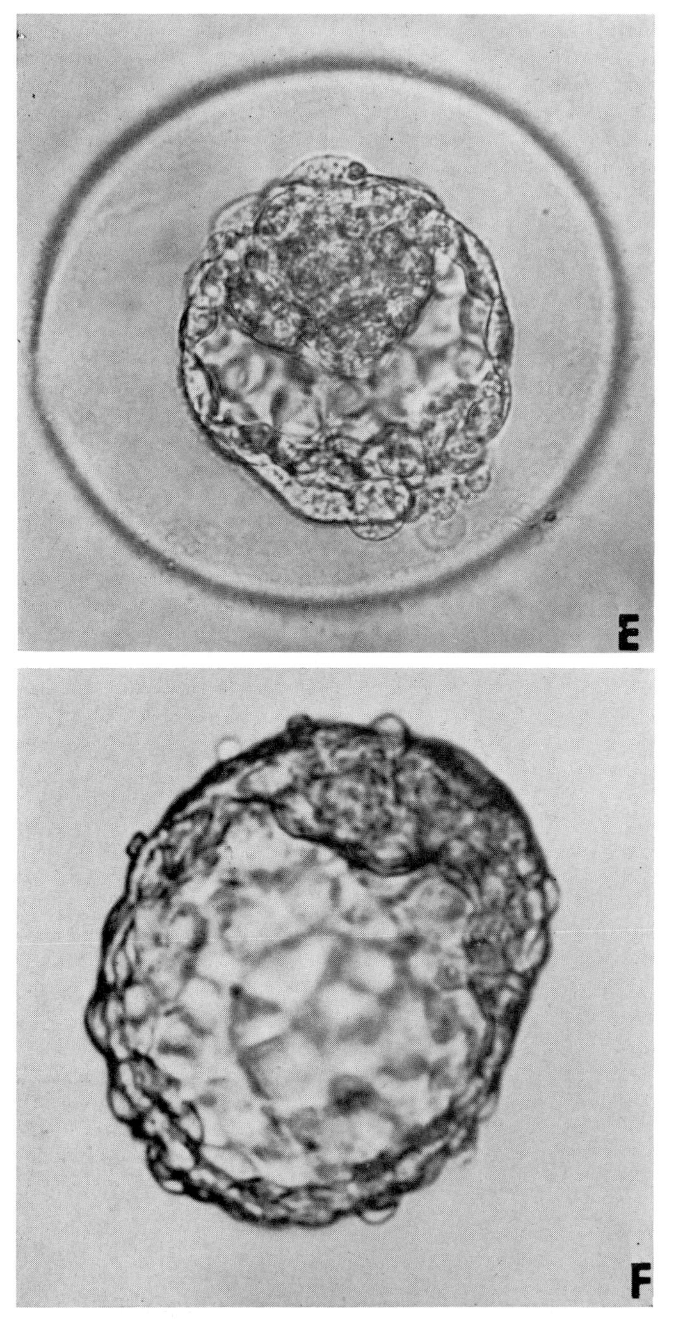

Figure 13-1. (Legend appears on page 341)

The process of implantation in primates is a sequence of integrated phenomena which may be divided into three separate phases, namely apposition, adhesion and invasion. The actual function of these mechanisms varies greatly among mammalian species.

A. Apposition and Adhesion

In order for implantation to occur, the blastocyst must be brought into direct contact with the internal wall of the uterus, apposition. In many nonprimate species such as the rabbit, apposition is accomplished by a swelling of the blastocyst against the wall of the uterus (Böving, 1965). In the rat and mouse, it is the swelling of the uterine wall which clasps the blastocyst. In these species, apposition may precede adhesion by as much as twenty-four to forty-eight hours. However, in primates where the blastocyst does not fill the uterine cavity for some time after implantation, this type of mechanism is of little significance. In these species, the blastomeres exhibit a truly "sticky" surface to the extent that a blastocyst will adhere so strongly to the bottom of a glass dish in

---

←

Figure 13-1. Preimplantation stages in the baboon. All photographs are of unstained material. A and F and B-E were photographed at approximately the same magnification. None of the stages were in any way flattened prior to photography. A. Pronuclear stage (1 day). The large male pronucleus (lower center) is situated next to the smaller female pronucleus (above right). Note the large size of the nucleoli. The first polar body is located to the bottom right of the male pronucleus. B. Syngamy stage (1 day). The male and female pronuclei have combined to form a single chromosome group. Three polar bodies are visible in the perivitelline space which is expanded and probably artifact. The second polar body (bottom) is segmenting.
C. Four cell stage (2 days). One of the blastomeres is largely out of the plane of focus. The polar bodies are still apparent. D. Morula stage (5 days). Note the appearance of large peripheral primitive trophoblast cells. Note also that the zona pellucida contains many sperm (top).
E. Blastocyst (6-7 days). The blastomeres now constitute a trophoblast around the margin of the blastocyst and an embryonic (inner) cell mass at one pole (top). F. Blastocyst (7-8 days) after shedding the zona pellucida. (From Hendrickx & Kraemer, 1968)

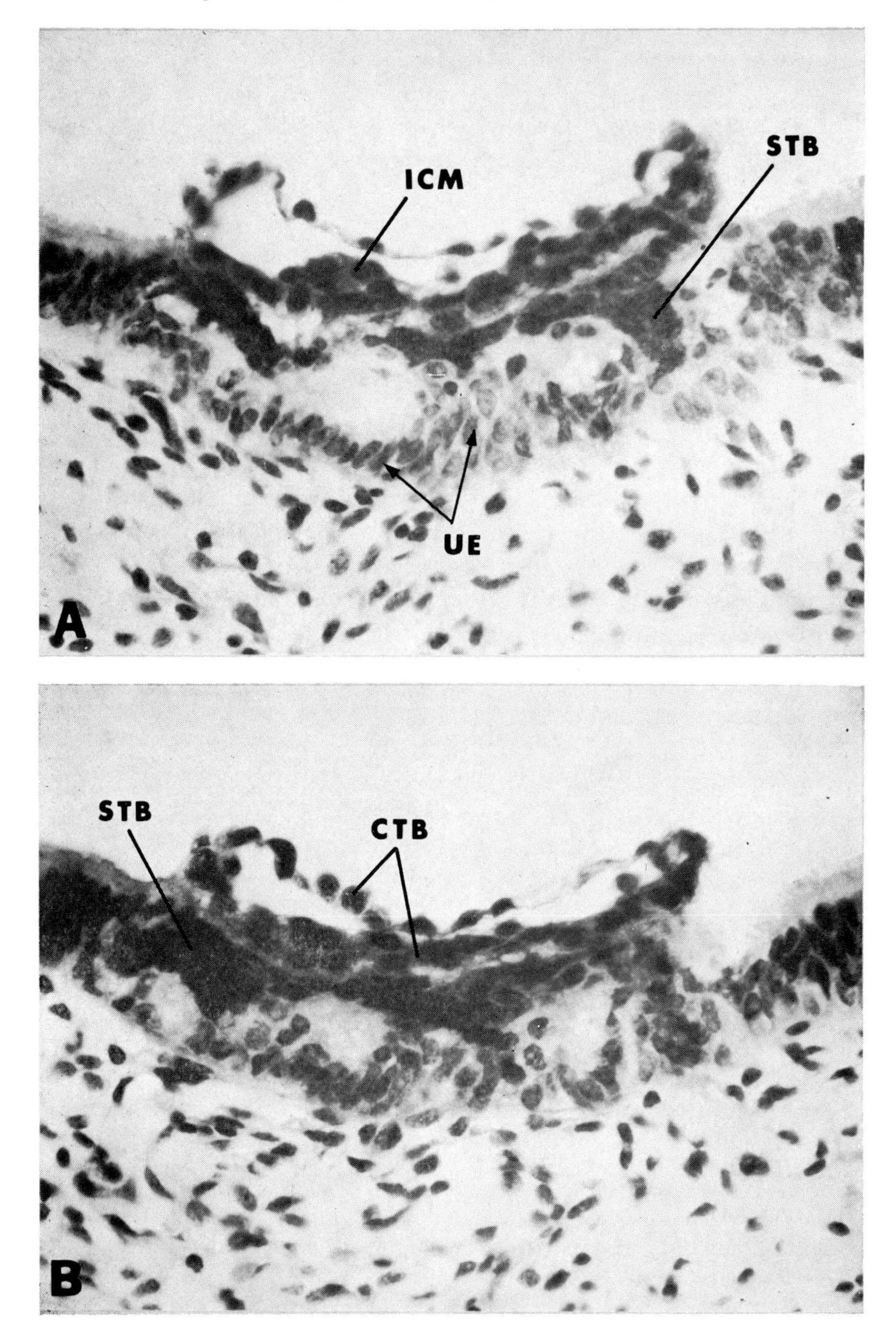
ICM
STB
UE
A
STB
CTB
B

which it has been collected that great care must be taken in dislodging it so that it will not be destroyed. This phenomenon is dependent on the pH of the medium in which it is contained. Thus, in primates, apposition is dependent on adhesive properties of the blastocyst, and thus these two phases of implantation occur simultaneously in the sense that only when a cohesive bond is formed between the blastocyst and endometrium is the blastocyst fixed in position.

Upon entering the uterine cavity, the blastocyst remains covered by the zona pellucida. Most nonprimate species implant with a very specific orientation of the embryonic pole of the blastocyst to either the mesometrial or antimesometrial pole of the uterus, the primate blastocyst seems to have little preference to implanting on the anterior or posterior wall of the uterus. At implantation, however, the embryonic pole makes first contact with uterine epithelium and the attachment is here set up which further develops implantation (Fig. 13-2). Although the specific mechanism by which this orientation is accomplished is unknown, evidence indicates that two factors may be involved. First is the shape of the blastocyst and secondly a specific adhesiveness of certain areas of the blastocyst.

B. Invasion

In some primate species such as the Galago, in which there is little or no destruction of maternal tissue, implantation is essentially complete after the adhesion of the blastocyst to the uterine wall is complete. *Galago senegalensis* and *G. crassicaudatus* (Butler and Adam, 1964, Butler, 1967a) as well as tarsius present an

---

Figure 13-2. Photomicrographs of an early implantation site of a baboon blastocyst. Note that pole of the blastocyst on which the inner cell mass (ICM) is located is the one which attaches to the uterine wall. The trophoblast is divided into cytotrophoblast (CTB) and syncytiotrophoblast (STB) and in areas where syncytiotrophoblastic penetration is active the uterine epithelium (UE) is disorganized. However, note the lack of necrosis among the cells of the uterine epithelium. (From Hendrickx *et al*, 1970).

initial mode of attachment in which only a small area of the uterine epithelium is disrupted (Fig. 13-3). However, this minor disruption of the uterine epithelium is soon lost, the epithelium replaced and the mature placenta is a diffuse, indeciduate, epitheliochorial type in virtually all of the Oriental and African Lorisidae. The only apparent exception seems to be *Galago demidovii* which Gérard (1932) described as initially having an interstitial type of implantation which secondarily becomes superficial with the growth of the conceptus until by midgestation the placenta appears identical to the other Galago species.

Most primates however, form their placenta greatly at the expense of the maternal tissue, so that in these species the early penetration of the uterine epithelium is considered a final stage of implantation. Almost immediately after adhesion, penetrating tongues of trophoblast have been seen extending between healthy uterine epithelial cells in several nonprimate species (Enders and Schlafke, (1969). Although this has not been directly observed in primate species, the similarity of the light microscopic observations of the species at implantation leads one to assume the same phenomena exist in the primate.

The extent of further penetration of the endometrium is dependent on the species. Both Old and New World monkeys, after the establishment of anchoring strands of trophoblast through the uterine epithelium, destroy or slough off the epithelial cells. In these species, this represents the limit of implantation. Although much further penetration of maternal tissue takes place, it is involved with the process of villous formation and thus considered a process of placentation. The earliest stages of implantation known in the new New World monkey consist of fused twin blastocysts of a marmoset (*Hapole jacchus*) (Wislocki, 1932 and 1939) and a somewhat older blastocyst of a squirrel monkey *(Chrysothrix sciureus*) (Hill, 1932). Additional specimens of early marmoset blastocysts have been described by Wislocki and Streeter (1938) and Benirschke (1969). In the earliest of these specimens the uterine epithelium is already eroded and a still smooth, avillous trophoblast is in contact with the underlying stroma. A relatively large epithelial plaque is present in the area of the implantation.

The mode of implantation in several species of Old World mon-

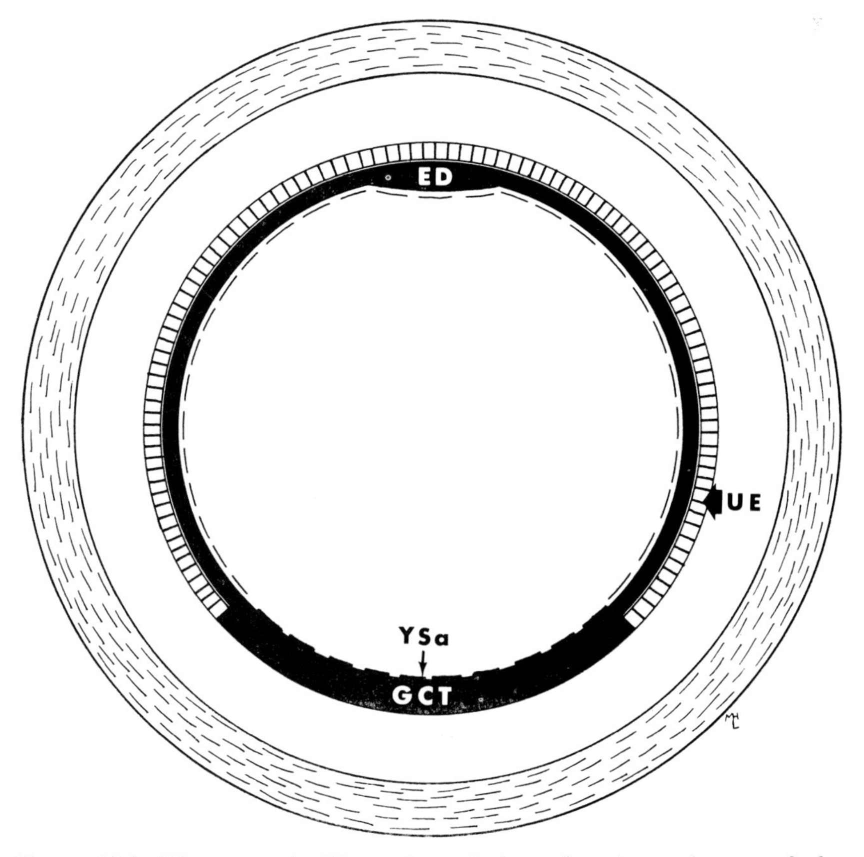

Figure 13-3. Diagrammatic illustration of the primary attachment of the blastocyst of Galago. Attachment is accomplished at the pole of the blastocyst opposite the embryonic disc (ED) by an area of giant cell trophoblast (GCT). The uterine epithelium (UE) is disrupted in this area but this condition is transient, disappearing in later development. Note the attachment of the yolk sac (YSa) to the area of giant cell trophoblast. (Adapted from Butler, 1967a)

keys, namely the rhesus monkey and baboon, has been studied in detail and they represent the only species in which the temporal as well as the morphological factors have been studied. In the baboon and rhesus monkey, the earliest phase of attachment of the blastocyst to the uterine epithelium occurs on days eight and nine (Fig. 13-2) (Wislocki and Streeter, 1938; Houston, 1969a,b, and 1970). Immediately after contact with the uterine epithelium is established, the trophoblast in the area of contact differentiates into an external layer of syncytiotrophoblast and an internal cytotrophoblast. The attachment of the synctiotrophoblast to the uterine epithelium is usually limited to several small areas peripheral to the embryoblast which enlarge and blend with one another resulting in a total opposition of the embryonic pole to the uterine epithelium. Cytolysis occurs in the uterine epithelium at the contact points due to the presence and activity of the invading trophoblast. In man and the other anthropoid species, implantation extends well beyond the penetration of the uterine epithelium, penetrating well into the substance of the uterine stroma (Heuser, 1940). With the "healing over" of the point of penetration, the blastocyst comes to lie completely within maternal tissue, no longer within the uterine cavity. (Hamilton and Boyd, 1960; Hertig, Rock, and Adams, 1956).

Three main types of implantation are recognized, based on the relationship of the blastocyst with the uterine cavity. These are eccentric, central and interstitial. In *eccentric* implantation the blastocyst embeds in a uterine crypt or recess off the main channel of the uterine cavity. This type is common to many rodents, but is not found in any of the primate species which have been studied in detail. The *central* type of implantation, in which the blastocyst remains within the uterine cavity, is most common among primates. Only the anthropods exhibit *interstitial* implantation in which the blastocyst penetrates entirely beneath the level of the uterine epithelium into the substance of the endometrium.

IV. GASTRULATION

Gastrulation is the process by which the inner cell mass, the embryoblast, is segregated into three germ layers, ectoderm, endoderm and mesoderm. The process of gastrulation in primates is unclear but can be regarded as following the same pattern as other mammals. In the first stage of gastrulation the inner layer of the germ disc, the endoderm, forms by the migration or delamination of cells from the deep surface of the inner cell mass (Fig. 13-4). In the second stage of gastrulation there is a migration of cells from the ectodermal disc to the axial region of the caudal portion of the embryonic disc to form the primitive streak. From this streak cells migrate from the primitive streak to form the intraembryonic mesoderm and possibly the extraembryonic mesoderm. Extraembryonic mesoderm may arise from the trophoblast. The notochordal process originates from the cephalic end of the primitive streak. The process is intercalated in the axial region of the endoderm, but separates from it to form the notochord early in the fourth week of development. The primitive streak is a temporary structure, and as the embryo differentiates from the cepahlic end, caudally, the parts that remain become incorporated into the intervertebral disc.

V. ORGANOGENESIS

Organogenesis is the period of embryonic development during which the three germ layers are subdivided into smaller, more specialized groups of cells, each of which will form an organ or organ system. From the primitive streak forward to nearly the cephalic edge of the embryonic disc the thickened ectoderm rises into rounded ridges, the neural folds, on each side of the notochord and prochordal plate, (Fig. 13-5). The neural folds come together dorsally to form the neural tube. The cephalic end of the neural tube expands into a large vesicle with three subdivisions which correspond to the future forebrain, midbrain and hindbrain. The more caudal part of the neural tube develops into the spinal cord. Other derivatives of the ectoderm include the skin and coat cover, sensory organs and most of the glands.

Early in the third week the mesoderm which has migrated from the primitive streak and has come to lie along both sides of the notochord becomes organized into segments, the somites. The somites differentiate and form skeletal and muscular components as well as the dermis of the skin. The major components of the heart and circulatory system and urogenital system are also derived from mesoderm. Mesoderm also forms the supportive and connective tissues of other systems.

With the formation of the head fold and tail fold and growth of the embryo, a portion of endoderm which formed the inner lining of the vitelline sac becomes enclosed in the embryo proper as the primitive gut. The diverticulum of the primitive gut which occupies the head is the *foregut,* the part in direct communication with the vitelline sac is the *midgut,* and the part that is located caudal

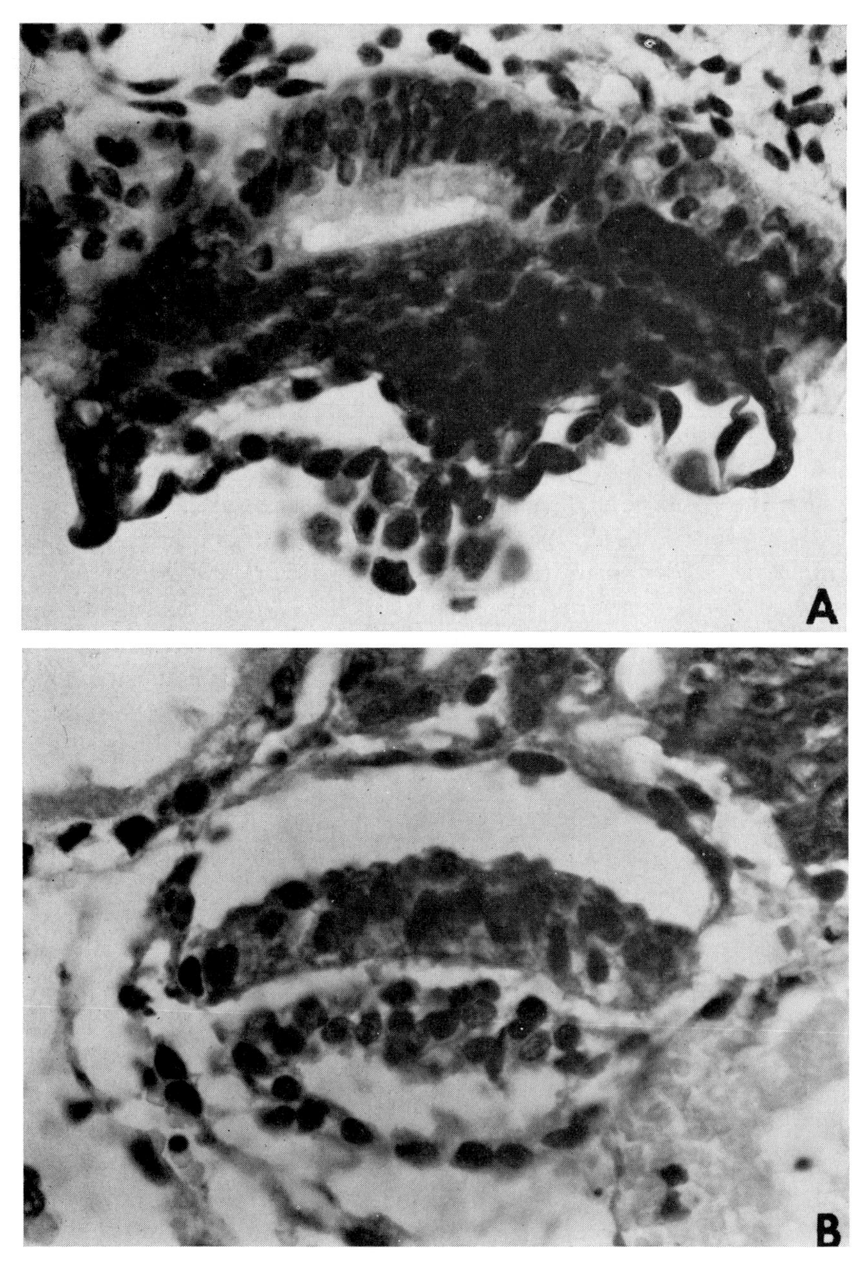

Figure 13-4. Gastrulation stages in the baboon. All photographs are of sectioned and stained material. A. Implanting blastocyst (9 days). Note the two points of attachment of the trophoblast to the uterine epithelium, the embryonic cell mass and collapsed trophoblast. B. Early bilaminar embryonic disc (11-12 days). The embryonic disc consists of an ectodermal plate that borders the amniotic cavity and an endodermal plate that borders the vitelline cavity.

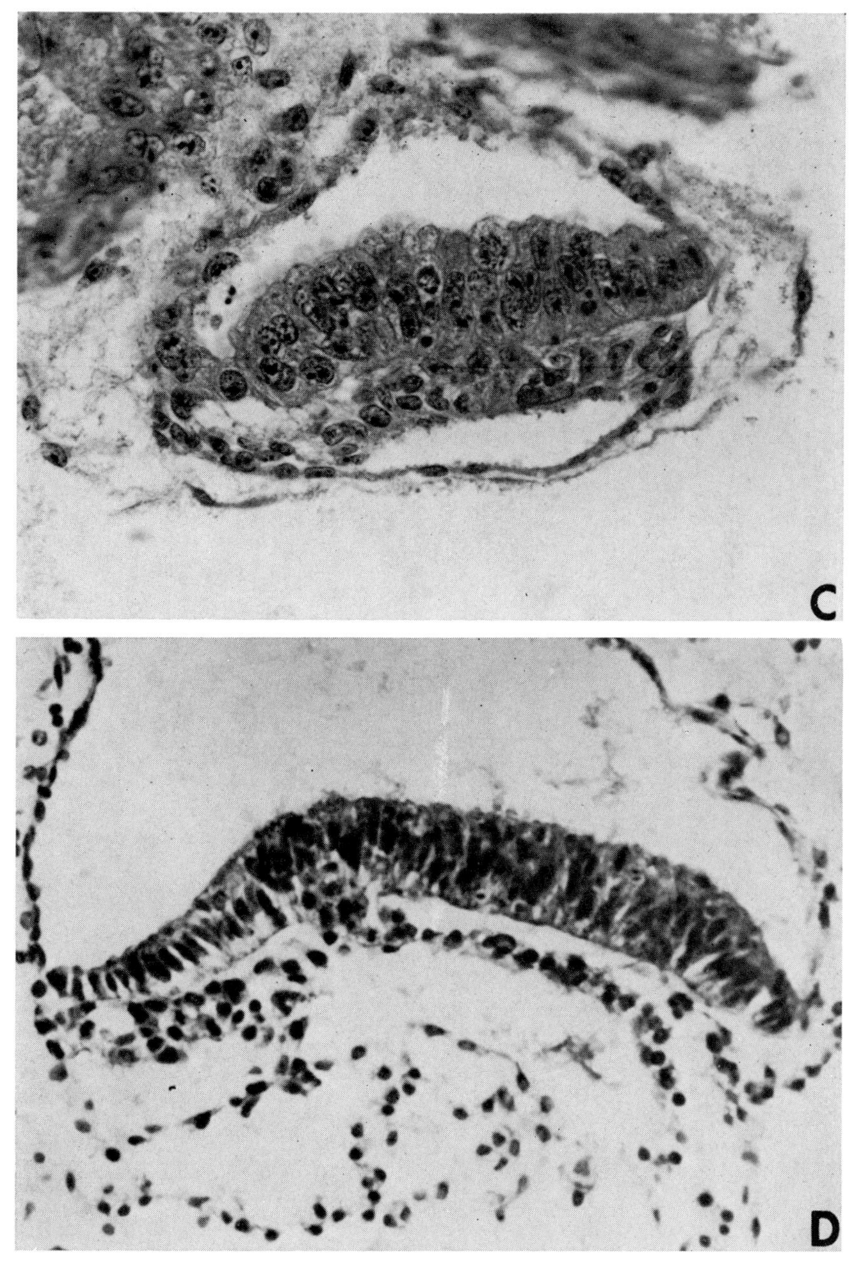

C. Late bilaminar embryonic disc (13-15 days). Note that the ectodermal and endodermal plates are closely apposed. The exocoelomic membrane is visible just below the vitelline wall. D. Early primitive streak stage (16-18 days). Note the primitive streak in its early stages of formation. Intraembryonic mesoderm is sparse but extraembryonic mesoderm is proliferating on the margins of the embryonic disc.

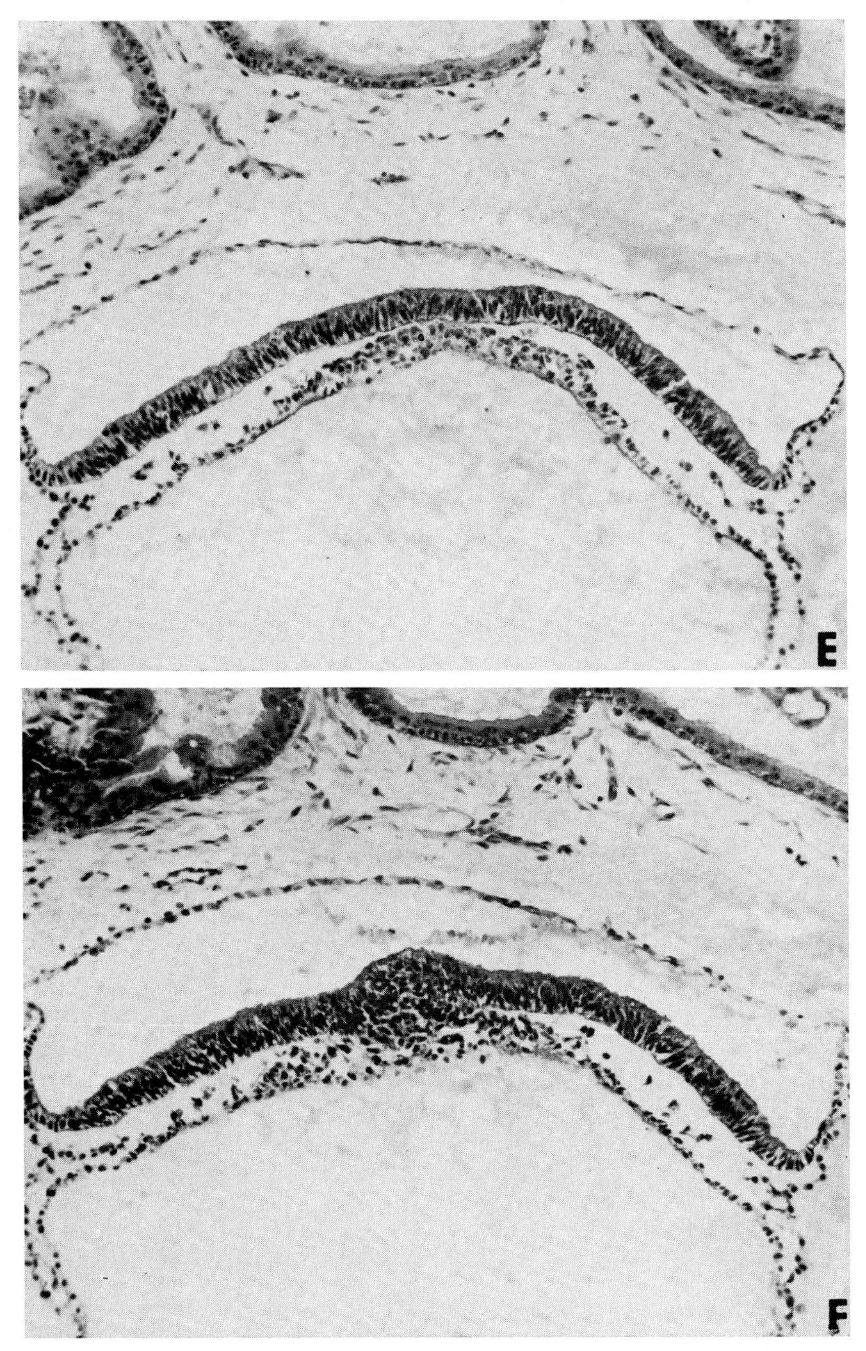

E and F. Primitive streak stage (19-21 days). Sections are from the same embryo. E. is through the prochordal plate and F is through the primitive streak. Note the proliferation of the mesoderm from the primitive streak (F) in comparison to the small amounts of mesoderm cranially (E). (From Hendrickx *et al.*, 1970).

to the body stalk is the *hindgut*. The communication between the foregut, midgut, and hindgut, and the vitelline sac is gradually reduced to a slender tube, the vitelline duct, and the vitelline sac remains as a rudimentary structure, often recognizable on the surface of the placenta at birth.

The endoderm forms the lining of the alimentary and respiratory passages apart from the nose, mouth, and the lower part of the anal canal. The liver, pancreas, serous, mucous and gastric glands progressively differentiate from the alimentary canal.

While the various organs are being formed the shape of the embryo changes. The main changes during the period of organogenesis are elongation of the body, subdivision of the body into head, trunk and tail, development of the appendages and separation of the embryo from the extraembryonic parts (Fig. 13-5 and 13-6).

The changing appearance of embryos makes it possible to distinguish certain *stages* which can be referred to when it is necessary to determine the progression in development of an embryo. A table of "normal stages" is available for the baboon (Table 13-I). Three criteria are used to distinguish one stage from another: the age of the fetus; the size of the fetus; and selected developmental horizons of the fetus.

Criteria for age determination of embryos and fetuses are based on copulation and fertilization time for most laboratory species. This is a reliable method for most experimental studies. The only problem that arises is the designation of the day of copulation. It is becoming generally accepted that the day of mating (sperm present in vagina) be considered *day zero* of pregnancy although a number of laboratories still designate the day after mating as day zero. Measurements of embryos are useful, particularly in research where the size and gestation age are correlated and compared to a control. When measurements are taken they should be done according to a standard procedure (Fig. 13-7). The preferred and accepted method is to base the normal stages on morphological characteristics of the fetus especially external features. During gastrulation, the shape of the primitive streak may be used and after gastrulation the neural plate is an easily recognizable feature. The number of pairs of somites has often been used to define the stage of development during early organogenesis. In still later stages, the

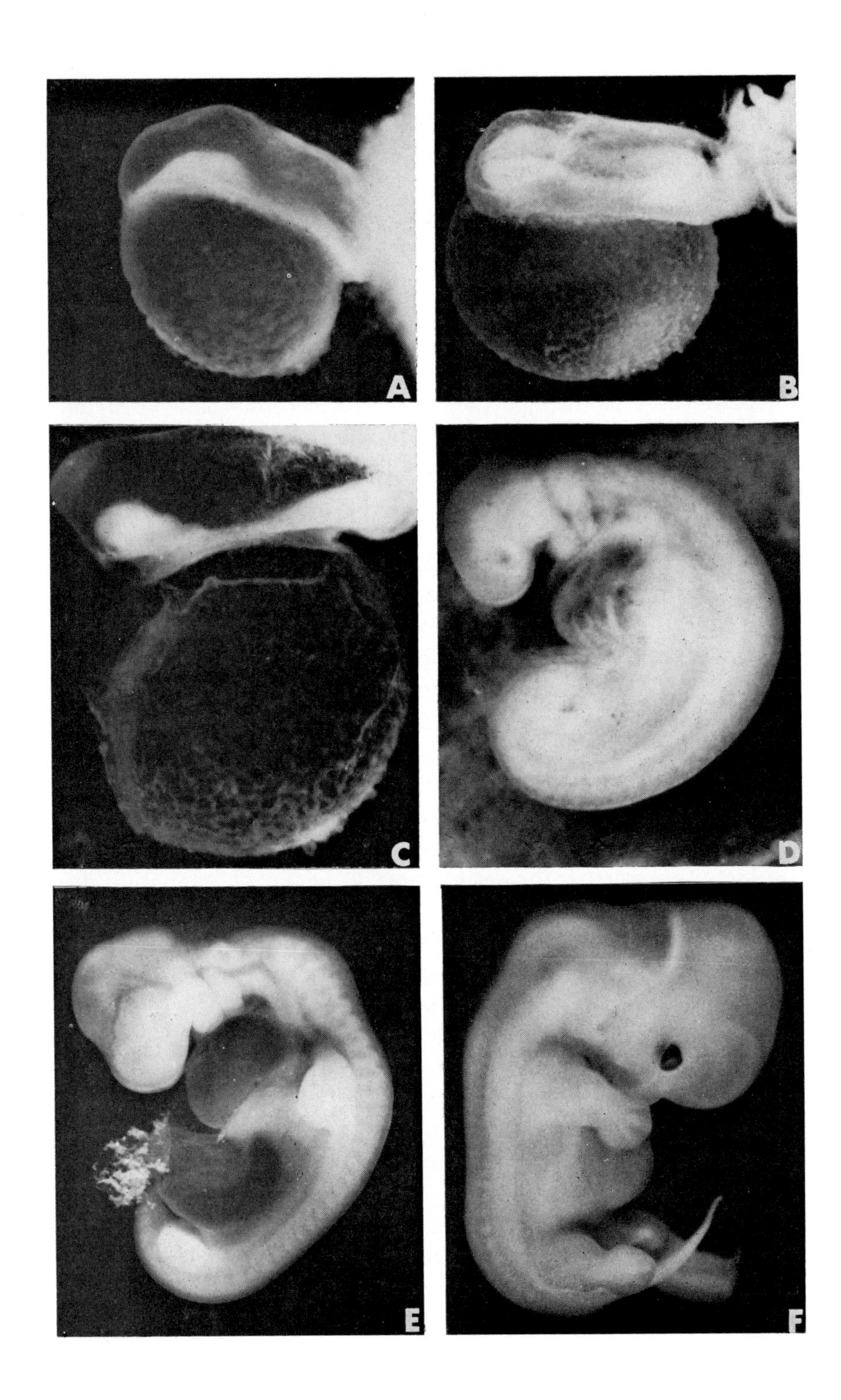
A
B
C
D
E
F

development of the appendages present easily distinguishable and reliable characters for the definition of normal stages (Heuser and Streeter, 1941; Hendrickx *et al.,* 1970).

VI. PLACENTATION

A. Formation

Viviparity, the giving of birth to live young, is associated with the formation of a placenta. This is necessitated by the fact that the embryo in viviparous animals contains insufficient nutritive supply to sustain it until birth, and a functional relationship with the maternal tissues must therefore be established.

The extraembryonic membranes consisting of the amnion, yolk sac, allantois and chorion are very similar in form and size in the higher primate species, varying most markedly in the Prosimian species (Fig. 13-8). Of these, the chorion and allantois are most commonly involved in the formation of the placenta. The chorion consists of an outer layer of trophoblast lined internally by a fibrous mesenchyme. It is the trophoblast that comes into contact with the uterine wall and undergoes various modifications to form the major embryonic tissue of the placenta. The allantois, an outgrowth from the posterior portion of the embryonic gut, consists of endoderm covered by a layer of mesenchyme which, in contrast

---

Figure 13-5. Stages of organogenesis in the baboon. All photographs are of fixed whole specimens which are unstained. A. Late primitive streak stage (19-21 days). Note the embryonic disc which is curved from front to back and side to side, and is bordered by the amniotic sac (top) and vitelline sac with a fine vascular network (bottom). Note also the body stalk (right) connecting the embryo to the placenta. B. Neural fold stage (23 days). The neural folds extend over the cranial two-thirds of the embryo.
C. Neural tube stage (25 days). D. Twenty-eight day old embryo showing the characteristic C-shape which develops with the appearance of the major organ systems.
E. Thirty-day embryo. The brain, pharyngeal arches, heart and limb buds are particularly conspicuous. F. Thirty-seven day embryo. Note the formation of the external ear, pigmentation of the eye and the finger and toe rays. (From Hendrickx *et al.*, 1970).

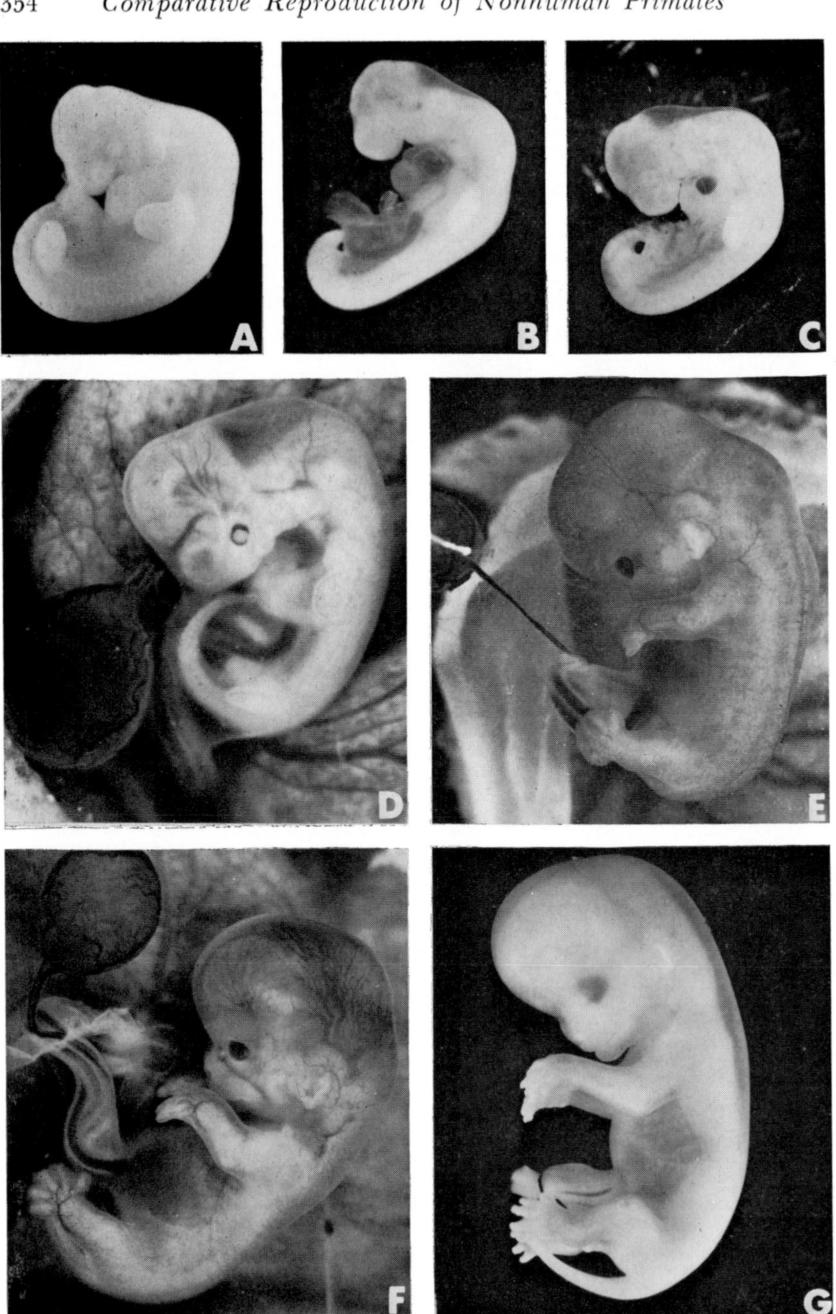
A
B
C
D
E
F
G

to the chorionic mesenchyme, is highly vascular. Thus, by combining the two membranes, a highly vascular chorioallantois is formed, the condition common to the Prosimian species (Fig. 13-8B) (Butler, 1967b; Luckett, 1968). In higher primate species, the actual allantoic vessicle remains rudimentary and vascular elements of its mesodermal layer extend out into the chorion. Thus, the chorion is vascularized by allantoic vessels without the actual presence of an allantoic vesicle (Fig. 13-8A).

B. Types

Outgrowth of the chorion known as *chorionic* villi are developed as the means of increasing the surface of contact between maternal and fetal tissues. The distribution of the villi forms one of the methods by which placentae are classified and on the basis of this four types (diffuse, cotyledonary, zonary, and discoid) are recognized. Of these, only the diffuse and discoid types are found on primates.

Diffuse. Villous formation is generalized over the entire chorionic surface in apposition to the uterine mucosa, but the villi are usually rather rudimentary in their development of length and branching. In the Galago the chorion is merely thrown into irregular folds which correspond with folds of uterine mucosa.

Discoid. Villi are extremely complex in length and branching pattern and are limited to an area of attachment with the uterine wall which is in the shape of a round to oval disc. It was from the observation of this type of placenta as found in man that the word

---

Figure 13-6. Embryos of different species. A. Thirty-day *Macaca irus* embryo. B. Thirty-day *Macaca radiata* embryo. C. Thirty-eight day *Galago crassicaudatus* embryo. D. Thirty-four day *Cercocebus fulliginosus* embryo. The *M. irus* embryo is slightly more advanced in development than the *M. radiata* that has a similar gestation period, and the *C. fulliginosus* embryo is more advanced than the *G. crassicaudatus* that has a shorter gestation period. However, the variation in development for *M. irus* and *M. radiata* is within the normal range. E. Thirty-eight day *M. mulatta* embryo. F. Forty-three day *M. mulatta* embryo. Note the development of peripheral circulation. G. Forty-eight day *M. mulatta* embryo. This stage of development represents the end of the embryonic period.

TABLE 13-I

DEVELOPMENTAL STAGES OF THE BABOON

Stage	*Estimated Fertilization Age (days)*	*Size*		*Characteristics*
		Zona Pellucida		
		Diameter (μ)	*Thickness (μ)*	
I	1	140–180	12–26	Fertilized ovum
II	2–5	150–200	14–26	Segmenting embryo
III	5–8	180–200	9–10 (or absent)	Free blastocyst
		Greatest Length (mm)		
IV	9 ± 1	0.04		Implanting blastocyst, inner cell mass
V	10 ± 1	0.08		Blastocyst implanted but still avillous, bilaminar embryonic disc I
VI	11–15	0.12–0.20		Primitive chorionic villi, bilaminar embryonic disc II
VII	16–18	0.20–0.35		Branching chorionic villi, embryonic shield I
VIII	19–21	0.60–0.90		Angioblasts in chorionic villi, embryonic shield II
IX	23 ± 1	1.0–2.0		0–3 paired somites, formation of neural folds
X	25 ± 1	2.0–3.5		4–12 paired somites
XI	27 ± 1	2.0–4.5		13–20 paired somites
		Crown-rump Length (mm)		
XII	28 ± 1	3.3–4.5		21–29 paired somites
XIII	29 ± 1	4.5–6		Lens placode present inner layer of optic cup thickened, nasal placode present
XIV	30 ± 1	6–7		Lens pit formed, optic cup invaginated, nasal placode thickened, metanephric diverticulum appears.
XV	31 ± 1	6–8		Lens pit closed, optic stalk formed, retinal fissure closed, nasal pit formed, metanephric diverticulum (ureter) elongated and expanded at distal end.
XVI	33 ± 1	7–9		Lens vesicle connection to ectoderm thin, numerous pigment granules, retinal fissure fusing, maxillary process and nasal fin present, renal pelvis and metanephrogenic mass present.

TABLE 13-I (Continued)

DEVELOPMENTAL STAGES OF THE BABOON

Stage	*Estimated Fertilization Age (days)*	*Size*	*Characteristics*
		Crown-rump Length (mm)	
XVII	35 ± 1	10–13	Lens cavity small, retinal fissure fused, nasal fin expands, renal major calyces formed.
XVIII	37 ± 1	14–17	Lens separated from ectoderm, cavity slit-like, pigment granules of retina migrating forward, primary polate formed, nasal fin degenerates, renal minor calyces formed, primorduim of renal capsule present, subdivision of metanephragenic mass.
XIX	39 ± 1	16–17	Cornea, a thin loose cellular layer, neural and pigment layers of optic cup evident lateral palatine processes blunt and project medially metanephric cap on ends of collecting tubules.
XX	41 ± 1	17–18	Cornea discrete layer, eyelids cover one-fifth of eye surface, lateral palatine process project to floor of oral cavity, metanephric vesicles S-shaped and fusing with collecting tubules.
XXI	43 ± 1	18–21	Cornea three discrete layers of cells, anterior chamber appears between cornea and pupillary membrane, premaxillary and maxillary bone formed, primitive Bowman's capsule partially invaginated, renal corpuscles differentiating.
XXII	45 ± 1	21–23	Eyelid covers one-third of eye surface, bucconasal membrane ruptures, lateral palatine processes rotated medially but remain beneath the tongue, Bowman's capsule invaginated, layers thinner, glomeruli enlarge.
XXIII	47 ± 1	25–28	Eyelids nearly cover eye and begin to fuse, lateral palatine processes in horizontal position above the tongue and are fusing, renal corpuscles and Bowman's capsule attaining definitive shape.

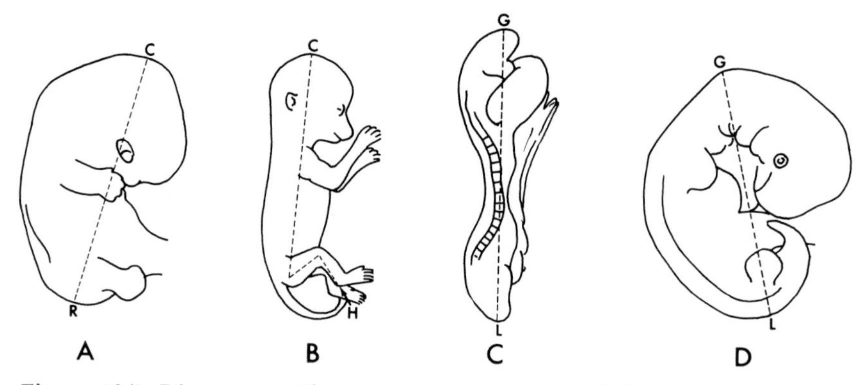

Figure 13-7. Diagram to illustrate measurements used for estimation of age and growth rate of mammalian embryos and fetuses. A. Crown-rump length (CR), or sitting height; distance from vertex to breech; B. Crown-heel length (CH), or standing height; C. Greatest length (GL), practical for young embryos; D. Neck-rump length (NR), useful when head is greatly flexed. (Adapted from Arey, 1965)

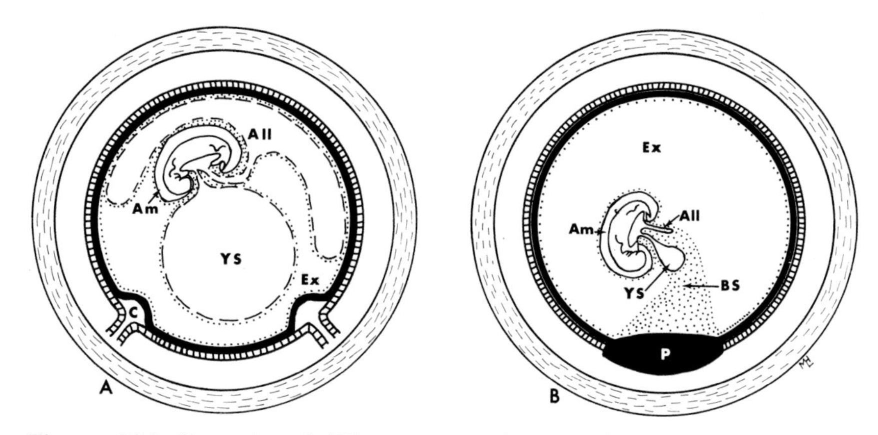

Figure 13-8. Examples of different types of extraembryonic membrane configurations found among laboratory primates. The amnion (Am) remains essentially the same in all species, but the allantois (All), which is large in species such as the Galago (A) is extremely rudimentary in higher primates (B). YS = yolk sac, Ex = exocoelom, BS = Body stalk, C = chorionic vesicle. (Adapted from Butler, 1967a)

placenta (flat cake) was first coined. However, the term is now universally accepted as applying to all types of fetal-maternal connections as defined previously. Discoid placentae are common to all the higher primates and may appear as a single disc (monodiscoid) as in man, baboon and chimpanzee, or in two separate discs (bidiscoid) as in the rhesus monkey.

Another method of placental classification has been proposed by Grosser based on the number of membranes or cell layers forming the "placental barrier" or "placental membrane" between fetal and maternal blood. The chorion, although perhaps modified, remains intact over the fetal capillaries throughout gestation. Certain maternal tissue layers are, however, broken down and disappear during placental formation so that the name of each group reflects the maternal tissue which remains in contact with the chorion in the final, functional form of the placenta. One is left then with the following:

Epitheliochorial, in which no maternal tissue is broken down and there remains the normal fetal compliment of capillary endothelium, connective tissue and chorionic epithelium and the uterine epithelium, endometrial stroma and capillary endothelium on the maternal side (Fig. 13-9a);

Syndesmochorial, in which the uterine epithelium is destroyed and chorionic epithelium comes into contact with the underlying endometrial connective tissue (Fig. 13-9B);

Endotheliochorial, where the chorion becomes contiguous with the endothelium of the maternal capillaries (Fig. 13-9C); and

Hemochorial, in which the maternal capillary endothelium is also destroyed and maternal blood bathes the chorion directly (Fig. 13-9D).

In primates, the epitheliochorial type is found in many of the lower forms such as the Galago, lemur and loris, but the more advanced species (Old and New World monkeys, anthropoids) display the hemochorial type of placenta. The structure of the epitheliochorial placenta such as found in the Galago however should not be regarded as the simplicity of uterine epithelium lying flat against chorion. Although little maternal tissue is broken down and the basic relationship remains epitheliochorial, many complex

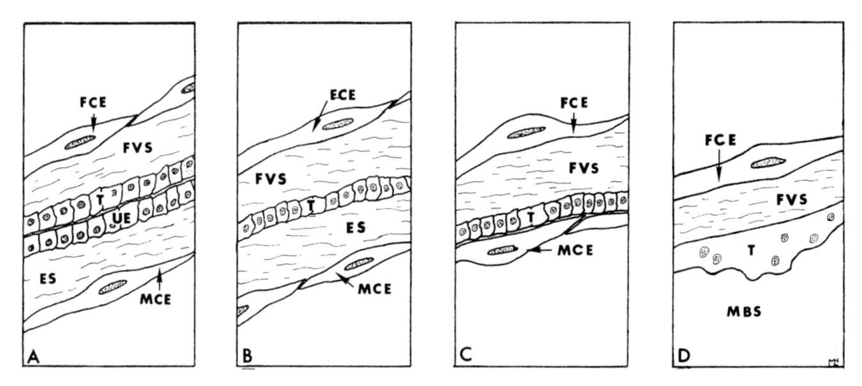

Figure 13-9. The relationship of fetal and maternal blood in different types of placentae forms the basis of the "Grosser system" of placental classification. A. Epitheliochorial; C. Endotheliochorial; D. Hemochorial. FCE = Fetal Capillary endothelium; FVS = Fetal Villous Stroma; T = Trophoblast; UE = Uterine Epithelium; ES = Endometrial Stroma; MCE = Maternal Capillary Endothelium; MBS = Maternal Blood Space.

specializations of the contiguous surfaces of both tissues are formed (Fig. 13-10) serving both anchoring and transport functions. No syndesmochorial or endotheliochorial types of placentae are known to exist in primate species. Although the hemochorial placentae of primate species take on various gross shapes, the internal histological structure is amazingly similar. For example, the first classifications of placentae by this method were based on light microscopic observations by which it was found that in hemochorial placentae the maternal blood bathed the layer of trophoblast directly. Thus many widely diverse species such as the rat, guinea pig, rabbit, monkey, and man were found in the same hemochorial group. However, with the advent of the electron microscope, Enders (1965) found that this layer of trophoblast varied from a single layer in some species to as many as three separate layers in others. Thus, this group is further divided into hemomonochorial, hemodichorial and hemotrichorial classes for one, two and three trophoblastic layers, respectively. Of the hemochorial primates thus far studied (man, rhesus and baboon) all conform to the hemomonochorial configuration (Fig. 13-11), (Boyd and Hamilton, 1967; Houston, 1969b; Ashley, 1965; Luckett, 1970; Panigel, 1970). Other, more specific, structural differences among the three higher

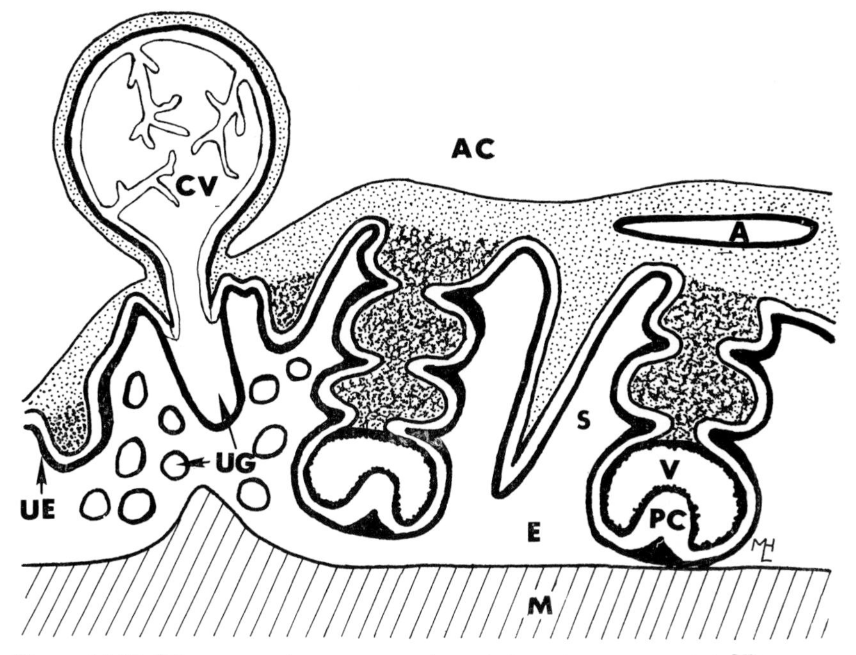

Figure 13-10. Diagrammatic representation of the relationship of the chorionic and maternal tissues in the mature allantoic placenta of the Galago. Note that the uterine epithelium is intact even though involved in several various structural specializations. A = Allantoic Vesicle; AC = Amniotic Cavity; CV = Chorionic Vesicle; E = Endometrium; M = Myometrium; PC = Pit and Cone at Villous Tip; S = Connective Tissue Septum; UE = Uterine Epithelium; UG = Uterine Glands; V = Bulbous Tip of Chorionic Villus. (From Butler, 1964)

primate species which have been most thoroughly studied are summarized in Table 13-II.

C. Circulation in the Placenta

As the function of the placenta is the transmission of materials between maternal and embryonic (fetal) blood, the structure of the placenta must necessarily perform the task of bringing the two blood streams into close enough proximity that efficient exchange may take place. Thus, the placenta, practically speaking, contains two separate blood-vascular systems, the structure of which will be discussed separately.

The structure of the fetal circulation is dependent upon the

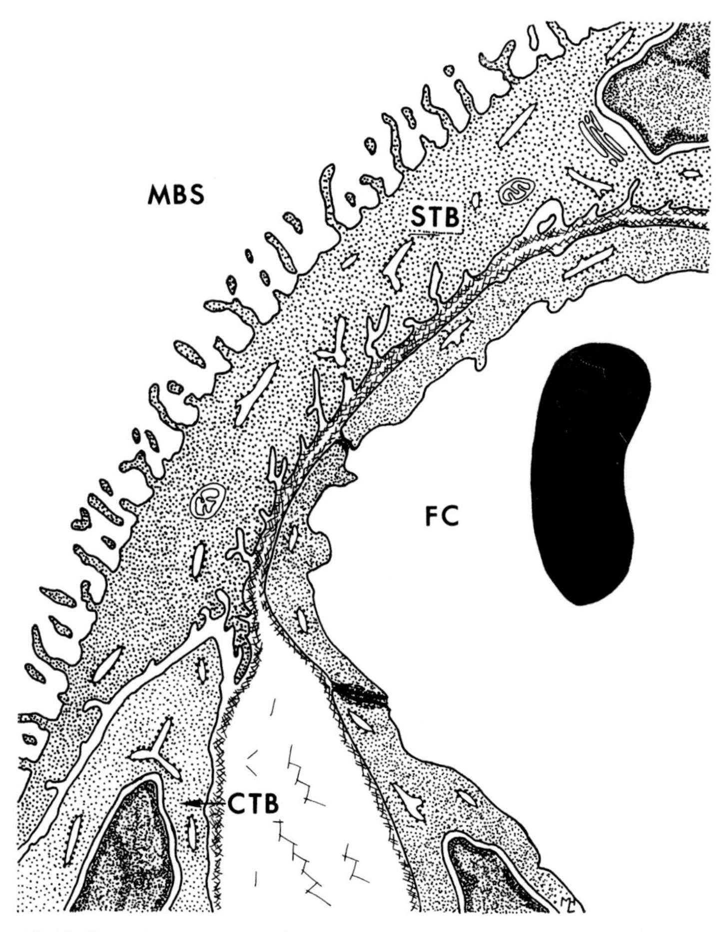

Figure 13-11. Drawing from an electron micrograph of a baboon placenta showing the hemomonochorial condition which exists. CTB = Cytotrophoblast; FC = Fetal Capillary; CBS = Maternal Blood Space; STB = Styncytiotrophoblast.

configuration of the chorionic villi in which the blood vessels course (Ramsey and Harris, 1966; Harris and Ramsey, 1966; Houston and Hendrickx, 1968). In Figure 13-12, the first column represents the structure of the villous tree in such higher species as man, rhesus monkey and baboon, and column two demonstrates how fetal blood vessels course through the cores of these villi. It should be noted that the structure of the villus is such that the dis-

TABLE 13-II

COMPARISON OF THE MAIN PLACENTAL FEATURES OF THE RHESUS MONKEY, MAN AND BABOON*

Rhesus Monkey	*Man*	*Baboon*
	Implantation	
Superficial No decidual reaction Transitory epithelial plaque Secondary placenta	Interstitial Pronounced decidual reaction No epithelial reaction No secondary placenta	Superficial (central) Partial decidual reaction; developing somewhat more slowly than in man No epithelial reaction No secondary placenta
	Trophoblast	
Boundary between maternal and fetal tissues—straight No penetration of myometrium by trophoblast No trophoblastic wandering cells	Boundary between maternal and fetal tissues—very irregular Penetration of inner third of myometrium by trophoblast Trophoblastic wandering cells prominent	Boundary between maternal and fetal tissues—straight No penetration of myometrium by trophoblast No trophoblastic wandering cells
	Arteries	
Intravascular cells very early—17th day Migration of intravascular cells in lumen only Elastic tissue extending halfway up in endometrium Multiple openings to intervillous space from single stems—infrequent	Intravascular cells later—peak at 12th week Walls also traversed by intravascular cells Little elastic tissue beyond myoendometrial junction Multiple openings—common	Intravascular cells very early—16th day Intravascular cells in lumen only Elastic tissue extends well into endometrium Multiple openings—common

* From Houston, 1969a.

tal end is firmly attached to the basal plate with free floating branches protruding into the intervillous space along the length of the main villous trunk. Each villous trunk carries both arterial vessels sending vessels into the smaller terminal villi, and venous return vessels, returning the blood through the same villous trunk. There are no anastomoses between the villi themselves, or between the vascular channels within a villus or between villi.

The remaining three columns of Figure 13-12 represent the circulation of the maternal blood within the placenta. In this villous

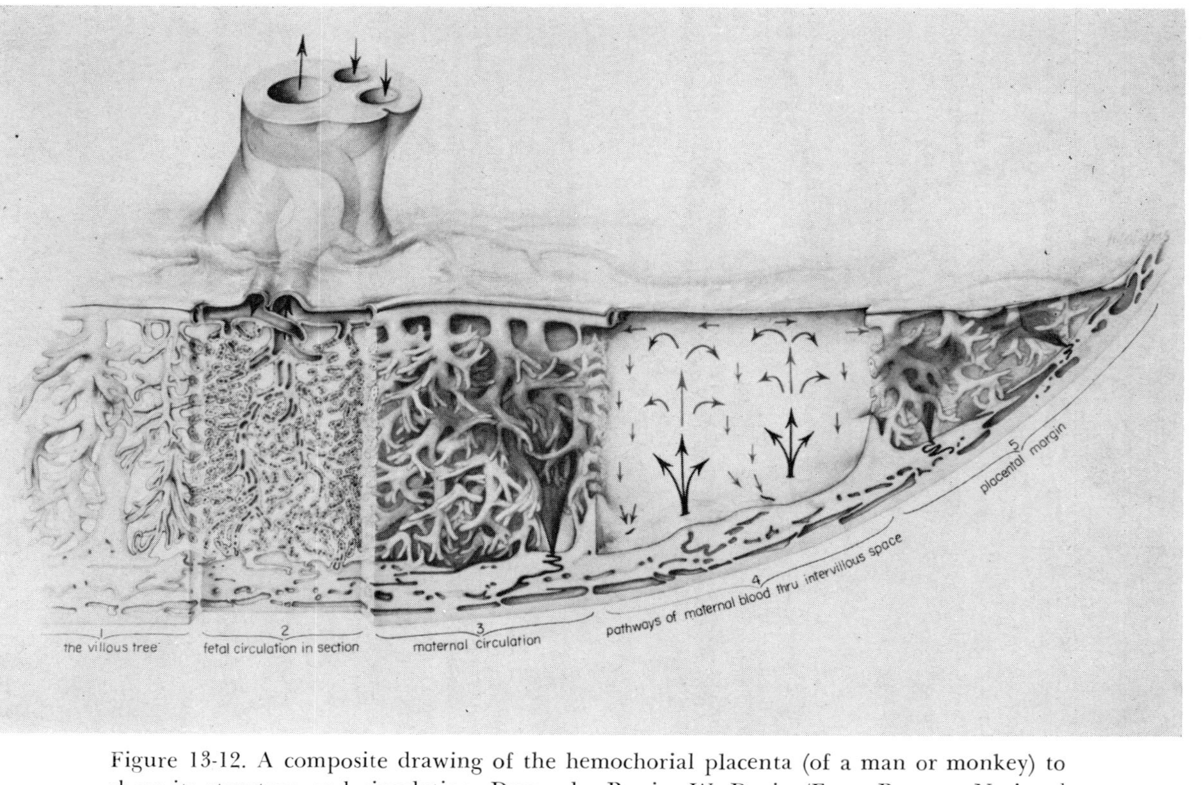

Figure 13-12. A composite drawing of the hemochorial placenta (of a man or monkey) to show its structure and circulation. Drawn by Ranice W. Davis. (From Ramsey, National Foundation Reprint Series, Courtesy of Carnegie Institution of Washington).

hemochorial placenta, there are no preformed channels through which maternal blood courses, but instead the maternal blood enters at the base into the amorphous space between the villi. However, in the absence of preformed channels the flow of maternal blood within the intervillous space is not as random as one might expect. Because the blood pressure in the maternal vessels entering at the base of the placenta is much greater than in the intervillous space, the blood is driven well toward the chorionic plate of the placenta, as shown in column four. Along the course of this stream loose semiattached fronds of villi are encountered which baffle the flow and direct portions of the blood laterally. The force of the blood entering the intervillous space pushes blood out through the venous exits also located in the basal plate so that the circulatory pathway of the maternal blood is governed by the pressure under which it enters the intervillous space. This basic pattern of spurts of maternal blood into the intervillous space is varied by the state of the uterus, relaxed or contracted. Contractions of the uterus occur throughout pregnancy and vary greatly in intensity. Strong contractions may completely inhibit the flow whereas weaker contractions seem merely to reduce flow.

VII. DIFFERENTIATION

The term differentiation is commonly defined as an increase in complexity and organization of cells and tissues during development. The characteristic changes associated with the differentiation of the ovary and testis from undifferentiated cells are typical of this process for the mammalian embryo. A summary of the major changes are shown in Table 13-III.

VIII. FETAL GROWTH

The term *growth* is commonly used for the aspects of maturation which can be reduced to a measurement of size. Several criteria are useful in measuring growth. During the prenatal period measurements of body length are commonly applied as well as measurements of specific body regions (Schultz, 1929). Weights of the whole body and selected organs as well as radiographs of the skeleton are also reliable indicators of growth. Although there is no substitute for knowing the conception age or the birth date, the

TABLE 13-III

SEQUENCE OF DEVELOPMENT OF THE MACAQUE EMBRYONIC AND FETAL OVARY AND TESTIS—(MACACA MULATTA)*

Conception Age (Days)	*Crown-rump Length (mm)*	*Characteristics*	
		Ovary	*Testis*
30–31	8–10	No ventromedian thickening of mesothelium.	
32–35	11–12	*Genital ridge* present; thickened mesothelium, cords of mesothelial cells extend into mesenchyme, a few primordial germ cells.	
36–42	13–21	*Undifferentiated gonad;* (presumptive ovary) compactly cellular, suggestion of cords, mesovarium formed.	Testis differentiated by days 38–40; cords of epithelial-like cells present, tunica albuginea irregular in width with closely packed spherical nuclei, seminiferous tunica albuginea.
43–55	22–34	*Definitive ovary;* a few larger, possibly sex cells present, primary tunica albuginea interrupted by epithelial cords continuous with surface.	Sustentacular cells with spherical nuclei, mesorchium formed, tunica albuginea regular in width, compact cellular, by day 50 cells elongate and resemble fibroblasts, seminiferous tubules (cords) oriented to hilus, spermatogonia identified, glandular interstitial cells recognizable as larger cells below tunica albuginea which gradually increase in number, connective tissue increases between tubules.
56–70	35–80	*Definitive cortex* established; tunica albuginea testis indistinct and transient.	Precursors of straight and rete tubules cordlike.
70–90	81–110	*Inner cortex* divided into lobules; epithelial components in medulla decrease, sex cells enlarged and in prophase of miosis, *small cell zone* at periphery of cortex.	Nuclei of sustentacular cells basal in tubule, cytoplasm central, glandular interstitial cells approaching maximum number, cytoplasm differentiating, spermatogonia near basement membrane, straight and rete tubules become patent.
90–110	111–140	*Outward progression of miotic activity*, through ⅔'s of cor-	Spermatogonia larger, more numerous and more clearly

TABLE 13-III (Continued)

Conception Age (Days)	*Crown-rump Length (mm)*	*Characteristics*	
		Ovary	*Testis*
		tex, lobulation maximally distinct, oocytes enlarging at corticomedullary junction.	outlined, glandular interstitial cells decrease in numbers and reduced to small round cells in connective tissue, outer layer of tunica albuginea fibrous, inner layer a loose vascular zone, connective tissue concentric in arrangement around tubules, seminiferous tubules convoluted peripherally.
110–130	141–170	*A few primordial follicles* present; prophase of miosis extends outward into subepithelial cords, medulla free of epithelial components.	
132–136	160–170	*Multiple primordial follicles;* tunica albuginea ovarii forming	
140–155	170–180	*Primordial follicles occupy more than half of cortex;* A few follicles with cuboidal granulosa, occasional vesicular follicle, miotic activity extends to periphery of cortex, degenerative products accumulate at corticomedullary junction.	Intertubular collagenous fibers increase, septi continuous with tunica albuginea separating seminiferous tubules.
Perinatal 153–181	190–220	*Oocytes* in surface epithelium, in subepithelial cords perforating tunica albuginea ovarii, and in remnants of primitive cortical lobules, increased atresia, occasional vesicular follicles, increased connective tissue in tunica albuginea and throughout ovary.	
Postnatal 3–6 mo.		Small vesicular follicles more common than in perinatal period.	Nuclei of sustentacular cells scattered less central cytoplasm.

* Adapted from van Wagenen and Simpson, 1965.

growth of the fetus can be determined when several of these criteria are correlated and compared to standard values. The same criteria are of practical value in estimating the stage of undated pregnancies. Data on the physical growth of the fetus are available for a variety of species (Schultz, 1937 and 1956; van Wagenen and Catchpole, 1965; van Wagenen and Asling, 1964; Swindler *et al.*, 1968; Kerr *et al.*, 1969; Hendrickx *et al.*, 1970).

A. Embryonic Period

No increase in size is noted during fertilization and cleavage although the cell populations are increasing. The growth process commonly measured in later periods appears to start after the completion of cleavage. An increase occurs relatively rapidly once the neural plate is established. The increase in size mainly occurs by the overgrowth of the central region of the embryonic disc. The margin of the disc (e.g. the junction between the embryo and amnion) stops growing and gradually becomes narrower. This constriction forms first the body stalk and then the umbilicus. Late in the fourth week, shortly after the embryo is constricted from the yolk sac, it becomes markedly curved and the head increases rapidly in size. During the sixth week the curvature of the embryo is diminished and by the end of the seventh week the flexure of the head is gradually reduced and the neck is slightly lengthened and the back is straight.

B. Fetal Period

The period from the beginning of the third month (end of the seventh week) to the end of intrauterine life is known as the fetal period in the Old World monkeys. It is characterized by the rapid growth of the body. By the end of the seventh week the head and body remain in the same relative position so that the crown-rump length (sitting height) is a reliable indication of growth (Fig. 13-13). Thus, the age of the fetus may be conveniently expressed as the crown-rump (C.R.) length or sitting height. The crown-heel (C.H.) length or standing height, the measurement from the vertex of the skull to the heel is commonly used in expressing the age of human fetuses, but may be less appropriate for other primates because of their quadrupedal type of locomotion. Unlike the data

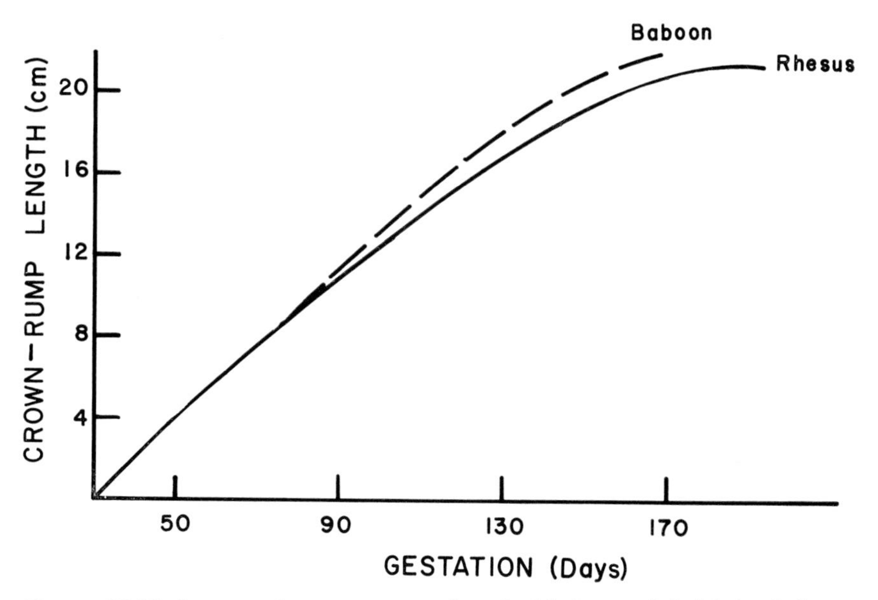

Figure 13-13. Increase in crown-rump length (sitting and height) of rhesus monkeys and baboon fetuses of known gestational age. (From van Wagenen and Catchpole, 1965; Hendrickx *et al.*, 1970)

for man, the crown-rump length as an assessment of fetal age for other primates is based on carefully dated pregnancies (van Wagenen and Catchpole, 1965; Kerr *et al.*, 1969a; Hendrickx *et al.*, 1970). Therefore, its application to the estimation of age in undated pregnancies is quite reliable. The study of morphology of the fetus and the utilization of age-length graphs based on data accumulated from accurately dated pregnancies will yield more trustworthy information of the age of the embryo than can be obtained from anything except complete and accurate clinical and breeding histories. Knowledge of the size that a fetus should have attained at any given time after the beginning of the pregnancy may be the means of diagnosing intrauterine death of the fetus, or of differentially diagnosing a pregnancy and a uterine tumor.

The growth rate of the organs of rhesus monkey fetuses has been studied (Kerr *et al.*, 1969). For most organs, an increase in weight is observed with increasing body weight and advancing gestation (Appendix V a, b). The only exceptions to this pattern of growth are seen in the lungs and thymus, both of which show a decrease in weight between 150 and 175 days gestational age. The percent of the total body weight accounted for by each fetal organ is presented in Appendix V c. The brain, spleen, kidneys, thyroid and heart constitute about the same proportion of the total body weight throughout fetal life, however, the liver shows a decrease in its relative growth rate throughout gestation. The adrenal glands show a similar decrease except for an apparent increase in growth rate between 150 and 175 days gestational age. The lungs and thymus show a relative decrease between the same ages. The ratio of placental to fetal weight shows a rapid decrease during early and

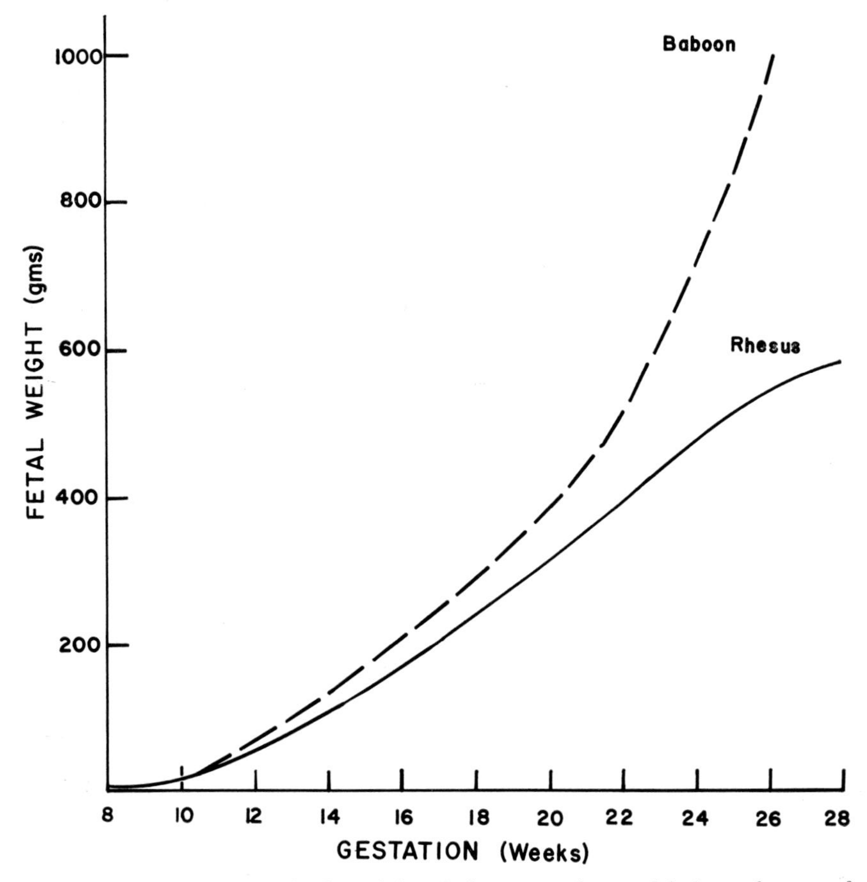

Figure 13-14. Increase in body weight of rhesus monkey and baboon fetuses of known gestational age. (From van Wagenen and Catchpole, 1965; Hendrickx *et al.*, 1970)

mid gestation; the decrease occurs at a slower rate during late gestation.

The baboon and rhesus monkey fetus develop at a parallel rate up through approximately the eleventh gestational week (Fig. 13-14). From the eleventh week to the end of gestation the growth of the baboon is accelerated so that it is approximately 2 cm longer than the rhesus monkey at birth. The rates of growth of fetal organs in the rhesus monkey are generally similar to the data available for the human fetus (Greenwald and Ming, 1960; Schulz *et al.,* 1962). However, there are some obvious species differences. The brain of the monkey has reached over 65 percent of its adult size by the end of full-term gestation in comparison to the corresponding figure of approximately 30 percent for the human fetus (Kerr, *et al.,* 1969).

C. Ossification of the Skeleton

Timing of appearance of ossification centers by roentgenography is known to be useful in estimating fetal age, predicting the time of parturition, and following the course of normal pregnancy as well as deviations from the normal such as twinning and fetal death. Basic data obtained from *M. mulatta* fetuses *in utero* and from fetuses separated from their mothers is available and provides the basis for the following discussion (van Wagenen and Asling, 1964). The new osseus centers and the growing zones, particularly the relative lengths of the diaphyseal centers provide the important dimensions for bone growth.

Although the axial skeleton is less definitive as a maturity indication than the appendicular skeleton it shows early signs of ossification at fifty days gestation, but no appendicular centers are discernible before day fifty-six. The development of appendicular ossification centers throughout gestation are summarized in Figures 13-15 and 13-16.

D. Estimation of Fetal Age in Utero

Although favorable fetal positions and roentgenographic contrast are not always obtained in the fetus *in utero* and small newly developing centers may be missed because of small amounts of ossification or their masking by shadows of larger bones, it is possible

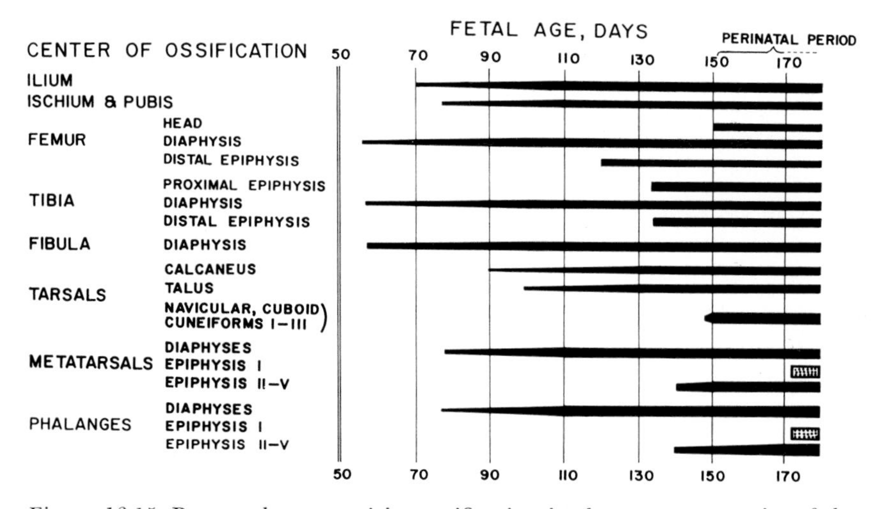

Figure 13-15. Bar-graph summarizing ossification in the upper extremity of the *M. mulatta* fetus. Expanding portions of solid bars indicate period during which the bone is attaining its definitive (neonatal) proportion. Stippled bars indicate variability in presence of the ossification center. (From van Wagenen and Asling, 1964)

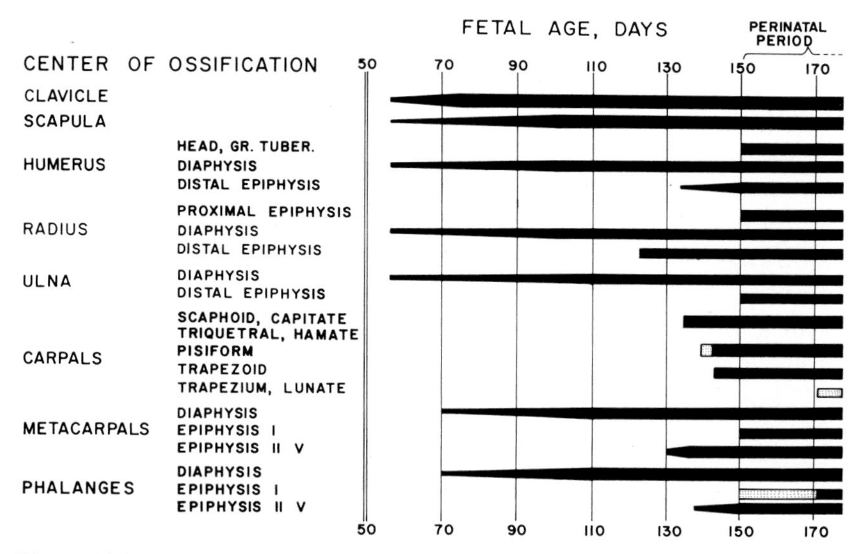

Figure 13-16. Bar-graph summarizing ossification in the lower extremity of the *M. mulatta* fetus, with symbols as in Figure 13-11.

TABLE 13-IV

ESTIMATION OF FETAL AGE BY ROENTGENOGRAPHY OF OSSIFICATION CENTERS (MACACA MULATTA)

Period	*Days*	*Characteristics*
1	1–60	No bone shadows
2	60–75	Shadows of cranium and axial skeleton, primary ossification centers in the girdle and main long bones.
3	75–125	Shadows of metacarpus, metatarsals, phalanges and caudal vertebrae. Hand shadows better defined than foot shadows early in period.
4	125–150	Carpal, tarsal and epiphyseal ossification center of long bones appear including, metacarpals, metatarsals and phalanges.
5	150–Parturition	Remaining epiphyseal centers of the large long bones appear, particularly the proximal femoral and distal ulnar epiphyses, later the greater tuberosity of humerus and proximal radial epiphyses. Sex differences in fetuses are based on time of appearance, initial size and density of small centers.

to divide pregnancy into five major time periods on the basis of fetal bone shadows and obtain a rather accurate estimate of fetal age (Table 13-IV).

IX. POSTNATAL DEVELOPMENT

A wide variety of genetic and environmental factors probably influence the postnatal growth and development. Although the limitations of the sample noted for prenatal growth also exist for postnatal growth and development, sufficient data has been accumulated to provide reasonably accurate indication of the growth pattern from birth to adulthood for several species (Hurme and van Wagenen, 1956; 1961; van Wagenen and Catchpole, 1956, van Wagenen and Asling, 1958; Berkson, 1968; Rahlmann and Pace, 1969; Bowen and Koch, 1970). Measurements of body length, body weight, the eruption pattern of the deciduous and permanent teeth and radiographs of the long bones are useful in expressing postnatal growth. A large normal range exists for all species and for both sexes.

A. Body Weight

Saimiri sciureus infants are extremely large at birth relative to the size of their mothers (Long and Cooper, 1968). The birth weight of *Saimiri sciureus* represents 12-16 percent of maternal nonpregnant body weight, which is considerably higher than that in most other species. There is usually a drop in body weight during the first several weeks following birth. Most full-term rhesus monkey infants regain their birth weight within two weeks and double their birth weight by the age of approximately ninty days (van Wagenen and Catchpole, 1956). The time required for doubling the birth weight seems to bear no relation to sex. The growth rate of animals is usually increased by laboratory-controlled formula feeding over that of nurslings. Until three months of age, body weight seems to increase at about the same rate in both males and females. From three to fourteen months of age, males gain weight more rapidly than females in the squirrel monkey, rhesus monkey, and baboon (Figs. 13-17 and 13-18). Weight gain continues until several years after puberty if a normal diet is maintained. In the female rhesus monkey the growth curve flattens after five years of age, and the overall variability becomes larger. The male weight curve surpasses that of the females and shows no plateauing through the sixth and seventh years. The relatively high rate of growth at birth falls off in the first six months, and is then resumed after a levelling off period at about eighteen months of age in the females and twenty-four months in

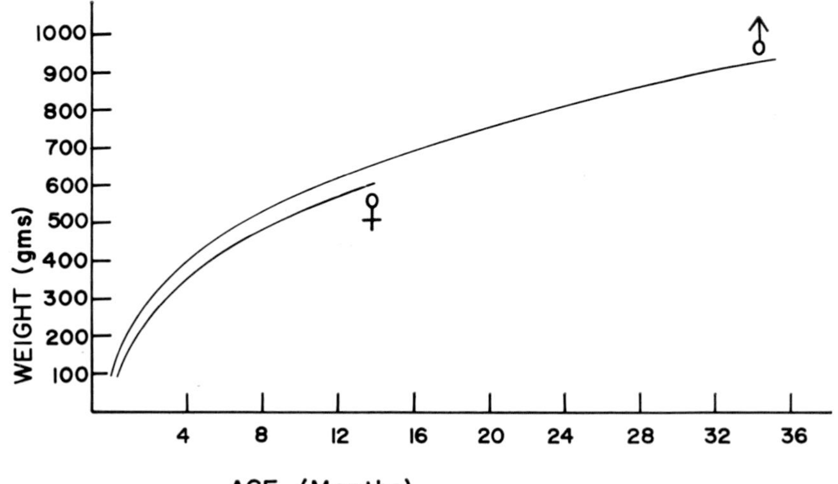

Figure 13-17. Body weight of male and female *Saimiri sciureus*. (From Long and Cooper, 1968)

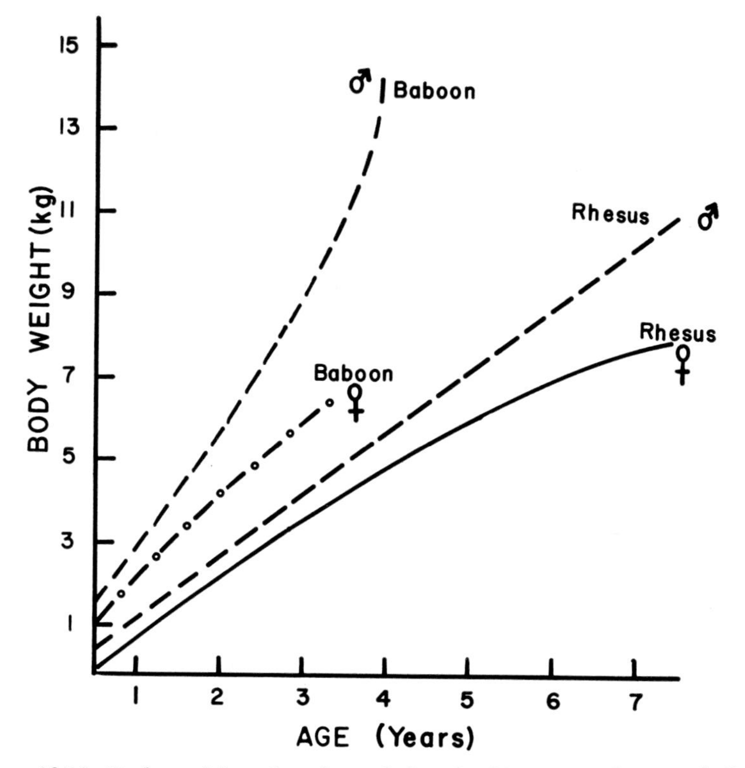

Figure 13-18. Body weight of male and female *Macaca mulatta* and *Papio cynocephalus* with known birth dates. (From van Wagenen and Catchpole, 1956, and Snow, 1967)

the males, corresponding to the initiation of maturation. The "adolescence" growth spurt coincides closely with the menarche and appears first in early maturing females and is delayed in late maturing females.

B. Body Length (Crown-Rump)

Increases in sitting height are greatest during the first year in both sexes of *Macaca mulatta* (Fig. 13-19). There is a slight but definite increment in sitting height occuring at the time when sexual maturity is being achieved, which corresponds to the weight increase. The effect is smaller and briefer in the male than in the female. In the male a distinct increase in sitting height begins at 2.5 years and continues into the 4th and 5th years, surpassing the increments for females.

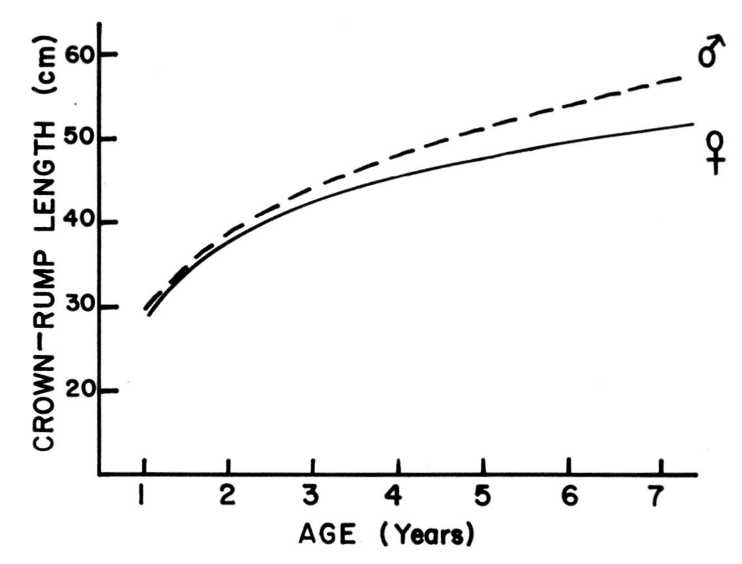

Figure 13-19. Crown-rump length (sitting height) of rhesus monkeys with known birth dates. (From van Wagenen and Catchpole, 1956)

C. Dentition

Eruption of teeth serves as an excellent indicator of both physiological and chronological age. Reasonably reliable conclusions can be drawn by observations on a limited number of teeth, providing suitable statistical standards of reference are available. Practically speaking, it is possible to estimate the age of young animals with no recorded birth dates by single dental examinations. However, properly spaced repeat examinations are far more reliable. The sex of the animal should be considered in all estimations of age. The emergence of teeth is characterized by considerable variability, which increases with age. As variability increases with age, so do temporal asymmetries in the emergence of right and left teeth. Postnatal variability in the ages of emergence is partially accounted for by variations in the length of gestation (Hurme and van Wagenen, 1956). The longer the period of intrauterine development, the sooner after birth do the teeth appear. Infants with long gestation periods average earlier and faster development of their dentition than those with a relatively short prenatal span of existence.

Deciduous teeth. The eruption sequence of the deciduous dentition in *Saimiri sciureus* and *Macaca mulatta* is summarized in Appendix VI a, b. The deciduous dentition of *Saimiri sciureus* consists of two incisors, one canine, and three premolars on either side of the maxilla and mandible for a total of twenty-four teeth (Long and Cooper, 1968). All eruptions tend to proceed in order from the front to the rear of the jaw with individual mandibular teeth usually appearing before their maxillary counterparts. The eruption of deciduous dentition is generally complete by nine weeks of age and by twelve weeks of age the last deciduous tooth (maxillary third premolar) reached complete occulusion. Dentition remains unchanged from the third to the fifth month postpartum. The first permanent tooth to erupt is the mandibular first molar during the fifth month postpartum. Usually the mandibular first incisor is the first deciduous tooth to be replaced by a permanent tooth.

The deciduous dentition of the *Macaca mulatta* consists of two incisors, one canine and two molars on either side of the maxilla and mandible for a total of twenty teeth (Hurme and van Wagenen, 1961). In general, the eruption sequence in *Macaca mulatta* is similar to *Saimiri sciureus* although the time sequence is different. The permanent first molar in *Macaca mulatta* emerges from the mandible at about sixty-eight weeks (seventeen months) postpartum. Usually the *permanent first molar* in the female is the first permanent tooth to replace a deciduous tooth.

Permanent dentition. Saimiri sciureus have a total of thirty-six permanent teeth compared to the permanent replacement for all twenty-four deciduous teeth plus three molars on either side of both the maxilla and the mandible. *Macaca mulatta* have a total of thirty-two permanent teeth composed of permanent replacements for all twenty deciduous teeth plus three premolars on either side of both the maxilla and the mandible. The eruption sequence of the permanent dentition in *Saimiri sciureus* and *Macaca mulatta* is summarized in Appendix VI c, d. The emergence pattern of premolars and canines is later in the *Macaca mulatta* male than the female, the canines in particular appearing considerably later in the male. The emergence of the first molars is more variable in the male than in the female. On the other hand, the third molar erupts later in the female than in the male. Dental maturation is slower in the *Macaca irus,* than in the *Macaca mulatta* while the

Ceropithecus aethiops is faster at all stages of its dental development. The rate of odontiasis in the *Macaca mulatta* is roughly triple that of man.

No apparent sex-related differences appear in the dental eruption data for either deciduous or permanent teeth in *Saimiri sciureus,* but there is a sex-related difference in the time of emergence in *Macaca mulatta,* are approximately 12 months apart for the teeth of males and 7 months apart for the teeth of females. The wide ranges of variation in tooth emergence stress the necessity for caution in appraising the overall rate of maturation of the individual based on dentition.

D. Ossification of the Appendicular Skeleton

The accurate age of monkeys is seldom known because the majority of monkeys are obtained by capture from the wild state. The criteria mentioned above such as weight, body length, and dentition provide a means of approximation, but may be influenced by variation in nutrition. Determination of age by use of roentgenograms of the extremities is commonly accepted in clinical medicine and the standards are established for *Macaca mulatta* (van Wagenen and Asling, 1958). Roentgenograms provide age estimates for the developmental period with an accuracy of within three months of chronologic age. Maturation of the skeleton present at birth in the majority of epiphyses and in nearly all wrist and ankle bones differs in the two sexes, epiphyseal fusion occurs later in males than in females. At birth, females are slightly more advanced than males, and during adolescence females are approximately six to ten months ahead of males. In general, fusion of the epiphyses occurs first at the elbow, and then in the hip, ankle, knee, wrist and shoulder. Epiphyseal fusion of hands, feet, and ankle occurs at approximately the same time. The extremities were completely ossified at sixty-three months in females and at seventy-two to seventy-eight months in males.

REFERENCES

Arey, L. B. (1965): *Developmental Anatomy.* Philadelphia, Saunders, p. 103.

Ashley, C. A. (1965): Study of the human placenta with the electron microscope. *Arch Path, 80,* 377-390.

Benirschke, K., and Layton, W. (1969): An early twin blastocyst of the golden lion marmoset, *Leontocebus rosalia L. Folia Primat, 10,* 131-138.

Berkson, G. (1968): Weight and tooth development during the first year in *Macaca irus. Lab Anim Care, 18:*No. 3, 352-355.

Böving, B. G. (1965): Implantation. In Wynn, R. M. (Ed.): *Fetal Homeostasis.* New York Academy of Sciences, vol. I, 138-177.

Bowen, W. H., and Koch, G. (1970): Determination of age in monkeys (*Macaca irus*) on the basis of dental development. *Lab Anim, 4,* 113-123.

Boyd, J. D., and Hamilton, W. J. (1967): Development and structure of the human placenta from the end of the 3rd month of gestation. *J Obstet Gynaec Brit Comm, 74,* 161-226.

Butler, H. (1967a): Blastocyst implantation and phylogeny in lorisoids. In Starck, D.; Schneider, R., and Kuhn, H. J. (Eds.): *Neue Ergebnisse der Primatologie.* Gustau Fischer Verlag, Stuttgart.

Butler, H. (1967b): The giant cell trophoblast of the Senegal galago (*Galago senegalensis senegalensis*) and its bearing on the evolution of the primate placenta. *J Zool, 152,* 195-207.

Butler, H., and Adam, K. R. (1964): The structure of the allantoic placenta of the Senegal bush baby *(Galago senegalensis senegalensis*). *Folia Primat, 2,* 22-49.

Dukelow, W. R., and Chernoff, H. N. (1969): Primate sperm survival and capacitation in a foreign uterine environment. *Amer J Physiol, 216,* 682-686.

Enders, Allen C. (1965): A comparative study of the fine structure of the trophoblast in several hemochorial placentas. *Amer J Anat, 116,* 29-67.

Enders, Allen C., and Schlafke, Sandra. (1969): Cytological aspects of trophoblast-uterine interaction in early implantation. *Amer J Anat, 125,* 1-30.

Gérard, P. (1932): E'tudes sur l'ovoginese et l'ontogenese chez les Lemuriens de genre *Galago. Arch Biol (Belgium) 43:*93-151.

Gruenwald, P., and Ming, H. H. (1960): Evaluation of body and organ weights in perinatal pathology. I. Normal standards derived from autopsies. *Amer J Clin Path, 34,* 247-253.

Hamilton, W. J., and Boyd, J. D. (1960): Development of the human placenta in the first three months of gestation. *J Anat, 94,* 297-328.

Harris, J. W. S., and Ramsey, E. M. (1966): The morphology of human uteroplacental vasculature. *Carnegie Contrib Embryol, 38,* 45-58.

Hartman, C. G. (1933): Pelvic (rectal) palpation of the female monkey, with special reference to the ascertainment of ovulation time. *Amer J Obstet Gynec, 26,* 600-608.

Hendrickx, A. G., and Kraemer, D. C. (1968): Preimplantation stages of baboon embryos (*Papio sp*). *Anat Rec, 162:*111-120.

Hendrickx, A. G., and Kraemer, D. C. (1970): Primates In Hafez, E. S. E. (Ed.): Reproduction and breeding techniques in laboratory animals. Philadelphia, Lee and Febiger.

Hendrickx, A. G.; Houston, M. L.; Kraemer, D. C.; Gasser, R. F., and Bollert, J. A. (1970): Embryology of the baboon. Chicago, University of Chicago Press.

Hertig, A. T.; Rock, J., and Adams, E. C. (1956): A description of thirty-four human ova within the first seventeen days of development. *Amer J Anat, 98,* 435-494.

Heuser, C. H. (1940): The chimpanzee ovum in the early stages of implantation (about 10½ days). *J Morph, 66,* 155-173.

Heuser, C. H., and Streeter, G. L. (1941): Development of the macaque embryo. *Contr Embryol Carneg Inst, 29,* 15-55.

Hill, J. P. (1932): Developmental history of the primates (Croonian Lecture). *Phil Trans, B. 221:*45-178.

Houston, M. L. (1969a): The villous period of placentogenesis in the baboon (*Papio sp.*). *Amer J Anat, 126,* 1-16.

Houston, M. L. (1969b): The development of the baboon (*Papio sp.*) placenta during the fetal period of gestation. *Amer J Anat, 126,* 17-31.

Houston, M. L. (1970): The placenta. In Hendrickx, A. G. (Ed.): *The Embryology of the Baboon.* Chicago, Univ. of Chicago Press.

Houston, M. L., and Hendrickx, A. G. (1968): Observations on the vasculature of the baboon placenta (*Papio sp.*) with special reference to the transverse communicating artery. *Folia Primat, 9,* 68-77.

Hurme, V. O., and van Wagenen G. (1956): Emergence of permanent first molars in the monkey (*Macaca mulatta*). Association with other growth phenomena. *Yale J Biol Med, 28:*538-567.

Hurme, V. O., and van Wagenen, G. (1961): Basic data on the emergence of permanent teeth in the rhesus monkey (*Macaca mulatta*). *Proc Amer Philosophical Soc, 105:*1, 109-140.

Kerr, G. R. *et al* (1969): Growth and development of the fetal rhesus monkey. I. Physical growth. *Growth, 33,* 201-213.

Lewis, W. H., and Hartman, C. G. (1941): Tubal ova of the rhesus monkey. *Contr Embryol Carnegie Inst Washington, 29,* 7-14.

Long, J. O., and Cooper, R. W. (1968): Physical growth and dental eruption in captive-bred squirrel monkeys, *Saimiri sciureus* (Leticia, Colombia). Rosenblum and Cooper (Ed.): *The Squirrel Monkey.* New York, Aacademic Press, chap. 7, pp. 193-205.

Luckett, W. P. (1968): Morphogenesis of the placenta and fetal membranes of the tree shrews (Family Tupaiidae). *Amer J Anat, 123,* 385-427.

Luckett, W. P. (1970): The fine structure of the placental villi of the rhesus monkey (*Macaca mulatta*). *Anat Rec., 157:*141-164.

Marston, J. H., and Kelly, W. A. (1968): Time relationships of spermatozoan penetration into the egg of the rhesus monkey. *Nature 217 (No. 5133),* 1073-1074.

Mastroianni, L., Jr. (1967): Contraceptive action of intrauterine devices in the rhesus monkey. *Nature, 215 (No. 5016),* 1172-1173.

Panigel, M. (1970): Structure et ultrastructure comparees de la membrane placentaire chez certains primates non humains (*Galago demidovii, Erythrocebus patas, Macaca irus (fascicularis), Macaca mulatta* et *Papio cynocyhalus*). *C R Ass Anat, 145,* 319-337.

Rahlmann, D. F., and Pace, N. (1969): Anthropordimetric and roentgenographic growth changes in young pig-tailed monkeys (*Macaca nemestrina*). *Proc 2nd Int Congr Primat, 2,* 171-180.

Ramsey, E. M., and Harris, J. W. S. (1966): Comparison of uteroplacental vasculature and circulation in the rhesus monkey and man. *Carnegie Contrib Embryol, 38,* 61-70.

Schultz, A. H. (1929): The technique of measuring the outer body of human fetuses and of primates in general. Carnegie Inst. Wash. Pub. No. 394, *Contrib Embryol (No. 117), 20,* 213-257.

Schultz, A. H. (1937): Fetal growth and development of the rhesus monkey. Carnegie Inst. Pub. 479, *Contrib Embryol (No. 155), 26,* 71-97.

Schultz, A. H. (1956): Postembryonic age changes. In Hofer, H.: Schultz, A. H., and Starck, D. (Eds.): *Pimatologia.* Karger, New York, vol. I, pp. 887-964.

Schulz, D. M. *et al.* (1962): Weights of organs of fetuses and infants. *Arch Path, 74,* 80-86.

Snow, C. C. (1967): Some observations on the growth and development of the baboon. In Vagtborg, H. (Ed.): *The Baboon in Medical Research.* Austin, University of Texas Press.

Starck, D. (1956): Primitiventwicklung and Plazentation der Primaten. In Hofer, H.; Schultz, A. H., and Starck, D. (Eds.): *Primatologia. Handbuch der Primatenkunde.* Basel, Karger, vol. 1, pp. 723-886.

Swindler, D. R.; Jenkins, T. W., and Weiss, A. W. (1968): Biology of the howler monkey *(Alouatta caraya)* IV Fetal growth and development. *Bibl Primat, No. 7,* pp. 28-47.

van Wagenen, G., and Asling, C. W. (1958): Roentgenographic estimation of bone age in the rhesus monkey. *Amer J Anat, 103:*163-185.

van Wagenen, G., and Asling, C. W. (1964): Ossification in the fetal monkey. (*Macaca mulatta*). Estimation of age and progress by roentgenography. *Amer J Anat, 114:*107-132.

van Wagenen, G., and Catchpole, H. R. (1956): Physical growth of the rhesus monkey (*Macaca mulatta*). *Amer J Phys Anthrop, 14:*245-273.

van Wagenen, G., and Catchpole, H. R. (1965): Growth of the fetus and placenta of the monkey (*Macaca mulatta*). *Amer J Phys Anthrop, 23:*23-34.

van Wagenen, G., and Simpson, M. (1965): Embryology of the ovary and testis *Homo sapiens* and *Macaca mulatta.* New Haven, Yale University Press.

Wislocki, G. B. (1932): Placentation in the marmoset, with remarks on twinning in monkeys. *Anat Rec, 52,* 381-399.

Wislocki, G. B. (1939): Observations on twinning in marmosets. *Amer J Anat, 64,* 445-483.

Wislocki, G. B., and Streeter, G. L. (1938): On the placentation of the macaque (*Macaca mulatta*), from the time of implantation until the formation of the definitive placenta. *Carnegie Contrib Embryol, 27,* 1-66.

Chapter 14

PARENTAL AND INFANT BEHAVIOR

G. MITCHELL

I. MATERNAL BEHAVIOR

Most of the details concerning maternal behavior in primates have been found in the laboratory and primarily involve the genus *Macaca*. This chapter will therefore rely heavily upon the species *M. mulatta,* the rhesus monkey, but some sections will also include brief description of other primates.

A. Maternal Behavior in Free-ranging Monkeys

Kaufman (1966) studied the maternal behavior of *Macaca mulatta* in a free-ranging colony on Cayo Santiago (Puerto Rico) until the infants were three months old. The newborn infant usually clings to the mother's ventral surface unaided by the mother, but occasionally the mother touches the infant or makes sure the infant is in position before moving. The infant is carried below the mother (on her ventral surface) most of the time, but some infants are carried on the mother's back part of the time as early as one week of age.

Macaca mulatta mothers in nature restrict their infants' movements and social interactions for about seven weeks following birth. Although the mother often allows her older offspring to contact the newborn infant, even from the first day, contacts with other immatures are severely limited, particularly during the first month. The mother begins to allow play with other infants at around seven weeks following birth. Other mature females often gather around a new mother and groom her, and such females are frequently permitted to touch the newborn infant during the first week. Primiparous mothers, according to Kaufmann, are restrictive in allowing their infants to leave them in nonsocial situations.

Older female offspring are often solicitous towards their newborn siblings, and these older sisters care for the infant when the mother leaves. They also chase away intruders and take their sibling infant away from adult females other than the mother. After the infant is seven weeks of age, other mature females groom and hold it, but the infant does not cling to them and usually breaks away or is taken away by a sibling, usually an older sister.

Mothers are very tolerant of their older young when a new infant is born. Siblings often carry infants during the first two months, and Kaufmann observed some mothers carrying an infant and a yearling at the same time, one dorsally and one ventrally.

With few exceptions, the development of maternal behavior in *Macaca mulatta* in the wild is comparable to that found in most laboratories. There are a few large differences in the ages at which behaviors are first observed. For example, Kaufmann first observed bipedalism in the infants during the second week of life, whereas one laboratory study, utilizing outdoor pens, reported the beginning of bipedalism to occur during the seventh week (Hinde *et al.,* 1964). Carrying the infant dorsally was seen by Kaufmann from the fourth day on, whereas Hinde *et al.,* did not see their infants ride dorsally until the third or fourth week in the outdoor laboratory pens, and mothers in the laboratory do not encourage their infants to do this. Hinde *et al.* reported grooming of the infant by other mature females at four months, while at Cayo Santiago this was seen during the first week. Despite these differences in development between the laboratory and the wild, Kaufmann estimated the age of independence from the mother (2 to 3 months) to be the same as that reported in laboratory studies (Hansen, 1966). Active rejection of the infant by the mother seems to be accentuated by the captive situation (Kaufmann, 1966). There are, in general, more aggressive and fearful behaviors in captivity than in the wild, and less calm, casual grooming in captivity (Mitchell, 1970). In general, maternal behavior in the wild and maternal behavior in the laboratory are very similar.

B. Maternal Behavior in Captivity

Seminatural Groups. Rhesus monkey maternal behavior has been studied in groups kept in captivity (cf. Spencer-Booth and

Hinde, 1966; Rowell, 1963; Hinde and Spencer-Booth, 1967; Spencer-Booth *et al.,* 1965; Hinde *et al.,* 1964; and Rowell *et al.,* 1964). The seminatural group provides a more complex social situation than standard laboratory cages and gives both the mother and the infant a chance to interact with other animals. The behavior of other adult females directed toward the infant ("aunt" behavior) has been emphasized (Rowell *et al.,* 1964). The presence of other adult or adolescent females results in the young rhesus infant ranging less freely from its mother. Two main sets of differences between group-living and isolated mother-infant rhesus pairs have been reported. The isolate infants range more freely, spend less time on the nipple, spend more time off the mother, and have longer periods each time off the mother than do group-living infants. The presence of social companions results in the infant's *returning* to the mother less often, and in consequence being rejected by the mother less often. Grooming is higher between mother-infant isolate pairs (Spencer-Booth *et al.,* 1965).

Most immature animals (in the rhesus monkey) direct maternal-like behavior toward siblings (Sade, 1965; Koford, 1963a), but seminatural groups do not have families extending over several generations. "Aunts" near females in labor and parturition occasionally protect the female giving birth in a seminatural situation as well as cuddle and groom new infants (Fig. 14-1). Generally, "aunts" without infants of their own are the most attentive and begin to groom the infant at the fifth week following birth. "Aunts" become aggressive at about the second month; the same time the mother begins to reject the infant. "Aunts" can influence mother-infant interactions in a group and often protect orphans (Rowell *et al.,* 1964). In general, both *M. radiata* and *M. nemestrina* display the same kind of maternal behavior as does the rhesus. However, *M. radiata* punishes and restrains her infant less often than *M. nemestrina* and *M. mulatta* mothers (Rosenblum and Kaufman, 1967).

Mother and Infant Playpens. The Hansen-designed playpen (1966), made of a series of four living cages and a play area, can be subdivided into four individual play cells, each of which abuts a large living cage (Fig. 14-2). A 3.5 inch by 5.5 inch opening cut into the wall of each living cage and the adjoining play cell allows

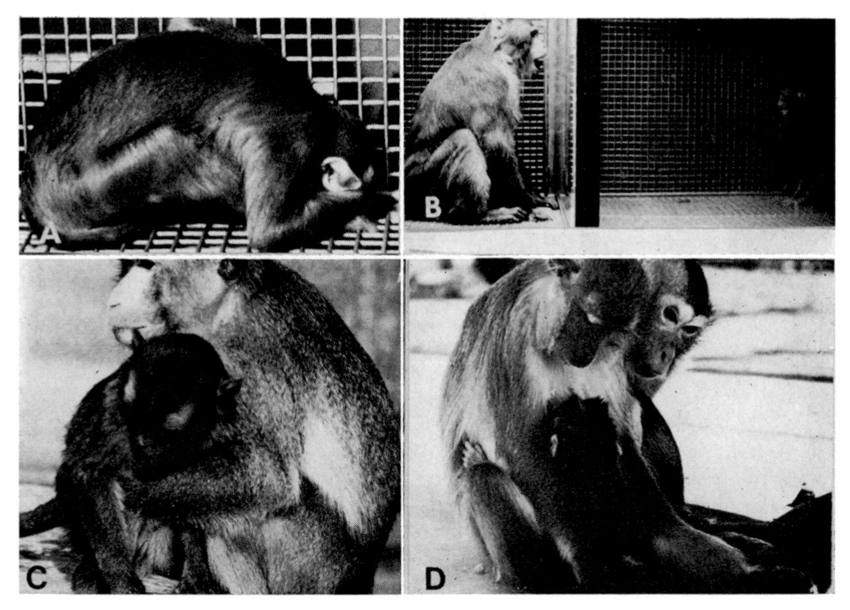

Figure 14-1. A, Juvenile isolate-reared *Macaca mulatta;* B, Isolate-reared male rhesus monkey (12 years old) threatening a juvenile (*M.* mulatta); C, Paternalistic behavior in a young adult male crab-eating macaque *(M. fascicularis);* D, Mother and infant crab-eating macaques (*M. fascicularis*) and an attentive "aunt."

free passage of the infant while effectively restricting the mother to the living cage. The apparatus, constructed of stainless steel wire mesh, permits full view of the animals (Harlow *et al.,* 1963).

Although not as natural as the seminatural group testing situation, playpens provide at least two advantages. Since the play area can be subdivided, the infants can be denied any interaction with each other until the observer wishes to see infant-infant play. This alteration increases the chances of actually observing infant-infant interaction when the observer is there. Another advantage of the playpen situation is that it effectively separates each mother-infant dyad without necessarily depriving the infants themselves of peer interaction or, indeed, even interaction with another adult female at some distance from the home cage. Thus, although it is not a natural social situation, it is efficient and has provided developmental data not too different from Kaumann's (1966) field study of mother-infant relations in *M. mulatta.*

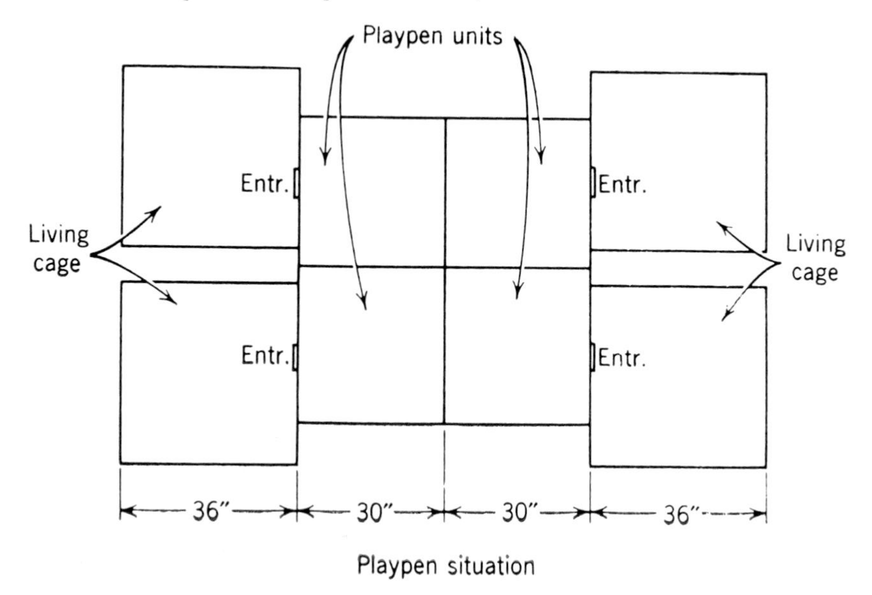

Figure 14-2. Playpen situation (from Harlow *et al.*, 1963).

There are two developmental stages in the expression of maternal behavior (Hansen, 1966). A stage of maternal attachment and protection is characterized by intensive infant-mother contact and maternal care-giving behaviors. A second transitional stage begins when the care-giving behaviors decrease and negative responsiveness to the infant on the part of the mother increases.

The development of monkeys raised by real mothers was compared to that of monkeys reared by surrogate or dummy mothers (see Harlow and Zimmerman, 1959, for a description of the surrogate mothers used by Hansen). This procedure permitted an experimental rather than a mere observational comparison of the influence of maternal responsiveness vs. infant responsiveness on the mother-infant bond. Real mothers oriented the infant toward and maintained the infant in contact with the mother's ventral surface. In the transitional stage, real mothers played a role in emancipating the infant from the intense early infant-mother bond.

The newborn rhesus infant is quite capable of holding onto his mother, but the real mother aids him. An inanimate surrogate-mother is an indifferent mother. She does not protect her infant nor does she punish him. She may provide security in the face of danger. With no other source of animate interaction except a mother, the real mother actively socializes her infant to real monkeys while, with the dummy mother, the infant is passively socialized to a surrogate. If the infant is not provided with at least peers, he will continue to be an outcast among his conspecifics, even though he is still "accepted" by an inanimate species of surrogates. The surrogate mother is *not* a mother; it is a tool used to study maternal behavior (Harlow and Suomi, 1970).

Mother and Infant Alone. A monkey mother and a monkey infant maintained by themselves in an individual home cage are both socially deprived to a degree. The mother is deprived of help and hindrances in rearing the infant that she would normally receive in the wild and, in addition, she is often distracted by the infant. Mothers maintained alone with their infants from the first four months to the first year of their infants' lives develop unstable relationships with their offspring. They are sometimes very tolerant and eventually also very punishing as compared to control mothers (Harlow and Harlow, 1969). Isolated mothers groom their infants more often than mothers maintained in seminatural groups (Spencer-Booth, 1969).

Mother-infant Separation. Both mother and infant protest intensely when they are separated. Maternal behavior changes in a predictable way at separation, while separated, and at reunion. *M. nemestrina* mothers separated from their infants become more active and vocal than either nonmother females or males (Simons *et al.*, 1968; Jensen, 1968). Their activity and response vocalizations increase during presentations of infant calls. At separation, they react initially with agitation and, eighteen days after separation, they appear to be depressed. Two months after separation all of the measures suggesting depression return to preseparation levels. This depression in *M. nemestrina* mothers is more subtle than the depression seen in their infants following separation.

M. mulatta mothers also become depressed when they are separated from their infants, and repeated separations have long-term effects on the mother. Mothers which had experienced brief repeated separations from their infants throughout the first eight months exhibited a greater preference for their own infants than control mothers (Mitchell, 1970).

Forced separation may produce exceptionally strong attachments. However, the repeatedly separated mother is less likely to interact with infants than with other adult females unless her infant (from whom she had been separated) is one of the choice objects.

M. mulatta mothers initially protest separation by moving rapidly about the cage and vocalizing frequently. Mother-infant pairs in adjoining cages which observe a separation but which are not themselves separated show an increase in mother-infant physical contact. The neighbor mothers also show an increase in "coo" vocalization while witnessing the separation.

Abnormal Maternal Behavior. Sexually mature female *M. mulatta* which have been raised in social isolation exhibit infrequent adult sexual behavior (Mitchell, 1970). Such isolate-reared females are occasionally impregnated with some difficulty and deliver apparently healthy babies. Since these mothers were never mothered themselves, they have been called "motherless mothers" (Seay *et al.,* 1964). All or most of such females direct inadequate maternal behavior toward their first infants.

Some isolate-reared mothers are very brutal toward their infants and some are indifferent. Occasionally a motherless mother will abandon and retreat from her infant so that the baby must be hand-fed by humans. In attempting to remove the baby from a brutal or indifferent mother for hand feeding, often the mother violently attacks her infant instead of the human catcher (Seay *et al.*, 1964).

Amount of punishment directed toward the infant is not necessarily inversely related to the amount of nursing and cradling displayed by a *M. mulatta* mother. It appears that each isolate-reared mother has her own characteristic and rather arbitrary pattern of inadequacy. Most of the infant-directed punishment in insolate-reared mothers appears in the first ninety days of the infant's life. Normal mothers punish less severely and usually not until the second three months of life. Male infants are punished more than female infants by both normal and abnormal mothers (Mitchell, 1970).

When these abnormal isolate-raised mothers give birth to a second infant, they improve. Second and third infants of isolate-reared mothers who have been brutal or indifferent with their first infants are often treated adequately and are almost always treated less abusively than first-born infants (Harlow *et al.,* 1966). This may be partly due to both a change in the mother's age and the rehabilitative value of the first infant (Arling *et al.,* 1969; Mitchell, 1970).

Maternal Experience. Abnormally brutal mothers improve in their maternal behavior as a function of age and/or experience. Even in normal mothers there is a change in maternal behavior with age or experience. The mode of delivery of the infant at parturition, the length of the labor, and the degree of difficulty of the labor are functions of maternal age and/or experience (Mitchell, 1970).

Following delivery, the maternal behaviors of primiparous and multiparous mothers differ. The primiparous rhesus monkey mother normally gives adequate care to her infant but appears to show higher "anxiety" and greater protectiveness than the multiparous mother. Mother-infant grooming and maternal punishment occur more frequently in normal multiparous mothers (Seay, 1966). Primiparous mothers, on the other hand, stroke their infants frequently and threaten, lipsmack, and fear grimace to other social stimuli more frequently than older experienced mothers (Mitchell and Brandt, in press, Mitchell and Stevens, 1968).

II. PATERNALISTIC BEHAVIOR

The term father monkey is seldom used seriously by primate behaviorists because it is anthropomorphic. Yet anthropologists, psychologists, and zoologists have shown some interest in what has been called paternalistic behavior (Mitchell, 1969). Paternalistic behaviors include those behaviors between adult males and immatures (Fig. 14-1).

A. Paternalistic Behavior in Normal Males

Many free-ranging infant rhesus monkeys are killed by adult males, especially in an artificially crowded but free-ranging population (Collias and Southwick, 1952). Under normal circumstances, the adult male rhesus monkey has little interest in infants most of the time. At the birth of an infant in a seminatural setting, they occasionally appear to be sexually excited (Rowell *et al.*, 1964), but even here they usually ignore the infant.

Mothers with infants in the field groom adult males, and by eight weeks of age their infants may even approach, touch, and climb onto adult males. The rhesus male may respond with no reaction or with aggression. The infant ignores the male's threats but the mother may threaten or even attack him (Kaufmann, 1966; 1967). Occasionally, adult male rhesus monkeys will play with infants, but four-year-old males play twice as frequently as older males. Young subadult males of four different species (*M. mulatta, M. arctoides, M. fascicularis,* and *M. radiata*) play with infants and juveniles much more frequently than the older males in their respective groups. In macaques, at least, young adult males display the greatest amount of paternalistic behavior.

There are also seasonal differences. Play with infants is most common during the birth and mating periods when they increase their associations with females and immatures. Between the birth and mating periods, four-year-old males continue to play with infants at high levels, while the dominant male's play declines at this time (Kaufmann, 1967). Adult males interact primarily with infants of close relatives (siblings, first cousins); thus genetic factors also affect paternalistic behavior (Koford, 1963a, 1963a; Sade, 1967).

Hormones may play a role in paternalistic behavior. Ten male rhesus monkeys were castrated and released among normal rhesus monkeys in free-ranging colonies. Two of the castrated males, one castrated at four years of age and the other castrated at five, showed exaggerated affectional behavior toward infants (Wilson and Vessey, 1968).

B. Normal and Abnormal Development

Behavior directed toward newborn infants appears in *M. mulatta* before one year of age. The newborn infant is often an object of interest to his one-year-old brother. Although brothers are not attracted as much to their newborn sibling as are sisters, paternalistic behavior apparently begins before one year of age (Koford, 1963b).

There are basic sex differences in the development of infant-directed behaviors in rhesus monkeys, just as there are basic sex differences in the development of play. Chamove *et al.* (1967) reported that fifteen juvenile males directed significantly more hostility toward a one-month-old infant than did fifteen juvenile females.

Monkeys who have been reared from birth in social isolation display brutal parental behavior (Arling and Harlow, 1967). Female and male isolates are apparently affected in much the same way, that is, male *M. mulatta* raised in isolation display brutal "paternal" behavior, females brutal "maternal" behavior. Isolate-raised males between the ages of three and five years direct physical aggression toward one-year-old infants. Mother-raised males of the same age do not aggress the infants. The isolate-raised subadult males also threaten the infants significantly more often than do the controls. Since four years of age is the age when one usually observes a peak in paternalistic behavior in *M. mulatta,* this behavior is apparently destroyed by early social deprivation just as is maternal behavior (Mitchell, 1969).

Behaviors directed visually by much older (12 years old) isolate-raised rhesus monkey males toward infants are not different from visually directed behaviors of control males (Fig. 14-2). There are no differences in the number of threats displayed by isolate males as opposed to control males at this age. Previously mentioned differences between isolate (motherless mothers) and control females in infant-directed hostility also decrease as a function of age and/or experience. However, in the case of both isolate-reared females and isolate-reared males, this decrease with age in socially directed hostility is apparently specific to infants as social objects. Isolate females and isolate males remain hyperaggressive toward age-mates throughout adulthood (Arling *et al.,* 1969).

III. INFANT BEHAVIOR

The behavior of *M. mulatta* infants is not only affected by the mother, but by the other adult females, adult males, peers, and particularly by relatives (Koford, 1963a). The infant affects these other animals' behavior, and maternal behavior is a function of the behavior being displayed by a particular infant. For example, male infants elicit different responses than female infants (Mitchell, 1968).

A. Infant Behavior in a Free-ranging Situation

The free-ranging infant rhesus monkey lives in a more complex environment than does the laboratory-raised infant, yet, the wild-reared infant probably is not nearly as stressed as is the laboratory-reared infant. Crowding, restricted social experiences, repeated separations from the mother, unnatural group composition, boredom, partial sensory deprivation, and the breaking down of long-established families all add up to the conclusion that laboratory monkeys, at least in the average present-day primate laboratory, are behaviorally stressed. In the case of an infant monkey something can be done about the degree of stress occurring in captivity. A monkey brought into the laboratory as an adult will be stressed irrespective of the environment, but the adult animal's stress can be eased somewhat by housing him with familiar animals in a large enough enclosure to approximate natural composition. If an adult laboratory-raised monkey is put into the wild, the same rule applies. Monkeys, like man, become "imprinted" to many or most of the salient stimuli in their rearing environments (Sluckin, 1965).

Singh (1968) compared rhesus monkeys captured in Indian cities to those captured in the jungle. The urban monkeys were active, manipulative, and not timid of people; the forest-reared monkeys were extremely timid. Monkeys become attached to their rearing environments, including the other monkeys in these environments. Removing them from these environments upsets them. The only primatologists who grasp the overwhelming implications of this principle for the future of primate research are the primate behaviorists.

Adult monkeys brought into captivity from the feral state show behavioral instability, but stable and reasonably natural rearing environments can be provided for those animals which are born in captivity, and this can be done with no greater than current expenditures.

With emotional stress at a low level, and it is the role of the primate behaviorist to make sure that it is, infant *M. mulatta* in the laboratory behave as do infant *M. mulatta* in the wild.

B. Infant Behavior in Captivity

Normal Infant Behavior in the Laboratory. Hinde and Spencer-Booth (1967) believe that too often an increase in experimental control (as with the use of the Hansen [1966] playpen) is obtained at the cost of excessive impoverishment. They studied the development of behavior in eight rhesus monkey infants living with their mothers in small social groups for the first two-and-a-half years of life. They believe that the less natural but more experimental mother-infant studies have failed to recognize the complexity of the developing interacting nature of the mother-infant relationship. Yet there are parallel age-changes and sex differences in many aspects of mother-infant interaction when the two environments are compared in a general way. Kaufmann (1966) was satisfied that his field data were substantially in agreement with *both* the Hansen (1966) study and with that of Hinde *et al.* (1967). It is certainly fortunate that the natural complexity of the interaction has been observed, described, and emphasized by Hinde *and* that Hansen attempted to isolate diverse factors influencing infant development, even though the latter approach may have diverted attention away from the complex interactions between the factors.

Infant rhesus monkeys raised by real mothers display a greater degree of social sophistication in peer interaction than do surrogate-reared infants. Surrogate-raised infants are less aware of other infants than are real-mothered infants and show a lack of social organization. This large difference between the two groups tends to disappear as intensive peer interaction compensates for the effects of inadequate mothering. The temporary conclusion is that infant rhesus monkeys do not need mothers at all, at least not as long as peers are provided (Hansen, 1966).

It was felt that normal mothering alone was not enough to produce socially adequate offspring even though normal peer relations in association with surrogate mothering *was* sufficient (Harlow and Harlow, 1962). This clearly makes the presence or absence of peers the prominent problem. Peers, apparently, can compensate for the lack of a mother, but the mother, apparently, cannot compensate for the absence of peers. Two studies have since been completed which do not support this last hypothesis (Harlow and Harlow, 1969; Spencer-Booth, 1969).

The effects of peer deprivation on infants provided normal mothering from birth have been studied in a Hansen playpen (Harlow and Harlow, 1969, describe the history of this study). Each mother-infant dyad was effectively isolated by placing opaque panels between adjacent cages and playpens. One of these groups interacted with both mothers and peers for eight months. Two other groups were denied all association with peers but were raised by normal mothers. One of these two experimental groups was deprived of peers for four months and the other for eight months.

Peer-deprived infants make rapid and effective heterosexual and social adjustments when allowed to interact with peers. Monkeys that are peer-deprived for eight months take longer to adjust than those deprived for four months.

Peer-deprivation does alter social behavior. Peer-deprived monkeys initially avoid contact with other animals and show more agonistic responses relative to controls (Harlow and Harlow, 1969). Nevertheless, they show normal sexual and play behavior, indicating that real mothers can compensate for the absence of age-mates. Just as surrogate-mothered infants find socializing substitutes in real peers, so do peer-deprived rhesus infants find compensation in a real mother. Neither group is as completely socialized as infants provided both peers and a parent, but both groups do play, reproduce, and adjust socially. Peer-deprived infants in a seminatural setting also show a smaller readiness to respond socially to other individuals, but their social interactions are qualitatively normal (Spencer-Booth, 1969). Quantitative differences in normal infant behavior in the laboratory can also be related to the sex of the infant and the experiences of the mother (Mitchell, 1970).

Abnormal Infant Relations with the Mother. The term abnormal is defined here only with respect to some arbitrary yet familiar control group. For example, infants in the wild are rarely separated from their mothers or mother substitutes. This is an abnormal condition. If they were separated in the wild, they would not survive.

The Bowlby separation syndrome occurs when an infant is removed from his environment or when he is removed from his mother. Although the Bowlby syndrome is formulated to describe the behaviors of institutionalized human infants (Bowlby, 1961), it is applied quite readily by primate behaviorists to monkey mother-infant separation. Bowlby's syndrome has three phases. The first phase, called *protest,* involves crying (cooing) and extreme agitation when the mother first leaves. The second stage, called *despair* or *depression,* is accompanied by marked inactivity and withdrawal from social contact. The third and final phase, called *detachment* or *denial,* is characterized by initial withdrawal from or aggression toward the mother upon reunion.

Infant rhesus monkeys at any age between one month and three years exhibit the protest phase (screeching, struggling, and often fear grimacing) of a Bowlby syndrome when separated. During the second stage, there is decreased behavioral activity, depression, crouching, and increased cooing which gradually declines. At reunion, if the separation lasts for about forty-eight hours, some rhesus infants will not return directly to their mothers and may actually run away from them repeatedly (Mitchell, 1970). This last phase, detachment, is described as occurring in one separated rhesus infant by Seay *et al.* (1962). Detachment is usually found in males at around three months of age.

Several factors affect the outcome of a separation. Being able to see the mother during separation increases aggressiveness toward peers during separation and at reunion (Seay and Harlow, 1965). The severity of the separation effect varies directly with the degree of preseparation protection (Hinde *et al.,* 1966). There are long-term effects on the infant which have been attributed to both single and repeated separations (Mitchell *et al.,* 1967). The entire syndrome can occur with a forty-eight-hour separation, but even repeated separations of two-hour lengths produce long-term effects. Previous separations do not reduce but rather increase the disturbing effects of subsequent separations (Mitchell, 1970). Repeatedly separated infants remain behaviorally subordinate to their peers for at least a year following their final separation. They emit more coo vocalizations and show more fear grimaces. Separation in a seminatural group setting reveals species differences which probably would not be prominent in more controlled settings. *M. nemestrina, M. fascicularis* and *M. mulatta* monkeys exhibit the entire syndrome in a group; *M. radiata* do not because they are immediately adopted (Rosenblum and Kaufmann, 1968; Hinde *et al.,* 1966). Rhesus monkeys maintained with their mothers until twenty-six months of age and then separated display at least the first two stages of the syndrome. The earlier the separation in *M. mulatta,* at least down to eight weeks of age, the more likely the chances for detachment, particularly if the infant is a male (Mitchell, 1970).

All of the infants of isolate-reared and often brutal mothers continue to approach their mothers for physical contact (Seay *et al.,* 1964). Such infants show marked preferences for their real mother over an inanimate but nonpunishing surrogate. The responses of the infants, along with repeated approach, include marked disturbance, excessive cooing in the first two months, and (initially) excessive self-mouthing. At around one year of age, infants of brutal mothers, particularly male infants, show exaggerated aggressiveness (Arling and Harlow, 1966), and this hyperaggressiveness continues at least up to the third year and perhaps beyond (Chamove *et al.,* 1967; Mitchell *et al.,* 1967). Thus, early maternal punishment is positively correlated with later aggression, and this appears to be true within the normal range of maternal rejection and punishment as well as for "motherless mother" punishment.

Behavior of Motherless Infants. This subject does not belong in a chapter on parental and infant behavior. The abnormal behaviors displayed by a rhesus monkey reared in isolation from other animals change with the age of the animal (Fig. 14-2). The Isolate-raised monkey starts life as a rocking, digit-sucking, grimacing, self-clutching recluse, and gradually changes as he matures to a pacing, masturbating, sexually abnormal, self-threatening, self-mutilating adult who often exhibits bizarre postures and movements (Mitchell, 1970). The complete absence of parental protection or peer play makes the monkey himself his only external animate object of attachment. Since monkeys (and other animals) become attached to the salient stimuli in their rearing environments, the isolate becomes attached to himself.

REFERENCES

Arling, G. L., and Harlow, H. F. (1967): Effects of social deprivation on maternal behavior of rhesus monkeys. *J Comp Physiol Psychol, 64,* 371-377.

Arling, G. L.; Ruppenthal, G. C., and Mitchell, G. D. (1969): Aggressive behavior of the eight-year-old nulliparous isolate female monkey. *Anim Behav, 17,* 109-113.

Bowlby, J. (1961): Separation anxiety: A critical review of the literature. *J Child Psychiat Psychol, 1,* 251-269.

Chamove, A. C.; Harlow, H. F., and Mitchell, G. (1967): Sex differences in the infant-directed behavior of preadolescent rhesus monkeys. *Child Develop, 38,* 329-335.

Collias, N., and Southwick, C. H. (1952): A field study of population density and social organization in howling monkeys. *Proc Amer Philos Soc, 96,* 143-156.

Hansen, E. W. (1966): The development of maternal and infant behavior in the rhesus monkey. *Behaviour, 27,* 107-149.

Harlow, H. F., and Harlow, M. K. (1962): Social deprivation in monkeys. *Sci Amer, 207,* 136-146.

Harlow, H. F., and Harlow, M. K. (1969): Effects of various mother-infant relationships on rhesus monkey behaviors. In Foss, B. M. (Ed.): *Determinants of Infant Behavior.* London, Methuen, IV, pp. 15-36.

Harlow, H. F., and Suomi, S. J. (1970): Nature of love—simplified. *Amer Psychol, 25,* 161-168.

Harlow, H. F., and Zimmerman, R. R. (1959): Affectional responses in the infant monkey. *Science, 130,* 421-432.

Harlow, H. F.; Harlow, M. K., and Hansen, E. W. (1963): The maternal affectional system of rhesus monkeys. In Rheingold, H. L. (Ed.): *Maternal Behavior in Mammals.* New York, Wiley, pp. 254-281.

Harlow, H. F.; Harlow, M. K.; Dodsworth, R. O., and Arling, G. L. (1966): Maternal behavior of rhesus monkeys deprived of mothering and peer association in infancy. *Proc Amer Philos Soc, 110,* 58-66.

Hinde, R. A., and Spencer-Booth, Y. (1967): The behaviour of socially living rhesus monkeys in their first two and a half years. *Anim Behav, 15,* 169-196.

Hinde, R. A.; Rowell, T. E., and Spencer-Booth, Y. (1964): Behaviour of socially living rhesus monkeys in their first six months. *Proc Zool Soc London, 143,* 609-649.

Hinde, R. A.; Spencer-Booth, Y., and Bruce, M. (1966): Effects of six-day maternal deprivation on rhesus monkey infants. *Nature (Lond), 210,* 1021-1023.

Jensen, G. D. (1968): Reaction of monkey mothers to long-term separation from their infants. *Psychon Science, 11,* 171-172.

Kaufman, J. H. (1966): Behavior of infant rhesus monkeys and their mothers in a free-ranging band. *Zoologica, 51,* 17-27.

Kaufman, J. H. (1967): Social relations of adult males in a free-ranging band of rhesus monkeys. In Altmann, S. A. (Ed.): *Social Communication Among Primates.* Chicago, Univ. of Chicago Press, pp. 73-98.

Koford, C. B. (1963a): Group relations on an island colony of rhesus monkeys. In Southwick, C. H. (Ed.): *Primate Social Behavior.* Princeton, N.J., Van Nostrand, pp. 136-152.

Koford, C. B. (1963b): Rank of mothers and sons in bands of rhesus monkeys. *Science, 141,* 356-357.

Mitchell, G. (1968): Attachment differences in male and female infant monkeys. *Child Develop, 39,* 612-620.

Mitchell, G. (1969): Paternalistic behavior in primates. *Psychol Bull, 71,* 399-417.

Mitchell, G. (1970): Abnormal behavior in primates. In Rosenblum, L. A. (Ed.): *Primate Behavior: Developments in Field and Laboratory Research.* New York, Academic Press, vol. I.

Mitchell, G., and Stevens, C. W. (1968): Primiparous and multiparous monkey mothers in a mildly stressful social situation: First three months. *Develop Psychobiol, 1,* 280-286.

Mitchell, G.; Arling, F. L., and Møller, G. W. (1967): Long-term effects of maternal punishment on the behavior of monkeys. *Psychon Sci, 8,* 209-210.

Mitchell, G.; Harlow, H. F.; Griffin, G. A., and Møller, G. W. (1967): Repeated maternal separation in the monkey. *Psychon Sci, 8,* 197-198.

Mitchell, G., and Brandt, E. M. (in press): Behavioral differences related to experience of mother and sex of infant in the rhesus monkey. *Develop Psych.*

Rosenblum, L. A., and Kaufman, I. C. (1967): Laboratory observations of early mother-infant relations in pigtail and bonnet macaques. In Altmann, S. A. (Ed.): *Social Communication Among Primates.* Chicago, Univ. of Chicago Press, pp. 33-41.

Rosenblum, L. A., and Kaufman, I. C. (1968): Variations in infant development and response to maternal loss in monkeys. *Amer J Orthopsychiat, 38,* 418-426.

Rowell, T. E. (1963): The social development of some rhesus monkeys. In Foss, B. M. (Ed.): *Determinants of Infant Behavior* II. New York, Wiley, pp. 36-46.

Rowell, T. E.; Hinde, R. A., and Spencer-Booth, Y. (1964): Aunt-infant interactions in captive rhesus monkeys. *Anim Behav, 12,* 219-226.

Sade, D. S. (1965): Some aspects of parent-offspring and sibling relations in a group of rhesus monkeys with a discussion of grooming. *Amer J Phys Anthrop, 23,* 1-17.

Sade, D. S. (1967): Determinants of dominance in a group of free-ranging monkeys. In Altmann, S. A. (Ed.): *Social Communication Among Primates.* Chicago, Univ. of Chicago Press, pp. 99-114.

Seay, B. M. (1966): Maternal behavior in primiparous and multiparous rhesus monkeys. *Folia Primat, 4,* 146-168.

Seay, B. M., and Harlow, H. F. (1965): Maternal separation in the rhesus monkey. *J Nerv Ment Dis, 140,* 434-441.

Seay, B. M.; Alexander, B. K., and Harlow, H. F. (1964): Maternal behavior of socially deprived rhesus monkeys. *J Abnorm Soc Psychol, 69,* 345-354.

Seay, B. M.; Hansen, E. W., and Harlow, H. F. (1962): Mother-infant separation in monkeys. *J Child Psychol Psychiat, 3,* 123-132.

Simons, R. C.; Bobbitt, R. A., and Jensen, G. D. (1968): Mother monkeys (*Macaca nemestrina*) responses to infant vocalizations. *Percept Motor Skills, 27,* 3-10.

Singh, S. D. (1968): Effect of urban environment on visual curiosity behavior in rhesus monkeys. *Psychon Sci, 2,* 83-84.

Sluckin, W. (1965): *Imprinting and Early Learning.* Chicago, Aldine.

Spencer-Booth, Y. (1969): The effects of rearing rhesus monkey infants in isolation with their mothers on their subsequent behaviour in a group situation. *Mammalia, 33,* 80-86.

Spencer-Booth, Y., and Hinde, R. A. (1966): The effects of separating rhesus monkey infants from their mothers for six days. *J Child Psychol Psychiat, 7,* 179-198.

Spencer-Booth, Y.; Hinde, R. A., and Bruce, M. (1965): Social companions and the mother-infant relationship in rhesus monkeys. *Nature (London), 208,* 301.

Wilson, A. P., and Vessey, S. H. (1968): Behavior of free-ranging castrated rhesus monkeys. *Folia Primat, 9,* 1-14.

IV. INFERTILITY

Chapter 15

REPRODUCTIVE FAILURE

A. G. HENDRICKX AND V. GILES NELSON

THE reproductive efficiency of a given species of nonhuman primates depends on many factors including the time required for adjustment to environment, the duration and frequency of the sexual season and cycle, ovulation rate, the duration of pregnancy, the frequency of multiple births, the number of viable young, and nursing period, the age at puberty, the duration of the reproductive period in the animal's life as well as nutrition and the inherent health of the parents and offspring. The alteration of any of these factors may constitute reproductive failure.

I. ANESTRUS AND AMENORRHEA

A. Importation and Conditioning Period

Importation of all species for research purposes is essential for the establishment of breeding programs since few laboratories are able to produce and raise sufficient numbers of offspring to meet their needs. The stress of capture, transportation and confinement in cages has an adverse effect on reproduction. Most species experience a period of variable length during which cyclicity and conceptions occur at a low frequency. Galagos (*Galago senegalensis moholi* and *Galago crassicaudatus pangensensis*) probably conceive within the first year of captivity and possible in the first breeding season (Doyle *et al.*, 1967). Squirrel monkeys *(Saimiri sciureus)* kept in the Monkey Jungle near Miami, Florida experience their first mating season approximately one year after being placed in the compound (DuMond, 1968). Female squirrel monkeys that are recent arrivals in the laboratory exhibit irregular cycles (Lang, 1967). Colony-caged squirrel monkeys conceive as early as seven months after arriving in the laboratory, although the range in the time of first conception varies between seven to forty-seven months (Hopf, 1967; Bantin, 1969).

Adult female baboons (*Papio cynocephalus*) transported from Africa experience a period of infertility following arrival in the laboratory (Hendrickx and Kriewaldt, 1967; Kriewaldt and Hendrickx, 1968). This period of infertility generally is characterized by an initial period of amenorrhea followed by cyclic menstrual activity but low conception rates. Cycle lengths are quite variable during the first six months in captivity. During the next six

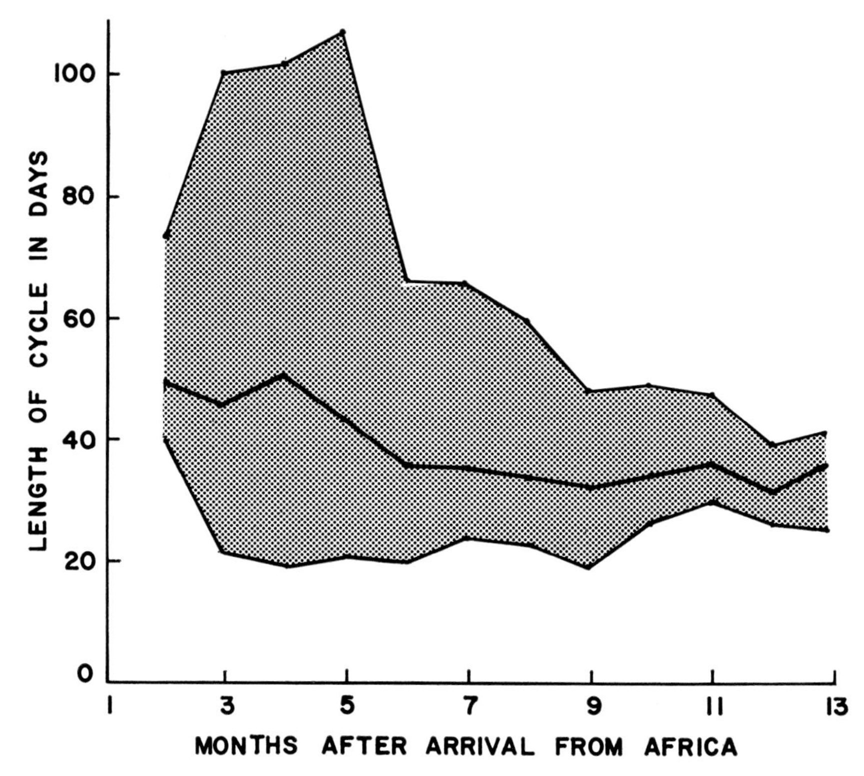

Figure 15-1. The effect of adaptation to captivity on cycle duration in the baboon (*Papio sp.*). Cycle length varies from 20 to 110 days during the first six months. By the 12th month both the range (dotted line) and mean (solid line) are similar to those of conditioned animals (Hendrickx and Kriewaldt, 1967).

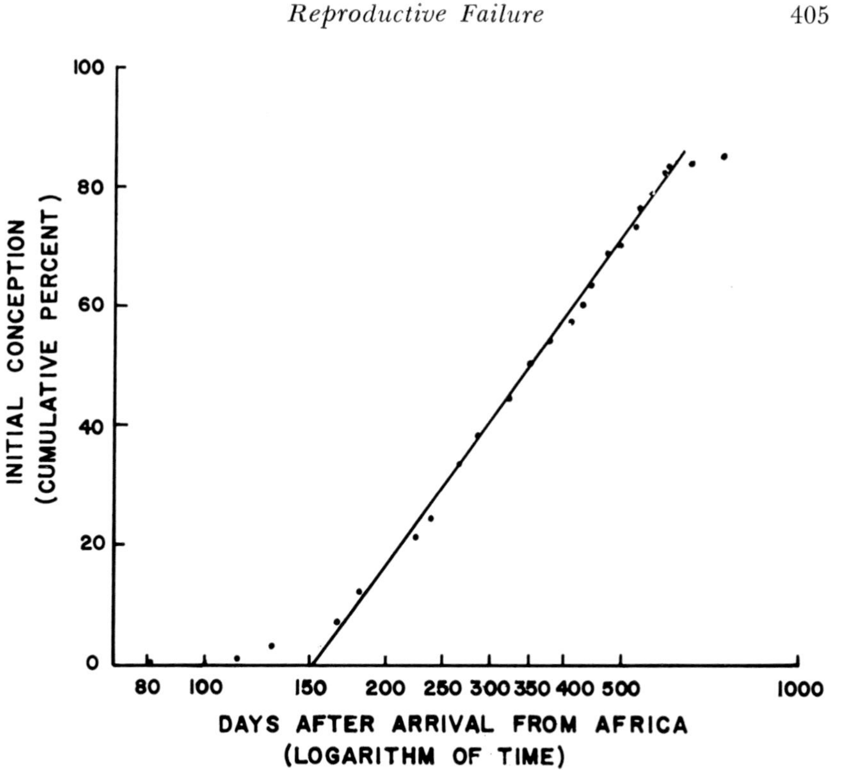

Figure 15-2. The interval of time between initial conception in San Antonio, Texas and the time of arrival from Africa for the baboon (*Papio sp.*). Conceptions occur at a semilogarithmic rate. Approximately 10% of the females conceived within 180 days of arrival, 40% conceived between 350 and 700 days after arrival (Kriewaldt and Hendrickx, 1968).

months the range in cycle lengths is reduced to that found in stable populations (Fig. 15-1). Approximately 10 percent of the baboon females conceive within six months of arrival. Forty percent conceive between six and twelve months, and 35 percent conceive between twelve and twenty-four months after arrival (Fig. 15-2). Approximately 15 percent of the females imported do not conceive. No field data are available for yearly conception rates in baboons or rhesus monkeys in the laboratory, but approximately 85 percent of the rhesus monkeys observed in the field for one year conceived (Conaway and Koford, 1965). The reproductive rate, the ratio of newborn infants to mature females, in the field may vary with the year and the group (Koford, 1965). The reproductive rate increases from 73 percent to 85 percent over a four year period. For newly mature females, four years old, the increase in the rate is more striking, increasing from 63 percent to 100 percent. This high rate is notable because in many mammals observed in the laboratory, including primates, the reproductive rate of the youngest class of breeding females is usually lower than that for older animals. Most other Old World monkeys require a similar period of adjustment. Chimpanzees *(Pan satyrus)* trapped in social groups and maintained under similar social conditions in captivity begin to cycle and accept the male within ten to twelve weeks after arrival in the laboratory (Hummer *et al.,* 1969). The influence of the natural breeding season on cyclicity and onset of conception in captivity is undetermined.

Importation of nonpregnant mature females *Macaca mulatta* is a more efficient way to establish a long-term breeding colony than importing pregnant animals (Valerio *et al.,* 1969b). The incidence of death during the first six months in imported pregnant mothers is significantly greater than in imported nonpregnant animals. In addition the number of culls is greater in an imported pregnant group than in a nonpregnant group (Table 15-I). Despite the advantage of obtaining young quite rapidly, imported pregnant animals are usually considered to be inferior breeding stock.

TABLE 15-I

OUTCOME OF SHIPMENT FOR *M. MULATTA* AND *M. IRUS* WHICH WERE IMPORTED PREGNANT TO THE NATIONAL CENTER FOR PRIMATE BIOLOGY, DAVIS, CALIFORNIA

	M. mulatta	*M. irus*
No. Imported	83	23
Died	44	4
Survived	39	19
No. Abortions & Stillborn	7	11
No. Viable Births	32	8
No. Viable Neonates	11	7

B. Atypical Estrus and Menstrual Cycles

Anovulatory menstrual cycles occur frequently in rhesus monkeys (*Macaca mulatta*) during all periods of the year (Hartman,

1932). The baboon also has anovulatory menstrual cycles which occur approximately 15 to 20 percent of the time. Anovulatory estrous cycles appear to be more common in New World monkeys and in the Greater Apes than in the Old World monkeys. In young rhesus monkeys menstrual flow is heavier, but the cycles vary more in length. Amenorrhea usually occurs for a variable period of time during the nursing period (van Wagenen, 1945a).

Both *Pan satyrus* and *Papio cynocephalus* exhibit sexual skin cyclicity during pregnancy. In the chimpanzee it occurs quite regularly, making it difficult to confirm the pregnant condition. In the baboon it occurs less frequently and is rarely accompanied by menstrual flow.

C. Season

The rhesus (*Macaca mulatta*) and probably bonnet macaques (*Macaca radiata*) maintained in the laboratory have a period of amenorrhea or oligomenorrhea during the hot summer months, beginning as early as June and extending into September. Rhesus monkeys kept indoors in Davis, California without natural lighting exhibit seasonal amenorrheic and oligomenorrheic conditions similar to those exposed to natural lighting in other geographic areas. This period of irregular cycling varies somewhat with geographic location. The reason for seasonal variation under artificial conditions is unknown, however, seasonal amenorrhea is known to decrease with time in captivity, although the tendency for cycle length variability remains. Both the baboon and macaque have normal menstruation in the absence of ovulation, which may be associated with seasonality.

Seasonality in males is also a factor in reproductive failure. In species with a true seasonality (see Chap. 7) the male and female breeding season occur at the same time.

D. Lactation

A condition of anestrus or amenorrhea usually occurs during the nursing period. The Galago (*Galago senegalensis*) and tree shrew (*Tupaia montana*) are exceptions to this, however, because estrus occurs within several days after parturition (Doyle *et al.*,

1967, Sorenson and Conaway, 1968). A number of other species including *Semnopithecus entellus, Cercopithecus aethiops, Papio cynocephalus, Macaca radiata, Macaca mulatta* and *Macaca irus* occasionally menstruate toward the end of the nursing period, and *Semnopithecus entellus* and *Cercopithecus aethiops* may conceive while nursing their young. Rhesus monkeys in the field nurse their young well into the next pregnancy. The weaning process is not complete until a few weeks before the next delivery.

E. Aging

The importation of sexually immature animals is an obvious factor in reproductive failure. Well-defined criteria for selection of the sexually mature from imported stock are only partially available. However, weight and tooth eruption are of use in both sexes for establishing age. Sexual maturity may be determined by complete eruption of canine teeth and minimum weights of 8 kg for males and 4 kg for females in *M. mulatta* (Valerio *et al.,* 1969b). Semen evaluation and rectal palpation of the female genital tract are also useful parameters.

The effects of aging on reproduction in *Prosimians* and *New World Monkeys* are unkown. Recently Van Wagenen (1970) observed that rhesus females begin to cycle irregularly between twenty-two and twenty-five years of age. Cycle irregularity is followed by cessation of menstruation. The effects of aging on reproduction in males remains unknown.

II. ENVIRONMENTAL AND SOCIAL STRESS

A. Caging and Handling

Stress factors related to group and individual caging and handling contribute to reproductive inefficiency. Over a three year period (1967-69) female rhesus monkeys caged indoors in groups of three to eight animals per cage had a much lower conception rate than females caged alone under similar conditions. The conception rate, i.e. the percentage of pregnancies per year, is approximately three times greater in *Macaca mulatta* individually caged than it is in those caged in a group. The conception rate in baboons does not vary significantly in animals housed in group outdoor cages from those kept indoors in individual cages. However, baboons transferred from outdoor to indoor cages in the first trimester of pregnancy have a high incidence of abortion.

In breeding programs in which males and females are caged individually except for short periods of mating at the expected time of ovulation, commonly referred to as timed or controlled mating programs, fighting and sexual incompatibility is observed in most species of macaques and baboons. The degree of fighting may vary from the production of mild bite and scratch wounds involving both sexes to severe lacerations inflicted by the male, which in some instances may eliminate the female for breeding for one or more cycles.

All species require a period of variable adjustment to being handled. Abortions and stillbirths may occur after handling unadjusted animals. In baboons unaccustomed to being handled, fetal wastage is higher in those handled under light sedation (Sernylan®) than in those receiving heavy sedation.

B. Sexual Receptivity

Rhythmic fluctuations in sexual activities of both males and females occur in relation to the menstrual cycle (Ball and Hartman, 1935; Carpenter, 1942; Michael, 1965; Michael, Herbert and Walegalla, 1966, 1967; Michael and Saayman, 1967; Michael, Saayman and Zumpe, 1967, 1968; Michael and Walegalla, 1968; Michael and Plant, 1969 and Everitt and Herbert, 1969a, b). The change in sexual behavior is brought about by two principal types of male-female interactions. In one, males stop making mounting attempts, although females continue to invite them (i.e. loss of female attractiveness); in the other, males continue to attempt to mount, but females stop inviting and begin to refuse them, (i.e. loss of female receptivity). Bilateral ovariectomy of females abolishes all rhythmic variations, and the behavioral interactions are reduced to low levels. Subcutaneous injections of estradiol into the females restore the behavioral interactions, while administration of progresterone decreases sexual attractiveness. This indicates that the male-female interaction during the menstrual cycle is influenced by the secretory activity of the ovaries. Testosterone and adrenal androgens probably have a similar effect (Herbert and Trimble, 1967; Everitt and Herbert, 1969a).

In group situations, the dominant males usually copulate more frequently than less dominant males, and some females seem to mate infrequently (Conaway and Koford, 1965). The less favored females mate with the less dominant males. Sexual preference by individual males for particular females occurs in most species. Baboons and rhesus monkeys form a temporary *consort* relationship which lasts as long as the female remains in estrus. During this time they copulate and sit together, and the female exercises privileges, e.g. access to available food, not allowed by the male at other times. This relationship is ended when the female's estrous phase is over and another female then takes her place (Herbert, 1968). Some males have favorite females whose status is retained regardless of the stage of their menstrual cycle. When the male is caged along with a nonfavorite, he will copulate and groom with her, in contrast to his behavior if the favorite female is present. Thus, the nonfavorite female is sexually attractive only in the absence of the favorite female. It appears that the formation of a consort relationship between a male and female may exclude, for a time, sexual interaction with other females. The degree to which the male, particularly in the rhesus, dominates the female may prevent her from expressing a sexual preference for another male. The rate of mounting by the males is usually highest during the follicular phase of the cycle and lowest during the luteal phase. Ejaculation times are shortest and mounting rates highest near ovulation. Under indoor breeding conditions sexual receptivity can be determined by confirming copulation during the follicular phase of the cycle and pairing only compatible pairs during the ovulatory phase of the cycle.

Pheromones are also important factors in sexual interactions. These substances that are produced by one individual and evoke a response in another, may be secreted by the skin or by specialized glands and exert their effects via sensory receptors. Under laboratory controlled conditions male *Macaca mulatta* rendered anosmic by plugging the nasal olfactory area and by cutting the nerve supply to the organ of Jacobson show no interest in ovariectomized females receiving estrogen intravaginally (Michael and Keverne, 1968). After restoration of olfactory acuity males again demonstrate a preference for females receiving intravaginal estrogen. Application of vaginal secretions from donor females onto the sex skin of ovariectomized females (*M. mulatta*) also evokes male response (Michael and Keverne, 1970).

III. FERTILIZATION FAILURE

Fertilization failure may be the result of death of the ovum before sperm entry, structural or functional abnormality in the ovum or sperm, or it may result from mating either too early or too late in the menstrual cycle. In addition, sexual incompatibility of the females is a factor in fertilization failure. Under laboratory conditions, baboons, rhesus, bonnets, and cynomolgus monkeys may be unreceptive during the estrous phase. This is due in part to sexual incompatibility and in part to the stress of caging, or it may be related to the inhibitory effects of differences in social status. In controlled or timed mating programs, the inability to predict the right day or days for mating due to the variability in cycle length is also a contributing factor.

IV. PRENATAL MORTALITY

A. Embryonic Factors

Prenatal mortality occurs at all stages of gestation. Early embryonic mortality occurs most often before implantation and in decreasing numbers shortly after implantation with a further reduction in incidence during the period of organogenesis. The incidence of early embryonic mortality appears to vary little between species. In the baboon approximately 30 percent of the preimplantation embryos were morphologically abnormal (Hendrickx and Kraemer, 1968). Similar results are observed in the rhesus monkey. Defective segmenting ova are characterized by necrotic blastomeres, multinucleated blastomeres, distortion or malposition of embryonic or trophoblastic blastomeres, and distortion in the overall shape of the morula or blastula. Approximately 15 percent of the postimplantation embryos are abnormal in the baboon (Hendrickx *et al.*, 1970); one of two implantation sites was abnormal in the chimpanzee (Heuser, 1940). This postimplantation period of approximately two weeks includes the period from implantation to the onset of organogenesis. In the postimplantation embryo degenerative changes occur in the form of cellular pyknosis in the embryonic disk, associated membranes, and placental components.

The causative factors leading to early embryonic mortality are difficult to delineate, but several factors merit consideration. The apparent time of ovulation is probably the most important factor leading to defective ova and early mortality. In the baboon mating early or at the optimal time in the ovulatory phase of the cycle resulted in a higher conception and pregnancy rate than mating late in the ovulatory phase of the cycle. Although this is indirect evidence that an intrafollicular oocyte released from the ovary at the optimal time of maturation is more likely to result in a normal offspring, it substantiates to some degree a similar observation made by Hertig (1967) in man. Hertig shows that there is a sevenfold difference in favor of ova developing normally if they are ovulated on or before day fourteen of the cycle in contrast to ovulation after day fourteen. A similar condition may exist for sperm. Aged sperm nearing the end of their fertilizing capability probably produce more defective zygotes than those which are properly capacitated.

No evidence of embryonic mortality is observed in the baboon for the period of organogenesis which begins early in the fourth week and extends through the seventh week of pregnancy. However, abnormal embryos are observed in the rhesus monkey (Padgett, 1968).

B. Congenital Malformations

Developmental malformations represent one of the most obvious malformations of reproductive failure. The incidence of spontaneous congenital malformation is less than 0.5 percent (Wilson and Gavan, 1967, Lapin and Yakovleva, 1963; Hendrickx, 1966; Courtney and Valerio, 1968). The incidence of specific defects is very low; however the types of defects recorded include anencephaly, hydrocephaly, anophthalmia, cutaneous angioma on the face, diaphragmatic hernia, pigmented nevus, subdural hydroma, congenital blindness, hermaphrodism, agenesis of the genitalia, renal malformations, cleft lip, cleft palate, polydactylism, meromelia, amelia and numerous other skeletal defects (Hendrickx and Gasser, 1967; Koford *et al.*, 1966; Maruffo and Cramer, 1967; Schultz, 1956; Sullivan and Drobeck, 1966).

TABLE 15-II

PRIMATES BRED UNDER CONDITIONS PERMITTING DETECTION OF EXTERNAL MALFORMATIONS*

Specific Name	*Number of Deliveries*	*Number Malformed*
Callitrix jacchus	26	0
Erythrocebus patas	4	0
Macaca irus	579	2
Macaca mulatta	1567	6
Macaca nemestrina	40	0
Macaca speciosa	17	0
Oedipomidus oedipus	75	0
Pan troglodytes	172	1
Pango pygmaeus	3	1
Papio sp.	382	2
Saimiri sciurea	77	1
Tupaia chemensis	8	0
Totals	2950	13
Estimated Incidence	0.44%	

* Wilson & Gavan, 1967.

C. Placenta

The involvement of the placenta and umbilical cord in reproductive failure also is made apparent in human studies. Although deficiencies exist in our knowledge of placental abnormality in the nonhuman primate, its role appears to be equally important in all species. Gross placental malformations appear to be infrequent in most primates although in one study five malformations were found in approximately two-hundred cases: three double placentas, one circumvallate placenta, and one placenta with a membranous insertion of the umbilical cord. Two cases of placenta praevia have been reported (Ruch, 1959). In another study a single umbilical artery was observed in the baboon in one of 165 cases (Houston and Hendrickx, 1968). Variations in the transverse communicating artery, the artery between the two umbilical arteries, are commonplace and occur at about the same frequency as reported for man. Variations in lobe size in species with a bidiscoid placenta also occur.

OTHER DISORDERS OF PREGNANCY

A. Stillbirth and Abortion

Stillbirths and abortions remain one of the most common causes of reproductive failure. The incidence may vary with species, parity, season, housing conditions, degree of handling, time in captivity and other factors, but the main causes of abortion and stillbirth are unknown.

The incidence of stillbirth and abortion often are reported as one figure, therefore it is difficult to determine the relative incidence. Furthermore the incidence varies with the laboratory, geographic location, type of caging and other factors. The reported combined incidence for abortion and stillbirth is approximately 15 percent for the rhesus monkey (Valerio *et al.*, 1969b). Lapin and Yakovleva (1963) report an incidence of stillbirth of 12.3 percent in macaques (mainly *M. mulatta*), 13.6 percent in baboons, and 14.6 percent in green marmosets. The incidence is only 5 percent in *C. atys, M. mulatta,* and *M. radiata* and 20 percent in *M. nemestrina (Fig. 15-III)*.

Koford (1965) reports a decrease in the abortion rate in ba-

TABLE 15-III

INCIDENCE OF ABORTION, STILLBIRTH, PREMATURE BIRTHS, AND VIABLE BIRTHS FOR A THREE YEAR PERIOD (1967-69) AT THE NATIONAL CENTER FOR PRIMATE BIOLOGY

Species	*Abortion*	*Stillbirth*	*Premature Birth*	*Normal*	*Total*
Cercocebus atys	4	6	1	40	51
Cercopithecus aethiops	3	3	3	36	45
Macaca irus	45	33	7	115	200
Macaca mulatta	105	36	6	465	612
Macaca nemestrina	35	26	3	96	160
Macaca radiata	33	16	2	125	176
Macaca speciosa	13	8	5	44	70
Semnopithecus entellus	1	3		11	15

boons and macaques over a five year period from 14.1 percent to 4.6 percent. The decrease is attributed to avoiding the restraint of animals in the early stages of pregnancy, avoiding changes in caging environment, and creating conditions most suitable for reproduction. The abortion rate in other species, including macaques, ranges from 4 to 16 percent. The abortion rate is approximately 4 percent in baboons for both indoor and outdoor housing (Hendrickx, 1966).

The incidence of stillbirths and abortions is highest in primigravid animals; it decreases after the first pregnancy and increases again in later pregnancies. The stillbirth rate is higher in winter than in summer, and the rate is lower in pens than in cages. Complications of pregnancy and delivery are lower in monkeys imported than in those born in captivity, and the incidence decreases with time in captivity (Lapin and Yakovleva, 1963). The most frequent cause of stillbirth is traumatic injury of the fetus during parturition. Prolonged gestation may be related to the birth of a dead fetus, but the specific determination of the condition must be based on species with known gestation length and in individual animals with a known gestational age. The fetus may give the appearance of gross enlargement as death and initial maceration may have occurred some time prior to delivery. A conception age of 181 days for *M. mulatta* is used as a routine time for performing surgery on females which have not yet delivered (Pickering, 1966).

The occurrence of early abortion, those occurring during the first fifty days of pregnancy, is difficult to detect clinically, and the reported incidence is often based only on rectal palpation of the uterus. Accurate diagnosis requires familiarity with the history of the animal, especially the size and condition of the uterus and adnexa. Unvisualized abortion, abortion without signs of external bleeding or expulsion of placental or fetal tissue, is fairly common. In one study involving seventeen sexually mature *Saimiri sciureus*, and fifteen *Cebus albifrons*, six of twelve Cebus and nine of eleven Saimiri presumed pregnant carried young to term (Castellanos and McCoombs, 1968). Histologic examination on necropsy specimens from females presumed to have aborted showed changes compatible with the assumption.

B. Dystocia

The high incidence of night births in nonhuman primates in part may account for the low incidence of recognized and reported cases of dystocia. The most obvious causes of dystocia are abnormal size relationships, positional abnormalities, and uterine inertia. Dystocia in the larger nonhuman primates has not been a frequent finding. One case occurred in a thirty-five year old chimpanzee from blockage of the cervix by a uterine fibroid tumor (Guilloud, 1969). Two cases of dystocia secondary to pelvic abnormalities appear in the literature. Deformity from osteomalacia occurred in a Barbary ape *(M. sylvanus)* and a pig-tailed macaque (*M. nemestrina*) (Ruch, 1959). Dystocias related to fetal size and hydramnios have occurred.

The most obvious positional abnormality leading to dystocia in nonhuman primates is facial presentation. The surviving infants have bruised faces and often periorbital edema. Close observation of these animals may reveal an inability to nurse, necessitating removal and tube feeding. Posterior presentation is the second most obvious positional abnormality and may show perineal edema as the only sign. Other presentations generally occur in conjunction with premature births or abortions and may necessitate embryotomy.

Uterine inertia may be primary or secondary. Primary inertia has not been reported in nonhuman primates, but the absence of normal uterine contractions in domestic animals is associated with lack of exercise, excessive fat, twins or multiple pregnancy, and increasing age. Secondary uterine inertia either follows or results from prolonged labor. Initiating factors may be malposition, maternal pelvic abnormalities, and cephalo-pelvic disproportion.

C. Neonatal Mortality

Prematurity is one of the major factors contributing to neonatal mortality. Criteria to use in establishing a prematurity index include weight, development of haircoat, and degree of activity (Valerio *et al.*, 1969a). Weights regarded as depicting prematurity for infants of various species at the National Center for Primate Biology are as follows:

	less than
Cercopithecus aethiops	250 gm.
Cercocebus atys	450 "
Macaca irus	250 "
Macaca mulatta	300 "
Macaca radiata	250 "
Macaca speciosa	300 "
Semnopithecus entellus	500 "

Deaths among infants in reduced gestation groups occur most often during the first week of life and in general are related to immature respiratory systems (Pickering, 1966).

Premature labor may occur in twin pregnancies; however, delivery at term of both offspring in a viable state is possible. The incidence of twinning varies considerably in the different genera. In the *Tupaiiformes* and in *Microcebus* the number of young at birth varies between one and four, one being found very rarely (Schultz, 1956). Lemurs may have one to three offspring at a time (Petter-Rousseaux, 1964). In the prosimian genera *Lemur, Loris* and *Galago,* multiple births occur less frequently than single births. There appear to be subspecific differences in the incidence of twin births in *Galagos* with twin births being common to *Galago senegalensis moholi* and twin births rare in *Galago senegalensis senegalensis* and *Galago senegalensis braccatus* (Doyle *et al.,* 1967). Twinning occurs in the Capuchin monkey (*Cebus sp.*), *Alouatta,* and the *Callithricidae* frequently have twins and occasionally triplets.

The *Cercopithecidae* (Old World monkeys) and apes are normally monovulatory species. However twins and even triplets do occur. The reported incidence of twinning in Old World Monkeys varies between species and colonies. The incidence of twinning in baboons in approximately 0.23 percent to 0.50 percent (Lapin and Yakovleva, 1963; Hendrickx *et al.,* 1968) and approximately 0.26 percent to 1.0 percent for rhesus monkeys (Lapin and Yakovleva, 1963; van Wagenen and Asling, 1964; Koford, Farber and Windle, 1966). Of the seven pairs of twins recorded by the authors (1 pair in 56 births for *Cercopithecus atys,* none in 269 births for *Macaca irus,* four pairs in 840 births for *Macaca mulatta,* one pair in 199 births for *Macaca radiata,* one pair in eighty-two births for

Macaca speciosa) four were aborted or stillborn. Two pairs from *Macaca mulatta* were aborted late in gestation, one set being male-female and the other both females; the *Macaca speciosa* twins were found at necropsy early in gestation, and one *Macaca radiata* female gave birth to female twins, one alive and one dead. Twinning also occurs in *Cynopithecus, Cercopithecus,* and *Nasalis* (Schultz, 1956).

Twin births in apes are very rare. Gorilla twins were born alive in the Frankfurt Zoo, the first report of such an event in captivity although gorilla twins were aborted in the Kansas City Zoo (Kirchshofer, *et al.,* 1968). There are no records of gorilla females nursing twins in the wild. There are records of seven twin births for chimpanzees and one triplet birth at Yerkes Regional Primate Research Center. All have occurred in captivity and the young had to be hand-reared. It is questionable whether ape mothers are able to feed and care for twins.

Stillbirths, aglactia, and cannibalism by the male were the major problems encountered in breeding *Tupaia glis* and *Tupaia tana* in zoos. Infant tree shrews in captivity have high mortality rates, which is often due to maternal abandonment and carnivorous actions of the mother or other adults (Conaway and Sorenson, 1966; National Academy of Sciences, 1968). In squirrel monkeys, deaths of infants in the perinatal period may be lessened significantly by waiting forty-eight hours following parturition before handling the mother in order to examine the infant (Bantin, 1969). Prematurity, stillbirths, and rejection of the young occur in most species. In addition to the more common species used in laboratories reports are available for the Colobus monkey, black-faced spider monkey, and lar gibbon, and gorilla.

A hemolytic disease resembling erythroblastosis fetalis occurs in marmosets and is related to the interbreeding of the subspecies of *Saguinus fusciocollis* (Gengozian, 1969). Megaloblastic anemia of pregnancy is common in captive squirrel monkeys (Rosenblum, 1968). Supplementation of the diet with folic acid for approximately the last nine weeks of pregnancy reduces fetal loss, but does not entirely correct the problem. Low rates of absorption of folic acid may be the basic difficulty in eliminating the problem.

VI. PATHOLOGY

Information on pathology of the reproductive tract leading to reproductive failure is limited.

A. Malposition and Rupture

Natural cervical and uterine malposition is observed infrequently in nonhuman primates. Cervical prolapse occurs at a relatively low incidence, and it usually is in conjunction with pregnancy. Prolapsed uterus, while it occurs fairly commonly in species of domestic animals, occurs comparatively infrequently in nonhuman primates. Thirty years of breeding in Russia yielded one case out of 1,693 births (Lapin and Yakovleva, 1963); the present authors have seen one case in 1,190 rhesus births. Uterine torsion occurred in a pregnant baboon and led to its death two days following a physical examination (Lapin and Yakovleva, 1963). In the same colony over a six year period, three out of 715 births led to uterine rupture (2 of 352 births in baboons, 1 of 286 births in macaques). Ruptures occurred at the cervico-uterine junction and were attributable to cephalo-pelvic disproportion. In the case occurring in the macaques, rupture was secondary to a retained placenta and was situated basally on the uterus. Of four uterine ruptures observed by the authors, two cases in *M. mulatta* were along previous cesarian section scars, while the cases in a *M. nemestrina* and a *Cercocebus atys* were spontaneous. Ruptures occur dorsal to the broad ligament in nonpregnant uteri with retrograde flushing (Hartman, 1944).

B. Extrauterine Pregnancy

Extrauterine pregnancies also occur infrequently. Incidence in one colony has been three out of 1,892 pregnancies and occurred in a rhesus monkey, a baboon (*Papio hamadryas*), and a green marmoset (Lapin, Yakovleva, 1963). Abdominal ectopic pregnancy in a rhesus monkey resulted in survival of mother and infant following surgical termination of the pregnancy (Pickering, 1966).

C. Endometriosis

The increasing frequency of reported cases of endometriosis in recent years probably results from increasing awareness of the problem. Old reports include four cases in *M. mulatta* and one case in *M. irus;* two were asymptomatic, one had dysmenorrhea, and two had received dienestrol (Ruch, 1959). Examinations of 493 genital tracts yielded five cases of endometriosis (Lapin and Yakovleva, 1963). In animals with previous cesarian sections, reproductive failure and malaise may be related to the development of endometriosis. In one study nine of eleven infertile animals developed debilitating bowel obstructions within five years following surgery (Pickering, 1966). Widespread endometriosis occurred in a rhesus monkey with a history of irradiation but no abdominal surgery (McClure *et al.,* 1969). Twenty-one additional cases from a single colony included many found only on microscopic examination. Coincident reproductive disease included endometrial and endocervical polyps, uterine leiomyomas, and mucinous cystadenoma of the ovary (McCann and Myers, 1970). In a control group of animals without endometriosis, reproductive tract disease included two uterine leiomyomas, three endometrial polyps, and five functional ovarian cysts. In a study involving *Cercopithecus aethiops aethiops,* two animals of unknown age had polymenorrhea and menorrhagia. Gross abnormalities of the ovary and endometrium were observed but no histological examination followed (Butler, 1967). The appearance did not parallel that of endometriosis. Cystic endometrial hyperplasia has not occurred spontaneously in nonhuman primates, but is inducible through estrogen stimulation and may lead to endometrial polyps with prolonged bleeding (Ruch, 1959). Benign cervical and uterine polyps may lead to varying signs of reproductive abnormality. Vaginal abnormalities such as hyperkeratosis and papillomatosis remain etiologically obscure (Lapin and Yakovleva, 1963). Other abnormalities of the female reproductive tract include cystic ovaries, (2 cases in gibbons secondary to the filaria *Tetrape talonema digitate).* (Ruch, 1959), an aberrant ovary in a baboon, pelvic fat causing genital prolapse in a mandrill as well as infantile uteri and ovaries (van Wagenen, 1945b).

D. Neoplasm

Although the exact effect of neoplastic changes in the reproductive tract has not appeared in the literature, some will affect reproductive efficiency. Lapin and Yakovleva (1963) reported one malignant tumor, an ovarian sarcoma, in a baboon, while Valerio (1969b) found a granulosa cell tumor as the only tumor in a six year period. Reports of mammary gland pathology have been infrequent and generally associated with experimental procedures such as ovariectomy and administration of estrogenic compounds (Ruch 1959). There have been two reports of spontaneous mammary gland cancer.

Reports of abnormalities of the male reproductive system appear infrequently. Prostatic enlargement and a primary prostatic carcinoma have been reported for the *Macaca mulatta* (Ruch, 1959). Eunuchoidism in a *Comopithecus hamadryas* and *M. mulatta* as well as a number of cases of cryptorchidism have also been reported. A report of primary sterility in a *Lemur fulvus rutus* resulting from abnormal cellular changes of spermatocytes, spermatogonia, and Sertoli cells and a report of testicular atrophy in a gorilla also have appeared. Pseudohermaphrodism as a spontaneous malformation has not been reported, although experimental induction occurs with testosterone injections during pregnancy. The occurrence of true hermaphrodites and freemartins have not been reported for nonhuman primates. A study on the effects of immobilization on *M. nemestrina* testicles show that beginning degenerative changes of Sertoli cells and spermatogonia A occur in seven days and that the changes following two weeks of immobilization are reversed sixty days after release (Zemjanis, 1970).

REFERENCES

Ball, J. and Hartman, C. G. (1935): Sexual excitability as related to the menstrual cycle in the monkey. *Amer J Obstet Gynec, 29,* 117-119.

Bantin, G. C. (1969): Reproduction in the squirrel monkey (*Saimiri sciureus*). *J Inst Anim Tech, 20,* 83-90.

Butler, H. (1967): Seasonal breeding of the senegal Galago (*Galago senegalensis senegalensis*) in the Nuba Mountains, Republic of the Sudan. *Folia Primat, 5,* 165-175.

Carpenter, C. R. (1942): Sexual behaviour of free-ranging rhesus monkeys

(*Macaca mulatta*). I. Specimens, procedures and behavioral characteristics of estrus. *J Comp Psychol, 33,* 113-142.

Castellanos, H., and McCombs, H. L. (1968): The reproductive cycle of the New World monkey; Gynecologic problems in a breeding colony. *Fertil Steril, 19,* 213-227.

Conaway, C. H., and Koford, C. B. (1965): Estrous cycles and mating behavior in a free-ranging band of rhesus monkeys. *J Mammal, 45,* 577-588.

Conaway, C. H. and Sorenson, M. W. (1966): Reproduction in tree shrews. In Rowlands, I. W. (Ed.): Comparative biology of reproduction in mammals. New York, Academic Press, pp. 471-492.

Courtney, K. D., and Valerio, D. A. (1968): Teratology in the *Macaca mulatta. Teratology, 1,* 163-172.

Doyle, G. A.; Pelletier, A., and Bekker, T. (1967): Courtship, mating and parturition in the lesser bushbaby (*Galago senegalensis moholi*) under seminatural conditions. *Folia Primat, 7,* 169-197.

DuMond, F. V. (1968): The squirrel monkey in a seminatural environment. In Rosenblum, and Cooper (Eds.): *The Squirrel Monkey*. New York, Academic Press, pp. 88-146.

Everitt, B. J., and Herbert, J. (1969a): Adrenal glands and sexual receptivity in female rhesus monkeys. *Nature, 22,* 1065-1066.

Everitt, B. J., and Herbert, J. (1969b): The role of ovarian hormones in the sexual preference of rhesus monkeys. *Anim Behav, 17,* 738-746.

Gengozian, N. (1969): Marmosets: Their potential in experimental medicine. *Ann NY Acad Sci, 162,* 336-362.

Guilloud, N. B. (1969): The breeding of apes: Experience at the Yerkes Regional Primate Research Center and a brief review of the literature. *Ann NY Acad Sci, 162,* 297-299.

Hartman, C. G. (1932): Studies in the reproduction of the monkey macacus (*Pithecus*) rhesus, with special reference to menstruation and pregnancy. *Contrib Embryol Carnegie Inst Washington, DC,* 23, 1-161.

Hartman, C. G. (1944): Recovery of primate eggs and embryos. *West J Surg Obstet Gynec, 2,* 41-61.

Hendrickx, A. G. (1966): Teratological findings in a baboon colony. *Proceedings: Conference on Nonhuman Primate Toxicology*. Washington, D.C., Food & Drug Administration, pp. 120-123.

Hendrickx, A. G., and Gasser, R. F. (1967): A description of a diaphragmatic hernia in a sixteen week baboon fetus (*Papio sp.*). *Folia Primat, 7,* 66-74.

Hendrickx, A. G., and Kriewaldt, F. H. (1967): Observations of a controlled breeding colony of baboons. In Vagtborg, H. (Ed.): *The Baboon in Medical Research*. Austin, University of Texas Press, 2, pp. 69-83.

Hendrickx, A. G., and Kraemer, D. C. (1968): Preimplantation stages of baboon embryos (*Papio sp.*). *Anat Rec 162,* 111-120.

Hendrickx, A. G.; Houston, M. L., and Kraemer, D. C. (1968): Observations on twin baboon embryos (*Papio sp.*). *Anat Rec, 160,* 181-186.

Hendrickx, A. G.; Houston, M. L.; Kraemer, D. C.: Gasser, R. F., and Bollert, J. A. (1970): Embryology of the baboon. Chicago, University of Chicago Press.

Herbert, J. (1968): Sexual preference in the rhesus monkey *Macaca mulatta* in the laboratory. *Anim Behav, 16,* 120-128.

Herbert, J., and Trimble, M. R. (1967): Effect of oestradiol and testosterone on the sexual receptivity and attractiveness of the female rhesus monkey. *Nature, 216,* 165-166.

Hertig, A. T. (1967): The overall problem in man, In Benirschke, K. (Ed.): *Comparative Aspects of Reproductive Failure.* New York, Springer-Verlag, pp. 12-43.

Heuser, C. H. (1940): The chimpanzee ovum in the early stages of implantation. *J Morph, 66,* 155-173.

Hopf, S. (1967): Notes on pregnancy, delivery and infant survival in captive squirrel monkeys. *Primates, 8,* 323-332.

Houston, M. L., and Hendrickx, A. G. (1968): Observations on the vasculature of the baboon placenta (*Papio sp.*) with special reference to the transverse communicating artery. *Folia Primat, 9,* 68-77.

Hummer, R. L.; May, H. C., and Knight, W. K. (1969): Observations during the first year of operation of a chimpanzee breeding colony. In Hofer, H. O. (Ed.): *Recent Advances in Primatology.* Basel & New York, Karger, chap. 2, pp. 1-8.

Kirchshafer, R.; Weisse, K.; Brenz, K., and Klose, L. (1968): A preliminary account of the physical and behavioral development during the first 10 weeks of the hand-reared gorilla twins born at Frankfurt Zoo. In Jarvis, C. (Ed.): *Inter Zoo Yearbook, 8,* 121-128.

Koford, C. B. (1965): Population dynamics of rhesus monkeys on Cayo Santiago. In Devore, I. (Ed.): *Primate Behavior.* pp. 160-174.

Koford, C. B.; Farber, P. A., and Windle, W. F. (1966): Twins and teratisms in rhesus monkeys. *Folia Primat, 4,* 221-226.

Kriewaldt, F. H., and Hendrickx, A. G. (1968): Reproductive parameters of the baboon. *Lab Anim Care 18,* 361-370.

Lang, C. M. (1967): The oestrous cycle of the squirrel monkey (*Saimiri sciureus*), *Lab Anim Care, 17,* 442-451.

Lapin, B. A., and Yakovleva, L. A. (1963): Comparative pathology in monkeys. U.S. Joint Publ. Res. Service, transl. Thomas, Springfield, pp. 209-235.

Maruffo, C. A., and Cramer, D. L. (1967): Congenital renal malformations in monkeys. *Folia Primat, 5,* 305-311.

McCann, T. O., and Myers, R. E. (1970): Endometriosis in rhesus monkeys. *Amer J Obset Gynec, 106,* 516-523.

McClure, H. M.; Graham, C. E., and Guilloud, N. B. (1969): Widespread endometriosis in a rhesus monkey (*Macaca mulatta*). *Proc 2nd Inter Cong Primat, 3,* 155-161.

Michael, R. P. (1965): Some aspects of the endocrine control of sexual activity in primates. *Proc Roy Soc Med, 58,* 595-598.

Michael, R. P.; Herbert, J., and Welegalla, J. (1966): Ovarian hormones and grooming behaviour in the rhesus monkey (Macaca mulatta) under laboratory conditions. *J. Endocr, 36,* 263-279.

Michael, R. P.; Herbert, J., and Welegalla, J. (1967): Ovarian hormones and the sexual behaviour of the male rhesus monkey (*Macaca mulatta*) under laboratory conditions. *J Endocr, 39,* 81-98.

Michael, R. P., and Saayman, G. (1967): Individual differences in the sexual behaviour of male rhesus monkeys (*Macaca mulatta*) under laboratory conditions. *Anim Behav, 15,* 460-466.

Michael, R. P.; Saayman, G., and Zumpe, D. (1967): Sexual attractiveness and receptivity in rhesus monkeys. *Nature (London), 215,* 554-556.

Michael, R. P.; Saayman, G., and Zumpe, D. (1968): The suppression of mounting behaviour and ejaculation in male rhesus monkeys *(Macaca mulatta)* by administration of progesterone to their female partners. *J Endocr, 41,* 421-431.

Michael, R. P., and Keverne, E. B. (1968): Pheromones in the communication of sexual status in primates. *Nature (London), 218,* 746-749.

Michael, R. P., and Welegalla, J. (1968): Ovarian hormones and the sexual behaviour of the female rhesus monkey (*Macaca mulatta*) under laboratory conditions. *J Endocr, 41,* 407-420.

Michael, R. P., and Plant, T. M. (1969): Contraceptive steroids and sexual activity. *Nature (London), 222,* 579-581.

Michael, R. P., and Keverne, E. B. (1970): Primate sex pheromones of vaginal origin. *Nature (London), 225,* 84-85.

National Academy of Sciences (1968): *Nonhuman Primates: Standards and Guidelines for the Breeding, Care and Management of Laboratory Animals.* No. 1677, Washington, D.C.

Padget, D. H. (1968): Spina bifida and embryonic neuroschisis—A causal relationship. *Johns Hopkins Med J, 123,* 233-252.

Pickering, D. E. (1966): The laboratory—confined mulatta macaque monkey. Reproduction characteristics. *Proceedings: Conference on Nonhuman Primate Toxicology.* Washington, D.C., Food and Drug Administration, pp. 102-113.

Petter-Rousseaux, A. (1964): Reproductive physiology and behaviour of the Lemuroidea. In Buettner-Janusch, J. (Ed.): Evolutionary and Genetic Biology of Primates. New York, Academic Press, vol. II, pp. 91-132.

Rosenblum, L. A. (1968): Some aspects of female reproductive physiology in the squirrel monkey. In Rosenblum, and Cooper (Ed.): New York, Academic Press, pp. 147-170.

Ruch, T. C. (1959): Diseases of the endocrine, reproductive, and urinary systems. In *Diseases of Laboratory Primates.* Philadelphia, Saunders, pp. 443-471.

Schultz, A. H. (1956): The occurrence and frequency of pathological and teratological conditions and of twinning among nonhuman primates. *Folia Primat, 1,* 965-1014.

Sorenson, M. W., and Conaway, C. H. (1968): The social and reproductive behaviours of *Tupaia montana* in captivity. *J Mammal, 49,* 502-512.

Sullivan, D. J., and Drobeck, H. P. (1966): True Hermaphrodism in a rhesus monkey. *Folia Primat, 4,* 309-317.

Valerio, D. A.; Pallotta, A. J., and Courtney, K. D. (1969a): Experiences in large-scale breeding of simians for medical experimentation. *Ann NY Acad Sci 162,* Art 1, 282-296.

Valerio, D. A.; Miller, R. L.; Innes, J. R. M.; Courtney, K. D.; Pallotta, A. J., and Guttmacher, R. M. (1969b): *Macaca mulatta: Management of a Breeding Colony.* New York, Academic Press, pp. 59-78.

van Wagenen, G. (1945a): Optimal mating time for pregnancy in the monkey. *Endocrinology, 37,* 307-312.

van Wagenen, G. (1945b): Mating in relation to pregnancy in the monkey. *Yale J Biol Med, 17,* 745-760.

van Wagenen, G. (1970): Menopause in a subhuman primate. *Anat Rec, 166,* 392.

van Wagenen, G., and Asling, C. W. (1964): Ossification in the fetal monkey (*Macaca mulatta*). Estimation of age and progress of gestation by roentgenography. *Amer J Anat, 114,* 107-132.

Wilson, J. G., and Gavan, J. A. (1967): Congenital malformations in nonhuman primates: Spontaneous and experimentally induced. *Anat Rec, 158,* 99-110.

Zemjanis, R.; Gondos, B.; Adey, W. R., and Cockett, A. T. K. (1970): Testicular degeneration in *Macaca nemestrina* induced by immobilization. *Fertil Steril, 21,* 335-340.

Chapter 16

INFECTIOUS DISEASES INFLUENCING REPRODUCTION

D. C. KRAEMER AND N. C. VERA CRUZ

I. NONGENITAL INFECTIONS

NONHUMAN primates are subject to many infectious diseases (Ruch, 1959; Lapin and Yakovelva, 1963; Fiennes, 1967) which do not directly influence the reproductive organs, but which nevertheless have indirect influence on reproduction. These effects may be mediated via the hypothalamus, pituitary, and/or adrenal glands. They may result from circulating toxins produced by the infectious agent or from elevated body temperature, altered blood circulation or by combinations of these and other factors. The type of influence which is exerted upon the reproductive process by a nongenital infection depends, at least in part, upon the location, severity and duration of the infectious process. Diseases such as influenza which cause nausea and depression may only temporarily decrease libido, whereas a protracted infectious diarrhea with accompanying malnutrition and dehydration may disrupt the menstrual cycle or decrease the rate of spermatogenesis. Although debilitating diseases such as pneumonia and malaria are not considered reproductive diseases, they do, as is the case with every potentially fatal disease, influence the reproductive process at some point as they progress. These influences are seldom recorded except in cases of abortion, because the primary concern is generally for survival of the animal rather than for such a specialized function as reproduction.

II. VIRAL INFECTIONS

Evidence linking viruses with congenital and/or teratogenic abnormalities, abortions and stillbirths in nonhuman primates and a variety of laboratory and domestic animals has been reviewed (Wilson and Gavan, 1967; Elizan and Fabiyi, 1970). Of the various viruses reviewed for their ability to affect the fetus of man and various animal models, only rubella virus and cytomegalovirus affect man and only rubella is known to affect nonhuman primates.

A. Rubella

Common laboratory primates, *Erythrocebus patas* (Sigurdardottir *et al.,* 1963; Draper and Laurence, 1969) *Macaca mulatta* (Parkman *et al.,* 1965; Sever *et al.,* 1966) and *Papio cynocephalus* (Hendrickx, 1966), share with man a susceptibility to wild and attenuated strains of rubella virus.

M. mulatta and *M. fascicularis* experimentally infected with rubella virus at various stages of pregnancy show high incidences of fetal size reduction, fetal mortality, stillbirths and abortions (Table 16-I) in addition to otic, cutaneous, chorionic, osseous and vascular abnormalities. The virus affects the products of conception, often involving the placenta. Fetal abnormality, mortality and

TABLE 16-I

EXPERIMENTAL TRANSMISSION OF RUBELLA VIRUS IN PREGNANT M. MULATTA AND M. FASCICULARIS*

Species	*State of Gestation*	*Route of Administration*	*Effects*
M. mulatta	28–133 days	Intravenous or intramuscular	Successful experimental transplacental transmission; limited intrauterine infection.
M. mulatta	—	Intravenous	Successful experimental transplacental transmission; no evidence of fetal infection.
M. mulatta	20–44 days	Intravenous, intramuscular and/or intranasal; topical eye application	Lens changes; otic, cutaneous chorionic and osseous lesions; reduced fetal size; high incidence of abortion.
M. fascicularis		Not specified	9 abortions, 3 had cataracts and 3 normals out of 14.
M. mulatta	1st trimester	Intra-amniotic	1 premature stillbirth, 1 stillbirth delivered 3 wks. post-term; 1 term fetus which died (abnormal arterial communication; 1 normal out of 4.

* From Parkman *et al.*, 1965; Sever *et al.*, 1966; and Delahunt, 1966.

TABLE 16-II

EFFECTS OF RUBELLA INOCULATIONS IN PREGNANT BABOONS*

Treatment	*Case No.*	*Day of Treatment (Fertilization Age)*	*Results*
	1	49	abortion 4 days postinoculation
	2	49	abortion 7 days postinoculation
5 cc rubella	3	63	abortion 7 days postinoculation
$GML_{20}VK_3$ $10^{-3.5}$, inoculated I.V.	4	30	caesarean section 8 days postinoculation; embryo appeared normal but showed signs of autolysis
	5	98	postnatal death
	6	23	caesarian delivery at term; died 7 days postnatally
	7	32	abortion 4 days after exposure
airborne	8	98	stillbirth (3 weeks overdue)
exposure	9	63	normal infant (living)

* (*P. cynocephalus*) (Hendrickx, 1966)

abortions are more frequent when animals are infected early in pregnancy.

Experimental infection of pregnant baboons (Hendrickx, 1966) increases the incidence of abortions and stillbirths when animals are inoculated with the virus intravenously and perhaps when exposed, by air-borne passage, to inoculated animals (Table 16-II). The incidence of abortions and stillbirths in *P. cynocephalus* compares closely with that in *M. mulatta* (Delahunt, 1966).

B. Cytomegalovirus

The cytomegaloviruses (CMV, cytomegalic inclusion disease virus, salivary gland virus) are classified among herpesviruses. These viruses induce a rapidly fatal generalized infection and increased intrauterine deaths in mice (Henson *et al.*, 1966; Medearis, 1964a) and reproductive failure in man (Medearis, 1967) as a result of fetal infection which "probably occurs secondary to viremia and diaplacental passage of the virus." Cytomegaloviruses are highly species-specific (Medearis, 1967; Kalter, 1969) and do not, in general, cross-react with CMV from other species. However, a cross reaction between a vervet cytomegalovirus and human strains has been reported (Black *et al.*, 1963). As early as 1935, Cowdry and Scott reported extranuclear inclusion bodies suggestive of

TABLE 16-III

HUMAN AND SIMIAN VIRUS ANTIBODIES IN PRIMATES: COMPLEMENT FIXATION AND SERUM NEUTRALIZATION RESULTS WITH HERPES SIMPLEX, B-VIRUS AND MYCOPLASMA†

	*Herpes**		*B-virus**		*Mycoplasma**	
Source of Serum	*No. of Sera Tested*	*% Positive*	*No. of Sera Tested*	*% Positive*	*No. of Sera Tested*	*% Positive*
Homo sapien	136**	7	25	52	110	16
Gorilla gorilla	1	nil	1	nil	1	100
Pan sp.	51	2	67	13	51	27
Pongo pygmaeus	27	nil	29	3	27	19
Hylobates	9	nil	9	nil	9	33
Papio sp.	138	5	199	49	90	17
Cercopithecus pygerythrus	22	nil	126	48	22	18
Macaca mulatta	44	nil	19	11	44	18

* CF Test
** SN Test
† (After Kalter *et al.*, 1967; Kalter, 1969).

CMV in the cebus monkey (*C. fatuellas*). A comprehensive survey of primate sera for antibodies to viruses of man and simians (Kalter *et al.*, 1967; Kalter, 1969) reveals that herpes-type viruses are present in a wide variety of nonhuman primate species as well as in man (Table 16-III). An attempt to produce cytomegalovirus infections in pregnant *M. mulatta* was unsuccessful (Medearis, 1964b).

C. Other Viruses

M. mulatta fetuses are susceptible to tumor formation following *in utero* inoculation with Rous sarcoma virus (Berman *et al.*, 1967). Intravenous inoculation appears to cause a higher incidence of abortion and embryo mortality than does intramuscular injection. Some fetuses with tumors survive to term and the tumors tend to regress spontaneously after birth. Adenovirus type 12 given to pregnant *P. cynocephalus* and *M. mulatta* by amnioinjection does not produce tumors, but does produce abortions in *P. cynocephalus* (Cotes, 1965; Kalter *et al.*, 1967). Trachoma and Inclusion Conjunctivitis (TRIC) virus from cervixes of infected women causes trachoma in infant baboons and *M. cyclopis* and also cervicitis in pregnant *M. cyclopis*. The experimental cervical infections however do not produce eye lesions in the offspring. Interestingly, there is increased susceptibility of these offspring to eye inoculations (Alexander and Chiang, 1967). Mumps, herpes simplex, rubeola, vaccinia, western equine encephalitis, chicken pox, smallpox and coxsackie B viruses have been implicated in reproductive failure in man, but none of these viruses have yet been implicated in nonhuman primate reproductive failure.

Many other viruses, while capable of altering fetal development in laboratory rodents and certain domestic animals have not been studied in nonhuman primates. However, as interest broadens in this area, the role of viruses in reproduction will be further elucidated. Viral surveys (Kalter *et al.*, 1967; Kalter, 1969; Gajdusek *et al.*, 1969) are major contributions to progress in this area. The latter's finding of a strain of chimpanzee virus (CV 52) which belongs to the Para 2 group of viruses (simian foamy virus 7) in the testes of a chimpanzee is noteworthy, although the implication relative to reproduction is not yet fully understood.

III. MYCOPLASMA INFECTIONS

Mycoplasma organisms are commonly found in the human urogenital tract. Although T-strain mycoplasms are as yet not definitely associated with genital infections, some species of mycoplasms are frequently associated with venereal disease, urethritis, cervicitis and other inflammatory diseases of the reproductive tract. Four cases of human infection with pleuropneumonia-like-organisms (PPLO) have been described: two of puerperal sepsis, one pyosalpinx, and one postoperative empyema (Stokes, 1955). The presence of *Mycoplasma hominis* in the blood of patients with febrile illness following therapeutic abortion has been described (Tully *et al.*, 1965; Tully and Smith, 1968). *M. hominis* septicemia was associated with spontaneous abortion and the organism was isolated from both the blood and cervical discharge of the mother and the liver of the fetus (Harwick *et al.*, 1967). Antibody to *M. hominis* is more frequent in patients after delivery or abortion (Jones, 1967a; 1967b; Tully *et al.*, 1965; Tully and Smith, 1968). The organism has also been isolated from an aborted fetus (Hayflick and Stanbridge, 1967; Jones, 1967a) and the lung of a stillborn infant (Pease *et al.,* 1967) and the placenta (Jones and Tobin, 1969). In cases where the organism was found in the aborted fetal tissues, placentitis was observed as part of the pathological process.

Antibodies to another species of PPLO (*M. pneumoniae*) occur in many species of nonhuman primate sera (Table 16-III). Results of a comprehensive survey on chimpanzees also reveal a high incidence of antibodies to PPLO (Kalter and Guilloud, 1970).

Madden *et al.,* (1970a), recovered mycoplasma, predominantly *M. orale II, M. salivarium,* and *M. hominis I* from 105 of the 920 specimens obtained from fifty-five conditioned, pregnant *M. mulatta.* No signs of disease were observed in these monkeys, but this does not insure that these species of mycoplasma are entirely nonpathogenic for these animals under all conditions. Several species of mycoplasmas were also isolated from *C. aethiops* within three weeks of capture (Madden *et al.,* 1970b). The predominant species isolated was *M. orale II. M. salivarium* and *M. laidlawii* were also isolated. The recovery of these organisms in animals soon after being captured suggests that they may have been present in the "wild" population.

Mycoplasma were isolated from 173 of 395 samples from various orifices (throat, nose, rectum and vagina) of nonhuman primates

TABLE 16-IV

THE INCIDENCE OF COMPLEMENT-FIXING ANTIBODY TO MYCOPLASMA PNEUMONIAE*

Species	*No. Tested*	*% Positive*
Homo sapien	86	16
Gorilla gorilla	14	7
Callitrix	39	3
Pan sp.	239	18
Cercopithecus talapoin	21	48
Pongo pygmaeus	74	16
Hylobates	9	33
Papio sp.	271	30
Cercopithecus sabaeus	47	11
Macaca mulatta	89	24
Erythrocebus patas patas	48	13
Macaca fascicularis	18	6

* (From Hutchison *et al.*, 1970).

(*P. cynocephalus, Cercopithecus sabaeus, M. mulatta* and *Pan troglodytes*). Identification attempts using growth-inhibition test and selected antisera (*M. pneumoniae, M. hominis T-1, M. orale 1, M. salivarium, M. fermentens* and *simian strain #698*) were negative (Hutchison *et al.,* 1970). Metabolic inhibition tests, however, demonstrated the presence of carbohydrate-fermenting and non-fermenting types. Serologically, using the complement-fixation test, it was demonstrated that a sizable number of these isolates had some antibodies common to *M. pneumoniae* (Table 16-IV). The isolation of mycoplasma species from two aborted chimpanzee fetuses is also noteworthy. However, a causal relationship between mycoplasms and nonhuman primate abortions remains in question.

IV. BACTERIAL INFECTIONS

A. Brucellosis

Although a worldwide infectious disease affecting a wide variety of mammalian species including man, brucellosis is not prevalent in nonhuman primates. In a survey (Kalter *et al.,* 1968), positive serology to *B. abortus* was seen in the sera of eight out of seventy-two *P. cynocephalus*. Brucella antibody was also detected in two of seventeen *Pan troglodytes* and in three of seventeen *Pongo pygmaeus*. No brucella antibodies were found in *M. mulatta, Cercopithecus pygerythrus* or *Gorilla gorilla.*

B. Vibriosis

Another bacterial infection which causes a great deal of reproductive wastage in many species of domestic animals is caused by *Vibrio fetus.* As with many reproductive disorders, very little has been published on this disease in laboratory primates. Serological studies on 212 *P. papio* in France revealed 192 animals to have antibodies agglutinating *V. fetus* (Jacotot and Vallee, 1960). At the same time, the sera of the monkeys were screened for brucella antibodies. Reactions were all negative. Vibrio organisms have been isolated from the abdominal fluid of one adult female *M. mulatta* which showed clinical signs of lethargy, weight loss and slight chronic diarrhea (Valerio *et al.* 1969). The clinical factors observed and the frequency of occurrence in the nonhuman primate appear to be completely different from those observed in other animal species. Vibrio infections of nonhuman primates are still poorly defined.

C. Leptospirosis

Of the many species of leptospira, the species *L. pomona* has been implicated in reproductive failure in domestic animals (Fennestad and Borg-Peterson, 1958). So far, this species has not been linked to disorders of reproduction of nonhuman primates and man (Lawson and Michna, 1966). However, another species belonging to this genus has been suspected of being involved in reproductive disorders in the nonhuman primate. In 1965 to 1966, an extensive epidemic of *Leptospira ballum* infection occurred at the baboon colony at the Southwest Foundation for Research and Education (Fear *et al.,* 1968). Associated with the outbreak was a significant rise in the incidence of abortions and stillbirths among pregnant *P. cynocephalus.* On hematological screening, the females which aborted showed mild leucocytosis, and approximately 25 percent of the group showed monocytosis. Monocytosis, however, is also present in about one-fourth of normal females near term. The relationship of monocytosis to leptospirosis is therefore questionable. Culture of samples from the aborted fetuses failed to show leptospira organisms, thus, there is no direct evidence to implicate leptospira with the abortions.

D. Puerperal sepsis

An early report describes the occurrence of puerperal sepsis in which infection was by way of the vagina, then through the cervix and oviduct which caused peritonitis and septicemia in a baboon (Brooks and Blair, 1903). No bacteriologic studies were conducted, however. Puerperal sepsis was observed in a chimpanzee in which streptococci were seen in the vaginal smears at approximately five and one-half months antepartum. Autopsy of the animal when she died fifteen days postpartum revealed pronounced uterine infection (Tinklepaugh, 1932).

E. *Staphylococcal infections*

Staphylococcus aureus has been implicated as a pathogen in cases of abortions and stillbirths, but no causative relationship has been established (Valerio *et al.,* 1969). Staphylococcal infections are found infrequently in laboratory primates. For instance, in a colony of 1500 animals only one animal, an *Erythrocebus patas* was observed to be infected with *Staphylococcus aureus.* At necropsy, abcesses were found in the lungs, liver, spleen and mesentery of the small intestine, and the ureters were swollen and filled with purulent material (Vickers, 1962). *S. aureus* and *Actinomyces sp.* were isolated from a *M. mulatta* with acute pyometra and hemopurulent vaginal discharge (Lang and Benjamin, 1969).

F. *Syphilis*

Apparently, simians are not naturally infected with *Treponema pallidum* (Ruch, 1959), the spirochete which is the causative agent of syphilis in man. Experimentally, however, various nonhuman primate species have been infected with the disease. In 1904, Zabolotnyi inoculated a *Mandrillus sphinx* with human infective material. A solid chancre developed at the site of inoculation. Secondary signs of syphilis were also observed. Four passages were made on animals of the same genus and positive results were also obtained. In another attempt to produce syphilis experimentally in laboratory primates, a *M. sphinx* inoculated with the serous liquid from a lesion of a syphilitic chimpanzee was observed to be refractory, whereas a young *P. hamadryas* inoculated with the "serosity" of "chaveriform" syphilids of a woman displayed typical lesions (Mechnikov and Ruch, 1905). After a period of thirty-five days, red spots covered with dry scales appeared on the inoculated areas of the superciliary zone. No secondary skin or mucous membrane involvement was observed during the four months of the experiment. The same investigators concluded that the syphilitic lesions observed in the *P. hamadryas* resembled more closely those of macaques than those of the anthropoids and of man.

In another attempt to produce experimental syphilis in monkeys and baboons, it was observed that *C. sabaeus* and *M. sphinx*

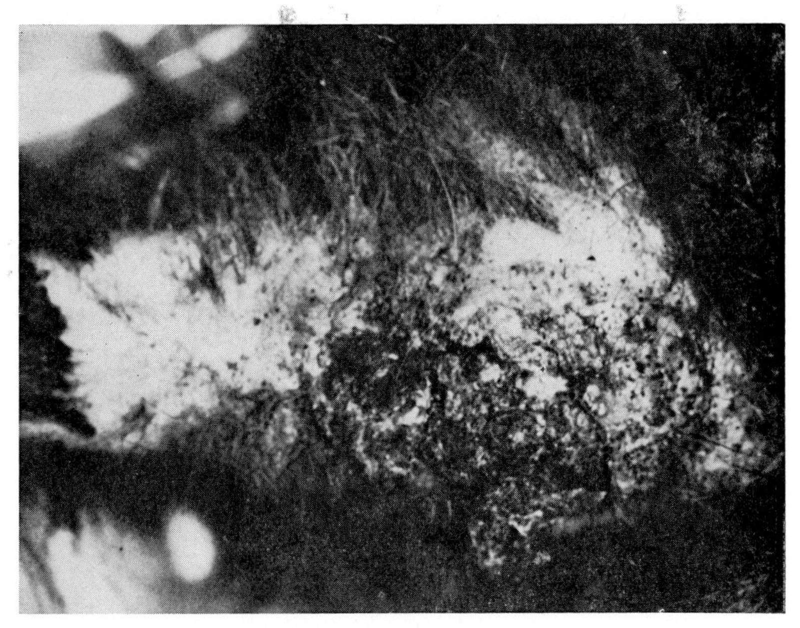

Figure 16-1. Skin lesion on base of monkey's back 10 months after intravenous inoculation with *T. pallidum*. (From Elsas *et al.,* 1968)

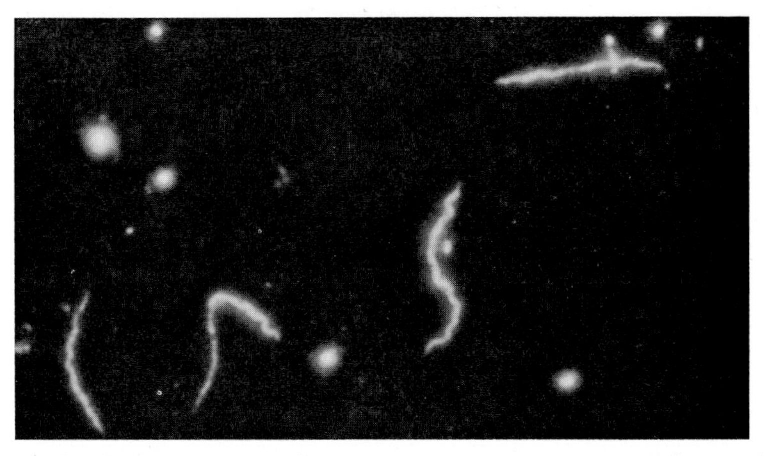

Figure 16-2. Treponemes found in the aqueous humour of the left eye of an owl monkey inoculated with *T. pallidum* (oil immersion dark field). (From Elsas *et al.,* 1968)

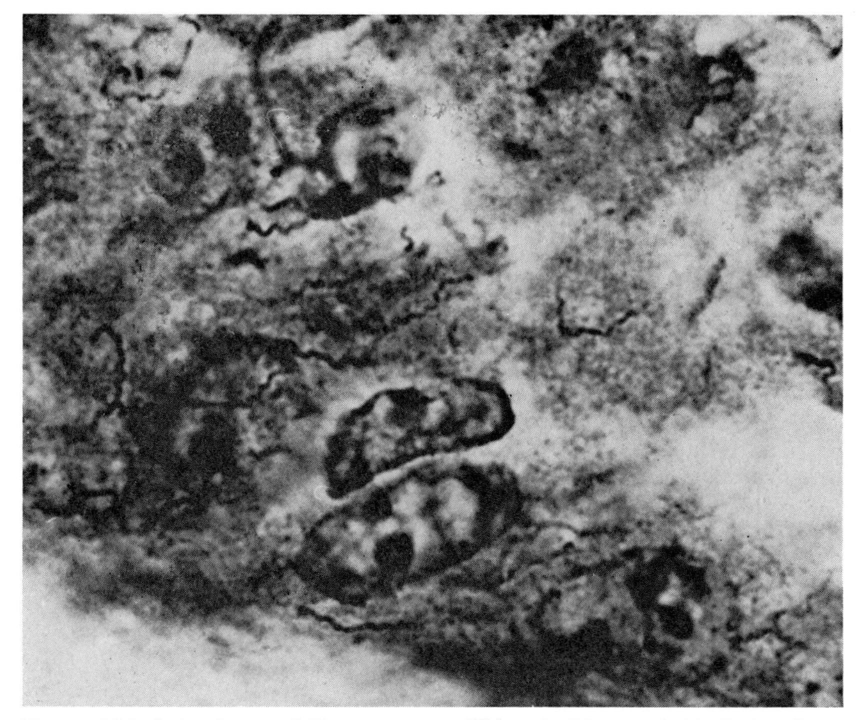

Figure 16-3. Spirochetes of *Treponema pallidum* in biopsy of skin lesion in an owl monkey (*Aotus trivirgatus*) (Krajian silver stain; oil immersion). (From Elsas *et al.*, 1968)

were not susceptible to infection with serous liquid from syphilitic chancre. *M. cynomolgus* were most susceptible among the macaques (Mechnikov and Ruch, 1904).

The occurrence of a large, crusted late syphiloderm was reported in an owl monkey (*Aotus trivirgatus*) eight months after intravenous injection with virulent *T. pallidum* expressed from a human penile chancre (Elsas *et al.*, 1968). A photograph of the skin lesion at the base of the monkey's back, and photomicrographs of treponemes found in the aqueous humor of the eyes, and of spirochetes in the biopsy of the skin lesion are shown in Figures 16-1, 16-2, and 16-3 respectively. The development of uveitis and the presence of spirochetes in the aqueous humor attest to the generalized syphilitic involvement. Histopathology of the lesion was considered as "consistent with *Condyloma latum*" (Smith, 1969). Occurrence of the disease in other species of monkeys are cited and the significance of the late manifestations of syphilis in experimental primates is discussed.

Pan troglodytes has also been experimentally infected with *T. pallidum* (Brown *et al.*, 1970). One chimpanzee was inoculated in the skin of the back with darkfield-positive serous material from a human primary syphilitic lesion. From the lesion which developed five more juvenile chimpanzees (2-4 years old) were inoculated with the infectious material into the skin at the base of the penis or into the left lip of the vulva. Three of these animals developed darkfield-positive lesions. Sera from the infected animals were reactive to various serological tests for syphilis.

It has also been reported (Kuhn *et al.*, 1968) that of 250 *P. tryglodytes* in the United States, 10 percent were reactive in the Venereal Disease Research Laboratory (VDRL) slide test, 16.4 percent were reactive in the *T. pallidum* Immobilization (TPI) test and 15.6 percent in the Fluorescent Treponemal Antibody-Absorption (FTA-ABS) test. This suggests that there is an enzootic treponematosis in captive chimpanzees in this country.

G. Gonorrhea

There are no reports of naturally occurring gonorrheal infections in nonhuman primates. However, gonococcal infections have been experimentally produced in *Pan troglodytes* by Lucas, Chandler, Martin and Schmale (Personal communication). This was achieved by inoculation of the exudate from infected human males into broth which was then transferred by catheter into the urethra of male chimpanzees.

H. Seminal Leucocytosis

Upon routine microscopic examination of semen samples collected from baboons in our laboratory, we obtained samples from one male with extensive leucocytosis (Fig. 16-4). Diphtheroid bacteria were isolated from one semen sample (Kalter, Personal communication). Treatment of the male with chloromycetin readily cleared the leucocytosis (Fig. 16-5).

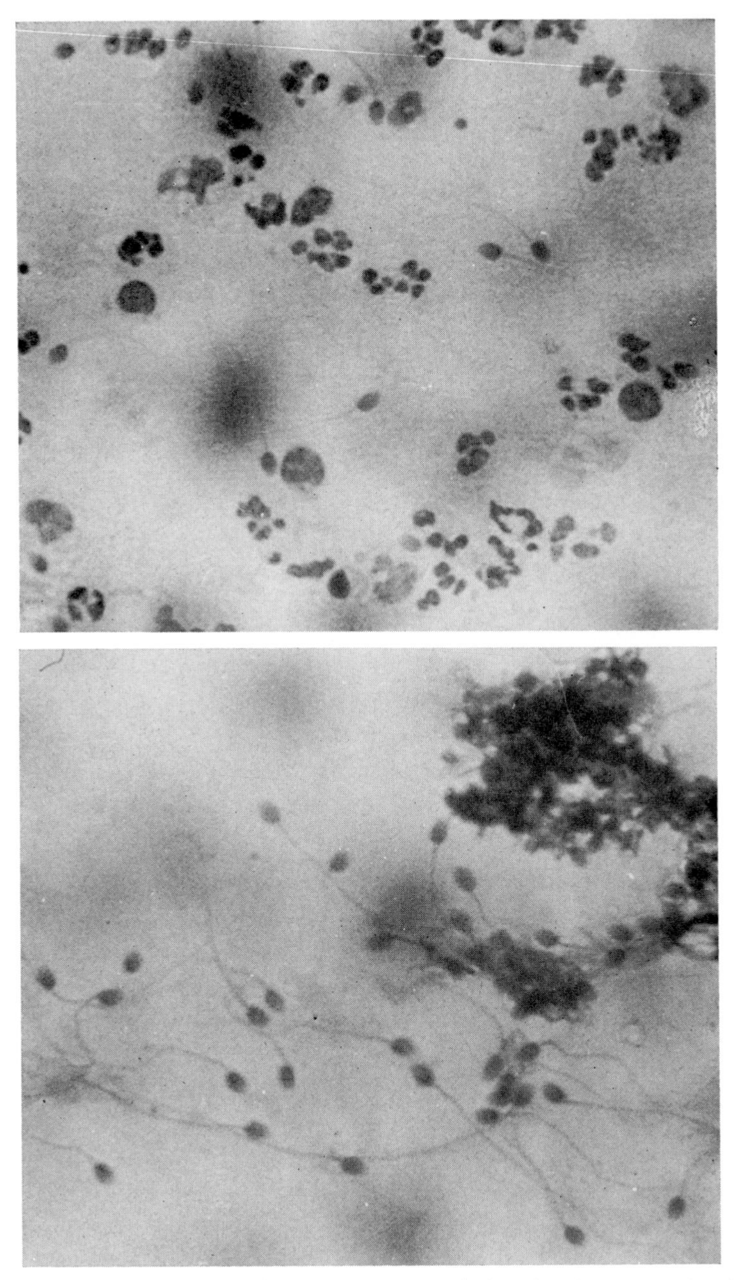

Figure 16-4. Semen sample from a *P. cynocephalus* showing extensive leucocytosis (700×); Figure 16-5. Semen sample from the same *P. cynocephalus* after antibiotic therapy. Note absence of leucocytes and a relatively greater cell concentration (700×).

V. MYCOTIC INFECTIONS

A. Candidiasis

Candida albicans is the primary etiologic agent in Candidiasis (moniliasis). It is normally a secondary invader to other infections in nonhuman primates and in man.

In a study by Al-Doory *et al.* (1967) on *P. cynocephalus, Candida* was the most frequently occurring yeast in the vagina, followed by *Trichosporon, Geotrichum, Cryptococcus, Rhodoto-*

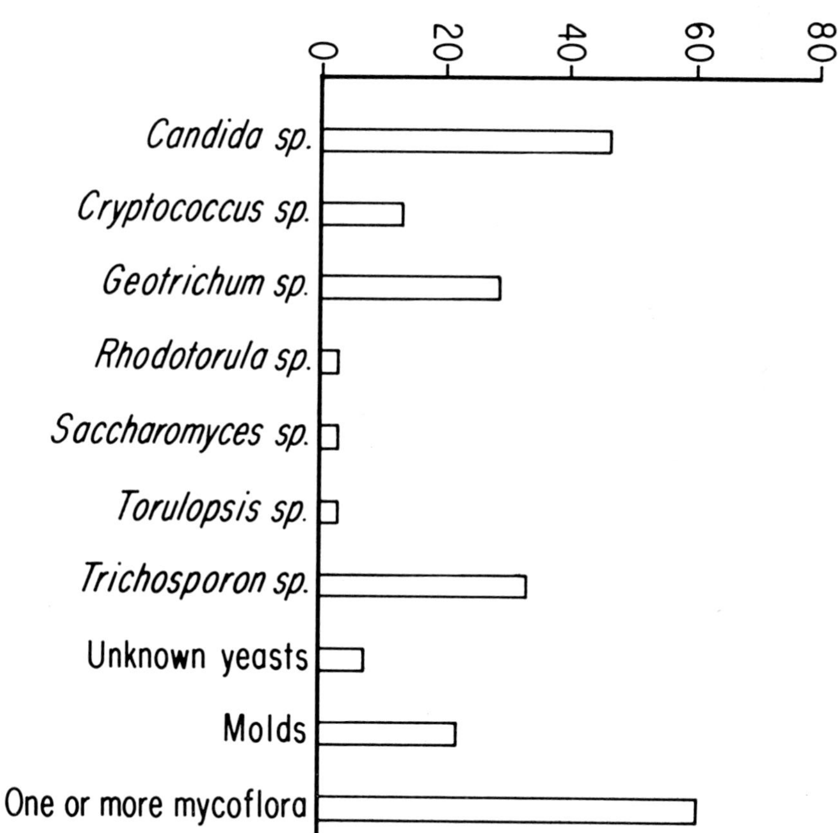

Figure 16-6. The incidence of mycoflora isolations from the vagina of *Papio sp.* (n = 127) (adapted from Al-Doory *et al.*, 1967)

rula, and *Saccharomyces* (Fig. 16-6) *Torulopsis* were also found in small numbers. The species of *Candida* obtained from the vaginal swabs were *C. albicans, C. brumptii, C. catenulata, C. claussenii, C. guilliermondi, C. intermedia, C. krusei, C. lipolytica, C. parapsilosis, C. pelliculosa, C. robusta, C. solani, C. stellatoidea, C. tropicalis, C. utilis, C. pulcherrima* and *Candida sp.* In addition to *Cryptococcus sp.,* the other species of *Cryptococcus* found in the vaginal swabs includes *Cr. albidus, Cr. diffluens* and *Cr. luteolus.*

P. cynocephalus is more susceptible to experimental candidiasis than *C. pygerythrus* (Al-Doory, 1970). Intravenous inoculation of *P. cynocephalus* with 5×10^6 cells of *C. albicans* isolated from a case of human vaginitis caused death five days postinoculation. General dissemination of the infection throughout the major organ systems was noted at necropsy of *P. cynocephalus,* whereas no significant signs of infection were seen in *C. pygerythrus.*

Balanitis (infection of the glans penis) was observed in an adult *M. mulatta* in conjunction with paronychia and onychia (Kerber *et al.,* 1968). The monkey was observed to spend considerable time manipulating the penis with its hand, and infection may have been transmitted from the penis to the hand (or vice versa) in this manner. The glans penis had a raw appearance, inflamed and granular. *C. albicans* was isolated from the lesion of the penis but not the hand.

B. *Actinomyces Species*

This organism was isolated from a *M. mulatta* which had acute pyometra (Lang and Benjamin, 1969). However, *S. aureus* was also isolated and these two organisms were suspected as the probable etiologic agents.

VI. PROTOZOAN INFECTION

A. *Trichomoniasis*

Trichomoniasis is an infection of the genital tract caused by a flagellated protozoan, *Trichomonas fetus,* causing fetal death, abortion, pyometra and eventually sterility in many species of domestic and laboratory animals. Fortunately, the flagellates of *T. fetus* do not survive in the vagina of common laboratory monkeys

(Ruch, 1959). Although the evidence is very scanty from a comparative standpoint, species lower in the primate series appear to be receptive hosts and harbor this organism. Trichomonads resembling *T. fetus* organisms were found in a tarsier (*Tarsius carbonarius*) which aborted before the infection was detected (Hill *et al.*, 1952).

Another species of trichomonad (*T. vaginalis*) thrives in the human and nonhuman primate vagina (Trussell, 1947; Trussell and McNutt, 1941; Vasquez-Colet and Tubanqui, 1936). Neither in spontaneously nor experimentally infected monkeys could gross pathologic lesions be attributed to this protozoan. *T. hominis* normally inhabits the intestines of man and monkeys and causes infection of the vagina of *M. mulatta* when artificially inoculated (Hegner, 1928; 1934). Other experiments (Kessel and Gafford, 1940; Trussell and McNutt, 1941) failed to produce any infection of the reproductive tract.

B. Toxoplasmosis

The close relationship between *Toxoplasma gondii* and human embryopathies has been reviewed by Frenkel (1967). Women with a positive toxoplasmin test had a 2.2, 6.6, and 3.0-fold increase of abortions, premature deliveries and dead newborns, respectively. Furthermore, sero-positive women had a 3.6-fold increase in abnormal pregnancies and a 2.6-fold increase in operative deliveries. The newborns in this group showed a 1.8-fold increase in prematurity and a 1.7-fold increase in abnormalities. Chronic toxoplasmosis can affect embryogenesis and fetogenesis with resulting fetal malformation and repeated abortions. Toxoplasma as a possible cause of reproductive failure in nonhuman primates warrants investigation since antibody to *Toxoplasma gondii* has been found in *Papio sp.* (Archer and Beverley, 1966).

VII. PARASITIC HELMINTH INFECTIONS

A. Schistosomiasis

Man and nonhuman primates are known natural definitive hosts of four species of schistosomes (*Schistosoma japonicum, S. haematobium, S. mansoni* and *S. bovis*). Of these, *S. haematobium* and

S. mansoni are the most commonly described both clinically and pathologically in the human urogenital tract. They cause bilharzial salpingitis, oophoritis, endometritis, metritis, vaginitis and vulvitis. In a study involving forty-five autopsies of adult African women suffering from schistosomiasis, all had a *S. haematobium* infestation and eighteen showed infection with *S. mansoni* (Gelfand, 1950). The ova of schistosomes were most frequently seen in the vagina (91% of the cases), followed by the cervix (87%), uterus (82%), ovaries (76%) and fallopian tubes (56%). In the majority of cases, the ova of *S. haematobium* were found more frequently than those of *S. mansoni. S. haematobium* eggs are also found in human vesicular glands, vas deferens and prostate gland (Ishak *et al.,* 1967).

Nonhuman primates are susceptible to schistosoma infections (Nelson, 1960). *C. aethiops* (Cameron, 1928) and *Papio sp.* (McQuay, 1952; Miller, 1960; Strong *et al.,* 1961) were naturally infected with *S. mansoni. Cercocebus sp.* was infected with the schistosome "*Bilharzia magna*" (Cobbold, 1859) which is neither *S. mansoni* nor *S. haematobium* (Leiper, 1918). *S. haematobium* was seen in one out of fifteen baboons in Kenya. The infected animal was an old male which had a severely contracted bladder encrusted with schistosome eggs. Eggs of the same species of schistosomes were found in the bowel of one out of twenty *C. aethiops* (Nelson, 1960). The same investigator also reported the presence of *S. matthui* in four of fifteen Kenya baboons.

Experimental exposure of ten primate species to *S. mansoni* reveals that all are susceptible to schistosomes although the type, intensity and course of infection varies considerably (Sadun *et al.,* 1966). In *M. mulatta, M. cynomolgus* and *M. speciosa,* there is a high rate of recovery of worms from the tissues following exposure, but a tendency for gradual self-cure. In *P. anubis* and *Pan troglodytes* worm recovery is lower but the egg excretion rate is maintained for long periods. In *Callithrix aurita, Saimiri sciureus* and *Tupaia sp.* the egg recovery rate is low and the infection tends to be aborted at an early stage. In *Ateles geoffroyi* and *Cebus apella* the number of parasites recovered is relatively low. While eggs of the schistosome were found in all the organs studied (lung, liver, intestines, spleen and kidney), apparently no attempts were made to recover eggs from the genital tract. However, Kuntz and

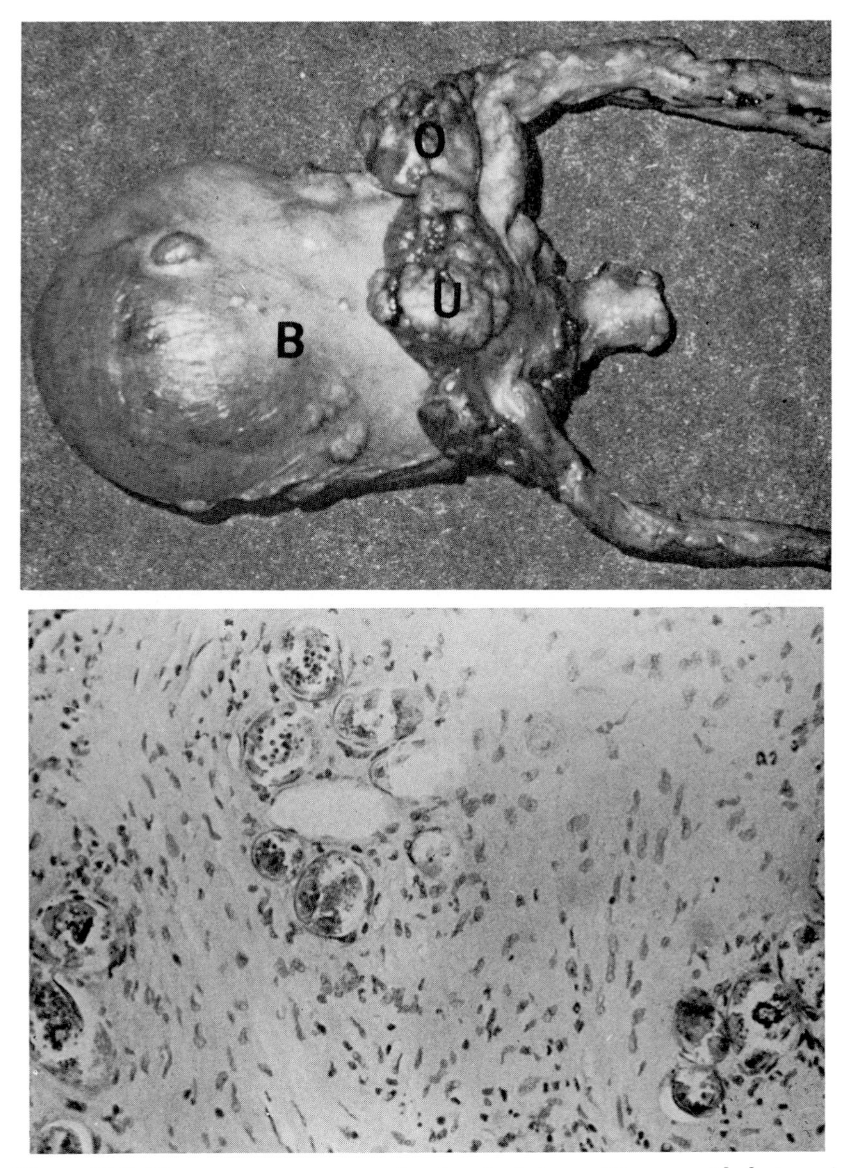

Figure 16-7. The gross appearance of a female baboon (*P. cynocephalus*) genital tract infected with eggs of *S. mansoni* (Kuntz and Myers, unpublished). (B—bladder; U—uterus; O—ovary); Figure 16-8. Myometrium of *P. cynocephalus* infiltrated with eggs of *S. mansoni* (approx. 150×). (Kuntz & Myers, unpublished)

Myers (Personal communication) found eggs of *S. mansoni* in the genital tract of *P. cynocephalus* (Fig. 16-7 and 16-8). Even though there are no data regarding the influence of schistosomes on reproduction of nonhuman primates, it is apparent that heavy deposition of eggs in the reproductive organs could impair fertility. Therefore, systematic surveys involving schistosomes should include the genital organs.

B. Filariasis

An isolated case of a filarid worm (*Tetrapetalonema digitata*) infection has been reported in two adult gibbons killed in habitat (Schultz, 1939). The ovaries were found to be invaded by the parasite.

VIII. SAMPLE COLLECTION FOR DIAGNOSIS AND SURVEY

A. Males

Cleansing of the area surrounding the male external genitalia is a requisite to proper collection of samples for diagnostic purposes. The hair surrounding these areas is first clipped. The entire area of the scrotum and the penis including the *fossa navicularis* is washed with a mild germicidal soap, and then rinsed thoroughly with sterile distilled water. A swab of the penile urethra is made by inserting a sterile cotton-tipped swab (for smaller males it may be necessary to reduce the amount of cotton on the tip) into the penile urethra approximately 2-3 cm (Fig. 16-9a). The swab is withdrawn and immediately placed in a sterile test tube containing the appropriate medium. This procedure is usually done before and after collecting semen samples (Fig. 16-9b). The semen is collected into sterile collection tubes.

B. Females

Preparatory to sample collection, the anal, perineal and the vulvar areas of the female are thoroughly washed with a mild germicidal soap and rinsed thoroughly with sterile distilled water. A sterilized speculum is inserted into the vagina. For collection of a specimen, a sterile cotton swab is inserted into the vaginal cavity be-

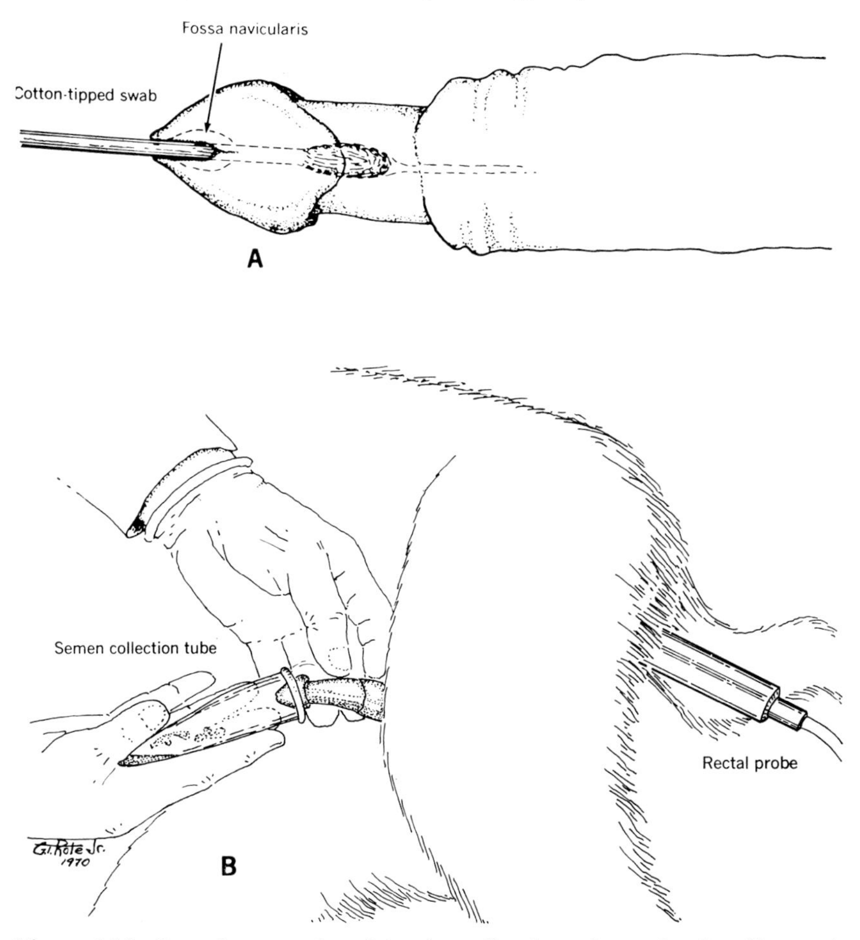

Figure 16-9. Procedure employed in the collection of samples for diagnostic and survey purposes from the male reproductive tract of baboons (*P. cynocephalus*). The cotton-tipped swab is inserted into the urethral opening (A) prior to and (B) after semen sample collection.

yond the tips of the speculum (Fig. 16-10a) and then rolled lightly over the vaginal lining. The swab is then carefully removed without further contact with the sides of the vagina or external genitalia. A wire loop has also been successfully employed to obtain vaginal samples (Schmale, personal communication). Cervical specimens are taken by first evacuating the vaginal cavity and douching with a mild germicidal agent. A cotton swab is then used to wipe

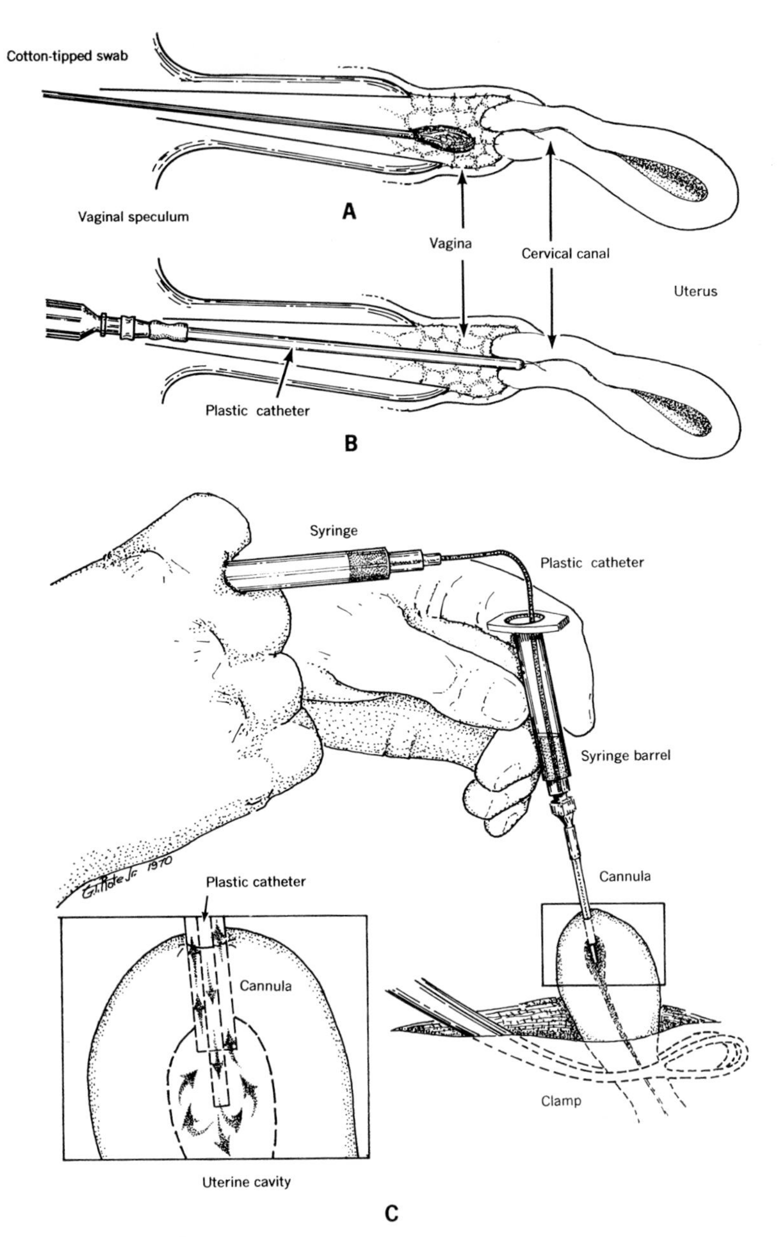

Figure 16-10. Procedure employed in the collection of samples for diagnostic and survey purposes from the female reproductive tract of baboons (*P. cynocephalus*). A sterile cotton swab is inserted into the vagina for vaginal sample collection (A); cervical samples are aspirated with a plastic catheter and a syringe (B); and uterine washings are obtained at laparotomy by introducing sterile saline through a small catheter and collecting return flow through a larger cannula (C).

the cervical opening before inserting a plastic catheter into the cervix. Cervical material is aspirated by means of a syringe (Fig. 16-10b). To avoid cervical contamination, specimens from the uterus are collected by laporatomy. The uterus is clamped at the internal cervical os (Fig. 16-10c). A double tubing (see inset) is inserted into the uterine lumen. Sterilized saline is pushed through the inner tubing and collected into a syringe barrel via the outer tubing. The samples are aspirated from the syringe barrel and transferred to sterile test tubes.

IX. PREVENTIVE MEDICINE

The true extent of spontaneous infections of the reproductive system of nonhuman primates is difficult to assess. The reproductive system is generally not even mentioned in pathological and microbiological surveys of nonhuman primates. The implication is that nonhuman primates are relatively free of spontaneous infections which influence reproduction. The results of the few serological and microbiological surveys of animals in the wild and the very limited number of cases which have been reported on reproductive diseases of these animals in captivity support this implication. However, the common practice of selecting only those animals which reproduce readily in captivity for reproductive studies and the use of nonreproducers for other studies, without diagnosis of the reproduction problems, very likely has both masked the true incidence of infections of reproductive tract and, fortunately, aided in control of any infection which may have been present.

This relatively favorable situation regarding the incidence of infectious diseases influencing reproduction in nonhuman primates is threatened by the susceptibility of these animals to numerous human diseases of the reproductive system. Therefore, preventive medicine procedures are of paramount importance, not only to prevent introduction of disease from nonhuman primates freshly introduced into breeding colonies, but even more important, to prevent the introduction of disease from the human population. The following general preventive medicine measures are therefore recommended:

1. Personnel involved in capture, transport, quarantine, maintenance, and experimentation must be monitored to assure that

they are not carriers of infectious diseases which influence reproduction.

2. Personnel must be trained in the use of, and must practice effective personal hygiene.

3. Animals with clinically obvious reproductive infections at the time of capture must be maintained separately for diagnosis and then either restricted for studies of therapeutic procedures or sacrificed.

4. Animal monitoring during quarantine must include physical examination of the reproductive system, serological testing for detection of possible exposures to reproductive tract pathogens, and microbiological screening of properly collected vaginal, cervical and semen specimens.

5. Causes of reproductive failure must be determined clinically. All animals must be examined postmortem for evidence of reproductive tract disorder.

6. Animal facilities must be maintained free of rodents and other pests which might transmit reproductive tract diseases.

REFERENCES

Al-Doory, Y. (1967): The mycoflora of the subhuman primates. II. The flora of the rectum and vagina of the baboon in captivity. Mycopathologia, *31,* 332-336.

Al-Doory, Y. (1970): An immune factor in baboon anti-*Candida* serum. *Sabouraudia* (In press).

Alexander, E. R., and Chiang, W. T. (1967): Infection of pregnant monkeys and their offspring with TRIC agents. *Amer J Ophthal, 63,* 1145-1153.

Archer, J. F., and Beverley, J. K. A. (1966): Immunofluorescence in the diagnosis of ovine abortion and to *Toxoplasma gondii. Vet Rec, 78,* 369-372.

Berman, L. D.; Cotes, P. M., and Simons, P. J. (1967): Tumors and immunological response in rhesus monkeys born after *in utero* inoculation with Rous Sarcoma Virus. *J Nat Cancer Inst, 39,* 119-134.

Black, P. H.; Hartley, J. W., and Rowe, W. P. (1963): Isolation of a cytomegalovirus from African green monkey. *Proc Soc Exp Biol Med, 112,* 601-605.

Brooks, H., and Blair, W. R. (1903): Annual report of the medical department of the Zoological Park for 1903. *Rep NY Zool Soc, 8,* 104-114.

Brown, W. J.; Kuhn, U. S. G.; Tolliver, E. A., and Norins, L. C. (1970): Experimental syphilis in the chimpanzee. Immunoglobulin class of early antibodies reactive with *Treponema pallidum. Brit J Vener Dis, 46,* 198-200.

Cameron, T. W. M. (1928): A new definitive host for *Schistosoma mansoni. J Helminth, 6,* 219-222.

Cobbold, T. S. (1859): On some new forms of Entozoa. *Trans Linn Soc Lond (Zool), 22,* 363-366.

Cotes, P. M. (1965): Discussion of the role of viruses in the etiology of leukemia in man and other animals. *Proc Symp Some Rec Dev Comp Med June 15-16, 1965.* London, Zoological Society.

Cowdry, E. V., and Scott, G. H. (1935): Nuclear inclusions suggestive of virus action in the salivary gland of the monkey, *Cebus fatuellas. Amer J Path, 11,* 647-658.

Delahunt, C. S. (1966): Rubella-induced cataracts in monkeys. *Lancet, 7441,* 825.

Draper, C. C., and Laurence, G. D. (1969): Susceptibility of *Erythrocebus patas* monkeys to Rubella virus. *J Med Micro, 2,* 249-252.

Elizan, T. S., and Fabiyi, A. (1970): Congenital and neonatal anomalies linked with viral infections in experimental animals. *Amer J Obstet Gynec, 106,* 147-165.

Elsas, F. J.; Smith, J. L.; Israel, C. W., and Gager, W. E. (1968): Late syphilis in the primate. *Brit J Vener Dis, 44,* 267-273.

Fear, F. A.; Pinkerton, M. E.; Cline, J. A.; Kriewaldt, F., and Kalter, S. S. (1968): A leptospirosis outbreak in a baboon (*Papio* sp.) colony. *Lab Anim Care, 18,* 22-28.

Fennestad, K. L., and Borg-Petersen, C. (1958): Fetal leptospirosis and abortion in cattle. *J Infect Dis, 102,* 227-236.

Fiennes, R. (1967): *Zoonoses of Primates. The Epidemiology and Ecology of Simian Diseases in Relation to Man.* Ithaca, N.Y., Cornell Univ Press, chap. IX, p. 190.

Frenkel, J. K. (1967): Toxoplasmosis In Benirschke, K. (Ed.): *Comparative Aspects of Reproductive Failure.* New York, Springer-Verlag, pp. 296-321.

Gajdusek, D. C.: Rogers, N. G.; Basnight, M.: Gibbs, C. J. Jr., and Alpers, M. (1969): Transmission experiments with kuru in chimpanzees and the isolation of latent viruses from the explanted tissues of affected animals. *Ann N.Y. Acad Sci, 162,* 529-550.

Gelfand, M. (1950): *Schistosomiasis in South Central Africa. A Clinico-Pathological Study.* Juta, Cape Town & Johannesburg, Juta, pp. 203-208.

Harwick, H. J.; Iuppa, J. B.; Purcell, R. H., and Fekety, F. R., Jr. (1967): *Mycoplasma hominis* septicemia associated with abortion. *Amer J Obstet Gynec, 99,* 725-927.

Hayflick, L., and Stanbridge, E. (1967): Isolation and identification of mycoplasma from human clinical materials. *Ann NY Acad Sci, 143,* 608-621.

Hegner, R. (1928): Experimental transmission of trichomonads from the intestine and vagina of monkeys to the vagina of monkeys (*Macacus rhesus*). *J Parasit, 16,* 91-92.

Hegner, R. (1934): Infections of the vagina of rhesus monkeys with *Trichomonas hominis* from man. *J Parasit, 20,* 247-248.

Hendrickx, A. G. (1966): Teratogenicity findings in a baboon colony. In

Miller, E. O. (Ed.): *The Proc. Conference on Nonhuman Primate Toxicology*. Warrenton, Virginia, Airlie House, pp. 120-132.

Henson, D.; Smith, R. D.; Gehrke, J. (1966): Non-fatal mouse cytomegalovirus hepatitis. Combined morphologic, virologic and immunologic observations. *Amer J Path, 49,* 871-888.

Hill, W. C. O.; Porter, A., and Southwick, M. D. (1952): The natural history, endoparasites and pseudoparasites of the tarsiers *(Tarsius carbonarius)* recently living in the Society's menagerie. *Proc Zool Soc London, 122,* 79-114.

Hutchison, V. E.; Pinkerton, M. E., and Kalter, S. S. (1970): Incidence of mycoplasma in nonhuman primates. *Lab Anim Care, 20,* 914-922.

Ishak, K. G.; Le Golvan, P. C., and El-Sebai, J. (1967): Malignant bladder tumors associated with Schistosomiasis. A gross and microscopic study. In Mastofi, F. K. (Ed.): *Bilharziasis.* New York, Springer-Verlag, p. 58-83.

Jacotot, H., and Vallee, A. (1960): Elements d'enquete serologique sur l'infection par *Vibrio foetus* en France. *Ann Pasteur (Paris), 98,* 601-604.

Jones, D. M. (1967a): *Mycoplasma hominis* in abortion. *Brit Med J, 1,* 338-340.

Jones, D. M. (1967b): *Mycoplasma hominis* in pregnancy. *J Clin Path,* 20, 633-635.

Jones, D. M., and Tobin, B. M. (1969): Isolation of mycoplasms and other organisms from the placenta after Caesarian section. *J Med Micro, 2,* 347-352.

Kalter, S. S. (1969): Nonhuman primates in viral research. *Ann NY Acad Sci, 162,* 499-528.

Kalter, S. S.; Al-Doory, Y.; Kuntz, R. E., and Pinkerton, M. E. (1968): Infectious diseases associated with the use of primates. In Vagtborg, H. (Ed.): *Use of Nonhuman Primates in Drug Evaluation. A Symposium.* Austin, Texas, University of Texas Press, p. 505.

Kalter, S. S., and Guilloud, N. B. (1970): Chimpanzee Viruses. In Bourne, G. A. (Ed.): *The Chimpanzee.* New York, Karger, vol. 2.

Kalter, S. S.; Ratner, I. A.; Britton, H. A.; Vice, T. E.; Eugster, A. K., and Rodriguez, A. R. (1967): Inoculations of baboon (*Papio* sp.) with adenovirus type 12: The effect of thymectomy, splenectomy, immunosuppressive drug (Immuran), radiation, and amnioinjection. In Vagtborg, H. (Ed.): *The Baboon in Medical Research, II.* Austin, Texas, University of Texas Press, pp. 683-695.

Kalter, S. S.; Ratner, J.; Kalter, G. V.; Rodriguez, A. R., and Kim, C. S. (1967): A survey of primate sera for antibodies to viruses of human and simian origin. *J Epidemiol, 86,* 552-568.

Kerber, W. T.; Reese, W. H., and Van Natta, J. (1968): Balanitis, paronychia and onychia in a rhesus monkey. *Lab Anim Care, 18,* 506-507.

Kessel, J. F., and Gafford, J. A. (1940): Observations on the pathology of *Trichomonas vaginitis* and on vaginal implants with *Trichomonas vaginalis* and *Trichomonas intestinalis. Amer J Obstet Gynec, 39,* 1005-1014.

Kuhn, U. S. G.; Brown, W. J., and Falcone, V. H. (1968): WHO/VDT/RES/68.137 cited by Brown *et al.* (1970): Experimental syphilis in the chimpanzee. Immunoglobulin class of early antibodies reactive with *Treponema pallidum*. *Brit J Vener Dis, 46,* 198-200.

Lang, C. M., and Benjamin, S. A. (1969): Acute pyometra in a rhesus monkey (*Macaca mulatta*). *J Amer Vet Med Assoc, 155,* 1156-1157.

Lapin, B. A., and Yakovleva, L. A. (1963): *Comparative Pathology in Monkeys*. Springfield, Thomas, chap. XVI, p. 272.

Lawson, J. H., and Michna, S. W. (1966): *Canicola* fever in man and animals. *Brit Med J, 2,* 336-340.

Leiper, R. T. (1918): Report on the results of the Bilharzia mission in Egypt, 1915. *J Roy Army Med Corps, 30,* 235-260.

Madden, D. L.; Hildebrandt, R. J.; Monif, G. R. G.; London, W. T.; Sever, J. L., and McCullough, N. B. (1970a): The isolation and identification of *Mycoplasma* from *Macaca mulatta*. *Lab Anim Care, 20,* 467-470.

Madden, D. L.; Hildebrandt, R. J.; Monif, G. R. G.; London, W. T.; McCullough, N. B., and Sever, J. L. (1970b): The isolation and identification of *Mycoplasma* from *Cercopithecus aethiops*. *Lab Anim Care, 20,* 471-473.

McQuay, R. M. (1952): Susceptibility of a Louisiana species of *Tropicorbis* to infection with *Schistosoma mansoni*. *Exp Parasit, 1,* 184-188.

Medearis, D. N. (1964a): Mouse cytomegalovirus. III. Attempts to produce intrauterine infections. *Amer J Hyg, 80,* 113-120.

Medearis, D. N. (1964b): Mouse cytomegalovirus infection. *Amer J Hyg, 80,* 103-112.

Medearis, D. N., Jr. (1967): Comparative aspects of reproductive failure induced in mammals by viruses. In Benirschke, K. (Ed.): *Comparative Aspects of Reproductive Failure*. New York, Springer-Verlag, pp. 333-349.

Mechnikov, E., and Ruch, E. (1904): La syphilis du chimpanzee. *Ann Inst Pasteur (Paris), 18,* 657-671.

Mechnikov, E., and Ruch, E. (1906): Studies on experimental syphilis. *Ann Inst Pasteur (Paris), 19,* 673-698.

Miller, J. M. (1960): *Papio doguera* (Dog Face Baboon), a primate reservoir host of *Schistosoma mansoni* in East Africa. *Trans Roy Soc Trop Med Hyg, 54,* 44-46.

Nelson, G. S. (1960): Schistosome infections as zoonoses in Africa. *Trans Roy Soc Trop Med Hyg, 5,* 301-315.

Parkman, P. D.; Phillips, P. E., and Meyer, H. H., Jr. (1965): Experimental rubella virus infection in pregnant monkeys. *Amer J Dis Child, 110,* 390-394.

Pease, P.; Rogers, K. B., and Cole, B. C. (1967): A cytopathogenic strain of *Mycoplasma hominis* Type 1 isolated from the lung of a stillborn infant. *J Path Bact, 94,* 460-462.

Ruch, T. C. (1959): *Diseases of Laboratory Primates*. Philadelphia, W. B. Saunders, pp. 443-471.

Sadun, E. H.; Lichtenberg, F. von, and Bruce, J. I. (1966): Susceptibility and comparative pathology of ten species of primates exposed to infection with *Schistosoma mansoni*. *J Trop Med Hyg, 15,* 705-718.

Schultz, A. H. (1939): Notes on diseases and healed fractures of wild apes, and their bearing on the antiquity of pathological conditions in man. *Bull Hist Med, 7,* 571-582.

Sever, J. L.; Meier, G. W.; Windle, W. F.; Schiff, G. M.; Monif, G. R., and Fabiyi, A. (1966): Experimental rubella in pregnant rhesus monkeys. *J Infect Dis, 116,* 21-26.

Sigurdardottir, B.; Givan, K. F.; Rozee, K. R., and Rhodes, A. J. (1963): Association of virus with cases of Rubella studied in Toronto: Propagation of the agent and transmission to monkeys. *Canad Med Ass J, 88,* 128-132.

Smith, J. L. (1969): Correspondence: Syphilis in the owl monkey. *Brit J Vener Dis, 45,* 170.

Stokes, E. J. (1955): Human infection with pleuropneumonia-like organisms. *Lancet, 1,* 276-279.

Strong, J. P.; McGill, H. C., and Miller, J. M. (1961): *Schistosomiasis mansoni* in the Kenya baboon. *Amer J Trop Med Hyg, 10,* 25-31.

Tinkelpaugh, D. L. (1932): Parturition and puerperal sepsis in a chimpanzee. *Anat Rec, 53,* 193-205.

Trussell, R. E. (1947): *Trichomonas vaginalis and Trichomoniasis.* Springfield, Thomas, chap. XII, pp. 277.

Trussell, R. E., and McNutt, S. H. (1941): Animal inoculations with pure cultures of *Trichomonas vaginalis* and *Trichomonas foetus. J Infect Dis, 69,* 18-28.

Tully, J. G., and Smith, L. G. (1968): Postpartum septicemia with *Mycoplasma hominis. JAMA, 204,* 827-828.

Tully, J. G.; Brown, M. S.; Sheagren, J. N.; Young, V. M., and Wolff, S. M. (1965): Septicemia due to *Mycoplasma hominis* type 1. *New Eng J Med, 273,* 648-650.

Valerio, D. A.; Miller, R. L.; Innes, J. B. M.; Courtney, D. A.; Pallotta, A. J., and Guttmacher, R. M. (1969): *Macaca mulatta. Management of a Laboratory Breeding Colony.* New York, Academic Press, p. 68.

Vasquez-Colet, A., and Tubangui, M. (1936): The identity and incidence of a flagellated parasite found in human urine. *J Phil Is Med Ass, 16,* 231-234.

Vickers, J. H. (1962): Generalized staphylococcic infection in a monkey. *J Amer Vet Med Ass, 141,* 256-257.

Wilson, J. G., and Gavan, J. A. (1967): Congenital malformation in non-human primates: Spontaneous and experimentally induced. *Anat Rec, 158,* 99-109.

Zabolotnyi, D. K. (1904): On experimental syphilis in baboons. *Ark biologicheskikhnauk, 11,* 155-164.

V. TECHNIQUES

Chapter 17

TECHNIQUES OF BREEDING AND REARING OF MONKEYS

C. MAX LANG

I. THE BREEDING COLONY

THE primary advantage of a breeding colony is the year-round availability of pregnant and young animals. This objective can be achieved only with laboratory breeding since pregnant monkeys are generally available for importation only during the winter and early spring—the months which follow their normal feral breeding season. Another advantage is that the percentage of live births is considerably higher among animals mated in the laboratory than among free-ranging monkeys. Monkeys reared in the laboratory also offer many advantages for experimental purposes: known age and parentage, prior nutritional history, and a far smaller incidence of parasitism.

In some cases, of course, the scientific community may be forced to raise nonhuman primates for research, or even to replenish those species which are in short supply.

An effective breeding program depends on a thorough understanding of the reproductive physiology of the species involved. This basic information is available for some species, and we are continually striving to increase our knowledge concerning reproduction in other species.

A. The Breeding Female

Considerable attention must be given to the breeding females in the colony. Because of the costs involved, one must be careful to keep only females that consistently produce healthy offspring. Females for the breeding colony usually have to be from imported groups since there are few established breeding colonies in the United States. There seems to be little, if any, advantage in buying pregnant females to start a breeding colony. Although pregnancy may indicate fertility, it does not predict the normal delivery of healthy offspring, nor subsequent fertility. Previous reports indicate that the incidence of abortions or stillbirths among imported pregnant *Macaca mulatta* is 59 percent, as compared to 12 percent in pregnancies produced by laboratory matings (Valerio *et al.*, 1968). Furthermore, the early mortality rate and incidence of tuberculosis are higher in the monkeys which are pregnant on arrival at the laboratory.

Some species of nonhuman primates have six to twelve months of anestrus when they are moved from the southern to the northern hemisphere (Lang, 1967). This phenomenon can also occur after the delivery of imported pregnant monkeys.

Following menarche, most species tend to have irregular and anovulatory cycles for a year before ovulation and regular cycles become established. As in the human female, menarche occurs at different ages, which tend to become lower with succeeding generations (Pickering, 1968).

Breeding females can be housed in a group pen or in individual cages. If the animals are housed indoors, a temperature of 70 $\pm$ 5° F. and a relative humidity of 40 $\pm$ 20 percent is recommended. Under these conditions and with good lighting, twelve hours each day, most species of monkeys show no seasonal or climatic variation in their estrous cycles and fecundity, whereas *M. mulatta* unprotected from seasonal or climatic changes may show marked variations in both (Pickering, 1968).

Commercial primate chows appear to be adequate for normal reproduction. Although many laboratories supplement this diet with vitamin preparations, fruits or vegetables, this practice is apparently not based on nutritional needs.

In general, nonhuman primates can be maintained in good health while bearing infants at intervals of approximately three times the normal gestation period. Fatiguing of the reproductive apparatus in *M. mulatta* occurs at about the sixth pregnancy (Pickering, 1968).

Drugs have been used to treat certain types of infertility problems in monkeys (Dede and Plentl, 1966; Rosenblum, 1968; Valerio and Courtney, 1968). While such compounds may be of benefit in the future or for use in investigative procedures or special genetic groups, they are not recommended for use in a normal production colony. Only fertile, healthy females should be used, and these should be carefully selected to ensure continuation of the colony in successive generations.

B. The Breeding Male

Breeding males are active for many years, although it has been reported that *M. mulatta* tend to fatigue after five to six years of activity (Pickering, 1968). A single *M. mulatta* male can easily be used to breed fifteen to twenty females per year if the breeding is adequately spaced.

Because of the maintenance costs, it is important that only proven breeding males (healthy adults that have a good semen count and motility) be used in the production colony. A surprisingly large number of males in a colony may be subfertile. It has been reported that sixteen of thirty-six *M. mulatta* (44.5 percent) were not responsible for a conception after at least two matings with fertile females (Eckstein and Kelly, 1966).

The housing and nutrition requirements for the male are the same as those described for the breeding female.

The canine teeth of breeding males should be removed or cut off to protect the animal handlers and reduce fighting wounds.

In free-ranging *M. mulatta,* according to some reports, there is extensive regression of the seminiferous tubules associated with cessation of spermatogenesis in the spring, and redevelopment of the testes in late summer (Conaway and Sade, 1965). Other investigators, however, have reported that the sexual life of male *M. mulatta* is not subject to seasonal influence (Van Wagenen, 1967).

C. Breeding Systems

The choice of a breeding system will depend on the investigator's requirements and the facilities available. In general, a group breeding system is more economical and more efficient than paired matings, whereas paired matings give more accurate information on breeding dates and parentage.

Probably the best method is a combination of the two systems where the females are kept in a group and the male in a separate pen or cage. The females can then be brought, one at a time, to the male for breeding and subsequently returned to the group pen. This system makes it possible to keep accurate breeding records and, at the same time, enjoy the lower cost of group housing. Certain species, however, can be bred only, or best, in pairs. Permanent monogamous matings appear to be the most efficient production method for *Tupaia glis* (Morris *et al.*, 1967).

It is expected that, under natural conditions, a given species in a given environment will, by a process of evolution, select the optimum time for breeding to ensure perpetuation of the species. Many writers have reported that monkeys have seasonal breeding periods even in the laboratory (Creager and Switzer, 1967; Dumond, 1968; Eckstein and Kelly, 1966; Fleischman, 1963; Hendrickx and Kriewaldt, 1967; Lang, 1967; Valerio *et al.*, 1968; Young, 1965). Some species probably do breed seasonally, but seasonal breeding may be an artifact in others. Most laboratories artificially maintain a breeding season by rebreeding imported pregnant monkeys at annual intervals.

1. Group Matings. In addition to the advantage of lower costs and a reduction in the amount of handling required, group matings make it possible for the male to be present when the female comes in estrus. This method, however, has some disadvantages: (a) the animal technician may not know when mating occurs; (b) there may be fighting when new females are introduced into the group; and (c) the male may be fatigued, especially if several of the females are in estrus at the same time. Inability to space the breeding is another disadvantage which may be important if the investigator needs a constant supply of young monkeys.

One fertile male for eight to twelve females seems to be an adequate ratio for most species.

2. Paired Mating. The advantages of paired mating are obvious. The major disadvantage is that more personnel time is required for handling the animals.

Mating is accomplished by placing the male and female together at the beginning of estrus, and leaving them together for at least three days. It does not seem to be important whether the female is brought to the male or vice versa. Since large-sized males are more difficult and dangerous to handle, many investigators prefer to bring the female to the male. In some cases, however, the male may consider the female as an intruder into his territory rather than as a mate, and fighting may result. If the first contact takes place in the female's cage, the male is more peaceful (Dubouch, 1969). This problem can usually be eliminated, or at least minimized, if the female is allowed to become accustomed both to the relatively close quarters of the mating cage and to the male by being kept in the same room, and in a cage similar to the male's, for at least a few days preparatory to mating. If she is frightened when they are put together, she is more likely to be attacked by the male and injured (Hartman, 1945). Pairs should be observed closely for about fifteen minutes when they are first put together, and daily thereafter; they should be separated immediately if any signs of serious aggression are seen.

Compatibility often depends upon the amount of experience the female has had and the patience and persistence of the male. The female may refuse to accept a particular male. In this case, mating should not be forced, and she should be placed with a different male in that and all subsequent matings. There are occasions, however, when the female will not accept any male, even though all external signs indicate that she is in estrus. In these cases, a vaginal smear usually reveals incomplete vaginal cornification which is indicative of a low estrogenic level and a consequent lack of receptivity. When vaginal smears are positive at the time of mating, the incidence of pregnancy is 25 percent (Pickering, 1968). Most *M. mulatta* ovulate between noon of the eleventh day of the estrous cycle and noon of the twelfth day (Young, 1965). The conception rate increases considerably as the animals adjust to their environment, even over a short period of time. In *Papio sp.* a conception rate of 19.4 percent has been observed over a one year period; this rate includes all matings, regardless of age, arrival time, parity, convalescent time after surgery, and seasonal fluctuations (Hendrickx and Kriewaldt, 1967). Approximately one half of all conceptions result from either the first or the second mating (Eckstein and Kelly, 1966). In *M. mulatta,* 94 percent of conceptions are followed by the regular onset of the subsequent period of menstruation at the expected time. The duration of this period, however, is much more variable than that of the average menstruation.

3. Artificial Insemination. Artificial insemination is primarily used for experimental purposes. If it could be used routinely, a large number of females could be bred to a proven sire, and fewer breeding males would be necessary.

4. Postpartum Estrus. The time of the first postpartum estrus is usually not of interest to an investigator unless he is taking the young at birth and is trying to get maximum production. Breeding at this time is not to be practiced as a rule, since it does not allow the female adequate time to recover between gestation periods.

In *M. mulatta* and *M. fascicularis,* estrous cycles usually occur one month after parturition if the baby is taken from the mother at birth (Fujiwara and Imamichi, 1966; Pallotta, 1969). If the baby is allowed to remain with its mother, there is a four or five month delay before onset of the estrous cycle. If postpartum estrus occurs one month after parturition it is usually assumed to be ovulatory in nonlactating animals and anovulatory in lactating animals. The average length of the postpartum amenorrheal period is longer for monkeys bred in the wild state than for laboratory-bred monkeys (Fujiwara *et al.,* 1969).

Galago sp. normally mate within two or three days postpartum (Gucwinski and Gucwinski, 1968).

II. CARE DURING PREGNANCY

The diagnosis of pregnancy is important and cannot be made solely on the basis of visual inspection of the abdomen. In species of medium size and larger, the most reliable criterion of pregnancy is an increase in the size of the uterus, detected by digital palpation through the rectum. An experienced individual can detect pregnancy by this technique as early as two to four weeks after conception (Creager and Switzer, 1967; Hendrickx and Kriewaldt, 1967). X-ray is usually not definitive before the end of the second trimester (Kuehn *et al.,* 1965; Valerio *et al.,* 1968), and its greatest usefulness probably lies in diagnosing obstetric problems in postmaturity cases.

Pregnant females should be given a complete physical examination at least once a month to make sure that gestation is proceeding normally.

A. Housing

There is little evidence that the pregnant female needs any special type of housing. Pregnant animals can easily be kept in a group, even with males, provided there is adequate space for the submissive females to escape from the dominant animals.

Although individual cages afford closer observation, the animals may be harmed when their cages are changed for cleaning.

B. Nutrition

Little information is available on the nutritional requirements of monkeys during gestation. Some nutritive increase is necessary to ensure a healthy baby and, at the same time, keep the mother in an optimal state of nutrition. Adequate nutrition is particularly important for *Saimiri sciureus,* whose babies weigh almost twice as much at birth, in proportion to the mother, as do most other primates. The newborn *Saimiri* weighs approximately one fifth as much as his mother; at this ratio, a human infant would weigh twenty-five pounds at birth (Goss *et al.,* 1968). The rapid growth of this species in the third trimester of pregnancy makes it necessary for the mother to consume large amounts of nutrients to supply the fetus and carry her through delivery and lactation (Dumond, 1968).

Pregnancies in nonhuman primates differ in many ways from those observed in other laboratory animals. While a pregnant rat on a deficient diet will frequently abort or produce grossly malformed offspring, the nonhuman primate usually has a healthy infant even in the presence of severe maternal malnutrition. Pregnant *M. mulatta* which were fed diets containing excess amounts of rather unpleasant tasting single amino acids produced infants whose weight and linear measurements were well within the normal range, even though the mothers showed a considerable degree of malnutrition (Kerr and Waisman, 1965). Some metabolities are prevented, by the placenta, from reaching the fetus, whereas others diffuse across the placental membrane with a zero gradient between fetal and maternal blood; a few are actively transported by the placenta to reach a higher level in the fetus than in the mother. The fact that amino acids belong to the last classification may serve to explain the rapid rate of fetal growth and the consequent fetal needs for unusually large amounts of nutrients.

C. Parturition

The length of labor in *M. mulatta* is comparable to that in human females—twelve to thirty-six hours. Labor is usually somewhat shorter in multiparous animals (Kerr and Waisman, 1965).

Little information is available on premature and prolonged gestation in monkeys. In 380 pregnancies among *M. mulatta* the neonatal mortality was twenty percent when gestation ended before 150 days and 18 percent when it lasted longer than 175 days (Kerr and Waisman, 1965). These figures are quite striking when they are compared with the 3 percent neonatal mortality for pregnancies terminating between these extremes.

Postmaturity may occur in caged females who voluntarily restrict their exercise. The chief risk of prolonged gestation is that of intrauterine anoxia due to failing placental function. The problems associated with postmaturity may be largely avoided if the mother is examined to determine the fetal position and presentation and to ascertain whether the fetus is still alive. A thorough examination and handling of the monkey frequently results in parturition within twenty-four hours.

In nonhuman primates the fetus begins to develop in a breech presentation. Normally, however, version occurs during the last weeks of pregnancy, so that the mature fetus lies in a cephalic presentation and is delivered in a vertex presentation. Version has been detected in *Saimiri sciureus* twenty-three to sixty-five days before delivery; in *M. mulatta,* four to eighty days before delivery; and in *Papio sp.* it has been known several times to occur within the last twenty-four hours before delivery (Bowden *et al.,* 1967).

The incidence of breech deliveries appears to be considerably higher in monkeys than in human females: in 12 and 16 percent of *M. mulatta* and *Papio sp.,* as compared with less than 4 percent of human pregnancies (Bowden *et al.,* 1967). The mortality rate in unassisted breech deliveries is quite high—approximately 90 percent. Although version is sometimes possible to manually correct, it is usually necessary to do a cesarean section when a breech presentation persists to the time of delivery.

Cesarean section has been done in several species. To minimize respiratory depression in the infant, this can be done under a local anesthetic until the fetus is removed; then general anesthesia can be administered. With the careful use of gas anesthetics, however, fetal depression is minimal. Through a low midline incision the site for needle puncture is selected by palpation of the uterus, care being taken to select a spot where the needle will not cause trauma to the infant or placenta. After the amniotic fluid is aspirated, a transverse uterine incision should be made just below the uterine attachment of the round ligaments. This incision is gently spread with the fingers until the infant can be delivered. The infant is held by the feet in an inverted position, so that mucus and fluid can drain from the oral cavity and trachea, and breathing is stimulated by a few slaps on the back. Suction should be available to assist in clearing the respiratory passages.

Complete removal of the bidiscoidal placenta and membranes can then be facilitated by delivering the uterus through the abdominal incision and everting it. After the placenta is gently wiped away or peeled off with gauze, the uterus is inverted, sutured with chromic catgut, and replaced in its normal position. Contraction of the uterus can be accomplished by gentle manual massage or by several small doses of ergonovine maleate injected into various parts of the uterine wall; the total of all injections should be approximately 1 ml (Valerio *et al.*, 1969).

Cesarean section in monkeys is sometimes followed by severe endometriosis (Pickering, 1968). This condition not only interferes with reproductive capability but may also pose a threat to normal body functions. In some cases, for example, severe intestinal obstruction has developed within five years after the cesarean section (Pickering, 1968).

The percentage of mothers which eat some or all of the placenta has been reported as 63 to 83 percent for *M. mulatta,* 47 percent for *M. nemestrina,* 69 percent for *Papio sp.* and 35 percent for *Pan sp.* (Bowden *et al.*, 1967).

III. CARE AND FEEDING OF THE YOUNG

All infants should be examined and weighed twelve to twenty-four hours after birth, but the mother and her infant should be left alone as much as possible in a quiet, normal environment.

A. Natural Rearing

The easiest and cheapest means of rearing infant monkeys is by leaving them with their mothers, and most females will instinctively provide adequate care for their young. The infants of most species climb onto their mother's back and cling there, even while sleeping, except when they come around to the front for nursing.

In most species, the mother assumes total responsibility for the rearing of the infant, although other females may show some protective interest. In the *Saguinus oedipus* species, however, both parents actively participate in infant care (Hampton and Hampton, 1967). The female may have exclusive care of the infants only during the first two or three days after birth. After that time, when nursing sessions are completed, the female begins to bite and scratch the infants in an effort to dislodge them from her back. The male parent then persuades the infants to come onto his back where they remain until they are hungry again. This procedure is followed until the infants are too large to be easily carried.

In captivity, infant *Tupaia glis* are often abandoned by the mother shortly after birth; occasionally they are eaten by the mother or by other adults in the cage. For this reason, it is also advisable to isolate female *Galago sp.* for parturition and during the early stages of infant development. The mothers often leave their infants alone in the nest box and they are very vulnerable to attack.

B. Artificial Rearing

Hand-rearing of infant monkeys may be desirable for some investigative procedures, or may be necessitated because the mother is unable or unwilling to care for her young.

1. Neonatal Care. If the infant is taken from the mother at birth, the umbilical cord should be cleaned with 70 percent alcohol and tied with silk 1/4 inch from the body; it is then cut distal to the knot, and the stump is painted with tincture of iodine. By the third or fourth day, the stump will slough off.

The infant, if soiled, may be bathed with warm water and a hexachlorophene emulsion, and then thoroughly dried. Hexachlorophene will minimize the possibility of infection picked up from the mother's vagina.

A cloth or rag should be given to the infant to satisfy the clutch reflex (Dubouch, 1969). This may be a turkish towel (Yang *et al.,* 1968) or a diaper which is preferred by infant *M. mulatta,* since it is lighter and easier to play with (Fleischman, 1963). The infant should have a towel or diaper for the first thirty days, a clean one being provided daily. Although it does not substitute for the presence of a mother, the infant learns early to cling to this cloth, and is more easily handled when removed from the cage if he is wrapped in a similar piece of cloth.

Most species of newborn monkeys have very poor thermal stability. The body temperature of a newborn *M. mulatta* separated from its mother is often in the range of 93 to 95° F, certainly an unphysiological drop from an ambient uterine temperature of about 100° F. An infant delivered when the room temperature is 70° F will need some protection until his own thermal mechanisms become established. Newborn infants taken from their mothers should be placed in an incubator at 37° C with adequate humidity, and oxygen should be supplied at the rate of two to three liters per minute (Munroe, 1966).

Hand-reared monkeys should be kept in a small cage until they are sufficiently coordinated to prevent injuries from falling. Balancing reflexes are usually developed in *M. mulatta* by twelve weeks of age.

2. *Feeding.* If an infant is taken from the mother at birth, it is recommended that a hypotonic saline solution be given *per os* four hours postnatally, followed by four feedings of a 5 percent solution of dextrose at two-hour intervals. After twelve hours, these may be replaced by commerical milk substitutes given on a two-hour schedule for the first five days. If the infant is unable to suck, no food should be forced during the first twenty-four hours. The primate infant, human or nonhuman, has a greater need for fluids than for calories during the first twelve to twenty-four hours, and aspiration pneumonia is less likely to be caused by a dextrose or saline solution than by milk preparations.

After the first five days, the infant should be fed every three hours for five more days, and then every four hours until he is one month of age. By this time, monkeys of most species are able to feed themselves. Healthy infants seldom need more than fifteen minutes for each feeding. After they are satisfied, they often fall asleep.

Vomiting is not uncommon during the first weeks of life, especially if the infant is not burped. Burping is essential at the end of a feeding, and may be done two or three times during the feeding; some infants, however, have a tendency to lose interest in feeding after being burped.

Monkey milk is similar to human milk in composition (Vickers, 1968); both contain much less protein and ash than cow's milk (Kerr and Waisman, 1965). Many commercial preparations meet the requirements of newborn monkeys.* If no commercial preparations are available, a mixture of whole cow's milk (8 ounces), water (2 ounces), and sugar (1 level teaspoon) can be used.

Infants of most species require 3 gm of protein per kilogram of body weight and a total intake of approximately 150 calories per day (Miller and Pallotta, 1965). For the larger species, the daily nutritional requirement is approximately 200 to 250 calories and 7 to 8 gm of protein per kilogram of body weight (Vickers, 1968). Multivitamins may be given, if desired, but there are no data to justify this practice. The commercial preparations probably contain many times more vitamins and iron than the amount required.

An important part of each feeding period is the use of a warm, damp tissue to induce urination and defecation.

As soon as possible (usually about one month of age) the baby should be allowed to feed himself and should begin receiving solid foods (mixed cereals and fruits). An excess of supplemental food items could result in an unbalanced diet.

C. Growth and Development

An initial weight loss is to be expected in newborn infants. Newborn *M. mulatta* lose about 10 percent of their birth weight by the end of the first thirty-six hours; then they slowly start to gain, reaching their birth weight by five days of age. Breast-fed monkeys gain more slowly than hand-reared ones (Vickers, 1968). In general, infants with the largest birth weight show the least to-

* Olac (Mead Johnson Laboratories, Evansville, Indiana), Similac (Ross Laboratories, Columbus, Ohio), and SMA Formulas I and II (Wyeth Laboratories, Philadelphia, Pennsylvania) are commonly used.

tal weight gain in the first few weeks. Birth weights and weight gains are generally larger in infants born to mother monkeys mated in cages than in infants of mothers which mated in their native habitat (Fujiwara and Imamichi, 1966).

The average daily weight gain for *M. mulatta* is 4 gm. In *Papio sp.* the rate of growth is greater for males (12 gm/day) than for females (7 gm/day) (Creager and Switzer, 1967). *Galago* infants gain about 80 percent of their birth weight per week during the first twelve weeks of life. *Gorilla gorilla* will usually double their birth weight by the eleventh week of age.

Both in the feral state and in the laboratory, *Saimiri sciureus* show some slowing of their weight gain at the fourth or fifth month and again at nine months (Hopf, 1967). In *Tupaia glis* monkeys, one infant of a litter appears to develop more rapidly than its litter mates during the first month, and is often twice as large as the other at three weeks. The smaller litter mates catch up around four or five weeks of age, and thereafter little difference is noted (Morris *et al.*, 1967).

D. Weaning

Weaning is a gradual process, which is actually started when the number of milk feedings per day is restricted. Weaning should be planned according to each individual monkey's growth and development rather than strictly according to age. Most species, however, should be introduced to soft solids at about four to six weeks of age. By gradually increasing the solids and more slowly decreasing the milk, the monkey can be completely weaned by the age of four to six months. It is important that the weaning process have no deleterious effects on normal growth curves (Zimmerman, 1969).

Hand-fed monkeys are gradually changed to a program of self-feeding by being offered small amounts of fruit, vegetables, or cereal mixed with the milk substitute and fed with an eye dropper. The amount of milk replacer is gradually decreased as the infant becomes accustomed to the more solid consistency. Hand-reared *M. mulatta* usually accept these foods eagerly and very quickly show a preference for solid foods over commercial milk preparations. If adequate space is available, this supplemental foodstuff can be offered to the young in an enclosure that does not permit entrance to the adult monkeys.

The following diet is readily accepted by a wide variety of species and provides all the nutritive requirements: Butter, 100 gm; casein, 200 gm; dextrin, 640 gm; Hegsted's salts mixture, 40 gm; complete vitamin mixture, 20 gm; flavoring (raisin, banana, etc.), 6 tsp; Sucaryl,* 7 tbsp.

This diet is suspended in agar, so that it can readily be eaten even by very young monkeys. The diet is prepared by mixing the flavoring and Sucaryl with the basic ingredients and then by adding this mixture to a 5 percent solution of boiling agar. After being poured into a pan and allowed to cool, the mixture can be cut into squares, each containing a prescribed amount of diet. The diet should be prepared weekly and kept in a refrigerator to prevent drying.

When infants reared by their mothers are separated from them at weaning time, they should be caged separately but within sight of their mothers. If the mother and child cannot hear loud vocalizations from each other, then they could initially be housed in separate areas. This procedure greatly reduces the stress of separation.

E. Primate Pediatrics

The purpose of primate pediatrics is to ensure the normal development of the young. Infants that are removed from their mothers should be examined and weighed daily; when the infants are left with their mothers these procedures can be done weekly. In order to detect early signs of anemia, hematologic studies should be done at monthly intervals on all infants, at least until they are weaned.

Diseases of young monkeys are not appreciably different from those of the adult, but the lack of cellular and fluid reserves in very young monkeys may make a difference. In severity and susceptibility respiratory diseases can be quite acute, and they require accurate diagnosis and intensive treatment. Respiration should be supported by placing the infant in an incubator with oxygen.

The greatest problems during infancy, however, are food re-

---

* Abbott Laboratories, North Chicago, Illinois.

fusal, constipation, and vomiting. As with all diseases, accurate diagnosis of the cause is of primary importance, and often depends upon adequate laboratory facilities. Food refusal may be related to diet or environment, or to some other underlying cause. Constipation is most likely to be a problem with hand-reared monkeys, and is usually precipitated by formula refusal, dehydration, or both. Glycerin suppositories should be used when necessary, and in extreme cases enemas of a mild-soap-water solution should be given (Blomquist and Harlow, 1961).

Protracted vomiting results in a loss of electrolytes and fluid, thereby inducing dehydration. Intravenous feeding is difficult, especially in the smaller species, and an alternative method is to feed the monkey with a stomach tube. Feedings should consist of a bland liquid diet of milk substitute suspended in an electrolyte solution containing sugar and 2 percent alcohol (Miller and Pallotta, 1965). If the infant is weak, it is better to give a 10 percent dextrose solution in electrolytes for twenty-four to forty-eight hours than to run the risk of having the milk formula aspirated into the lungs.

Diarrhea is probably the most common clinical sign of gastrointestinal illness in the monkey. Normal feces are yellow and pasty; green feces usually indicate that not enough calories are being consumed (Vickers, 1968). While the underlying cause of the diarrhea is being sought, electrolyte balance must be maintained. Diarrhea in monkeys is more often due to changes in environment than to bacterial infections, although the latter must always be considered.

Behavioral development is equally as important as physical development. Some writers (Harlow and Harlow, 1962) have emphasized the serious effects of social isolation of *M. mulatta* in infancy upon reproductive behavior in adulthood. According to these authors, animals reared in relative social isolation, sometimes with mother surrogates, often show marked inability to breed; if conception is achieved, they may prove to be poor mothers. These reports emphasize the "critical period" hypothesis, which holds that adult sexuality is learned during infancy and childhood. Other investigators, however, have reported essentially normal reproductive patterns in monkeys raised without the tactile stimulation usually afforded by the mother, siblings, and peers (Meier, 1965).

The seasonality of births in the feral state has the advantage of giving the young animals a group of playmates very close to his own age (Dumond, 1967). These seasonal birth groups seem to be important in fostering the development of early affectionate relationships between monkeys of the same age.

REFERENCES

Blomquist, A. J., and Harlow, H. F. (1961): The infant rhesus monkey program at the University of Wisconsin Primate Laboratory. *Lab Anim Care, 11,* 57-64.

Bowsen, D.; Winter, P., and Ploog, D. (1967): Pregnancy and delivery behavior in the squirrel monkey (*Saimiri sciureus*) and other primates. *Folia Primat, 5,* 1-42.

Conaway, C. H., and Sade, D. S. (1965): The seasonal spermatogenic cycle in free ranging rhesus monkeys. *Folia Primat, 3,* 1-12.

Creager, J. G., and Switzer, J. W. (1967): Some factors relating to growth and development of primate infants with special reference to the baboon. In Vagtborg, H. (Ed.); *The Baboon in Medical Research.* Austin, University of Texas Press, pp. 85-98.

Dede, J. A., and Plentl, A. A. (1966): Induced ovulation and artificial insemination in a rhesus colony. *Fertil Steril, 17,* 757-764.

Dumond, F. V. (1967): Semi-free-ranging colonies of monkeys at Goulds Monkey Jungle. *Int Zoo Yearbk, 7,* 202-207.

Dumond, F. V. (1968): The squirrel monkey in a seminatural environment. In Rosenblum, L. A., and Cooper, R. W. (Ed.): *The Squirrel Monkey.* New York, Academic Press, pp. 87-145.

Dubouch, P. (1969): Artificial rearing of baboons. *Primat Med, 2,* 96-99.

Eckstein, P., and Kelly, W. A. (1966): A survey of the breeding performance of rhesus monkeys in the laboratory. *Symp Zool Soc London, 17,* 91-112.

Fleischman, R. W. (1963): Care of infant rhesus monkeys (*Macaca mulatta*). *Lab Anim Care, 13,* 703-710.

Fujiwara, T., and Imamichi, T. (1966): Breeding of cynomologous monkeys as an experimental animal. *Jap J Med Sci Biol, 19,* 225-226.

Fujiwara, T.; Honjo, S.; Imaizumi, K., and Imamichi, T. (1969): The post partum menstruation of cynomologous monkeys kept under the laboratory conditions. *Jap J Med Sci Biol, 22,* 181-185.

Goss, C. M.; Popejoy, L. T., II; Fusiler, J. L., and Smith, T. M. (1968): Observations on the relationship between embryological development, time of conception, and gestation. In Rosenblum, L. A., and Cooper, R. W.: *The Squirrel Monkey.* New York, Academic Press, pp. 171-191

Gucwinski, H., and Gucwinski, A. (1968): Breeding the Zanzibar *galago Galago senegalensis zanzibaricus* at Wroclaw Zoo. *Int Zoo Yearbk, 8,* 111-114.

Hampton, S. H., and Hampton, J. K., Jr. (1967): Rearing marmosets from birth by artificial laboratory techniques. *Lab Anim Care, 17,* 1-10.

Harlow, H. F., and Harlow, M. K. (1962): Social deprivation in monkeys. *Sci Amer, 207,* 136-147.

Hartman, C. G. (1945): The mating of mammals. *Ann NY Acad Sci, 46,* 23-44.

Hendrickx, A. G., and Kriewaldt, F. H. (1967): Observations on a controlled breeding colony of baboons. In Vagtborg, H. (Ed.): *The Baboon in Medical Research.* Austin, University of Texas Press, pp. 69-83.

Hopf, S. (1967): Notes on pregnancy, delivery, and infant survival in captive squirrel monkeys. *Primates, 8,* 323-332.

Kerr, G. R., and Weisman, H. A. (1965): The rearing of the infant rhesus monkey (*Macaca mulatta*). *ISMR CB-ACP Bull,* 39, 6-8.

Kuehn, R. E.; Jensen, G. D., and Morrill, R. K. (1965): Breeding *Macaca nemestrina:* A program of birth engineering. *Folia Primat, 3,* 251-262.

Lang, C. M. (1967): The estrous cycle of the squirrel monkey (*Saimiri sciureus*). *Lab Anim Care, 17,* 442-451.

Meier, G. W. (1965): Other data on the effects of social isolation during rearing upon adult reproductive behaviour in the rhesus monkey (*Macaca mulatta*). *Anim Behav, 13,* 228-231.

Miller, R. L., and Pallotta, A. J. (1965): Comments on the maintenance of a small baboon colony. In Vagtborg, H. (Ed.): *The Baboon in Medical Research,* Austin, University of Texas Press.

Morris, J. H.; Negus, N. C., and Spertzel, R. O. (1967): Colonization of the tree shrew (*Tupaia glis*). *Lab Anim Care, 17,* 514-520.

Munroe, J. S. (1966): Viral oncogenesis in the rhesus monkey: Miscellaneous studies. *Symp Zool Soc London, 17,* 229-250.

Pallotta, A. J. (1969): Artificial rearing of macaques. *Primat Med, 2,* 100-102.

Pickering, D. E. (1968): Reproduction characteristics in a colony of laboratory confined mulatta macaque monkeys. *Folia Primat, 8,* 169-179.

Rosenblum, L. A. (1968): Some aspects of female reproductive physiology in the squirrel monkey. In Rosenblum, L. A., and Cooper, R. W. (Ed.): *The Squirrel Monkey.* New York, Academic Press, pp. 147-169.

Valerio, D. A., and Courtney, K. D. (1968): Treatment of infertility in *Macaca mulatta* with clomiphene citrate. *Lab Anim Care, 18,* 339-345.

Valerio, D. A.; Courtney, K. D.; Miller, R. L., and Pallotta, A. J. (1968): The establishment of a *Macaca mulatta* breeding colony. *Lab Anim Care, 18,* 589-595.

Valerio, D. A.; Miller, R. L.; Innes, J. R. M.; Courtney, K. D.; Pallotta, A. J., and Guttmacher, R. M. (1969): *Macaca mulatta. Management of a Laboratory Breeding Colony.* New York, Academic Press.

van Wagenen, G. (1967): Fertility of the colony-born male macaque. *Folia Primat, 5,* 241-246.

Vickers, J. H. (1968): Primate pediatrics. In Kirk, R. W. (Ed.): *Current Veterinary Practice*. III. *Small Animal Practice*. Philadelphia, Saunders, pp. 396-398.

Yang, C. S.; Kuo, C. C.; Del Favero, J. E., and Alexander, E. R. (1968): Care and raising of newborn Taiwan monkeys (*Macaca cyclopis*) for virus studies. *Lab Anim Care, 18,* 536-543.

Young, R. J. (1965): Monkey colony management. *J Amer Vet Med Ass, 147,* 1053-1062.

Zimmerman, R. R. (1969): Early weaning and weight gain in infant rhesus monkeys. *Lab Anim Care, 19,* 644-647.

Chapter 18

EXPERIMENTAL SURGERY

D. C. KRAEMER, G. T. MOORE AND N. C. VERA CRUZ

I. ANESTHESIA

PROPER anesthesia is essential for successful results in surgery. The following discussion is not intended to provide all the available information about anesthesia, but it does contain basic information on several anesthetics recommended for use in nonhuman primates. Three groups of anesthetics are discussed: local an esthetics, immobilizing agents, and general anesthetics. The dosage, route of administration, time to effect, and duration of action for short- and long-acting immobilizing agents, barbiturates and volatile anesthetics are outlined in Table 18-I.

A. Local Anesthesia

Local anesthesia is rarely used in surgery of nonhuman primates; however, selected procedures may be performed, if necessary, with combinations of local anesthetics and immobilizing agents. Examples of this type of procedure are vasectomy, castration and testicular biopsy. Spraying the pharynx to facilitate insertion of an endotracheal tube is another useful application of local anesthetics. Procaine, tetracaine, and lidocaine may be used safely for subcutaneous infiltration in concentrations of 0.5-2.0%, whereas sprays are used at 3-4%. In every instance the dosage should not exceed the lowest concentration and smallest quantity necessary to produce the desired effect.

B. Immobilizing Agents

Pharmacological immobilization of the nonhuman primate has come into wide usage in recent years. The most commonly used product for this purpose is Sernylan® (phencyclidine hydrochloride,

Bio-Ceutic Labs., Inc.). It has a wide margin of safety, is quick acting, conveniently administered and produces good immobilization. A closely related product, Ketalar® (ketamine hydrochloride, Parke-Davis) exhibits all these qualities with the added advantage of having a shorter duration of effect. With these agents an animal can be immobilized inside a conventional squeeze cage and removed without danger to the animal or animal technician. Once the animal is immobilized supplemental anesthesia can be administered if desired. Sernylan and Ketalar produce light anesthesia at the recommended dosages, however, local or general anesthetics may be necessary to provide good analgesia and proper muscle relaxation. These dosages may be adjusted slightly to produce varying levels of immobilization. These products should always be preceded by atropine sulfate (0.04 mg/kg) to prevent excessive salivation.

Tranquilizers have been used widely in an effort to produce immobilization; however, they usually fall short of producing the desired effect unless given in very high doses or in combination with other drugs. When used with Sernylan and Ketalar, tranquilizers have a synergistic effect. The animals sensitivity to its environment is reduced, but surgical anesthesia is not attained. Consequently, tranquilizers are not recommended for immobilization.

C. General Anesthesia

The recommended dosages of barbiturate and gas anesthetics (Table 18-I) reflect the amounts necessary to produce and maintain surgical anesthesia in animals previously immobilized with Sernylan or Ketalar. The barbiturate dose is a calculated amount which should be given slowly intravenously until the desired plane of anesthesia is obtained. Pentothal is not used intraperitoneally in prosimians because of its irritating properties if given extravascularly. However, Nembutal® is administered either intraperitoneally or intramuscularly at the recommended dosage. Both Pentothal and Nembutal provide excellent anesthesia in combination with Sernylan or Ketalar. Extended anesthesia with the barbiturates is obtained by supplementing with one-half the dosage described in Table 18-I. Other barbiturates (amobarbital and phenobarbital) have been used, but their durations of effect are too long for most procedures.

TABLE 18-I

IMMOBILIZING AGENTS AND GENERAL ANESTHETICS (BARBITURATES AND GAS) RECOMMENDED FOR NONHUMAN PRIMATES

	Dose		*Time to Effect (Min.)*		*Time to Recovery (Min.)*	
	A. Immobilizing Agents (mg/kg/IM)					
	Ketalar	*Sernylan*	*Ketalar*	*Sernylan*	*Ketalar*	*Sernylan*
Prosimians	6–8	0.8–1.0	8–10	10–15	50–60	80–95
New World	15–20	1.0–1.25	5–7	6–8	45–60	120–140
Old World	10–15	1.0–1.5	4–5	8–10	25–40	150–160
Baboons	9–15	0.8–1.0	3–4	14–16	40–45	140–150
Great Apes	12–17	0.75–1.25	2–3	12–15	35–40	160–180
	B. Barbiturates (mg/kg/IV)					
	Pentothal	*Nembutal*	*Pentothal*	*Nembutal*	*Pentothal*	*Nembutal*
Prosimians	NR	18–20*	—	15–20	—	300–360
New World	10–13	12–14	0.5–1.0	0.5–1.0	20–25	180–240
Old World	12–15	14–15	0.5–1.0	0.5–1.0	20–25	180–300
Baboons	8–10	14–15	0.5–1.0	0.5–1.0	25–30	120–180
Great Apes	8–12	14–15	0.5–1.0	0.5–1.0	35–40	120–240
	C. Gas (% Gas/Oxygen)					
	Nitrous Oxide	*Fluothane*	*Nitrous Oxide*	*Fluothane*	*Nitrous Oxide*	*Fluothane*
Prosimians	60–65	0.25–0.5	3–5	2	6–8	15–20
New World	60–65	0.25–0.5	4–6	2	5–7	10–15
Old World	65–70	0.5–0.75	4–6	3	4–5	10–15
Baboons	70–75	0.5–1.0	6–8	2–3	4–5	8–12
Great Apes	70–75	0.5–1.0	6–8	2–3	3–4	10–15

NR—Not Recommended
* —Given Intraperitoneally

The volatile anesthetics are usually safer to administer than barbiturates. They should be administered to animals previously sedated with either an immobilizing agent or a short-acting barbiturate. Table 18-I shows the percentage of gas/oxygen mixture necessary to maintain surgical anesthesia in various groups of nonhuman primates. These gas mixtures are administered using a closed or semiclosed circular anesthesia system.

Nitrous oxide is safe when used under 80 percent concentration in oxygen. Higher concentrations may produce hypoxia. Slightly higher concentrations than the recommended levels of Fluothane® may be necessary to induce surgical anesthesia. Both gases provide good anesthesia with rapid recovery and few toxic side effects. Ether, metofane, cyclopropane and chloroform have been used in nonhuman primates but are not as practical or effective as the two gases recommended. All gas anesthetics should be preceded by atropine sulfate (0.04 mg/kg) to insure an airway clear of secretions.

II. PREOPERATIVE AND POSTOPERATIVE PROCEDURES

A. Surgical Preparation

1. Food and water is withheld for twelve to fifteen hours prior to scheduled surgery. This preparation minimizes emesis and aspiration during and after surgery.

2. Immobilization is accomplished by intramuscular injection of phencyclidine hydrochloride (Sernylan) or ketamine hydrochloride (Ketalar). Atropine (0.04 mg/kg) is also given intramuscularly.

3. The hair, covering and immediately surrounding the surgical site, is clipped and shaved as close to the skin as possible.

4. The skin is thoroughly cleaned with hexachlorophene soap.

5. Each animal is intubated and surgical anesthesia is induced with either thiopental sodium (Pentothal® or Fluothane® (halothane).

6. The area surrounding the surgical site is disinfected with povidone-iodine solution (Betadine®) and covered with sterile drapes. Strict aseptic techniques, including use of sterile instruments, gowns and gloves, are adhered to during all surgical procedures.

B. General Surgical Technique

The skin is incised and the subcutaneous tissue is bluntly dissected to expose the desired surgical plane. Hemostasis during dissection is maintained by ligation and/or electrocautery. Further surgical detail is discussed under each procedure. After surgery the muscle fascia and subcutaneous tissue are closed with 000 chromic gut, and the skin with 00 silk, 000 nylon, or stainless steel wire (36 gauge).

C. Postoperative Care

After surgery the wound is sprayed with a topical antibiotic and the animal returned to its cage. If asepsis was not maintained during surgery the animal is supported with a combination of penicillin and streptomycin given systemically. All animals are observed following surgery for indications of systemic or wound infections, and antibiotics are used as each case warrants. The sutures are removed from all wounds seven to ten days postoperatively. Other special postoperative care will be discussed under each procedure.

III. TISSUE BIOPSIES IN THE MALE

An effective tissue biopsy technique is one which yields a tissue specimen of sufficient size to permit histological preparation and evaluation. The tissue collected must be free from mechanical distortions and the technique must not produce excessive damage to the tissue or organ being biopsied.

A. Testis

Biopsy techniques for serially sampling testes of *Macaca nemestrina* (Zemjanis *et al.,* 1969) and *Papio cynocephalus* have been adapted from techniques described for man (Rowley and Heller,

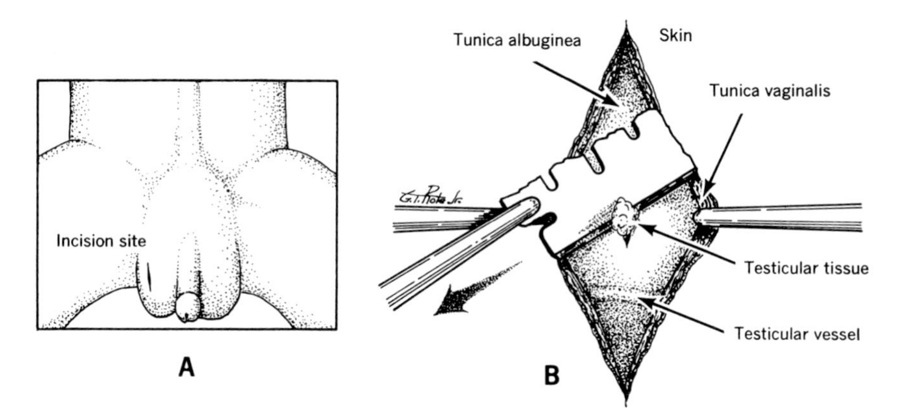

Figure 18-1. Testis biopsy. A. Incision site on the ventral aspect of the scrotum; B. Testicular tissue protruding through 0.5 cm incision in the tunica albuginea. Excision of biopsy specimen using a single slicing motion of an ultrathin razor blade held by a needle holder.

1966; Gouygou, 1969). The testis is held with minimal pressure by an assistant. An incision (4 cm) is made in the ventral aspect of the scrotum over the center of the testis (Fig. 18-1A). The exposed tunica vaginalis is incised to expose the testis. A 0.5 cm incision is made through the tunica albuginea with an ultrathin razor blade (Fig. 18-1B). Care is taken to avoid transection of the large blood vessels which traverse the tunica albuginea, however, if one is severed it is clamped temporarily and ligated during closure. The testicular tissue which protrudes is removed by a single slicing motion of the razor blade held by a needle holder (Fig. 18-1B). This procedure minimizes trauma on the excised tissue that could be caused by cutting with scissors or a heavy scalpel. Closure of tunica albuginea and tunica vaginalis are effected using simple interrupted sutures with 00000 plain gut. The skin is closed with 00 silk using simple interrupted sutures.

B. Prostate

The prostate of *Papio cynocephalus* is readily palpable through the rectal wall with the index or middle finger. With the other hand, a Silverman biopsy needle with a Franklin modification is inserted through the perineal wall and directed towards the gland. The tip of the biopsy needle with the stylet in place can be felt through the rectal wall, and is guided to the desired location on the surface of the prostate. The stylet is removed and the blades of the instrument are inserted through the sheath and pushed into the gland. The sheath is advanced over the blades and they are rotated before removal of the entire assembly (Fig. 18-2A & B). A sample of tissue from the caudal prostate is easily obtainable in this manner, but sampling the cranial prostate requires considerably more practice.

C. Bulbourethral Glands

The bulbourethral glands of *P. cynocephalus* are not as readily palpable as the prostate. However, they lie just posterior to the caudal lobes of the prostate (Fig. 18-2A). This anatomical relationship makes it possible, with practice, to obtain biopsy samples from these glands. Tissue samples are obtained using the same procedure and instruments described for the prostate (Fig. 18-2A &

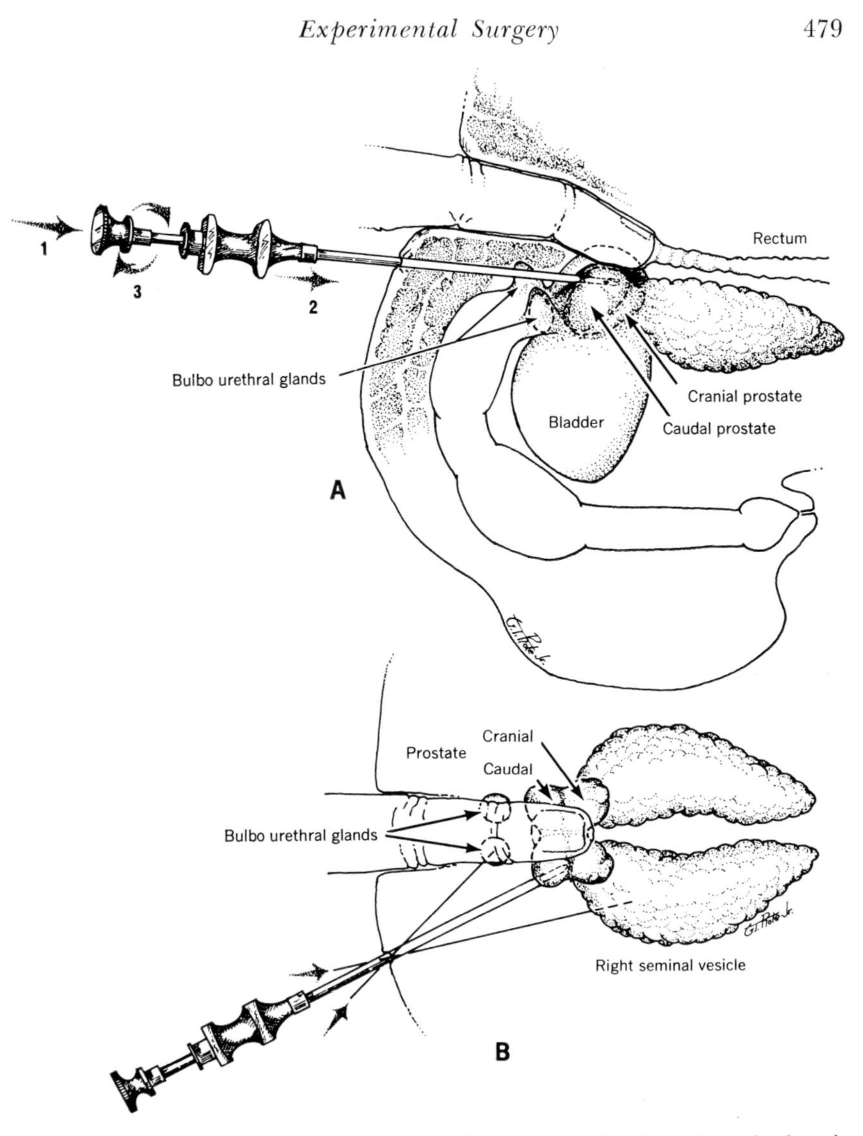

Figure 18-2. Needle biopsy of prostate, bulbourethral glands and seminal vesicles. A. Lateral view showing the finger in the rectum guiding the biopsy needle into the prostate. The blades are shown in position for insertion into the caudal prostate. The position of the blades after insertion (arrow 1) is shown by dotted lines. The sheath is advanced over the blades (arrow 2) which are then rotated (arrow 3) before removal of the entire assembly. Relative locations of bulbourethral glands and seminal vesicles are also shown. B. Dorsal view showing the relative angles of insertion of the biopsy needle for obtaining samples from the prostate, bulbourethral glands and seminal vesicles.

B). Where larger samples are required or where prior practice is not possible these glands are easily approached by the procedures described for gland removal (Sec. V-C) and a segment can be excised using a sharp blade or biopsy forceps.

D. Seminal Vesicles

Although the seminal vesicles of *Papio cynocephalus* can be reached with biopsy needle as described previously for the prostate and bulbourethral glands, the needle biopsy technique is not recommended because of the limited amount of tissue obtained and the possible danger of intraglandular hemorrhage. The method of choice is via a 4 cm lateroventral abdominal incision (Fig. 18-3A) through which the capsule of the gland is grasped with a pair of Allis tissue forceps. With slight tension on the forceps, the tip of the gland is exposed (Fig. 18-3B). The connective tissue capsule is dissected to expose a loop of tubule which is ligated before being excised (Fig. 18-3C). Closure of the capsule is not essential.

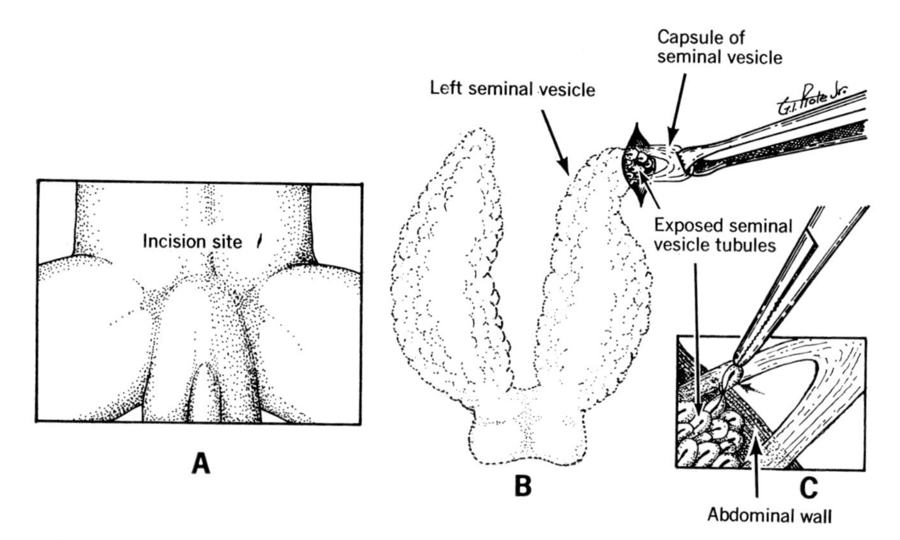

Figure 18-3. Transabdominal seminal vesicle biopsy. A. Incision site in lower abdomen; B. Seminal vesicle with the cranial tip exposed through the abdominal incision; C. A loop of seminal vesicle tubule ligated prior to excision (arrow). The tubule is supported by grasping the adventitia to avoid traumatizing the biopsy sample.

IV. COLLECTION OF FLUIDS FROM THE MALE

A. Testicular Fluid

The procedure for collection of testicular fluid in nonhuman primates is adapted from procedures reported for the bull (Voglmayr, *et al.*, 1970). The testis and the epididymis are exposed through an incision in the lateroventral aspect of the scrotal sac. The head of the epididymis is dissected from the tunica albuginea until the efferent tubules are exposed. Care must be taken to prevent excision of the adjacent vascular plexus which may be confused with the efferent tubules. Two ligatures are passed behind the tubules. While exerting tension on the tubules by means of one of the ligatures, a half spear point, extra fine dissecting scalpel (Clay-Adams) is inserted through the tubules into the rete testis (Fig. 18-4A). This incision is expanded by insertion of a fine mi-

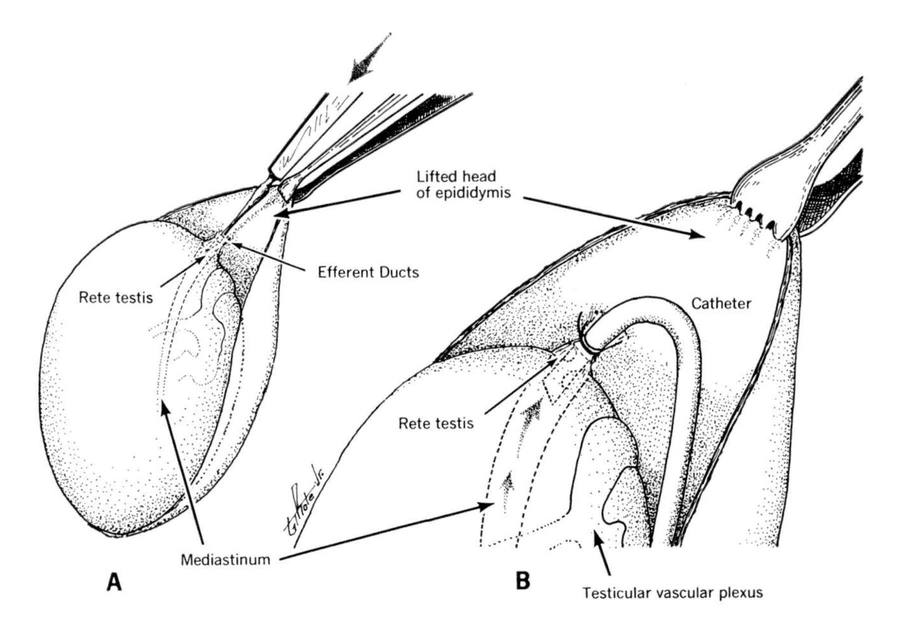

Figure 18-4. Collection of testicular fluid. A. Exposure of the efferent tubules by reflection of the head of the epididymis from the cranial aspect of the testis. An extra-fine scalpel is inserted through the efferent tubules into the rete testes towards the mediastinum; B. Insertion of the collecting catheter into the expanded opening of the efferent tubules. Catheter is stabilized by a ligature surrounding the efferent tubules below the site of insertion.

crodissecting forceps with rounded points. A flexible polyethylene catheter (1.0 mm O.D.) with an end and two lateral openings is inserted into the expanded incision towards the mediastinum testis (approx. 5 mm) and secured with the other ligature (Fig. 18-4B). The catheter is anchored to the tunica albuginea. Further stabilization is achieved when the head of the epididymis is sutured in its original position. Before wound closure, a small incision is made on the ventral apex of the scrotal sac through which the open end of the catheter is exteriorized and connected to a collection receptacle. The animal is placed in a restraining chair during the entire period of collection. Collection vessels may also be implanted under the skin of the scrotum, in which case, the animal may be maintained in an individual cage and chemically restrained for recovery of fluid from the collection vessel.

B. Epididymal

An incision is made on the lateroventral aspect of the scrotum and the testis is rotated to expose the tail of the epididymis (Fig. 18-5A). The ductus epididymis is isolated from the accompanying vessels and nerves by blunt dissection at the point where it becomes the ductus deferens (Fig. 18-5B). Several loops of the duct are isolated and stretched using right angle forceps. A small incision is made in the duct and a flexible polyethylene catheter (0.5 mm O.D.) is inserted into the lumen towards the tail of the epididymis. The catheter is secured by ligation around the epididymal duct between the stabilization cuffs of the catheter (Fig. 18-5D). Fluid collection is similar to that described previously (Sec. IV-A).

C. Ductus Deferens

The spermatic cord is palpated to determine the point of entry into the abdominal cavity. A 3 cm incision is made at this point (Fig. 18-5A). The cord is exposed by blunt dissection. The ductus deferens is isolated from the cord and an incision is made on the duct for insertion of a flexible polyethylene catheter (0.8 mm O.D.). The double-cuffed catheter is inserted a distance of approximately 5 mm towards the tail of the epididymis (Fig. 18-5 C & D). A ligature is applied to secure the catheter in the same man-

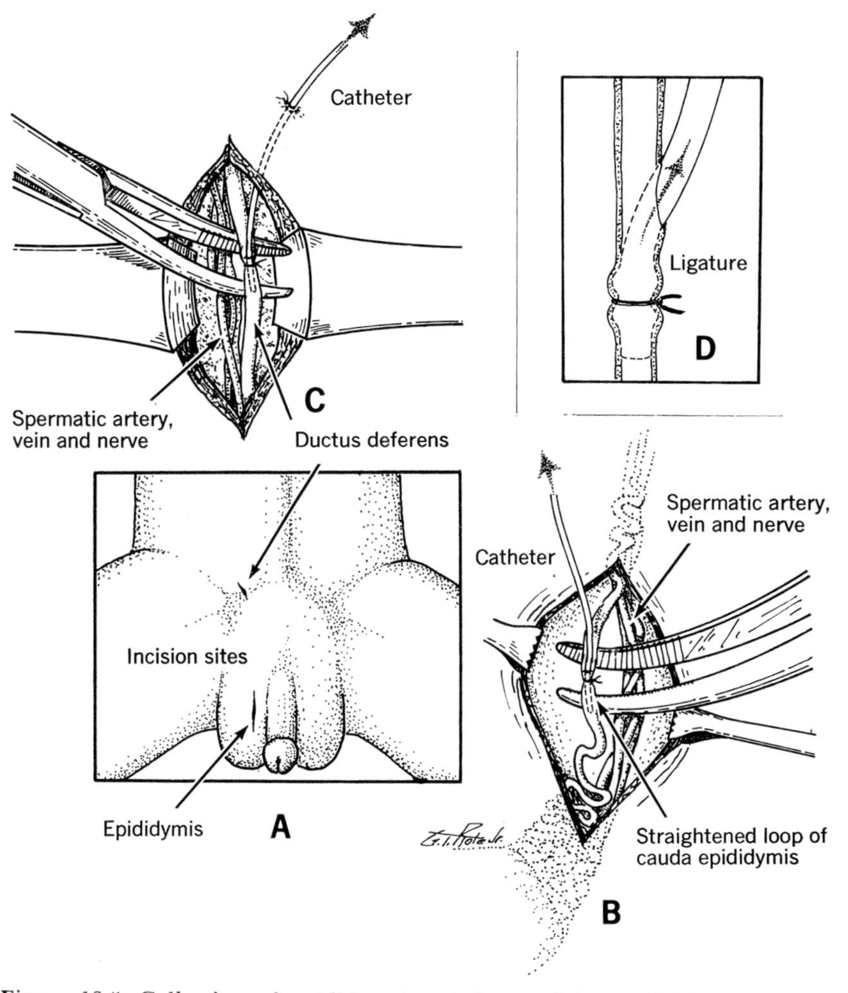

Figure 18-5. Collection of epididymal and ductus deferens fluid. A. Incision sites on the scrotum and over the spermatic cord for cannulation of the epididymis and ductus deferens, respectively; B. Catheter in straightened loop of the cauda epididymis; C. Catheter in ductus deferens directed towards the epididymis. The catheter is exteriorized cranially through a skin puncture which is ligated with a purse string suture. D. Method for stabilizing the catheters in the epididymis and ductus deferens.

ner as described above for the epididymis. The catheter is exteriorized cranially through a skin puncture and fluid collection is similar to that described previously (Sec. IV-A).

V. REMOVAL OF MALE GENITAL STRUCTURES

A. Castration

The testis is pushed craniad on the median raphe and an incision is made through the skin and underlying fascia to expose the tunica vaginalis which in turn is incised to expose the testicle. The tunica vaginalis is detached from the caudal pole of the testes by

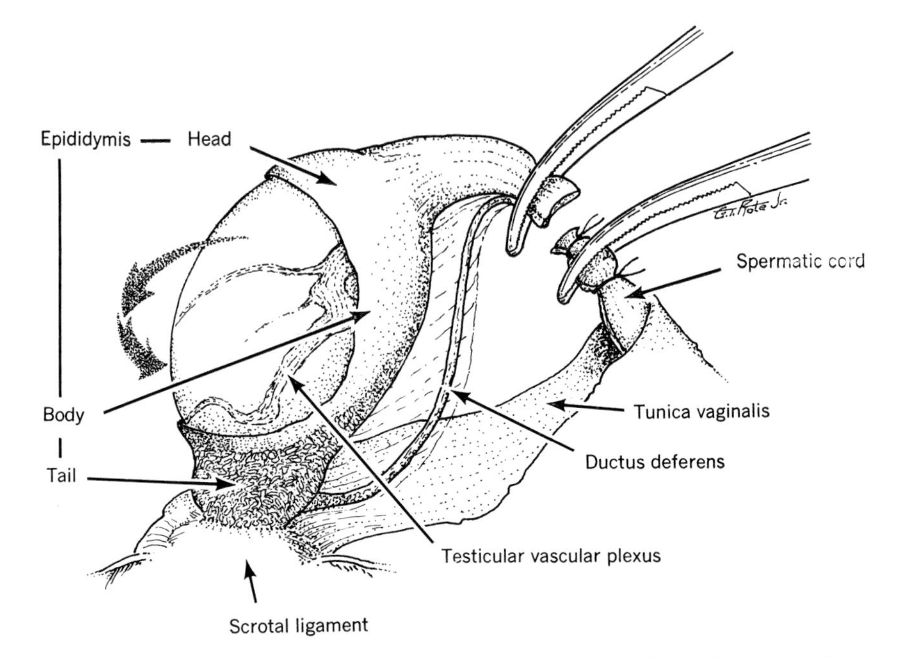

Figure 18-6. Castration. Ventral view of the right testis after being rotated out of the scrotal sac, showing severance of the spermatic cord distal to the double ligations.

cutting the avascular scrotal ligament. The exposed spermatic cord is double-ligated as shown in Fig. 18-6 preparatory to removal of the testis. Skin closure is by interrupted sutures leaving a 1 cm opening at the caudal apex of the scrotal sac for drainage.

B. Vasectomy

The surgical approach is similar to that described for fluid collection from the ductus deferens (Sec. IV.-C). A double ligature

(00 silk) is applied on the isolated ductus deferens. The duct is cut between the ligatures.

C. Bulbourethrectomy

The animal is placed in a prone position with the hind legs hanging over the elevated end of the surgical table. A horizontal skin incision is made in the perineal region approximately two-thirds the distance from the anus to the ischial callosities (Fig. 18-7A). The dorsal border of the incision is extended forward by blunt dissection between the sphincter ani externus and the levator ani muscles dorsally, and the bulbocavernosus muscle ventrally, to expose the bulbourethral glands (Fig. 18-7B), The bulbocavernosus muscle is retracted ventrally and the bulbourethral glands are isolated by blunt dissection until only the duct and vascular supply remain attached to the urethra. This connection is clamped with a curved forceps (Fig. 18-7C) and the gland is incised by passing a blade between the capsule of the gland and the forceps. A ligature is applied beneath the forceps (Fig. 18-7D). The wound is closed by skin closure only.

D. Prostatectomy

Several approaches have been employed in nonhuman primates to expose and remove the prostate gland. In *Papio ursinus,* the prostate was exposed via a midline suprapubic muscle-splitting incision through which the retropubic space was opened by excision of a wedge of the symphysis pubis and pubic bone (Schoonees and de Klerk, 1968). In *Macaca mulatta,* the retropubic approach has been employed successfully and recommended for removal of the cranial prostate (Greer *et al.,* 1968). In our experience, the perineal approach is the most satisfactory for removal of the caudal prostate in *P. cynocephalus* (Fig. 18-7E). When both lobes are to be removed, the perineal approach is also recommended; however, the retropubic approach is recommended when only the cranial prostate is to be removed. The positioning of the animal and the initial surgery are described in Sec. V.-C. The prostate gland lies immediately craniad to the bulbourethral glands (Fig. 18-7B) in close proximity to the urethra. In order to define the limits of the urethra, a catheter is inserted through the penile urethra into

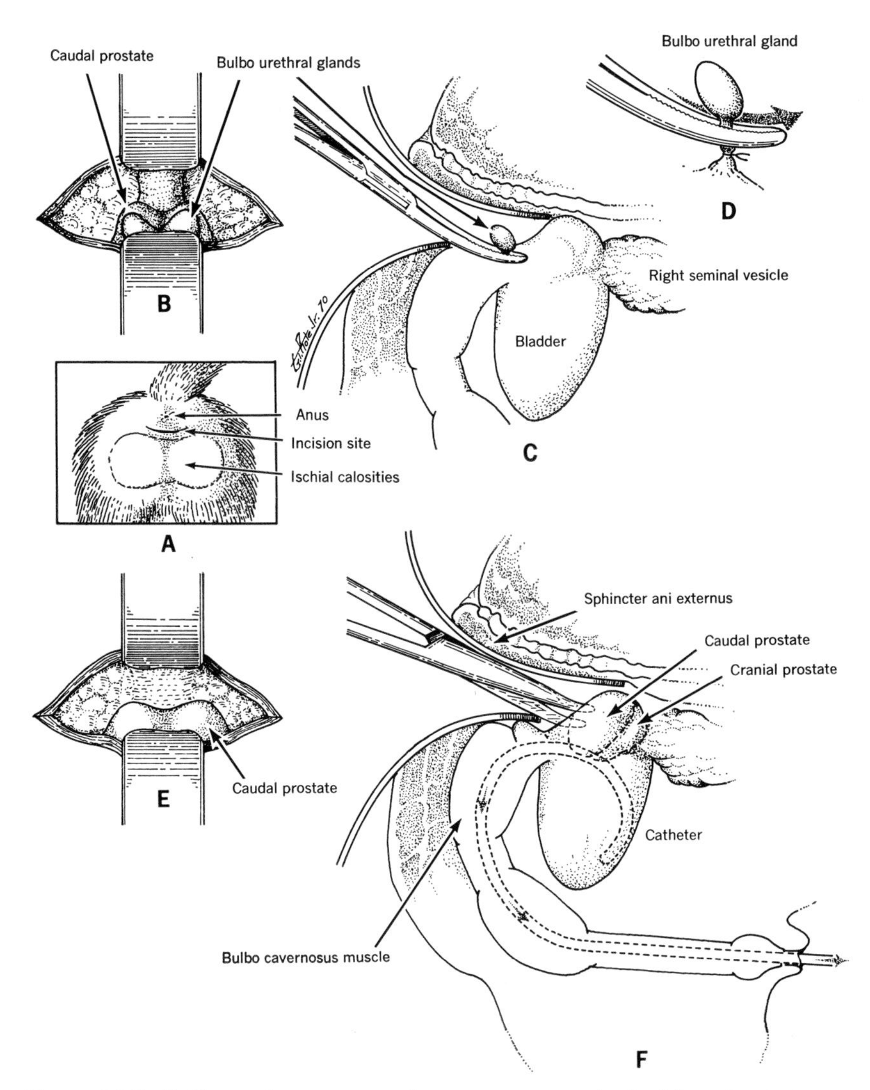

Figure 18-7. Bulbourethrectomy and prostatectomy. A. Incision site between the anus and ischial callosities; B. Perineal exposure of bulbourethral glands; C. Lateral view of the isolated right bulbourethral gland; D. Clamping, ligation and excision (arrow) of the bulbourethral gland; E. Perineal exposure of the prostate; F. Lateral view of dissection of the prostate.

the bladder. This procedure aids in the isolation and dissection of the prostate gland without traumatizing the urethra. Dissection of the gland is performed with a curved surgical dissecting scissors (Fig. 18-7F). As with bulbourethrectomy, wound closure is accomplished with skin sutures only.

E. Seminal Vesiculectomy

The seminal vesicles are exposed by way of a midventral incision extending from the pubis to the umbilicus (Fig. 18-8A). The tubules of the gland are bound together by a connective tissue capsule. This capsule is grasped using an Allis forceps and dissected from the gland until the base is exposed (Fig. 18-8B). Caution must be exercised not to damage the ductus deferens which lies medial at the base and crosses the gland ventrolaterally. The base of the seminal vesicle is exposed by applying tension on the dissected lobes of the gland and clamped with a curved forceps (Fig. 18-8C). With tension still applied, transection is accomplished by passing a scalpel blade over the concave surface of the forceps. A ligature is applied beneath the clamp.

VI. REMOVAL OF ENDOCRINE GLANDS

A. Hypophysectomy

A parapharyngeal approach for hypophysectomy of *Macaca mulatta* has been described (Smith, 1954; Knobil and Greep, 1959). A similar approach is described here for *Papio cynocephalus.* The animal is placed in a supine position with padding under the shoulders so that the head can be stabilized with the ventral border of the mandible in a horizontal position. A parasagittal incision is made through the skin and underlying fascia lateral to the larynx. The trachea and esophagus are retracted to the side (Fig. 18-9A). The recti capitis anterior muscles are exposed mainly by blunt dissection and followed craniad, along the medial ridge of the occipital bone, to their attachments on the basioccipital. At this point a V-shaped groove is palpable between the muscles near their attachments. The base of the skull is exposed by electrocautery of the connective tissue in this groove to expose the synchondrosis between the occipital and sphenoid bones. Using dental

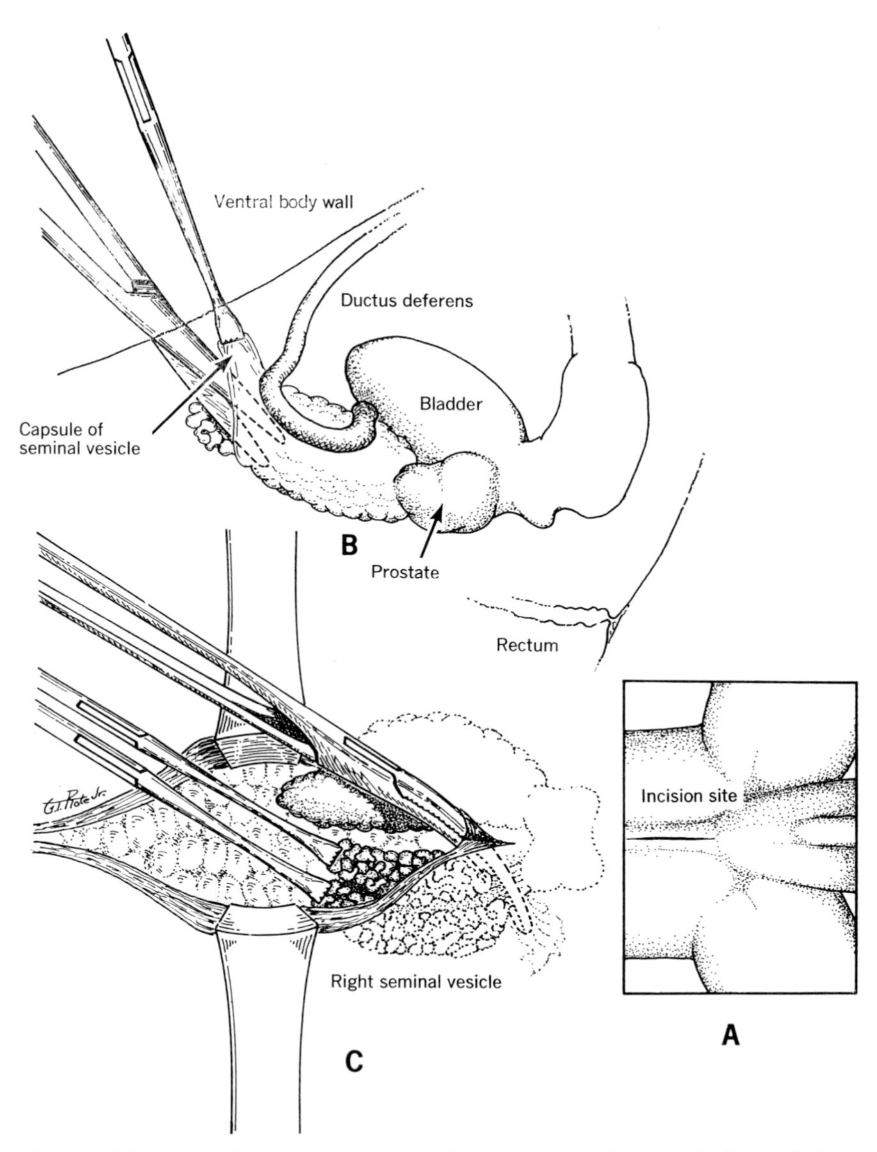

Figure 18-8. Seminal vesiculectomy. A. Midventral incision site; B. Lateral view showing blunt dissection of right seminal vesicle from its capsule; C. Ventral view of the dissected right seminal vesicle with a clamp on the base of the gland.

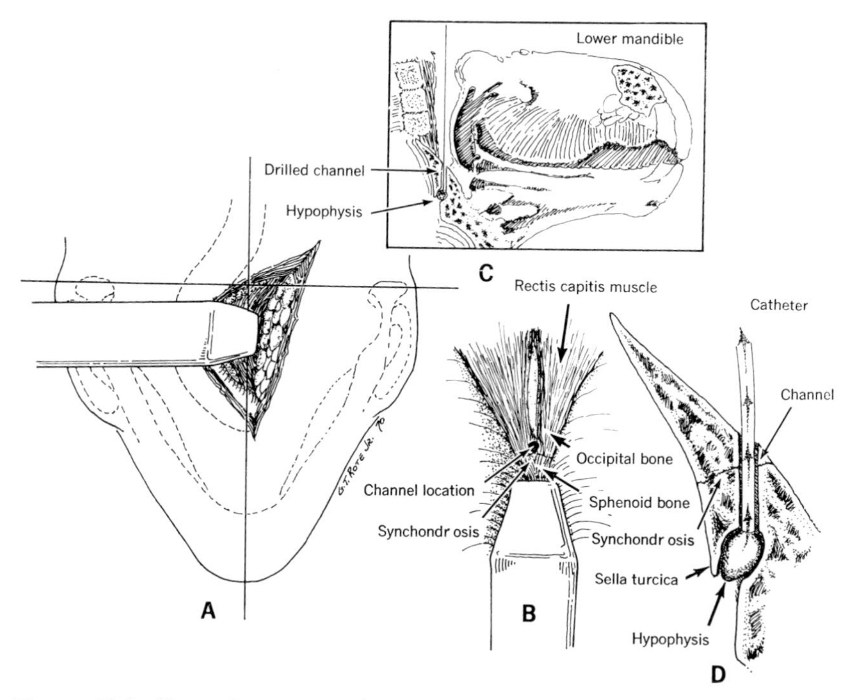

Figure 18-9. Hypophysectomy. A. Parapharyngeal incision site; B. Ventral view of the exposed synchondrosis between the basioccipital and sphenoid bones showing the channel location; C. Sagittal view of the surgical area for hypophysectomy showing the angle of approach to the sella turcica; D. Enlarged view of the drilled channel and hypophysis.

burrs a channel is drilled immediately posterior to the synchondrosis at an angle of approximately 40° to the basioccipital bone (Fig. 18-9B, C & D). The dura lining the sella turcica is thus exposed and incised with a sharp dura hook. A stainless steel atraumatic catheter with a slightly angled tip is lowered through the channel with the end in light contact with the side of the channel so that the entry of the catheter into the sella can be controlled. Suction is applied to the catheter using a 30 cc syringe. The catheter tip is moved about in the sella to facilitate removal of the entire gland. Chromic acid (3-5 percent) may be applied to the walls of the sella using a cotton tip applicator to destroy any remaining pituitary fragments. Closure of the channel in the occipital bone is not indicated and wound closure is limited to skin sutures. Postsurgical corticosteroid therapy (cortisone acetate, 5 mg/kg/day) may be administered to facilitate healing, but is not required for survival. Glucose (10 percent solution) is offered *ad libitum*.

The transorbital approach to the pituitary gland of the *Macaca mulatta* (Zervas and Pickren, 1968) provides access for purposes of pituitary biopsy or radio-frequency thermal destruction. Anatomically it appears that this approach should be equally effective for the *Papio cynocephalus;* however, it has not yet been applied to this species.

B. Thyroparathyroidectomy

The parathyroid glands in the *Papio cynocephalus* are embedded in the glandular parenchyma of the thyroid; therefore removal of the thyroid gland without the parathyroids is not practical. A midline incision is made in the neck from the thyroid cartilage to the suprasternal notch. The fascia and muscle sheaths are bluntly dissected and retracted laterally to expose the two lobes of the thyroid gland (Fig. 18-10A) which lie on each side of the first to third tracheal rings. The thin isthmus crossing the first tracheal ring is transected and a thin sheath of fascia surrounding the narrow band of isthmus is dissected free from the cartilage with a scalpel and retracted laterally. The lobes of the gland are isolated by blunt dissection (Fig. 18-10B), care being taken not to traumatize the recurrent laryngeal nerves which lie dorsal to the lateral lobes of the thyroid gland. The superior and inferior thyroid vessels are ligated and transected as they are exposed during the dissection. The use of cautery is not recommended because of possible damage to the recurrent laryngeal nerves.

C. Adrenalectomy

The technique for bilateral adrenalectomy using a transabdominal approach described for *Macaca mulatta* (Krahwinkle *et al.*, 1969) is also applicable to *Papio cynocephalus*. A midline incision is made extending from the xiphoid cartilage to the umbilicus. The left adrenal gland is exposed by packing the stomach, spleen and tail of the pancreas medially and the intestinal mass caudally with moist surgical towels held in place with retractors. The peritoneum over the gland is bluntly severed and the gland dissected

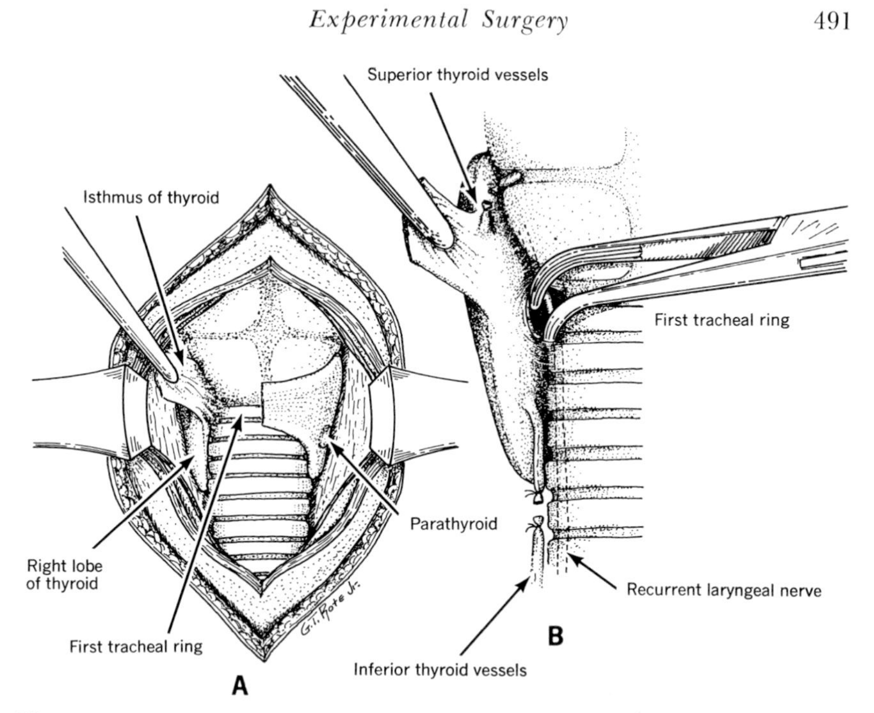

Figure 18-10. Thyroparathyroidectomy. A. Ventral view of the exposed thyroid gland showing the transected isthmus; B. Blunt dissection of the right lobe of the thyroid gland showing the recurrent laryngeal nerve and ligated thyroid vessels.

(Fig. 18-11A). Care must be taken to ligate or cauterize the numerous vessels surrounding the gland as they are encountered during the dissection. The smaller vessels are cauterized (Fig. 18-11D) and the larger vessels are double ligated and transected (Fig. 18-11B).

The right adrenal gland is more difficult to remove than the left because of its close proximity to the right kidney and the caudal lobe of the liver. Packing and retraction are performed as described previously. In addition, a padded retractor is used to retract the caudate process of the liver. A peritoneal opening is made over the cranial pole of the right kidney and retracted cranially over the lobe of the liver. This procedure minimizes the possibility of injuring the margin of the liver and also aids in exposing the right adrenal gland (Fig. 18-11C). The right adrenal gland is isolated and dissected in the same manner as described for the left gland. The peritoneal openings through which the adrenal glands were

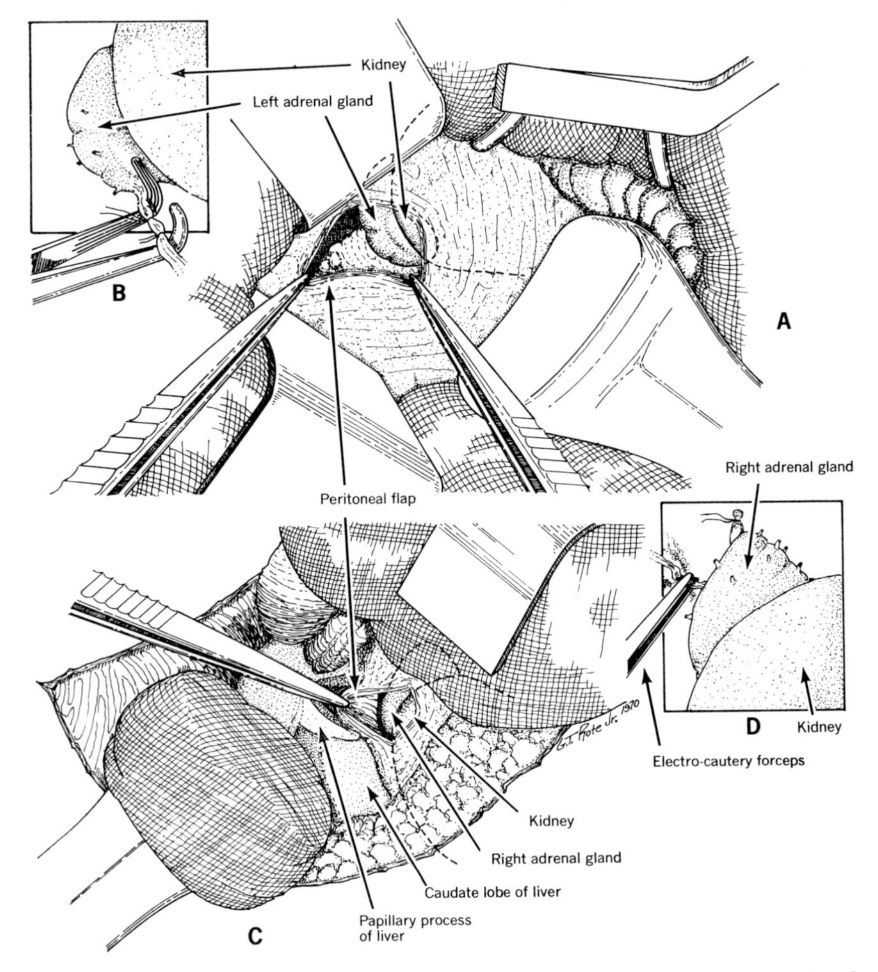

Figure 18-11. Adrenalectomy. A. Ventral exposure of the left adrenal gland through an incision in the suprarenal peritoneum; B. Double ligation of a larger vessel of the left adrenal gland; C. Ventral exposure of the right adrenal gland using the incised peritoneum to retract the adjacent lobe of the liver; D. Electrocauterization of a vessel of the right adrenal.

removed are closed by continuous sutures with 000 gut. Supportive therapy includes administration of hydrocortisone sodium succinate, cortisone acetate and desoxycortisone acetate (DOCA) according to the schedule reported by Krahwinkle *et al.* (1969) for *Macaca mulatta* (Table 18-II).

TABLE 18-II

DOSAGES OF DESOXYCORTICOSTERONE ACETATE (DOCA), HYDROCORTISONE Na SUCCINATE (HSS), AND CORTISONE ACETATE (CA) GIVEN ADRENALECTOMIZED RHESUS MONKEYS*

Time	*Drug*	*Dose*
Immediately after surgery	HSS	40 mg IV
	CA	10 mg/kg IM
	DOCA	0.12 mg/kg IM
6 hours after surgery	CA	10 mg/kg IM
	DOCA	0.12 mg/kg IM
Postoperative days 4–6	CA	7 mg/kg IM
	DOCA	0.08 mg/kg IM
Postoperative days 7–13	CA	3.5 mg/kg IM
	DOCA	0.05 mg/kg IM
Thereafter	CA	2.5 mg/kg IM
	DOCA	0.05 mg/kg IM

* After Krahwinkle *et al.*, 1969

D. *Pinealectomy*

The only report of pinealectomy of a nonhuman primate is that of Arland (1925) who successfully removed the pineal gland from "a large adult redfaced monkey." The procedures for anesthesia and control of hemorrhage were markedly different from those which are currently in use for pinealectomy of large animals. Anesthesia was achieved by intra-arterial (internal carotid) injection of cocaine hydrochloride and adrenalin hydrochloride in a 2 percent solution of gum acacia. The artery was clamped to restrict blood flow and the internal jugular vein was clamped after injection to "lock" in the injected solution as far as possible. Intracranial tension was diminished by drainage of the lateral ventricle.

The approach which has been applied to the *Papio cynocephalus* is similar to a technique for pinealectomy of the ewe (Roche and Dziuk, 1969) with modifications based upon the procedure for the dog (Dandy, 1915). The animal is placed in ventral recumbency with the head stabilized between two sandbags. A skin flap 4 cm wide, centered on the midline and its anterior edge on a line approximately one-third the distance from the base of the supraor-

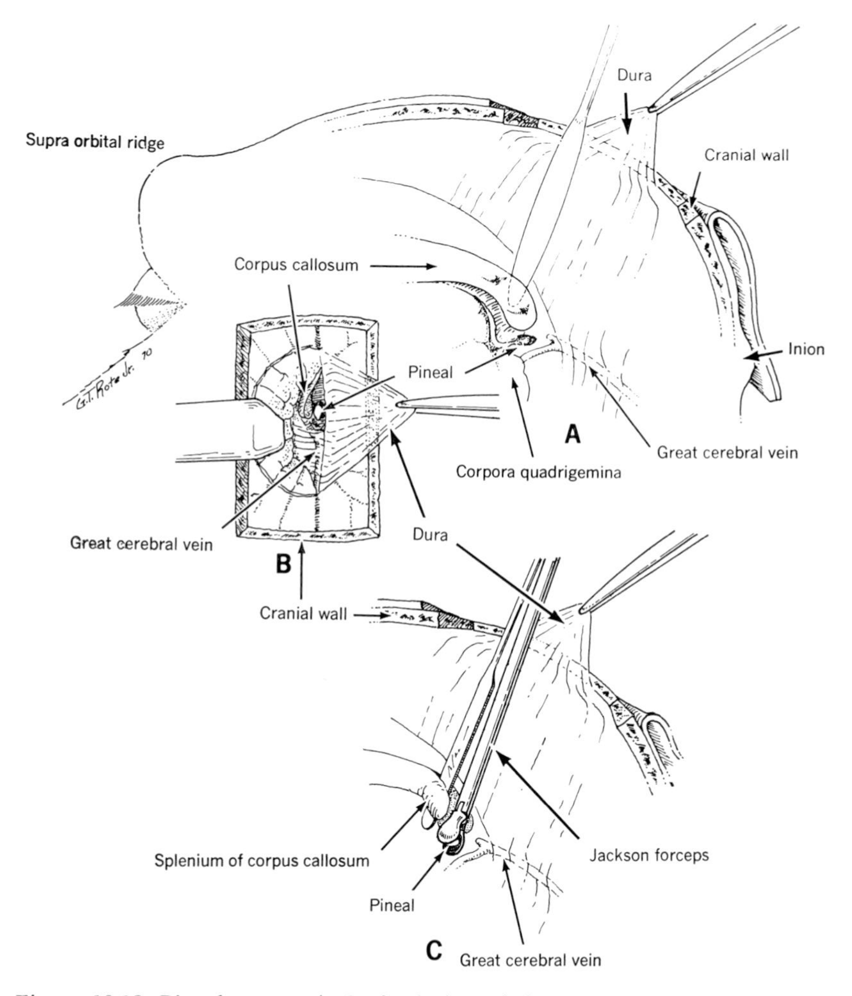

Figure 18-12. Pinealectomy. A. Sagittal view of the anatomical relationship of the pineal gland to the corpus callosum, corpora quadrigemina and great cerebral vein. The skin flap reflected posteriorly and the skull opening are also shown. The splenium of the corpus callosum is incised with tapered end of a micro spatula; B. Cranial view of the pineal gland following incision of the midline of the splenium of the corpus callosum; C. Removal of the pineal with a Jackson biopsy forcep.

bital ridge to the inion is reflected posteriorly approximately 5 cm (Fig. 18-12A). A parietal bone plate 2.5 × 3.5 cm, also centered on the midline, with its anterior edge located midway between the base of the supraorbital ridge and the inion, is cut using a vibrator saw (Fig. 18-12 A). When making this cut, care is taken to leave a thin layer of bone at the base of the grooves to avoid hemorrhage and damage to the brain. The bone plate is lifted with a scapel handle to expose the dura mater. Hyperventilation is used to reduce intracranial pressure and is begun before cutting the dura mater. The dura mater is lifted with a dura hook and a half-moon shaped flap is carefully incised with a Metzenbaum or a vascular scissor, and reflected across the dorsal sagittal sinus (Fig. 18-12B). Electrocautery and cotton strips are used to control hemorrhage.

The cerebral hemispheres are retracted laterally exposing the corpus callosum. A 12 mm wide malleable retractor is used on the hemisphere covered by the dura mater and a 6 mm wide spatula is used on the opposite hemisphere. The midline of the splenium of the corpus callosum is incised with the tapered end of a microspatula (Fig. 18-12A). As the surgical field is being cleared of cerebrospinal fluid and blood by aspiration, the pineal is removed with a Jackson biospy forceps (Fig. 18-12C). The area from which the pineal is removed is packed with gel foam to control hemorrhage. After hemorrhage has ceased the gel foam is removed, hyperventilation is stopped, and the dura is sutured with 00000 plain gut. The bone plate is fixed in position using 30 gauge stainless steel wire. The skin flap is sutured in position using 00 silk.

VII. TISSUE BIOPSY IN THE FEMALE

A. Endometrium

The transcervical suction biopsy technique which is in wide usage for serially sampling human endometrium is applicable to the great apes and to parous baboons. The perineum is thoroughly cleansed with a mild antiseptic. With the aid of a vaginal speculum, the vaginal canal is similarly cleansed. A Rock-Garcia (B-D Laboratories, Inc.) or Milex (Milex-Fertilex Co.) suction curette is passed through the cervical canal into the uterine lumen.

For passage through the baboon cervix it is necessary to bend the tip of the curette slightly and to rotate it several times during passage to negotiate the cervical folds. Only gentle pressure is applied to the curette during passage to avoid penetration of the cervical or uterine wall. Suction is applied with a 10 ml syringe as the endometrium is gently scraped with the sharp edge of the curette.

In the nonparous baboon and the smaller nonhuman primates the cervix is either too tortuous or its lumen is too small to allow penetration with the suction curette. Martin and Eckstein (1966) and Mastroianni and Rosseau (1965) have reported techniques for transcervical cannulation of the uterus in the rhesus monkey. However, these techniques are not generally applicable, for collection of endometrial biopsies. A technique for the formation of a partially exteriorized uterus in the monkey was developed by Van Wagenen and Morse (1940). Endometrial curettings were obtained and cyclic anatomical variations in the endometrium were observed. Good and Moyer (1966) developed a technique for preparing a chronic uterocutaneous abdominal fistula which permits repeated suction biopsy of the endometrium in the unanesthetized monkey. With the animal in a supine position a 7 to 8 cm incision is made in the lower abdomen, midway between the umbilicus and the symphysis pubis. The uterine fundus is grasped with a Babcock clamp and elevated to the level of the skin incision. The anterior peritoneum is closed circumferentially about the midsegment of the corpus so that the sutures unite peritoneum and serosa at the lower border of the peritoneal incision. The remainder of the peritoneal incision is closed. The fascia of the anterior rectus sheath is similarly sutured to the serosa at a more superficial site. Both peritoneum and rectus sheath support the uterus with the fundus lying at the level of the skin incision. A 7 to 10 mm diameter core of myometrium is removed to expose the anteriormost portion of the uterine cavity. The skin incision is closed and the myometrium is carefully sutured to the adjacent abdominal skin using 0 chromic gut. The fistula thus formed is sounded once or twice weekly to maintain patency. Endometrial biopsy is carried out with a suction curette attached to a 10 ml syringe by passing the instrument through the fistula into the uterine cavity and gently scraping the endometrium while applying suction.

B. Cervix

The animal is placed in ventral recumbency under chemical restraint. The external os of the cervix is exposed using a vaginal speculum. The vagina and portio of the cervix are cleansed with a mild surgical antiseptic and rinsed with sterile saline. The portio is grasped with a tenaculum. A wedge biospy sample is taken from the portio using a small scalpel. Hemorrhage is controlled when necessary by suture or by electrocautery. Tissue samples from the internal cervix are obtained using a suction curette in a manner similar to that described in Sec. VII-A. In the rhesus and most smaller species this procedure is limited to the area of the cervix posterior to the main cervical colliculus; however, in most baboons and in great apes the samples may be taken at any point along the cervical canal.

C. Vagina

Preparation of the vagina for biopsy is similar to that described above for cervical biopsy. With the speculum in place, a lateral fold of the vagina is grasped with a thumb forceps. A wedge section is taken from the fold lateral to the forceps. The wound is closed with 000 gut.

D. Mammary Glands

Biopsy of the mammary gland can be accomplished either by the punch or excision technique. Biopsies taken from the nonlactating gland present no postsurgical problems—however, a slight amount of drainage may occur following surgery during lactation especially with the excision technique.

The punch biopsy technique is performed using a Silverman needle. The area around the areolar mammae is shaved and thoroughly cleaned with an antiseptic agent. A puncture is made through the skin with either a trochar or scalpel approximately 1 cm from the edge of the areolar line through which the needle is introduced into the subcutaneous tissue. The needle is held at a plane horizontal with the skin. After the stylet is removed from the needle the blades are advanced forward into the mammary gland. The needle hub is pushed over the extended blades which are rotated and the entire assembly is withdrawn. It is usually not necessary to close the small hole in the skin.

For excision biospy the skin around the areolar mammae is shaved and cleaned with antiseptic solution. A 2 cm incision is made through the skin approximately 1 cm from the edge of the areolar tissue. The mammary tissue is exposed by blunt dissection. Mammary tissue is grasped with a thumb forceps, elevated up through the skin wound and a wedge of tissue is excised with a scalpel lateral to the forceps. Pressure is applied with dry sponges to control the small amount of hemorrhage encountered. The skin is closed with simple interrupted sutures using 00 silk.

VIII. COLLECTION OF FLUIDS FROM THE FEMALE

A. Oviductal Fluid

Several methods are used to collect oviductal fluid. One method involves laparotomy and ligation of both ends of each oviduct (Marcus and Saravis, 1965). The oviducts are exposed using the abdominal approach (Sec. IX). Both ends of the oviducts are ligated using 00 nylon or silk. The incision is closed using procedures as described in Sec. IX. The incision is reopened after a certain duration depending on the experimental design and the accumulated oviduct fluid is aspirated with a 27 gauge hypodermic needle. Also, laparoscopic techniques are applicable for collection of the accumulated fluid.

An external system has been applied successfully to the rhesus which allows continuous collection of oviduct fluid during the menstrual cycle (Mastroianni *et al.,* 1961). Oviductal fluid collected at room temperature in the unrestrained animal is usually contaminated with *E. coli.* In a modified external system, a low elliptical transverse incision is made on the abdomen (Mastroianni *et al.,* 1969). A stab wound is made in the lateral abdominal wall at the level of the ovaries. Cannulas are passed through the stab wound, inserted into the fimbriated end of the oviduct and affixed within the oviducts with a single silk suture. The oviducts are ligated at the uterotubal junction. The refrigerated collecting system is affixed to the skin with No. 1 silk sutures and supported on the abdominal wall just above the symphysis with adhesive tape.

B. Follicular Fluid

The ovaries are exposed via the abdominal approach (Sec. IX). The ovary is grasped between the thumb and index finger. A 27 gauge needle attached to 2 ½ ml syringe is inserted through the base of the follicle into the antrum with the bevel of the needle up. The fluid is aspirated slowly while moving the point of the needle downward until the follicle is totally collapsed.

Laparoscopic techniques may also be used for collection of follicular fluid. The ovarian ligament is grasped with an alligator forceps to orient the follicle so that the fluid can be aspirated using a long 22 gauge needle.

C. Uterine Fluid

Uterine fluid can be collected periodically using the technique described and illustrated in Chapter 16, Fig. 16-10C. Undiluted fluid may be obtained by inserting a plastic cannula into the uterine lumen after clamping the cervix. Fluid which rises into the cannula due to capillary action and intrauterine pressure is collected using a fine plastic catheter. For more complete collection of the uterine contents, the uterine cavity is flushed as illustrated in (Ch. 16, Fig. 16-10C).

D. Cervical Mucus

A method for periodic collection of cervical mucus is illustrated in Chapter 16, Figure 16-10B. Generally cleansing of the vagina is not indicated since this might alter the composition of the cervical mucus.

IX. REMOVAL OF FEMALE GENITAL STRUCTURES

The following abdominal approach and closure are generally used for removal of female genital structures. The rectus muscle sheath is exposed through a midline skin incision made from the symphysis pubis toward the umbilicus. Bleeding from subcutaneous vessels is controlled by electrocautery or ligation with 000 silk. The rectus sheath is incised and the muscle fibers bluntly separated to expose the peritoneum. The peritoneum is elevated with thumb forceps and a small cut is made with Metzenbaum scissors.

An index finger is introduced into the abdominal cavity to explore the peritoneum along the intended incision site for adhesions of abdominal viscera or omentum. The peritoneum is freed of any adhesions then opened with Metzenbaum scissors. A self-retaining abdominal retractor is placed in the incision. To expose the pelvic viscera, the lower abdominal viscera are packed anteriorly out of the surgical field with moist cotton sheets. This provides excellent exposure of the uterus and its adnexa.

A three tier technique is used to close the abdominal incision using a simple continuous suture pattern at each level. Size 000 gut is used in the peritoneum, 0 gut in the rectus muscle sheath, and 00 silk in the skin.

A. Ovariectomy

The ovary is elevated and the ovarian ligament is double clamped. The ligament is divided between the clamps and the cut ends are ligated below the clamps with 00 silk (Fig. 18-13A). The ovary is then elevated using the clamp on the attached portion of the ligament. The vasculature to the ovary arising from the tubal branch of the uterine vessels is carefully dissected away from the ovary and ligated with 000 silk (Fig. 18-13B). The infundibulo-pelvic ligament is ligated and transected close to the ovary (Fig. 18-13C). The fibrous connection between the ovary and fimbriae is then transected and the ovary removed.

B. Salpingectomy

A Crile clamp is placed on the fibrous attachment of the oviduct to the ovary. This fibrous union is severed and the oviduct is elevated away from the ovary (Fig. 18-13H). One then progresses down the tube toward the uterus clamping the mesentery near the oviduct and ligating the blood vessels between the ovary and tube (Fig. 18-13 D). After the tube has been isolated to the point where it inserts into the cornu of the uterus a mattress suture is placed through the uterine muscle and the oviduct is removed by a small wedge-shaped resection in the uterine wall (Fig. 18-13E). The mattress suture is tied to close the uterus. The peritoneum is closed over the ligated stumps of the vasculature with simple interrupted 000 gut.

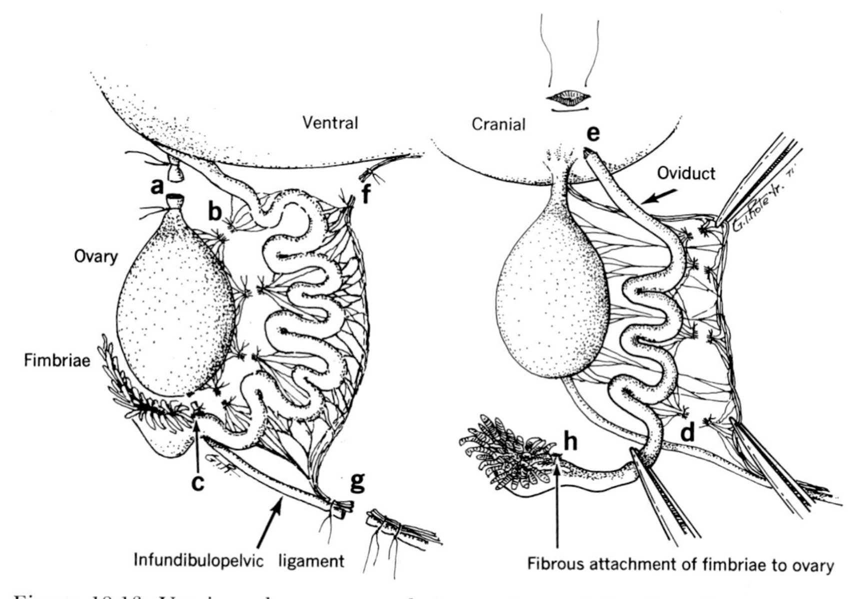

Figure 18-13. Uterine adnexa removal. Separation and ligation of (a) Ovarian ligament, (b) Ovarian vasculature, (c) Fibrous attachment of fimbriae to ovary, (d) Oviduct vasculature, (e) Isthmic end of oviduct. (f) Tubal branch of uterine vasculature and (g) Infundibulopelvic ligament and utero-ovarian vasculature.

C. Ovariosalpingectomy

The oviduct and ovary are elevated with a Crile or Kelly clamp to expose the infundibulopelvic ligament and utero-ovarian vessels. A stitch ligature of 00 silk is placed around the ligament and vessels. This ligature must be placed carefully to avoid including the ureter which lies near the ligament and vessels in this area. A Crile clamp is placed on the vessels and ligament between the ovary and ligature. The ligament and vessels are severed between the clamp and ligature. Another Crile clamp is placed on the ligated stump and a second ligature is applied (Fig. 18-13G). The tubal branches of the uterine vessels are isolated near the uterotubal junction. These vessels are double clamped, transected and ligated (Fig. 18-13F). A small part of the isthmic end of the oviduct traverses under the peritoneal covering of the uterus before it opens into the uterine lumen. Therefore, the oviduct must be carefully dissected away from the uterus before it can be removed at the uterotubal junction. A deep mattress suture is placed into the uterus at the uterotubal junction and the oviduct is removed by a wedge-shaped resection of the uterine wall (Fig. 18-13E). The mattress suture is tied to close the uterus. The ovarian ligament is divided as described in Sec. IX-A. A continuous suture of 000 gut is used to close the peritoneum, burying the infundibulopelvic ligament and utero-ovarian vessels outside the peritoneum.

D. Hysterectomy

A tenaculum is placed on the fundus of the uterus to facilitate elevation anteroventrally. The peritoneum is incised just below the round ligament on both sides of the uterus. The incision is continued across the uterus (Fig. 18-14A). The peritoneum is bluntly dissected away from the uterus and retracted posteriorly to expose the uterine artery and vein at the base of the cervix (Fig. 18-14B). Care is taken not to damage the anterior dome of the bladder (Fig. 18-14C).

A stitch ligature of 00 silk is placed through an avascular area of the broad ligament and around the oviduct. A clamp is placed on the oviduct near the uterus, and the oviduct is incised between the ligature and clamp. Another ligature is placed on the oviduct below the clamp and the clamp is removed. The ovarian ligament and tubal branches of the uterine vessels are ligated and incised using the same procedure (Fig. 18-14D). The opposite uterine adnexa are separated in the same manner.

A stitch ligature of 00 silk is placed through the round ligament and tied leaving the needle end of the suture attached. The ligament is clamped near the uterus and divided (Fig. 18-14E). The stump is ligated near the uterus and the clamp removed. In the reconstructive phase, after the uterus is removed, the round ligament will be approximated, using the attached suture, to the sectioned edge of the vagina. With gentle tension on the uterus, the broad ligament is sectioned down to the uterine vessels (Fig. 18-14D). These procedures are also performed on the other side of the uterus.

Sectioning the broad ligaments frees the uterus and allows it to be elevated and pulled posteriorly toward the pelvis to expose the

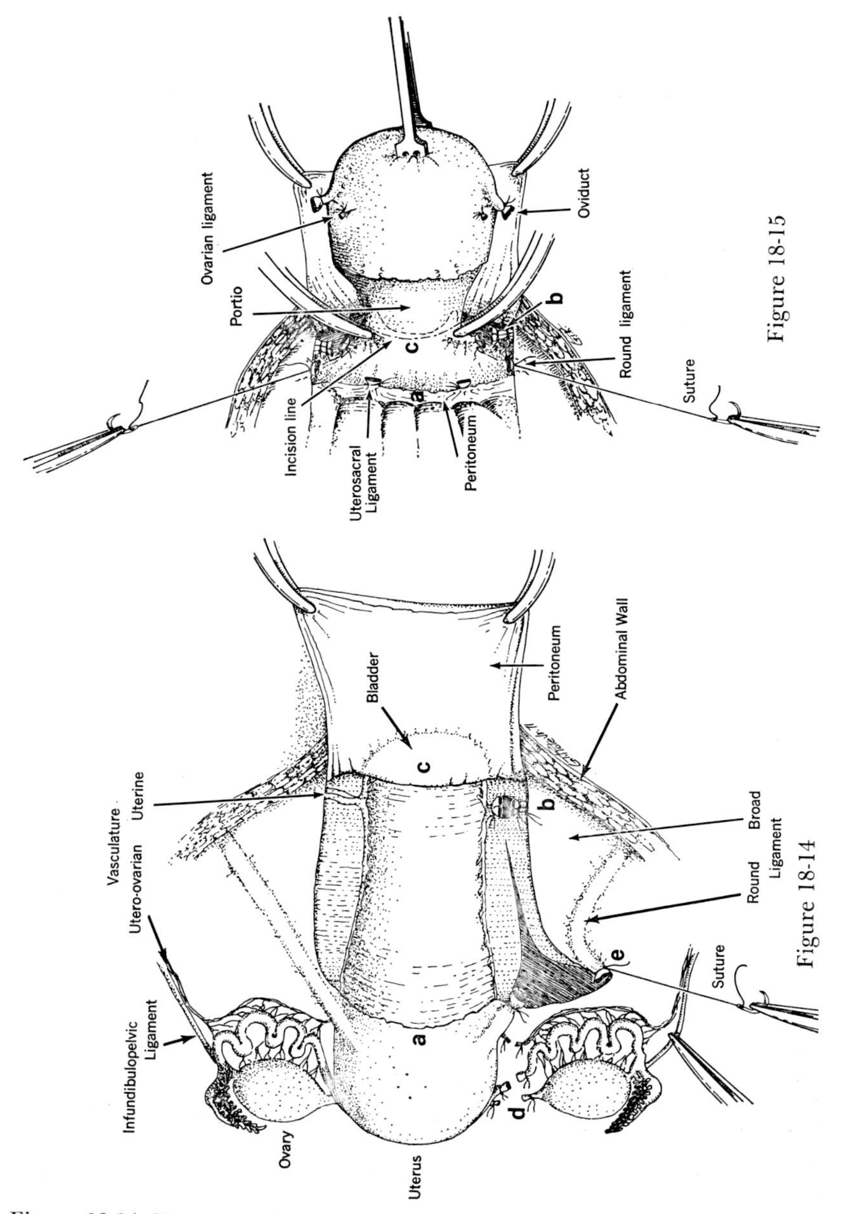

Figure 18-14. Ventral view of the uterus in its normal position, with the peritoneum of the lower uterus incised and reflected posteriorly over the bladder. The uterine adnexa is separated. The round ligament is divided and ligated leaving the needle end of the suture attached. The broad ligament is sectioned and the uterine vessels separated and double ligated.

Figure 18-15. The uterus is elevated posteriorly and the peritoneum covering its dorsal surface is incised and reflected toward the vagina. The uterosacral ligaments are divided and ligated. The uterus is excised along the dotted line below the portio. The suture on the severed end of the round ligament is used to connect the ligament with the lateral edge of the vagina after the uterus is excised.

uterosacral ligaments (Fig. 18-15). These ligaments are clamped and divided near the body of the uterus, and the stumps tied with 000 gut. Care must be taken at this point to avoid including the ureters when ligating the ligaments. The dorsal peritoneal covering of the uterus is divided between the uterosacral ligaments (Fig. 18-15A). Now all peritoneal attachments have been removed from the uterus.

The peritoneum is bluntly dissected to the level of the vagina to facilitate isolation of the uterine vessels. Traction of the uterus to one side permits the uterine vessels to be isolated and clamped near the cervix (Fig. 18-15B). Another clamp is placed approximately 5 mm from the first and the vessels separated near the first clamp. The vessels are ligated just below the second clamp. The cuff end of the vessels is clamped and another ligature is placed around the vessels. The same procedure is followed for the opposite side.

The uterus is elevated and clamps are placed on both sides of the vagina approximately 10 mm below the lateral edge of the cervix. The vagina is incised with a scalpel just above these clamps (Fig. 18-15C). After the uterus and cervix have been removed the vaginal musculature and epithelium are closed with a continuous locking suture of 0 gut. Care must be taken to include the vaginal epithelium with the muscle closure, otherwise the epithelium will retract carrying unligated vessels with it that may cause postoperative bleeding from the vagina. The round ligaments are sutured to the lateral edges of the vagina. A continuous suture with 000 gut is used to close the peritoneum. This helps prevent adhesions of the lower intestines to the operative sites.

E. Salpingohysterectomy

The oviducts are removed with the uterus, leaving the ovary and its blood supply intact. The oviducts are separated from the ovary as described in Sec. IX-B. The ovarian ligament and the tubal branches of the uterine vessels are clamped between the uterus and ovary. After they are transected the stumps are ligated with 000 silk (Fig. 18-13A,F). The hysterectomy is continued from this point as described in Sec. IX-D.

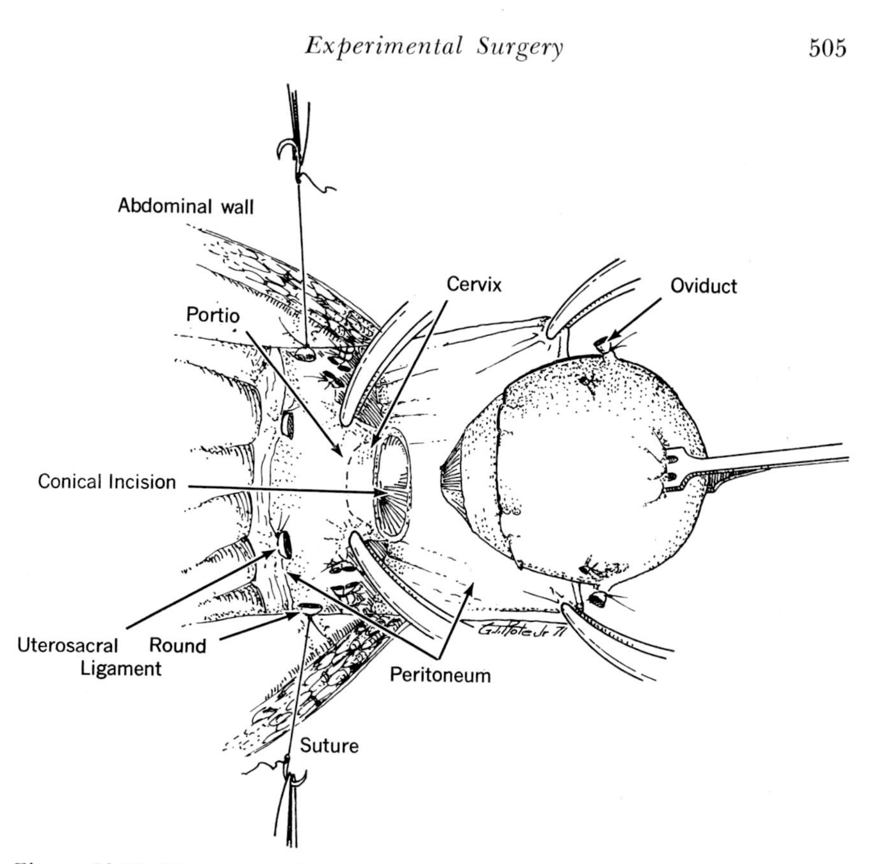

Figure 18-16. The uterus is elevated posteriorly and excised by a conical incision through the cervix.

F. Supracervical Hysterectomy

This procedure is identical with the one described in Sec. IX-D except the uterus is removed by excising the cervix above its external os in lieu of removing the entire cervix. After the peritoneum has been separated from the uterus and the uterine vessels have been ligated, the uterus is elevated to prepare for its removal. The scalpel blade is beveled to make a conical-shaped excision of the cervical musculature (Fig. 18-16). This method removes the endocervical lining and aids in closing the cervical stump. Closure of the cervical stump is with 0 gut using simple interrupted sutures. The peritoneum is approximated with a continuous suture of 000 gut.

G. Ovariohysterectomy

The basic procedure is described in Sec. IX-D. The peritoneum is separated from the uterus. The utero-ovarian vessels and infundibulopelvic ligaments are double ligated with 00 silk and transected. A clamp is placed on the ovarian side of the ligament to prevent back-bleeding. The round ligament is ligated and transected and the broad ligament sectioned down to the uterine vessels. These vessels are ligated and transected. The uterus is removed as previously described (Sec. IX-D or IX-F) and the operative site is covered with peritoneum.

H. Enucleation of Corpus Luteum

The ovary is held between the thumb and index finger. The germinal epithelium and ovarian stroma covering the corpus luteum is incised using the tip of a scalpel beginning at the stigma and ex-

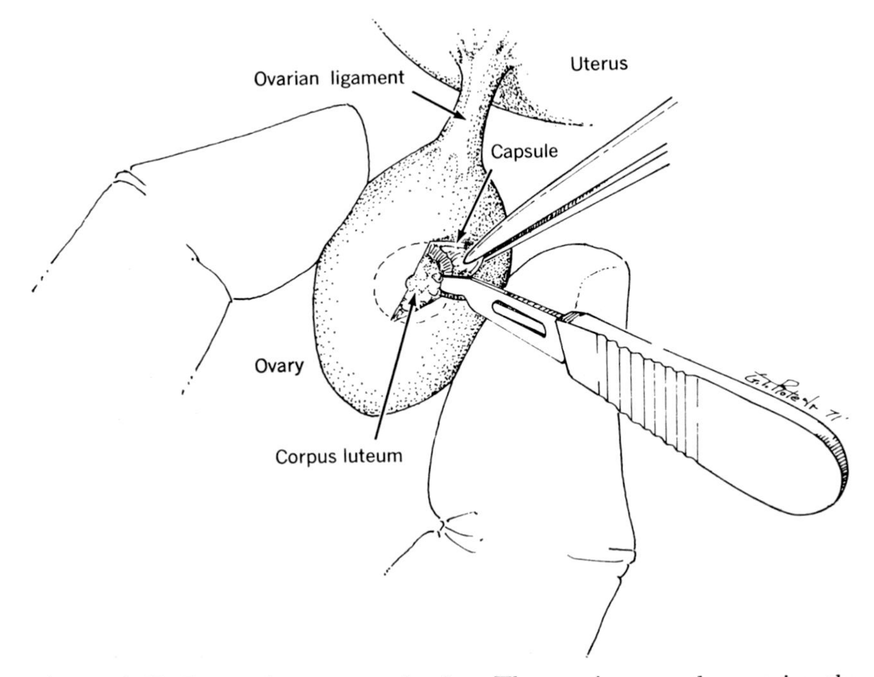

Figure 18-17. Corpus luteum enucleation. The ovarian capsule covering the corpus luteum is incised and reflected laterally and the corpus luteum is peeled out.

tending in opposite directions to the border of the gland. The epithelial and stromal layers are grasped with a fine serrated thumb forceps near the stigma. The corpus luteum, with its capsule, is enucleated by scraping it free at the highly vascular junction between the ovarian stroma and the capsule of the corpus luteum (Fig. 18-17). The resulting cavity is closed by continuous suture with 0000 gut.

I. Endometrial Enucleation

The procedure for enucleation of the endometrium from a nonpregnant animal is similar to that described for collecting early postimplantation embryos (Sec. X-B). In this case, unless otherwise dictated by the individual experiment, the endometrial sac can be opened *in situ*. This allows easier determination of the thickness of the endometrial layer being removed and permits removal of the endometrium without entering the myometrial layer. This is especially important during the early proliferative phase of the menstrual cycle when the endometrial layer is relatively thin. Endometrium can be collected four to six times from a given animal. The uterine lumen decreases in size with each enucleation.

J. Mastectomy

An elliptical skin incision is made on each side of the areolar mammae. The incision begins approximately 3 cm on the cranial side of the mammae and extends along the edge of the areolar tissue to a point directly below and approximately 3 cm from the ventral edge of the areolar mammae. The underlying mammary gland is bluntly isolated until it can be removed with the skin and areolar tissue. The skin is sutured with 00 silk using a simple interrupted pattern.

X. COLLECTION OF EMBRYOS AND FETUSES

A. Ova and Preimplantation Embryos

Unfertilized ova and preimplantation embryos can be collected by excising the uterus and oviducts and flushing their lumina with an appropriate fluid. However, the method is inefficient because it limits collection to only one per animal. *In vivo* collection procedures (Hendrickx and Kraemer, 1970) are applicable in *M. mulatta* and *P. cynocephalus* and allow repeated collections, usually at least four, from an animal. The number of collections which can be performed in a given animal depends upon the extent of the adhesions developed between the ovaries, the oviducts, and the uterus. These adhesions, which become increasingly severe with each succeeding collection, reduce the efficiency of ovum pick-up by the fimbriae of the oviduct and thereby decrease the chances of successful recovery of the ovum or embryo. Formation of these adhesions is minimized by handling the tissues with either moist gloves or blunt forceps to prevent damage to the serosal surfaces.

The uterus, ovaries and oviducts are exposed through a ventral midline incision. In *M. mulatta,* it is difficult to force fluid in a retrograde manner from the uterine cavity through the uterotubal junction. Thus, oviductal ova or embryos are collected by flushing the oviducts with fluid introduced in a retrograde manner into the oviductal lumen close to the uterotubal junction with a 25-30 gauge hypodermic needle. The same procedure may be used in baboons. However, baboon oviducts can also be flushed by clamping the cervix, and introducing fluid into the uterus and forcing the fluid through the uterotubal junction and out the oviduct. The fluid is collected in embryological watch glasses as it flows out of the fimbriae. The flushing fluids can also be transported to a receptacle by means of a fluted plastic cannula inserted approximately 3 mm into the infundibular ostium of the oviduct which is held in place with a ligature or clamp. This method avoids possible loss of the embryo in the fimbriae and generally yields washings which are free from blood.

To collect preimplantation embryos from the uterus, the vagina is cleansed with saline and a glass vaginal speculum is inserted. The animal is placed on its back with its buttocks extending over the end of the surgery table. The uterus is exposed by laparotomy. An 18 gauge I.V. catheter placement unit is inserted through the uterine fundus and anchored with a purse string suture. Flushing fluid is forced through the uterine lumen and out the cervix. In the baboon, the fluid flows out of the oviducts and the cervix. During the flushing procedure the vaginal speculum is held firmly around the cervical os to prevent leakage of fluid around the cervical end of the speculum as the fluid flows into the receptacle.

B. Postimplantation Embryos and Preterm Fetuses

Procedures for collecting postimplantation embryos from *M. mulatta* and *P. cynocephalus* have been described and illustrated (Hartman, 1944; Claborn *et al.*, 1967; Hendrickx and Kraemer, 1971). The gravid uterus is exposed by laparotomy and manually delivered through the incision. The cervix uteri is clamped with a sponge forceps to restrict the blood supply to the uterus. To expose the endometrium, an initial incision is made in the superficial layer of the uterine myometrium on the side opposite the implantation site and is carefully extended from the region anterior to the cervix uteri to the fundus. In early pregnancy, before the implantation site is palpable, the incision is made on either dorsal or ventral side of the uterus, whichever is more convenient for the surgeon. The incised edges of the myometrium are held in apposition with Allis forceps while the incision is being extended with a Strabismus scissors. Blood on the incision is washed away with physiological saline to clear the surgical field. The endometrial sac which varies in thickness with the stage of pregnancy (8 mm to 5 mm from the 3rd to 8th weeks) is removed by separating the decidual layer from the basal layer of the endometrium with Strabismus scissors and a dental spatula. The connective tissue septae are cut with scissors and the friable blood vessels are bluntly transected with the dental spatula. Digital pressure is applied to the uterine wall at the implantation site during the final stages of the dissection to partially evert the uterus and expose the base of the placenta. The endometrial sac containing the chorionic vesicle is excised anterior to the cervix. The uterine incision is closed using a modified Kushing suture in the myometrium and a simple continuous suture in the epimetrium with 000 chromic gut.

When collecting early implantation embryos, strips of myometrium are left on the endometrium to provide rigidity to the small delicate sac. Thus, physical damage and consequent artifacts on the embryo are minimized.

The endometrial sac is immersed in physiological saline immediately after removal, rinsed thoroughly to remove the blood from its surface and reimmersed in physiological saline. With a small forceps and dissecting scissors, the endometrial sac is carefully opened by cutting through the thin lateral walls until the implantation site is located. In the very young embryos, implantation may be indicated by small hemorrhages or deep red areas on the surface of the endometrium. In embryos twelve days or older, the implantation site is relatively large and easily identified. The membranous chorion is exposed by cutting the endometrial sac on one side and across the fundic margin or by cutting away the entire embryonic half of the endometrium.

The most frequently occurring artifact is the disruption of the placental surface. Maternal blood may also fill the amniotic and vitelline cavity and the embryo. The major complications of this surgery are the formation of adhesions between the omentum and the incision site, between the uterus and the adnexa, and between the adnexa, uterus and broad ligament. These adhesions are minimized by handling the tissues with either moist gloves or blunt forceps.

C. Term Fetuses (Caesarean Section)

The animal is chemically restrained with Sernylan and prepared for surgery. Fluothane is administered using a face mask to produce a light plane of surgical anesthesia. This light anesthesia permits entrance into the abdominal cavity and the gravid uterus. After the uterus is opened Fluothane administration is discontinued until the infant has been delivered and the umbilical cord clamped. After the cord is clamped the administration of Fluothane is resumed to maintain surgical anesthesia for the remainder of the procedure.

A ventral midline skin incision beginning just posterior to the umbilicus and extending to the symphysis pubis is used to open the abdominal cavity. Care must be exercised not to cut the gravid uterus while making the skin incision since the abdominal muscles are thin and the uterus lies very near the peritoneum. After the uterus is exposed the placental attachment is located. A small incision is made in the epimetrium opposite the placenta, and the chorionic vesicle is opened. The uterus is not delivered from the abdomen at this time. Allis tissue forceps are placed on the cut edges of the myometrium for support and the chorionic fluid is removed with suction. The opening in the uterus is enlarged to allow for delivery of the fetus. The fetus is delivered, the umbilical cord ligated, and the uterus is manually delivered out of the abdominal cavity. The uterus is then everted through the uterine incision and the placenta peeled away from the endometrium. The basal layer of endometrium is scraped thoroughly to remove all decidual tissue and then inverted to its normal shape. The uterine incision is closed using a modified Kushing suture in the myometrium and a simple continuous suture in the epimetrium. Both incisions are closed with 000 gut.

REFERENCES

Arland, J. P. (1925): Excision of the pineal body of a monkey under intra-arterial anesthesia. *Indian Med Gazette,* 361-362.

Claborn, L. D.; Hendrickx, A. G., and Kriewaldt, F. H. (1967): A proved technique for delivery of early-stage baboon embryos. In Vagtborg, H. (Ed.): *The Baboon in Medical Research.* Austin, University of Texas Press, pp. 825-848.

Dandy, W. E. (1915): Extirpation of the pineal body. *J Exp Med, 22:*237-247.

Good, R. G., and Moyer, D. L. (1966): Technique of serial endometrial biopsy in the monkey through a uterocutaneous fistula. *J Reprod Fertil, 12,* 573-574.

Gouygou, C. (1969): Testicular biopsy in male sterility. In Nabil Rashad, M., and Morton, W. R. M. (Eds.): *Selected Topics in Genital Anomalies and Related Subjects.* Springfield, Thomas, pp. 268-290.

Greer, W. E.; Roussel, J. D., and Austin, C. R. (1968): Prevention of coagulation in monkey semen by surgery. *J Reprod Fertil, 15,* 153-155.

Hartman, C. G. (1944): Regeneration of the monkey uterus after surgical removal of the endometrium and accidental endometriosis. *Western J Surg, 52, 87-102.*

Hendrickx, A. G., and Kraemer, D. C. (1970): *Primates.* In Hafez, E. S. E. (Ed.): Reproduction and Breeding Techniques for Laboratory Animals. Philadelphia, Lea & Febiger, pp. 316-335.

Hendrickx, A. G., and Kraemer, D. C. (1971): Methods used in collecting and studying embryos. In Hendrickx, A. G. (Ed.): *Embryology of the Baboon.* Chicago, University of Chicago Press.

Knobil, E., and Greep, R. O. (1959): The physiology of growth hormone with particular reference to its action in the rhesus monkey and the "species specificity" problem. *Recent Progr Hormone Res, 15,* 1-58.

Krahwinkle, D. J., Jr.; Hellerstein, L. J., and Anstadt, G. L. (1969): Adrenalectomy of the rhesus monkey (*Macaca mutatta*): Anatomy and surgical techniques. *J Amer Vet Med Ass, 155,* 1151-1155.

Marcus, S. L., and Saravis, C. A. (1965): Oviduct fluid in the rhesus monkey: A study of its protein components and its origins. *Fertil Steril, 16,* 785-794.

Martin, C. B., and Eckstein, P. (1966): Transcervical uterine catheterization in rhesus monkeys. *Amer J Obstet Gynec, 94,* 415-418.

Mastroianni, L., Jr.; Shah, U., and Abdul-Karim, R. (1961): Prolonged volumetric collection of oviduct fluid in the rhesus monkey. *Fertil Steril, 12,* 417-424.

Mastroianni, L., Jr., and Rosseau, C. H. (1965): Influence of the intrauterine coil on ovum transport and sperm distribution in the monkey. *Amer J Obstet Gynec, 93,* 416-420.

Mastroianni, L., Jr.; Urzua, M.; Avalos, M., and Stambaugh, R. (1969): Some observations on Fallopian tube fluid in the monkey. *J Obstet Gynec, 103,* 703-709.

Roche, J. F., and Dziuk, P. J. (1969): A technique for pinealectomy of the ewe. *Amer J Vet Res, 30,* 2031-2035.

Rowley, M. J., and Heller, C. G. (1966): The testicular biopsy: Surgical procedure, fixation and staining technics. *Fertil Steril, 17,* 177-186.

Schoonees, R., and de Klerk, J. N. (1968): Anatomy, radio-isotopic blood flow and glandular secretory activity of the baboon prostate. *S Afr Med J, 42 (Suppl),* 87-94.

Smith, P. E. (1954): Continuation of pregnancy in rhesus monkeys (*Macaca mulatta*) following hypophysectomy. *Endocrinology, 55,* 655-664.

Van Wagenen, G., and Morse, A. H. (1940): Cyclic changes in exteriorized uterus. *Endocrinology, 27,* 268-273.

Voglmayr, J. K.; Larsen, L. H., and White, I. G. (1970): Metabolism of spermatozoa and composition of fluid collected from the rete testis of living bulls. *J Reprod Fertil, 21,* 449-460.

Zemjanis, R.; Gondos, B.; Adey, W. R., and Cockett, A. T. K. (1969): Testicular degeneration in *Macaca nemestrina* monkeys used in prespace flight tests. *Aerospace Med, 40,* 1316-1322.

Zervas, N. T., and Pickren, K. S. (1968): Transorbital hypophysectomy in primates. *Endocrinology, 85,* 949-950.

Appendix I

A CLASSIFICATION OF LIVING PRIMATES

Order PRIMATES (Linnaeus, 1758)	
Suborder PROSIMII (Illiger, 1811)	
Infraorder TUPAIIFORMES (Schultz, 1953)	
Superfamily TUPAIOIDEA (Dobson, 1882)	
Family TUPAIIDAE (Mivart, 1868)	
Subfamily TUPAIINAE (Lyon, 1913)	
Tupaia (Raffles, 1822)	Tree shrew
glis (Diard, 1820)	
gracilis (Thomas, 1893)	
javanica (Horsfield, 1822)	
minor (Günther, 1876)	
montana (Thomas, 1892)	
nicobarica (Zelebor, 1869)	
tana (Raffles, 1821)	
Anathana (Lyon, 1913)	Indian tupaia
ellioti (Waterhouse, 1849)	
Dendrogale (Gray, 1848)	Mountain tupaia
melanura (Thomas, 1892)	
murina (Schlegel and Müller, 1843)	
Urogale (Mearns, 1905)	Philippine tupaia
everetti (Thomas, 1892)	
Subfamily PTILOCERCINAE (Lyon, 1913)	
Ptilocercus (Gray, 1848)	Feather tails
lowii (Gray, 1848)	
Infraorder LEMURIFORMES (Gregory, 1915)	
Superfamily LEMUROIDEA (Mivart, 1864)	
Family LEMURIDAE (Gray, 1821)	
Subfamily LEMURINAE (Mivart, 1864)	

Lemur (Linnaeus, 1758)	Lemur
catta (Linnaeus, 1758)	
fulvus (E. Geoffroy, 1812)	
macaco (Linnaeus, 1766)	
mongoz (Linnaeus, 1766)	
rubriventer (I. Geoffroy, 1850)	
variegatus (Kerr, 1792)	
Hapalemur (I. Geoffroy, 1851)	Gentle lemur
griseus (Link, 1795)	
simus (Gray, 1870)	
Lepilemur (I. Geoffroy, 1851)	Weasel, sportive lemur
mustelinus (I. Geoffroy, 1851)	
Subfamily CHEIROGALEINAE (Gregory, 1915)	
Cheirogaleus (E. Geoffroy, 1812)	Dwarf lemur
major (E. Geoffroy, 1812)	
medius (E. Geoffroy, 1812)	
trichotis (Günther, 1875)	
Microcebus (E. Geoffroy, 1828)	Mouse lemur
coquereli (A. Grandidier, 1867)	
murinus (J. F. Miller, 1777)	
Phaner (Gray, 1870)	Fork-marked mouse lemur
furcifer (Blainville, 1839)	
Family INDRIIDAE (Burnett, 1828)	
Indri (E. Geoffroy and Cuvier, 1795)	Indris
indri (Gmelin, 1788)	
Avahi (Jourdan, 1834)	Woolly indris
laniger (Gmelin, 1788)	
Propithecus (Bennett, 1832)	Sifaka
diadema (Bennett, 1832)	
verreauxi (A. Grandidier, 1867)	
Superfamily DAUBENTONIOIDEA (Gill, 1872)	
Family DAUBENTONIIDAE (Gray, 1870)	
Daubentonia (E. Geoffroy, 1795)	Aye-aye
madagascariensis (Gmelin, 1788)	
Infraorder LORISIFORMES (Gregory, 1915)	
Family LORISIDAE (Gregory, 1915)	

Subfamily LORISINAE (Flower and Lydekker, 1891)	
Loris (E. Geoffroy, 1796)	Slender loris
tardigradus (Linnaeus, 1758)	
Arctocebus (Gray, 1863)	Angwantibo
calabarensis (J. A. Smith, 1860)	
Nycticebus (E. Geoffroy, 1812)	Slow loris
coucang (Boddaert, 1785)	
Perodicticus (Bennett, 1831)	Potto
potto (Müller, 1766)	
Subfamily GALAGINAE (Mivart, 1864)	
Galago (E. Geoffroy, 1796)	Bush baby
alleni (Waterhouse, 1837)	
crassicaudatus (E. Geoffroy, 1812)	
demidovii (Fischer, 1808)	
elegantulus (Le Conte, 1857)	
senegalensis (E. Geoffroy, 1796)	
Infraorder TARSIIFORMES (Gregory, 1915)	
Family TARSIIDAE (Gill, 1872)	
Tarsius (Storr, 1780)	Tarsier
bancanus (Horsfield, 1821)	
spectrum (Pallas, 1778)	
syrichta (Linnaeus, 1758)	
Suborder ANTHROPOIDEA (Mivart, 1864)	
Superfamily CEBOIDEA (Simpson, 1931)	
Family CEBIDAE (Swainson, 1835)	
Subfamily CEBINAE (Mivart, 1865)	
Cebus (Erxleben, 1777)	Capuchin monkey
albifrons (Humboldt, 1812)	
apella (Linnaeus, 1758)	
capucinus (Linnaeus, 1758)	
nigrivittatus (Wagner, 1848)	
Saimiri (Voigt, 1831)	Squirrel monkey
boliviensis (d'Orbigny, 1834)	
madeirae (Thomas, 1908)	
oerstedi (Reinhardt, 1872)	
sciurea (Linnaeus, 1758)	
usta (I. Geoffroy, 1844)	

Subfamily ALOUATTINAE (Elliot, 1904)	
Alouatta (Lacépède, 1799)	Howler monkey
belzebul (Linnaeus, 1766)	
caraya (Humboldt, 1812)	
fusca (E. Geoffroy, 1812)	
palliata (Gray, 1848)	
seniculus (Linnaeus, 1766)	
villosa (Gray, 1845)	
Subfamily AOTINAE (Elliot, 1913)	
Aotus (Illiger, 1811)	Douroucouli, night monkey
trivirgatus (Humboldt, 1811)	
Callicebus (Thomas, 1903)	Titi monkey
moloch (Hoffmannsegg, 1807)	
torquatus (Hoffmannsegg, 1807)	
Subfamily ATELINAE (Miller, 1924)	
Ateles (E. Geoffroy, 1806)	Spider monkey
belzebuth (E. Geoffroy, 1806)	
fusciceps (Gray, 1866)	
geoffroyi (Kuhl, 1820)	
paniscus (Linnaeus, 1758)	
Brachyteles (Spix, 1823)	Woolly spider monkey
arachnoides (E. Geoffrey, 1806)	
Lagothrix (E. Geoffroy, 1812)	Woolly monkey
lagotricha (Humboldt, 1811)	
flavicauda (Humboldt, 1811)	
Subfamily PITHECIINAE (Mivart, 1864)	
Pithecia (Desmarest, 1804)	Saki
pithecia (Linnaeus, 1766)	
monachus (E. Geoffroy, 1812)	
Cacajao (Lesson, 1840)	Uakari
calvus (I. Geoffroy, 1847)	
melanocephalus (Humboldt, 1811)	
roosevelti (J. A. Allen, 1914)	
rubicundus (I. Geoffroy and Deville, 1848)	
Chiropotes (Lesson, 1840)	Cuxius, bearded saki

chiropotes (Humboldt, 1811)
albinasa (I. Geoffroy and Deville, 1848)
satanas (Hoffmannsegg, 1807)
Family CALLITHRICIDAE (Thomas, 1903)
Callithrix (Erxleben, 1777) — Tufted eared marmoset
argentata (Linnaeus, 1771)
aurita (E. Geoffroy, 1812)
chrysoleuca (Wagner, 1842)
flaviceps (Thomas, 1903)
geoffroyi (Humboldt, 1812)
humeralifer (E. Geoffroy, 1812)
jacchus (Linnaeus, 1758)
penicillata (E. Geoffroy, 1812)
Callimico (Ribeiro, 1911) — Goeldi's monkey
goeldii (Thomas, 1904)
Cebuella (Gray, 1866) — Pygmy marmoset
pygmaea (Spix, 1823)
Leontopithecus (Lesson, 1840) — Lion marmoset
chrysomelas (Kuhl, 1820)
chrysopygus (Mikan, 1820)
rosalia (Linnaeus, 1766)
Saguinus (Hoffmansegg, 1807) — Tamarin
bicolor (Spix, 1823)
devillei (I. Geoffroy, 1851)
fuscicollis (Spix, 1823)
graellsi (Espada, 1870)
imperator (Goeldi, 1907)
inustus (Schwarz, 1951)
labiatus (E. Geoffroy, 1812)
leucopus (Günther, 1876)
midas (Linnaeus, 1758)
mystax (Spix, 1823)
nigricollis (Spix, 1823)
oedipus (Linnaeus, 1758)
tamarin (Link, 1795)
Superfamily CERCOPITHECOIDEA (Simpson, 1931)
Family CERCOPITHECIDAE (Gray, 1821)

Subfamily CERCOPITHECINAE (Blanford, 1888)	
Cercopithecus (Brünnich, 1772)	Guenon
aethiops (Linnaeus, 1758)	
cephus (Linnaeus, 1758)	
diana (Linnaeus, 1758)	
hamlyni (Pocock, 1907)	
l'hoesti (Sclater, 1898)	
mitis (Wolf, 1822)	
mona (Schreber, 1775)	
neglectus (Schlegel, 1876)	
nictitans (Linnaeus, 1766)	
nigroviridis (Pocock, 1907)	
patas (Schreber, 1775)	
talapoin (Schreber, 1774)	
Cercocebus (E. Geoffroy, 1812)	Mangabey
albigena (Gray, 1850)	
aterrimus (Oudemans, 1890)	
atys (Audebert, 1797)	
galeritus (Peters, 1879)	
torquatus (Kerr, 1792)	
Macaca (Lacépède, 1799)	Macaque
arctoides (I. Geoffroy, 1831)	
assamensis (M'Clelland, 1839)	
cyclopis (Swinhoe, 1862)	
fuscata (Blyth, 1875)	
mulatta (Zimmerman, 1780)	
nemestrina (Linnaeus, 1766)	
nigra (Desmarest, 1822)	
radiata (E. Goeffroy, 1812)	
silenus (Linnaeus, 1758)	
sinica (Linnaeus, 1771)	
sylvana (Linnaeus, 1758)	
Papio (Müller, 1776)	Baboon
cynocephalus (Linnaeus, 1766)	
gelada (Rüppell, 1835)	
hamadryas (Linnaeus, 1758)	
sphinx (Linnaeus, 1758)	
Subfamily COLOBINAE (Elliot, 1913)	

Colobus (Illiger, 1811)	Guereza
badius (Kerr, 1792)	
polykomos (Zimmerman, 1780)	
verus (Van Beneden, 1838)	
Nasalis (E. Geoffroy, 1812)	Proboscis monkey
larvatus (Wurmb, 1784)	
Presbytis (Eschscholtz, 1821)	Langur
aygula (Linnaeus, 1758)	
carimatae (Miller, 1906)	
cristata (Raffles, 1821)	
entella (Dufresne, 1797)	
francoisi (Pousargues, 1898)	
frontata (Müller, 1838)	
johni (Fischer, 1829)	
melalophos (Raffles, 1821)	
obscura (Reid, 1837)	
phayrei (Blyth, 1847)	
pileata (Blyth, 1843)	
potenziani (Bonaparte, 1856)	
rubicunda (Müller, 1838)	
senex (Erxleben, 1777)	
Pygathrix (E. Geoffroy, 1812)	Douc langur
nemaeus (Linnaeus, 1771)	
Rhinopithecus (Milne-Edwards, 1872)	Tonkin monkey
avunculus (Dollman, 1912)	
roxellanae (Milne-Edwards, 1870)	
Simias (Miller, 1903)	Pagi langur
concolor (Miller, 1903)	
Superfamily HOMINOIDEA (Simpson ,1931)	
Family PONGIDAE (Elliot, 1913)	
Subfamily PONGINAE (Allen, 1925)	
Pongo (Lacépède, 1799)	Orangutan
pygmaeus (Linnaeus, 1760)	
Pan (Oken, 1816)	Chimpanzee, gorilla
gorilla (Savage and Wyman, 1847)	
paniscus (Schwarz, 1929)	
troglodytes (Blumenbach, 1779)	
Subfamily HYLOBATINAE (Gill, 1872)	

Hylobates (Illiger, 1811)	Gibbon, siamang
lar (Linnaeus, 1771)	
moloch (Audebert, 1797)	
syndactylus (Raffles, 1821)	
Family HOMINIDAE (Gray, 1825)	
Homo (Linnaeus, 1758)	Man
sapiens (Linnaeus, 1758)	

Appendix II

ALPHABETICAL LISTING OF VERNACULAR AND GENERIC NAMES*

Generic Name	*Vernacular Name*
Alouatta	Howler monkey
Anathana	Madras treeshrew
Aotus	Douroucouli
Aotus	Night monkey
Arctocebus	Angwantibo
Ateles	Spider monkey
Avahi	Avahi
Brachyteles	Woolly spider monkey
Cacajao	Uakari
Callicebus	Titi
Callimico	Goeldi's marmoset
Callithrix	Marmoset
Cebuella	Pygmy marmoset
Cebus	Capuchin monkey
Cercocebus	Mangabey
Cercopithecus	Guenon
Cercopithecus	Talapoin
Cheirogaleus	Dwarf lemur
Chiropotes	Bearded saki
Colobus	Guereza
Cynopithecus	Celebes black ape
Daubentonia	Aye-aye
Dendrogale	Smooth-tailed treeshrew
Erythrocebus	Oatas monkey

* From Napier and Napier (1968): *Handbook of Living Primates,* Academic Press, New York, N.Y.

Generic Name	***Vernacular Name***
Galago	Bushbaby
Galago	Galago
Gorilla	Gorilla
Hapalemur	Gentle lemur
Hylobates	Gibbon
Indri	Indris
Lagothrix	Woolly monkey
Lemur	Lemur
Leontideus	Golden lion marmoset
Lepilemur	Sportive lemur
Loris	Slender loris
Loris	Loris
Macaca	Rhesus monkey
Macaca	Barbary ape
Macaca	Macaque
Mandrillus	Drill
Mandrillus	Mandrill
Microcebus	Mouse lemur
Nasalis	Proboscis monkey
Nycticebus	Slow loris
Pan	Chimpanzee
Papio	Baboon
Perodicticus	Potto
Phaner	Fork-marked dwarf lemur
Pithecia	Saki
Pongo	Orang-utan
Presbytis	Langur
Presbytis	Leaf-monkey
Propithecus	Sifaka
Ptilocercus	Pentailed treeshrew
Ptilocercus	Feather-tailed treeshrew
Pygathrix	Douc langur
Rhinopithecus	Snub-nosed langur
Saguinus	Pinche
Saguinus	Tamarin
Saimiri	Squirrel monkey
Simias	Pagai Island langur

Symphalangus	Siamang
Tarsius	Tarsier
Theropithecus	Gelada
Tupaia	Treeshrew
Urogale	Philippine treeshrew

Vernacular Name	***Generic Name***
Angwantibo	*Arctocebus*
Avahi	*Avahi*
Aye-aye	*Daubentonia*
Baboon	*Papio*
Barbary ape	*Macaca*
Bearded saki	*Chiropotes*
Bushbaby	*Galago*
Capuchin monkey	*Cebus*
Celebes black ape	*Cynopithecus*
Chimpanzee	*Pan*
Douc langur	*Pygathrix*
Douroucouli	*Aotus*
Drill	*Mandrillus*
Dwarf lemur	*Cheirogaleus*
Feather-tailed threeshrew	*Ptilocercus*
Fork-marked dwarf lemur	*Phaner*
Galago	*Galago*
Gelada	*Theropithecus*
Gentle lemur	*Hapalemur*
Gibbon	*Hylobates*
Goeldi's marmoset	*Callimico*
Golden lion marmoset	*Leontideus*
Gorilla	*Gorilla*
Guenon	*Cercopithecus*
Guereza	*Colobus*
Howler monkey	*Alouatta*
Indris	*Indri*
Langur	*Presbytis*
Leaf-monkey	*Presbytis*
Lemur	*Lemur*
Loris	*Loris*
Macaque	*Macaca*

Vernacular Name	*Generic Name*
Madras treeshrew	*Anathana*
Mandrill	*Mandrillus*
Mangabey	*Cercocebus*
Marmoset	*Callithrix*
Mouse lemur	*Microcebus*
Night monkey	*Aotus*
Orang-utan	*Pongo*
Pagai Island langur	*Simias*
Patas monkey	*Erythrocebus*
Pentailed treeshrew	*Ptilocercus*
Philippine treeshrew	*Urogale*
Pinche	*Saguinus*
Potto	*Periodicticus*
Proboscis monkey	*Nasalis*
Pygmy marmoset	*Cebuella*
Rhesus monkey	*Macaca*
Saki	*Pithecia*
Siamang	*Symphalangus*
Sifaka	*Propithecus*
Slender loris	*Loris*
Slow loris	*Nycticebus*
Smooth-tailed treeshrew	*Dendrogale*
Snub-nosed langur	*Rhinopithecus*
Spider monkey	*Ateles*
Sportive lemur	*Lepilemur*
Squirrel monkey	*Saimiri*
Talapoin	*Cercopithecus*
Tamarin	*Saguinus*
Tarsier	*Tarsius*
Titi	*Callicebus*
Treeshrew	*Tupaia*
Uakari	*Cacajao*
Woolly monkey	*Lagothrix*
Woolly spider monkey	*Brachyteles*

Appendix III

ENDANGERED PRIMATE SPECIES*

Regulations implementing the Endangered Species Act (Public Law 91-135) were published in the Federal Register June 2, 1970, and became effective immediately except for a sixty-day delay in the requirement which restricts importation of all fish and wildlife to five designated ports of entry. A significant provision in the law is the limiting of importation of any wildlife to either New York, N.Y.; Miami, Fla.; Chicago, Ill.; San Francisco, or Los Angeles, Calif. The port of New Orleans, La. may be added to the list at a later date.

A Form 3-177 (Customs Declaration) must be filed for all primates imported showing common and scientific names, number, country of origin, whether or not on the Endangered Species List, together with an export permit from the country of origin showing that the animals were lawfully taken, transported or sold. The regulations also contain a list of species and subspecies considered to be threatened with extinction in other countries.

New world monkeys considered endangered are the Wooly spider monkey, White-nosed saki, Uakaris (all species), Goeldi's marmoset, Golden lion tamarins, four subspecies of spider monkeys found in Guatemala and Costa Rica, and the Red-backed squirrel monkey of Costa Rica.

Primates included on Endangered Species list (Federal Register, June 2, 1970):

Common Name	*Scientific Name*	*Where Found*
Aye-Aye	*Daubentonia madagascariensis*	Madagascar
Douc langur	*Pygathrixe nemaeus*	Indochina
Goeldi's marmoset	*Callimico goeldi*	Brazil

* From the National Society of Medical Research Bulletin, 1970, 21, (6), 1 and 4.

Common Name	*Scientific Name*	*Where Found*
Golden-rumped, golden-headed tamarin, golden	*Leontideus spp*	Brazil
Gorilla	*Gorilla gorilla*	Central and Western Africa
Indri, Sifakas, Avahis, all species	*Indriidae,* all members of of the genera *Indri, Avahi, Propithecus*	Madagascar and Comoro Islands
Kloss' gibbon	*Hylobates klossi*	Indonesia
Lemurs, all species	*Lemuridae,* all members of the genera *Lemur, Hapalemur, Lepilemur Cheirogaleus, Microcebus, Phaner*	Madagascar and Comoro Islands
Lion-tailed macaque	*Macca silenus*	India
Orangutan	*Pongo pygmaeus*	Indonesia, Malaysia, Brunii
Pagi Island langur	*Simias concolor*	Indochina
Pileated gibbon	*Hylobates Pileatus*	Malaysia
Red-backed squirrel monkey	*Saimiri orstedii (Saimiri sciurus orstedii)*	Costa Rica
Red colobus	*Colobus kirkii*	Kenya
Spider monkey	*Ateles geoffroyi frontatus*	Guatemala
Spider monkey	*Ateles geoffroyi geoffroyi*	Guatemala
Spider monkey	*Ateles geoffroyi ornatus*	Costa Rica
Spider monkey	*Ateles geoffroyi panamensis*	Costa Rica
Tana River mangabey	*Cerocebus g. galeritus*	Kenya
Uakari, all species	*Cacajao spp*	Peru, Colombia, Brazil, Venezuela and Ecuador
White-nosed saki	*Chiropotes albinasus*	Brazil
Wooly spider monkey	*Brachyteles arachnoides*	Brazil
Zanzibar red colobus	*Colobus badius rufomitratus*	Zansibar (Tanzania)

Appendix IV

GROWTH OF FETAL MONKEYS

A. THE GROWTH RATES OF FETAL ORGANS OF THE RHESUS MONKEY*†

(mg/g/day)

Organ	*50—75 Days*	*75–100 Days*	*100–125 Days*	*125–130 Days*	*150–175 Days*
Lungs	503.67	82.13	24.60	18.77	−13.60
Heart	317.65	101.55	46.10	21.76	13.49
Liver	447.53	89.85	23.93	23.46	2.80
Adrenals	318.72	44.57	15.51	14.04	60.02
Kidneys	572.13	139.74	26.97	9.37	10.04
Thyroid	—	105.52	31.23	32.72	20.07
Thymus	—	115.54	59.69	24.18	−20.92
Spleen	119.24	120.07	33.04	19.74	6.64
Brain	—	99.69	49.87	10.28	4.74
Placenta	73.02	24.86	7.21	17.79	9.77
Fetus	392.40	98.01	39.12	23.31	6.59

* Derived from change in mean weight of organs at each gestational age. Figures indicate mean value ±1 standard deviation.

† Kerr, G. R., *et al.* (1969): Growth and development of the fetal rhesus monkey. I. Physical growth. *Growth*, *33*, 201–213.

B. THE GROWTH IN WEIGHT OF MAJOR ORGANS DURING FETAL LIFE OF THE RHESUS MONKEY*†

Organ	*50*	*75*	*100*	*125*	*150*	*175*
Total Body wt. (gm)	4.003 ±.987	43.27 ±3.49	149.29 ±9.73	295.30 ±27.00	467.38 ±42.76	544.4 ±101.6
Placenta (gm)	21.23 ±6.59	59.99 ±12.23	97.27 ±14.66	114.82 ±21.28	165.88 ±33.82	206.40 ±49.52
Brain (gm)	—	5.26 ±.64	18.36 ±1.15	41.25 ±3.57	51.85 ±3.04	58.00 ±5.97
Spleen (gm)	.017	.068 ±.014	.271 ±.071	.495 ±.096	.739 ±.131	.861 ±.265
Thyroid (gm)	—	.015 ±.007	.054 ±.011	.096 ±.052	.175 ±.060	.263 ±.137
Kidneys (gm)	.017 ±.007	.225 ±.080	1.145 ±.155	1.92 ±.37	2.37 ±.37	2.96 ±.67
Adrenals (gm)	.007 ±.003	.065 ±.022	.138 ±.026	.192 ±.026	.259 ±.100	.649 ±.279
Liver (gm)	.148 ±.061	1.80 ±.40	5.84 ±.69	9.33 ±1.38	14.81 ±1.49	15.85 ±2.84
Heart (gm)	.025 ±.006	.226 ±.048	.800 ±.090	1.72 ±.39	2.66 ±.35	3.55 ±1.22
Lungs (gm)	.097 ±.041	1.32 ±.20	4.01 ±.88	6.48 ±1.42	9.53 ±1.27	6.29 ±.99
Thymus (gm)	—	.086 ±.035	.333 ±.126	.829 ±.277	1.331 ±.432	.635 ±.223

* Figures indicate mean weight ±1 standard deviation.

† Kerr, G. R., *et al.* (1969): Growth and development of the fetal rhesus monkey. I. Physical growth. *Growth*, *33*, 201–213.

C. THE RELATIVE GROWTH RATE OF FETAL ORGANS OF THE RHESUS MONKEY (PERCENT TOTAL BODY WEIGHT)*†

Organ	*Gestational Age (Days)*					
	50	*75*	*100*	*125*	*150*	*175*
Placenta	551.7 ±201.5	140.6 ±29.9	65.2 ±9.1	38.8 ±5.9	35.8 ±8.1	34.4 ±3.3
Brain	—	12.14 ±.99	12.30 ±.49	14.02 ±1.18	11.15 ±.88	11.14 ±1.88
Spleen	.70	.16 ±.03	.18 ±.05	.17 ±.03	.16 ±.02	.16 ±.04
Thyroid	—	.034 ±.016	.036 ±.008	.033 ±.019	.037 ±.010	.047 ±.020
Kidneys	.536 ±.061	.587 ±.164	.765 ±.071	.620 ±.118	.507 ±.038	.548 ±.102
Adrenals	.233 ±.039	.151 ±.055	.093 ±.017	.064 ±.012	.055 ±.021	.113 ±.037
Liver	4.05 ±1.27	4.14 ±.71	3.90 ±.25	3.16 ±.31	3.19 ±.30	2.93 ±.35
Heart	.657 ±.137	.525 ±.083	.543 ±.030	.581 ±.101	.561 ±.043	.646 ±.147
Lungs	2.63 ±.47	3.04 ±.43	2.68 ±.47	2.19 ±.42	2.04 ±.14	1.22 ±.26
Thymus	—	.201 ±.093	.224 ±.092	.280 ±.082	.283 ±.080	.118 ±.035

* Figures indicate mean value ±1 standard deviation.

† Kerr, G. R., *et al.* (1969): Growth and development of the fetal rhesus monkey. I Physical growth. *Growth*, *33*, 201–213.

Appendix V

ERUPTION SEQUENCE OF DENTITION

A. DECIDUOUS DENTITION IN *SAIMIRI SCIUREUS* (LETICIA, COLUMBIA)*

Tooth	In Weeks	
	Mean	*Range*
Maxillary		
I1	1.3	0–3
I2	2.2	1–3
C	3.4	2–4
P1	4.9	4–6
P2	6.1	5–7
P3	8.9	8–11
Mandibular		
I1	1.3	1–3
I2	1.4	1–3
C	3.4	3–4
P1	4.8	4–6
P2	5.7	5–7
P3	8.3	7–9

* Long, J. O., and Cooper, R. W. (1968): Physical growth and dental eruption in captive-bred squirrel monkeys, *Saimiri sciureus* (Leticia, Columbia). In Rosenblum and Cooper (Ed.): *The Squirrel Monkey*. New York, Academic Press, Chap. 7, pp. 193–205.

B. DECIDUOUS DENTITION IN *MACACA MULATTA**

Tooth		*In Weeks*	
		Mean	*Range*
Maxillary			
I1	♂	2.6	0–7.8
	♀	2.6	.5–4.3
I2	♂	5.7	1.6–11.8
	♀	5.7	2.0–9.4
C	♂	9.8	5.2–14.6
	♀	10.4	5.7–15.1
M1	♂	10.4	6.8–15.6
	♀	9.5	6.3–16.9
M2	♂	23.4	15.6–30.1
	♀	22.3	16.2–29.7
Mandibular			
I1	♂	2.0	0–6.2
	♀	2.0	0–5.2
I2	♂	3.1	.5–8.3
	♀	3.1	0–8.3
C	♂	9.8	5.2–18.3
	♀	10.9	5.7–16.7
M1	♂	10.4	6.8–15.6
	♀	10.4	7.3–14.1
M2	♂	21.9	15.2–28.2
	♀	21.5	15.1–26.6

* Hurme, V. O., and van Wagenen, G., (1965): Emergence of permanent first molars in the monkey (*Macaca mulatta*). Association with other growth phenomena. *Yale J Biol Med*, *28*:538–567.

C. THE PERMANENT DENTITION IN *SAIMIRI SCIUREUS* (LETICIA, COLOMBIA)*

Tooth	*In Months*	
	Mean	*Range*
Maxillary		
M1	5.5	5–6
M2	8.4	7–9
I1	9.7	8–12
I2	12.0	10–14
P2	13.0	12–15
P3	13.0	12–15
P1	14.7	14–15
M3	20.0	19–22
C	21.5	21–22
Mandibular		
M1	5.1	5–6
M2	7.0	7
I1	9.2	8–11
I2	9.6	8–11
M3	12.3	11–14
P3	12.8	12–15
P1	14.3	12–16
P2	15.0	15
C	20.5	19–21

* Long, J. O., and Cooper, R. W. (1968): Physical growth and dental eruption in captive-bred squirrel monkeys, *Saimiri sciureus* (Leticia, Colombia). Chapter 7, pp. 193–205. In Rosenblum and Cooper (Ed.), *The Squirrel Monkey*. New York, Academic Press, Chap. 7, pp. 193–205.

D. THE PERMANENT DENTITION IN *MACACA MULATTA**

Tooth		*In Months*	
		Mean	*Range*
Maxillary			
M1	♂	19.3	15.3–25.0
	♀	19.7	16.6–21.7
I1	♂	32.8	26.0–39.6
	♀	32.7	25.8–40.0
I2	♂	36.0	30.0–42.0
	♀	36.0	31.0–42.2
M2	♂	41.5	38.5–45.4
	♀	43.8	38.2–52.7
PM1	♂	48.2	41.4–59.5
	♀	44.7	36.0–62.7
PM2	♂	49.9	43.8–57.0
	♀	48.0	38.1–62.5
C	♂	53.1	45.0–60.0
	♀	46.7	38.1–65.7
M3	♂	75.5	65.7–109.5
	♀	84.3	65.5–144.5
Mandibular			
M1	♂	17.6	13.6–24.5
	♀	17.2	15.0–20.3
I1	♂	31.5	23.0–38.5
	♀	32.0	27.0–45.0
I2	♂	33.3	28.5–39.6
	♀	33.6	32.0–52.0
M2	♂	41.3	36.5–46.2
	♀	41.0	35.0–48.9
C	♂	49.2	43.2–54.5
	♀	41.8	32.7–56.0
PM1	♂	50.1	44.0–54.2
	♀	45.9	35.0–55.5
PM2	♂	51.9	46.7–56.5
	♀	46.6	33.7–61.0
M3	♂	72.1	64.1–90.0
	♀	80.6	61.7–99.5

* Hurme, V. O., van Wagenen, G. (1961): Basic data on the emergence of permanent teeth in the rhesus monkey (*Macaca mulatta*). *Proc Amer Phil Soc*, *105:*1, 109–140.

Appendix VI

RECOMMENDED PHARMACOLOGICAL AGENTS AND DOSAGE FOR IMMOBILIZATION OF NONHUMAN PRIMATES♯

Species	*Sernylan*			*Tiletamine Dosage**	*Ketamine Dosage**
	*Dosage**	*Time to Immobilize (Min)*	*Time to Recover (Min)*		
Baboons					
Papio cynocephalus	5				
P. doguera	1	8–10	120–180		
P. papio	1–2	6–10	100–240		
P. porcaruis	0.5–1	7–12	60–150		
Chimpanzee					
Pan sp.	0.5	10–15	180–240	1	2–3
Guenons					
Cercopithecus	2–3	3–5	60–120	4–6	8–18
Lemurs					
Lemur catta	1–2	10–30	40–300	2–4	4–12
Macaques					
Macaca fascicularis (crab-eating)	3–4	8–12	60–240	6–8	12–20
M. mulatta (rhesus)	2–3	4–8	120–150	4–6	8–18
M. nemestrina (pig tail macaque)	2–4	2–4	120–180	4–8	8–24
M. arctoides (stump-tail macaque)	2–4	2–4	120–180	4–8	8–24
Marmosets					
Hapale jacchus	1–5	5–10	15–30	3	6–9
Oedipomidas oedipus	2–5	3–7	30–120	4–10	8–30
Orangutan					
Pongo pygmaeus	0.75	8–10	180	1.5	3–4.5
Siamang					
Symphalangus syndactylus	0.5	10–15	180–240	2	—
Spider monkey					
Ateles = geoffroyi	3	4	240–300	6	12–18
Squirrel monkey					
Saimirai	2–4	4–10	30–75	4–8	20–35
Whitehanded gibbon					
Hylobates lar	0.5–1	7–10	400	2–4	4–12

* Dose in mg/Kg body weight, given intramuscularly.

♯ From the literature and proceedings of a symposium on VA Laboratory Guide on "Comparative Anesthesia in Laboratory Animals" *Fed Proc, 28* (No. 4), Courtesy of the Federation of American Societies for Experimental Biologists, Bethesda, Md.

Appendicies IV to VII compiled by A. G. Hendrickx.

Appendix VII

HANDLING OF MONKEYS

Method, in sequence (a-f), of capturing and restraining monkeys (*Macaca*) using a bare-hand technique. This procedure is recommended only for the well-trained researcher or animal handler. (Domino *et al.* (1969): *Fed Proc 28:* 1500)

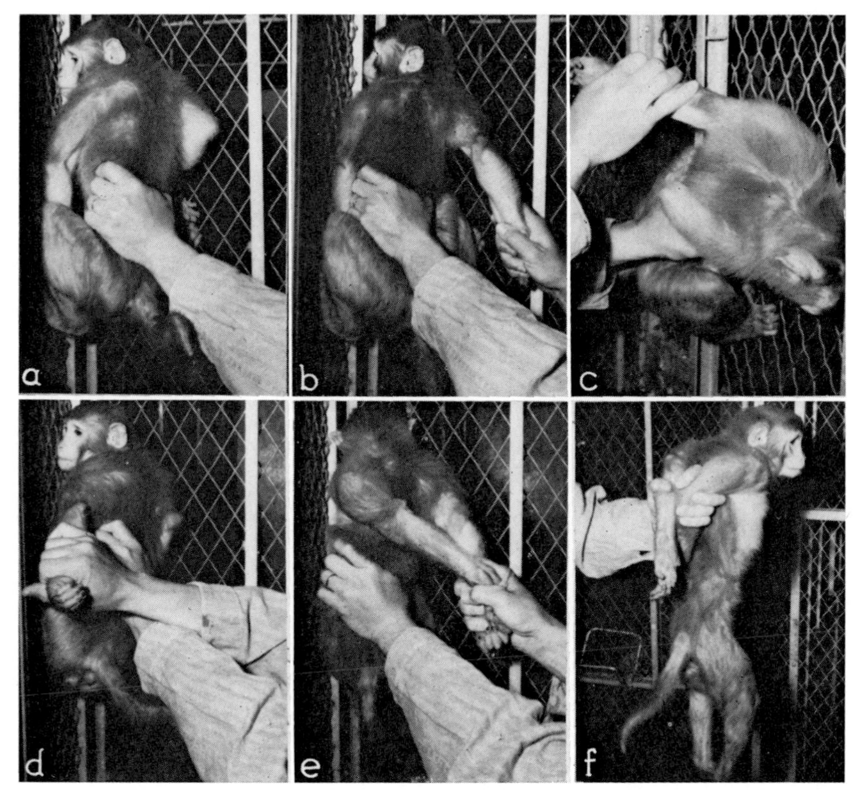

Appendix VIII

GENERAL REFERENCE BOOKS

Beveridge, W. I. B. (1969a): *Using Primates in Medical Research. Husbandry and Technology.* New York, Karger, vol. 2.

Bourne, G. H. (Ed.) (1968): 2nd Inter Cong Primat. New York, Karger, vol. 1 Behavior; vol. 2 Reproduction, Anatomy and Anthropology; vol. 3 Neurology, Physiology and Infectious Diseases.

Buettner-Janusch, J. (Ed.) (1963), (1964): *Evolutionary and Genetic Biology of Primates.* New York, Academic Press, vol. 1, 2.

Fiennes, R. (1967): *Zoonews of Primates.* London, Weidenfeld and Nicolson.

Hartman, C. G., and Straus, W. L. (1933): *The Anatomy of the Rhesus Monkey (Macaca mulatta).* New York, Hafner.

Hendrickx, A. G., Houston, M. L., Kraemer, D. C., Gasser, R. F., and Bollert, J. A. (1971): *Embryology of the Baboon.* Chicago, University of Chicago Press.

Hill, W. C. O. (1953-1967): *Primates.* Edinburgh, Edinburgh University Press, vol. 1-6.

Jolly, A. (1966): *Lemur Behavior.* Chicago, University of Chicago Press.

Lapin, B. A., and Yakovelva, L. A. (1963): *Comparative Pathology in Monkeys.* Springfield, Thomas.

Morris, D. (Ed.) (1967): *Primate Ethology.* London, Weidenfeld Press.

Napier, J. R., and Napier, P. H. (1967): *A Handbook of Living Primates.* New York, Academic Press.

Petter, J. J. (1962): Recherches sur L'Ecologie et L'Ethologie des Lemuriens Malgaches. *Memoires Mus Hist Nat, Nouvelle Series A., Z,* XXVII, 1 (36, Rue Geoffroy-Saint-Hilaire) Paris, France.

Petter-Rousseaux, A. (1962): Recherches sur la biologie des primates inferieurs. *Mammalia,* 26 (Suppl.), 1-88.

Reynolds, H. H. (1969): Chimpanzee. Central Nervous System and Behavior, a review. New York, Krager.

Riesen, A. H., and Kinder, E. F. (1952): *The Postural Development of Infant Chimpanzees.* New Haven, Yale Univ Press.

Rohles, F. H., Jr. (1969): *Circadian Rhythms in Nonhuman Primates.* New York, Krager.

Rosenblum, L. A. and Cooper, R. W. (1969): *The Squirrel Monkey. New York,* Academic Press.

Ruch, T. C. (1941): *Bibiolographia Primatologica.* Springfield, Thomas.

Ruch, T. C. (1959): *Diseases of Laboratory Primates.* Philadelphia, Saunders.

The Primates (1965): Life Nature Library, Time Incorporated, New York.

The Primates (1963): Sympos. No. 10. Zoological Society of London (Regent's Park, London, N.W. 1).

Sanderson, I. T. (1957): *The Monkey Kingdom.* Philadelphia, Chilton.

Vagtborg, H. (Ed.) (1965), (1967): *The Baboon in Medical Research.* vols. I & II. Austin, University of Texas Press.

Whitelock, O. V. St., (Ed.) (1960): Care and diseases of the research monkey. *Ann NY Acad Sci, 85,* 735.

Whitney, R. A., Johnson, D. J., and Cole, W. C. (1967): *The Subhuman Primate—A Guide for the Veterinarian.* EASP 100-26, Med Res Lab, Edgewood Arsenal, Maryland.

INDEX

S

T

Comparative reproduction of nonhuman primates. Edited by E.S.E. Hafez. Springfield, Ill., Thomas [1971]
557p. illus. 24cm.

Includes bibliographies.

1.Primates. 2.Reproduction. 3.Sexual behavior in animals. I.Hafrz, E.S.E., 1922- ed.